EX LIBRIS

D. V. Campbell

RED SPIES IN THE UN

Red Spies in the

UN

Pierre J. Huss

and George Carpozi, Jr.

Coward-McCann, Inc.

New York

I dedicate this book, for my part, to my daughters Marianne and Jacqueline Huss, to counsel them forever to cherish with courage the greatness of our land and the blessings of their heritage.

—PIERRE J. HUSS

Contents

RED SPIES IN THE UN

1 : Serpents in the House

ON the banks of the East River in Manhattan, in the area of the city known in the days of the American Revolution as Turtle Bay, a camping ground for the British Army's forces facing the valiant "rabble in arms" commanded by George Washington, stands now a complex of buildings which is world headquarters of the United Nations.

In a Dutch apple orchard several blocks up the street, Nathan Hale was hanged as a spy in 1776.

Today, nearly 200 years later, his ghost would be in good company among an unprecedented swarm of diplomatically cloaked professionals plying the ancient craft of espionage from within the UN's massive architectural cluster.

It is a strange and paradoxical situation which, morally and legally, has no place in this forum. The United Nations is an organization dedicated to keeping the peace of the world; it functions by virtue of the contributive membership of one hundred and twelve large and small nations of all races, colors, religions, and political ideologies.

A charter signed by fifty original allied nations in San Francisco in 1945 provided the ground rules and basic principles by which this deterrent to the "scourge of war" operates.

A voluminous treaty signed between the United States and the United Nations names and guarantees the rights and privileges of the world organization. The treaty, subject nowadays to a wide range of criticism in the United States—and elsewhere from time to time—creates an "international" enclave within the perimeter of 42nd Street, 48th Street, 1st Avenue and the banks of the East River. New York City has no jurisdiction in this tiniest of world states except by consent of the Secretary General. The Mayor and the City Council have no control over this choice piece of Manhattan real estate; nor does the Governor nor State Legislature nor, for that matter, the President and the Congress of the United States. In theory, those who step through the UN's gates have gained sanctuary. A fugitive from the Federal Bureau of Investigation or city police can be handed over to the law only if the Secretary General says so. Yet it is improbable that there will ever be a time when a Joe Valachi or a Willie Sutton will escape the law by taking asylum at the UN.

Nevertheless, as this book will show, a spy sent here with diplomatic credentials by a foreign power to steal military or defense secrets can take refuge behind the ramparts of the UN, remaining there in absolute safety until the machinery of our State Department grinds into motion and effects not his arrest but his deportation through "channels."

This privilege of immunity descends from traditional agreements and understandings enacted between governments, giving diplomats and consular employees carte blanche immunities from the laws of the land when they are stationed on each other's soil. Those enjoying this status are secure from arrest or prosecution while representing or working for their own governments abroad—regardless of the crime. They can only be declared personae non grata and expelled.

The extension of diplomatic immunity to members of missions accredited to the United Nations has become an increasing source of irritation. Particularly to the United States and the city of New York.

Over the years, privileges granted to a number of diplomats have been misused and abused. The violations have ranged from infractions of parking laws to doubtful behavior in hotels and public places; from exceeding speed limits and drunken driving on public highways to hit-and-run driving—and even murder.

But the ultimate crime, in that it can have the most far-reaching and widest effects, is that of espionage. Only a small handful of nations is known to have taken advantage of the freedom afforded at the UN to engage in subversion. Yet one nation—the Soviet Union —has managed to put the entire western hemisphere under a spy glass and has committed subversive acts repeatedly on U.S. shores.

It is the purpose of this book to focus America's and the world's attention on Soviet and satellite nation espionage as it emanates from the UN, and especially to show, by case histories obtained from the FBI, the State Department, the United Nations, and other sources, how the Russians operate this clandestine operation. These cases present documented proof that the Russians:

a) seized, with the help of the notorious Judith Coplon, a highly confidential file of FBI reports on the Red conspiracy in the U.S.;

b) launched a vast spying operation directed at gathering data and secrets of military and seaport facilities on the Atlantic Coast;

c) penetrated all but invulnerable security measures in order to seize intelligence manuals at the U.S. General Staff School in Leavenworth, Kansas;

d) obtained aerial photos and maps of military installations in the Midwest where some of America's key defense bases against Soviet nuclear-missile attack are situated;

e) stole top secret information on the location of missile and rocket launching sites and bases in the U.S.;

f) plotted a master plan to blow up our eastern seaboard via a terrifying campaign of sabotage that would have destroyed much of our resources and imperiled the lives of millions.

All of these plots and such others as we shall discuss in this book were initiated in one central location—the so-called Moscow "high command post," centered in a busy house not many blocks away from the United Nations: the Soviet Mission to the United Nations. Soviet nationals at the UN and staff employees from Iron Curtain satellites are part and parcel of this "high command post" housed in that unprepossessing building just off fashionable Park Avenue at 136 East 67th Street.

It is the nerve center on this side of the Atlantic Ocean for almost every phase of the Kremlin's subversive activities in North and South America. The fangs of this spy network rooted in the Soviet Mission and in the UN, as we shall show, extend miles beyond to the Soviet Embassy in Washington and its satellite diplomatic missions there, and beyond to Mexico, Panama City, Cuba, Brazil, and Canada.

While we abhor the methods employed and gains scored by the U.S.S.R. over the years in gathering secrets from us, we are forced to recognize the unfortunate truth that espionage is a necessary evil of international politics. To pretend that espionage is a crime exclusively of Russian origin would be hypocrisy, for we are dealing with a practice that is as old as recorded history.

The Egyptians were perhaps the first to realize the need for espionage when they organized a secret service and established schools to train spies. The first practical application apparently came during the reign of Egyptian King Tuthmosis III, when a Captain Thute managed, with the help of his spies, to smuggle into Jaffa two hundred armed soldiers who were sewn in sacks and carried into the city as a shipment of flour.

Perhaps the greatest of all espionage stories is to be found in the *Iliad*, in which Homer sings of the Trojan horse.

Down through the ages spying gained impetus and importance. We know Joan of Arc was betrayed by a spy, Bishop Pierre Cauchon of Beauvais, who was in the pay of the English king.

There was Benedict Arnold, of course, and during World Wars I and II we saw women such as Martha Cockaert of Belgium and Anne Marie Walters of France serve their respective countries as spies against German occupation forces.

It appears that Russia's first serious attempt to engage in espionage —domestic style—occurred in 1881 when the Okhrana or defensive police was organized to combat terrorism. By devious methods it succeeded in foiling not only the desperadoes threatening the czar, but the plotters in the government as well.

When the Bolshevists seized the government in 1917, Lenin organized the Extraordinary Commissions to Combat Counter-Revolution, Sabotage, and Speculation. Because it was such a mouthful even to the Russians, they called it Cheka. Nevertheless, it was Okhrana under a different name.

In 1922, Cheka was replaced by the State Political Administration, called the GPU, which grew into a far more fearsome secret police and spy organization. In 1934, the People's Commissariat of Home

Affairs took over from the GPU and became a tool of world-wide espionage. Readers may be more familiar with that spy machine's nom de guerre—the infamous NKVD which, in subsequent years, changed its name but never its objectives.

Before Lavrenti Beria, its chief, was executed in 1953, the NKVD slipped through a title change to MVD or Ministry of Home Affairs; then, its bull-faced boss eliminated by a firing squad, it became the KVD or Committee for State Safety—and finally the KGB.

The agents of this highly trained secret service form the nucleus of the Communist espionage conspiracy encircling the globe today and, with agents of the Comintern and Cominform, the international agencies of the Communist Party, have been carrying out the Kremlin's goal of spying in such diverse areas as politics, industry, business, commerce, agriculture, labor, transportation, and—most important—in the military.

With so many self-confessed former Communists telling us repeatedly about this, there is little doubt that the overriding interest and aim of Soviet spies centers chiefly in that last area—the military.

We also know that to be true because of the increasing number of spies uncovered in this country and, most especially, the preponderance of agents caught operating out of the United Nations.

The USSR has never admitted engaging in espionage, not even when its agents have been trapped red-handed with stolen secret data. On the contrary, they laugh at every unmasking and jibe us by saying: "You see a Communist spy behind every bush."

This is good form. An unwritten law of espionage is that one does not admit that one employs spies. It is not a question of etiquette. For maximum efficiency, a spy system must be entirely secret. An admission of ownership is an admission of failure; and in a world of secrecy, reputation is built upon what is unknown.

In the United Nations the dynamics of Soviet membership takes on special significance in the light of the many cases of espionage involving Moscow's diplomatic and consular corps, as well as its citizens who serve in the Secretariat's employ.

The UN Charter demands that staff employees, regardless of what country they come from or what capacity they hold, maintain a status as "international civil servants." That status is achieved by the signing of a loyalty oath before starting work in any UN post. The oath pledges the employee to serve the UN faithfully and impartially. It binds him to the world body and prohibits influences or acts of the home government to deflect the employee from his trust.

The oath obligates the entire UN staff—from the Secretary General down to the most obscure file clerk—to work in accordance with the UN rules and regulations. Strikingly, there is no suggestion in the oath for disloyalty to one's own country. Yet, on the other hand, a UN staffer is not allowed to exercise loyalty to country by passing, for example, UN documents to contacts on the diplomatic delegation of his native land or lobbying around UN departments for projects affecting his country.

The first nineteen years of the UN demonstrated fairly conclusively that the "international civil servant" can become enough of a reality to make a ponderous machine like the world organization work despite certain flaws and hazards in the loyalty system.

But the span of years also demonstrated that the Soviet Union, while subscribing to the loyalty rule at San Francisco, as it did to all Charter principles, had other ideas about the UN and the way it might serve the Kremlin.

Although until 1962 Soviet and satellite country UN employees signed the loyalty oath, if somewhat grudgingly, they nevertheless carried manifest instructions from Moscow. They were put in the UN not only to do their part for the Kremlin in world affairs, but also to carry out the secret orders issued by superiors seated in the Soviet Mission to the UN. Some of these Soviet nationals were trained as spies and saboteurs, yet came disguised as secretaries, clerks, typists, or officials from high Moscow posts to head UN departments.

We may be understating when we say "some" of the Soviet nationals are trained spies. The FBI prepared a report not long ago which it submitted to the Attorney General for use by the Subcommittee to Investigate the Administration of the Internal Security Act and Other Internal Security Laws.

In speaking of the United Nations, the report stated: "Attention is called to the fact that many of the incidents and cases [of spying] previously cited involved Soviet employees of the United Nations. They are guests of the United States and are supposedly dedicated to the cause of international peace but they are, in fact, carefully selected envoys of the international Communist conspiracy, trained in trickery and deceit and dedicated to the concept of fully exploiting the freedoms of the countries they seek to destroy. It is too much to expect that they would not prostitute the United Nations."

2 : Valentin Gubitchev,
the First UN Spy

THE shapely young woman dressed neatly but inconspicuously in black skirt and tan sweater with pearl necklace at her throat sat meditatively in her seat as the Pennsylvania Railroad's Washington-to-New York express rolled towards its destination—Pennsylvania Station. Her black cloth coat was neatly folded in the empty aisle seat beside her.

Now and then she looked out casually at the passing countryside. Now and then she turned and glanced at the other passengers in the half-filled coach.

Her name was Judith Coplon.

On that Friday, March 4, 1949, on the train which had left the capital at 1 p.m., two men in the same coach reclined in their own seats near the young woman. Judith Coplon, a plain-faced girl with intense dark eyes and brunette hair, was an analyst in the Internal Security Section of the Department of Justice in Washington. Although they were employed in the same service, the 27-year-old Miss Coplon did not know that the two men near her were FBI agents.

Nor did she know that they were trailing her.

Judith Coplon had been under surveillance for several weeks. The history of the case went back to late December, 1948, when Miss

Coplon first drew the suspicion of her superiors. A former fellow employee in the office of Foreign Agents Registration in the Internal Security Division of the Justice Department reported that Judith Coplon had been slanting her analyses and other reports so that they benefited the Soviet Union, favoring its friends and condemning its foes.

A loyalty investigation was begun and the springboard was the young woman's background. The probers found she was a native of New York City, born in Brooklyn. She was the daughter of Samuel M. and Rebecca Coplon and had been a student at Brooklyn's Madison High School where she averaged well above ninety percent for all subjects in her four years there. She then went on to Barnard College where she proved herself an equally brilliant student, winning two one-hundred-dollar scholarships in competitive examinations that tested both her academic potential and her character. She was graduated in 1943 cum laude and was listed by Barnard's placement bureau in the top category for ability, application, integrity, public spirit, leadership, and good breeding.

Almost immediately after graduation, Judith Coplon obtained a job as an economic journalist in the Economic Warfare Section of the Justice Department's New York City office. She remained there until January, 1945, and then, while World War II was still on, was transferred to Washington and assigned to the Foreign Agents Registration Section as an assistant political analyst. Her salary was $4,479 a year.

In her spare time in the capital, Miss Coplon also enrolled at American University to earn a master's degree in international relations. This opened a new phase in her life, giving her an opportunity to learn languages, and she was soon speaking French, German, and Russian.

Her work for the Justice Department was regarded highly, and in one instance, during February, 1946, Jesse M. MacKnight, chief of her Justice Department bureau, had occasion to report on the young woman's employment ability. He said she "showed herself a capable, industrious, and intelligent research worker. . . . Her language skills were more than adequate in French, and good in German and Russian . . ."

While the reports on her background were laudatory, sufficient information to raise some doubts about her loyalty was developed in just two days of investigation, prompting the Justice Department to assign special agents of the FBI to keep Miss Coplon under close surveillance.

Although nothing untoward had yet happened, the Justice Department nevertheless also took immediate steps to make certain she no longer had access to important secret defense information in the Government's files. The routine of her work, however, did not change: she continued to receive data she had been handling, but it was altered so as to make it worthless in the event it fell into the wrong hands.

The agents who were put on her trail came to know the suspect's habits quite intimately; one of them was making weekly trips to New York to visit her parents who were both ailing at the time.

The pattern of Judith Coplon's conduct remained virtually unchanged over the next few weeks, but in mid-January of 1949, the G-men assigned to keep an eye on her detected a variation. Miss Coplon's routine on this 14th day of January had started like all the other days. She reported for work in the Justice Department Building in the capital, put in an eight-hour day, then left for Union Station where she caught a Pennsylvania train for New York.

But this time, instead of going to the apartment of her father and mother in the Flatbush section of Brooklyn, Judith Coplon headed from Pennsylvania Station to the Independent Subway system's 8th Avenue line station at 34th Street and boarded an uptown express.

The two G-men who had followed her from Washington, Agents Richard T. Hradsky and Richard E. Brennan, were met by other FBI men at Penn Station and they, too, became shadows of Miss Coplon. The G-men all boarded the same subway train, then jammed by the rush hour crowds, and rode uptown. When she got off at the Fort Tryon Park station at 190th Street and Overlook Terrace in the section of Manhattan known as Washington Heights, the agents followed her off the train, into the elevator, and up to the street.

It was precisely 7:10 p.m. on Hradsky's wristwatch when Judith Coplon meandered out to the street and began looking in all directions as though she were planning to meet someone there and was impatient at the person's lateness.

Moments later, she walked east for two blocks to Broadway, then turned the other corner into Dyckman Street and headed to 143, which was the DeLuxe Italian Restaurant.

As the agents watched discreetly from the outside, they saw Judith Coplon walk to a table and sit down beside a somber-faced but handsome man with a receding hairline who looked to be in his early thirties. Beside the 5-foot, 100 pound Miss Coplon, the stranger seemed not much bigger. He was perhaps 5 feet 4, on the stocky side, about 165 pounds.

There was little opportunity for the agents to observe from the outside without attracting attention to themselves. At most they could only pass the restaurant in relays, mingling in the crowds of pedestrians, casting quick glances inside until they had determined what was going on. They soon found out. Miss Coplon and the man she had met were ordering from the menu.

Special Agent T. Scott Miller, Jr., was designated to go into the restaurant and take a booth near the couple to observe their activity from close range. Miller noticed the waiter brought food to the man but only a cup of coffee for Miss Coplon. As she sipped the coffee, Miss Coplon dropped nickels in the musicbox coin machine at the table.

Agent Miller was unable to hear their conversation through the blare of the juke-box music. Even during the moments of quiet he could not pick up any of the talk because the conversation, although animated, was conducted in whispers.

Finally Judith Coplon and her companion rose from the table and walked out of the restaurant. Their trail outside was picked up by the other G-men—Agents Hradsky, Brennan, and Daniel Garde—who followed Miss Coplon and the still unidentified man back to the IND subway station entrance where they stopped.

Miss Coplon, who was holding a folded newspaper, raised it and gesticulated. It seemed for a moment that she was going to strike the man, for she appeared angry now as she spoke with him. But they soon ended their heated conversation and went down into the subway. Agents followed them and rode on the train with the couple. At the 116th Street station the man suddenly got up and left the train. Agents Hradsky and Brennan followed him while the other operatives remained on Miss Coplon's trail, which led to Brooklyn, to the home of her parents.

Meanwhile, her companion hailed a taxi and went east on 116th Street. Hradsky and Brennan followed in another cab. The ride ended at Broadway and 116th Street where the pursued man headed to another subway, the IRT's Broadway-7th Avenue line.

The G-men were about to follow him, but just then their quarry turned and looked in their direction. The agents were standing less than ten feet away. Afraid the man might suspect he was being trailed, Hradsky and Brennan decided on discretion and ended their surveillance.

But the next morning one of those fortuitous strokes that often seems to guide the destinies of the FBI found Hradsky and Brennan standing outside the old Soviet Mission to the United Nations at 680 Park Avenue. Lo and behold, whom should they see but the man who had met Miss Coplon the night before!

To this day the FBI insists Hradsky and Brennan had no inside information but were only playing a hunch when they went to the Mission. As he was to explain later, when he first saw the man at the table in the restaurant with Miss Coplon, Hradsky thought he "looked like a Russian." And where but at the Russian Mission to the UN does one go looking for a Russian in New York?

The operatives picked up their prey's trail. It led to a fashionable six-story apartment house at 64 West 108th Street, between Manhattan and Amsterdam Avenues. In the lobby, the agents checked names on the mailboxes. The names meant nothing to them, so they called on the superintendent who lived on the ground floor.

From the agents' description of the man they had trailed, the superintendent told them he probably was Valentin Gubitchev, who lived with his wife in a $63.25-a-month four-room apartment on the fifth floor of the forty-two-family house.

"He works at the United Nations," the superintendent said as casually as if he were talking about a shipping clerk. What immediately lifted him above the ordinary to the FBI agents, though, was the superintendent's confirmation that Gubitchev was a Russian and that he was employed at the UN. Together with what the agents already suspected about Judith Coplon, the Justice Department girl, her association with Gubitchev took on an ominous configuration.

Agents Hradsky and Brennan notified their superiors immediately and a stakeout was ordered for Gubitchev's apartment house. G-men in cars kept a day-night vigil outside the building. In the morning, as Gubitchev came out and started downtown for his job at the UN, the agents shadowed him all the way to work. He went by bus and, while some of the FBI men followed in their cars, one agent, John F. Malley, boarded the Broadway bus and rode to 42nd Street in the seat right beside the suspect. When Gubitchev transferred to a 42nd Street crosstown bus for the ride across Manhattan to the UN Building, Malley was still with him.

During that day, the FBI, making discreet inquiries at the UN, whose headquarters at the time were still out in Lake Success on Long Island, determined just what Gubitchev's function was at the world organization. He was a civilian engineer, employed as third secretary of the Soviet delegation. He had come to the United States from the Soviet Union in July, 1946, as a member of the Soviet Delegation, but subsequently had severed his connections to become a $6,600-a-year tax-free member of the Secretariat which gave him international civil servant status. This was done, the FBI found, to enable Gubitchev to contribute his talents as an engineer in the planning of the new United Nations skyscraper headquarters on First Avenue which was now nearing completion.

When he resigned from the Soviet delegation on September 26, 1946, Gubitchev had signed the oath required of all Secretariat members. It read: "I solemnly swear (undertake, affirm, promise) to exercise in all loyalty, discretion and conscience the functions entrusted to me as a member of the International Service of the United Nations, to discharge those functions and regulate my conduct with the interests of my duties from any government and not to seek or accept instructions in regard to the performance of my duties from any government or other authority external to the organization."

This was the same oath taken by the more than score of other Soviet nationals who were caught in espionage activity in subsequent years; it was the same oath that Khrushchev would repudiate fifteen years later.

In the days that followed in the unmasking of Judith Coplon's companion, every step Gubitchev took was watched ploddingly. Every time he came out of the maze of construction that was shaping the UN Building, FBI agents were standing by to follow his trail. He never walked or rode in a public conveyance alone. Even when he took a cab or rode in a car, he was shadowed by FBI men in their own vehicles.

The FBI's investigation revealed that Gubitchev also had a child, a girl of thirteen, who had lived in New York City with her parents until the previous summer when the Russian Consulate, where the family had been staying, was closed. That action was forced on the Soviet Union as an aftermath of the celebrated Mme. Oksana Kosenkina case. Mme. Kosenkina was a teacher at a Russian school conducted by the Russian Consulate, at 7 East 61st Street, for children of Soviet officials and emissaries in the New York City area. Among the children who attended the school was Gubitchev's daughter. But when Mme. Kosenkina's husband was slain by the Reds, rather than return to Russia, Mme. Kosenkina went into hiding with the Countess Alexandra Tolstoy in Rockland County, just north of New York City. But Russian agents kidnapped Mme. Kosenkina and took her to the Soviet Consulate. While being kept a prisoner there pending her return to Russia, she escaped by leaping from a window. She was badly injured and spent several months in Roosevelt Hospital, but she achieved her goal: asylum in this country.

The FBI learned that in the same month as the Kosenkina incident, August, 1948, Gubitchev and his family had gone back to Russia briefly. When they returned a few weeks later, their daughter did not come back with them.

"We put her in school in Moscow," Gubitchev told one of his neighbors.

Digging further into his background, the FBI found that Gubitchev was born in Orel, Russia, on June 24, 1916. He was a student at the Moscow School of Construction, then went into the employ of the Soviet Ministry of Construction. He rose to deputy chief of the Ural Construction Trust in Chelyabinsk. Afterward he was transferred to the Soviet Foreign Office and came to the U.S. in July, 1946, as the third secretary of the Soviet Mission to the United Nations.

When the Soviet Union was allotted a quota to fill on the UN Secretariat staff, Gubitchev was designated and he resigned from the Soviet Mission to accept the new post which brought him back into the field of his first love—construction engineering.

Secretary General Trygve Lie provided the information that Gubitchev was one of the outstanding figures in the planning and design of the new UN Building. "He is a good man who has worked both inside and outside under the direction of Construction Co-ordinator James Dawson," Lie told the FBI.

While Gubitchev was kept under rigid surveillance, no less an effort was exerted to maintain a check on Judith Coplon's movements and activities. G-men followed her everywhere she went. When she left her parents' home the night after her furtive meeting with Gubitchev and went back to Washington, agents rode on the train to the capital and kept her in their sights constantly. They followed her cab to McClean Gardens, a substantial housing development in the capital where Miss Coplon resided in a two-room, $34.50-a-month apartment.

The next morning when she went to work, G-men were right behind her again. And when she sat down at her desk in the Justice Department, agents made it their business to know what Judith Coplon was doing at work.

So it went through the rest of January and into the middle of February. Nothing unusual occurred in this period. But on February 18, once again Miss Coplon headed for New York and once again she met Gubitchev in the same general locale in Washington Heights as their first meeting. But the pattern this time took on marked variation.

Instead of coming face to face in the restaurant, Gubitchev and Miss Coplon, with their respective FBI shadows behind them, appeared to come together for a rendezvous at the northeast corner of 193rd Street and Broadway. Yet they did not quite meet there. This time their actions were strictly cloak-and-dagger.

Gubitchev, who was being followed by Agent Malley and other operatives, had taken a bus from his home and reached the Washington Heights corner at 7:05 p.m. He loitered briefly there, looking around at the people passing. After a minute of this, he boarded a downtown Broadway bus. Malley and the other agents followed in their car and watched as Gubitchev got off at 166th Street. There he crossed Broadway and immediately got aboard an uptown bus that took him back to 192nd Street, which is on the fringe of Fort Tryon Park.

Meanwhile, agents following Judith Coplon rode with her on the IRT subway to the 191st Street station, where she got off and went up to the street. She, too, meandered about as though searching for someone.

The agents finally focused in on the play. Gubitchev had crossed the street and was standing on the west side of Broadway. Miss Coplon, on the east side, looked across the stream of cars and buses passing, seemed to spot Gubitchev and crossed over. As she reached the sidewalk, she started up Broadway, passing Gubitchev by as if he were a total stranger. The G-men watching the action noticed that as Miss Coplon passed the Russian, she shifted her pocketbook to her left arm. A second later, as if that movement were a signal, Gubitchev started after Miss Coplon. For a time, he stayed behind several paces, then finally hurried his step. As he drew alongside on her left, he held his right hand in front of the government girl and they walked together like that five or six steps. Then Gubitchev slowed his pace while Miss Coplon walked on.

Only one FBI man was close enough to see what was happening. He was Roger B. Robinson, a former Rose Bowl football star, a blocking back on the 1938 Duke University eleven which went undefeated, untied, and unscored on, and which beat Southern California 7 to 3 in the Tournament of Roses. Robinson saw Miss Coplon open her handbag as she lifted it up on her arm. Then passersby were in the way and the G-man could not see if Gubitchev took anything out of the bag as he walked alongside the girl with his arm stretched across her. Nor could he see if Miss Coplon had passed anything to the Russian.

But Agent Miller, who had ridden uptown on the subway with Miss Coplon, knew what she was carrying in her handbag—certain folded onion-skin papers. He had seen them when she opened her bag while he was standing beside her in the train. Such papers—they contained secret but erroneous information about the Amtorg Trading Corporation, the Russian purchasing mission in the U.S., and data about the use of geophones to measure pressure in U.S. atomic bomb tests—had been prepared as decoys and routed through Miss Coplon's desk in the Justice Department the day before she met Gubitchev.

For no valid reason, the papers had remained on her desk far longer than they should have. While no one could observe what was going on, the assumption was that Miss Coplon had copied the information on her own typewriter on the same kind of paper at her desk.

After his brief encounter with Miss Coplon, Gubitchev turned, walked to the corner of 192nd Street, and took a Broadway bus downtown. He got off at 108th Street and went into a supermarket. The agents watched the Russian as he filled a shopping cart with pumpernickel bread, cake, and a variety of meats, including a length of bologna. Then he went home.

Miss Coplon's movements were tracked by other FBI men. When Gubitchev had turned back after his brief and furtive encounter with the girl, she walked to the corner of 193rd Street, stopped momentarily, looked around, then walked back, entered the subway station, and took a train to her parents' home in Brooklyn.

The pattern of this get-together in which Gubitchev and Miss Coplon cautiously avoided all signs of recognition was reminiscent of the tactics used by the Canadian atom spy ring. In that case, the standard operating procedure was never to loiter at an appointed spot if a fellow conspirator was late, but to return later. The G-men who followed Gubitchev and Miss Coplon were convinced that the Russian had taken his short bus jaunt downtown because the Justice Department girl was late for her appointment. But what puzzled them was the change in procedure; they had previously met rather openly in the restaurant, as perhaps a couple of lovers might do on a date, but this time they exhibited the bizarre tactics of a couple of secret agents. Why the change?

The FBI decided that Gubitchev and Miss Coplon had probably begun to suspect they were being followed. That this was so could not be discounted because agents had made so many inquiries about Miss Coplon among her friends. It was deemed well within the realm of probability that some word of the investigation had seeped back to the suspect.

Miss Coplon's FBI shadows found that her trips to New York City did not always lead to rendezvous with Gubitchev. On at least five other occasions G-men found her involved in other situations.

On the night of January 19, FBI Agent Richard E. Brennan followed Judith Coplon to the Hotel Piccadilly off Times Square. There, after a long and impatient wait, he saw her come out of an elevator in the lobby with a tall, handsome, dark-haired man who certainly wasn't Gubitchev.

From the hotel, Brennan followed the couple to the Alps Restaurant at the Avenue of the Americas and 58th Street, and then to the Colony Theater where they watched the stage performance of *Kiss Me Kate*.

For the next three days, Brennan and other agents trailed Miss Coplon around Manhattan but she never met Gubitchev. Most of the time she was in town she went shopping—with a diplomatically distant escort of three FBI men, including Brennan. But all that the agents saw Miss Coplon buy on those days—she had four days off from her job because of President Truman's inauguration ceremonies in Washington—was a scarf.

On one more occasion, Miss Coplon went out without meeting Gubitchev. It was the night after that February 18 when she had the brief and clandestine encounter with the Soviet engineer up in Washington Heights. Miss Coplon went from her parents' home in Brooklyn to visit friends in the Fresh Meadows housing development in Queens. These friends also were later questioned by the FBI.

While agents continued to keep tabs on Gubitchev and Miss Coplon, other FBI men sought to determine what dealings were being transacted between the two suspects, what secrets the Justice Department girl was passing to the Russian—if, indeed, she was selling out.

Everything began to point toward that probability. For one thing, the investigators learned that Miss Coplon, for no apparent reason, had been calling for FBI data on embassies and consulates and embassy personnel. Then, finally, she asked her superior in the Justice Department, William Foley, for a secret file marked INTERNAL SECURITY-R. The "R" stood for Russian. And the data was classified information dealing with Red agents and national security.

For another thing, the meetings between Gubitchev and Miss Coplon paralleled in many respects the fantastic account bared during the previous summer of 1948 by Elizabeth Bentley and Whittaker Chambers, the confessed couriers for Communist espionage networks. Miss Bentley had told the House Un-American Activities Committee the details of clandestine meetings with government employees on street corners, meetings at which she admitted turning over vital government secrets. The FBI was convinced Miss Coplon was similarly engaged in espionage.

Now they decided the time had come to close in.

Late on March 3 the FBI in New York learned that Judith Coplon again planned to visit the city. How did they learn that? From a phone conversation Miss Coplon's mother in Brooklyn had with her daughter in Washington. The FBI had put a tap on the Coplons' phone.

That information prompted a teletype alarm to Washington which read in part: "Due to time Judy stated [in the phone conversation with her mother] she would be home [on March 4] strong possibility she may meet Gubitchev at 7 p.m. Wash Field should surveil her to N.Y. as in past. N.Y. coverage will be same."

William Foley, her superior in the Justice Department, was instructed to notify the FBI when Judith Coplon was leaving so the tail could be put on her. Late on the afternoon of March 3, Foley tipped the FBI that the suspect had made arrangements to go to New York the next day.

At 1 p.m. Friday, March 4, Miss Coplon left Union Terminal in Washington aboard a Pennsylvania Railroad train for New York. And sitting alone beside the window looking out at the landscape whizzing by, Judith had no idea that two seats behind her on the opposite side of the aisle, the two men sitting together had one overriding mission—never to let their eyes off her. They were the same two agents who had followed her on a number of previous occasions, Agents Hradsky and Brennan. They felt reasonably safe that Miss Coplon had not spotted them before and that she could not suspect they were following her now.

In New York, elaborate and painstaking preparations had been made for her arrival and expected meeting with Gubitchev. There was little doubt but that Judith Coplon would meet the Russian official, because this time the FBI strongly suspected she had made off with data slips containing extracts of FBI reports relating to Soviet affairs; word sketches of three government employees, and extracts from a decoy message prepared by the FBI and made available to her by her superior, Foley, on that Friday morning. The FBI was almost certain the petite Miss Coplon was going to transmit this data to Gubitchev.

The preparations were more elaborate than before because this time the FBI was prepared to close in and make arrests. Twenty

agents and seven radio-equipped cars were pressed into service in
New York. Five agents were assigned to watch Gubitchev—three at
the United Nations and two at his 108th Street home.

Another car with two agents covered the DeLuxe Restaurant on
Dyckman Street where Miss Coplon and Gubitchev had had their first
known meeting. Two more G-men were at the Broadway IRT subway's 191st Street station. Another two were put in a stationery store
at Broadway and West 193rd Street to watch the corner the suspects
had used previously for their hurried cloak-and-dagger rendezvous.
Two other agents were posted across the street.

Downtown, two cars, an agent in each, were designated to patrol
outside Pennsylvania Station, while five other agents—one a tall, wil-
lowy brunette named Sappho Manos, chief clerk in the New York
City FBI office—were in and around the station on foot.

As the train bringing Judith Coplon to New York passed through
the tunnel under the Hudson River and slowed down in its approach
to Pennsylvania Station, the slender, dark-eyed Miss Coplon rose
from her seat and straightened the wrinkles in her black skirt, adjusted her sweater, then reached for the black cloth coat which had
been on the seat beside her. She put on the coat, then walked forward
to the car's vestibule.

Agents Hradsky and Brennan remained in their seats but their eyes
were glued to the suspect.

When the train came to a halt and the doors opened, Judith Coplon stepped onto the platform and walked toward the stairs. Right
behind were the two agents who had followed her from Washington.
And when she reached the main terminal level, other alert but invisible hosts were there to greet her.

Miss Manos and FBI Agents Robert Granville and Edward Scheidt
quickly targeted in on Miss Coplon and, with several paces separating
each operative, fell in behind her as she threaded her way through the
incipient evening rush hour crowd to the IND's 34th Street station at
the far western end of the giant terminal.

Unknown to Judith Coplon, this same trio followed her through
the turnstile to the platform and into an uptown Washington Heights
express. Agents Hradsky and Brennan, on a signal from Granville
that his team had taken over, dropped out of the picture at the sub-

way entrance. They could not continue to tail the suspect without risking the chance that she would recognize what they were doing.

Nevertheless, Miss Coplon was in the clutches of a formidable array of operatives. At no time could she elude the scrutiny of at least one or all three of her watchers, even when the homebound crowd grew at each subsequent stop on the trip uptown.

The ride lasted less than a half hour. Shortly before 5 p.m., Miss Coplon wove her way to the train's door and stepped out onto the platform at the 190th Street station. Agent Granville was right behind her. At the same time Miss Manos and Agent Scheidt stepped off through a door at the other end of the car. They turned and walked toward Miss Coplon as she, seeming somewhat confused on the crowded platform, moved toward them.

Then came one of those incidents that if written into fiction would surely have been discounted as too melodramatically implausible.

Miss Coplon stumbled and literally bumped into Miss Manos. "Excuse me," the girl said, "I'm sorry." Then as she recovered, she added, "Excuse me again, but I seem to be lost. Can you tell me how I can get to Broadway?"

Heart in mouth but deadpan, as though nothing in the world could be amiss, Miss Manos turned a quick smile and answered in a steady voice, "That's quite all right. I'm sorry we can't help." She gazed at Scheidt and then at Miss Coplon again. "We seem to be lost, too. We were just trying to get our bearings. Sorry . . ."

And with that, Miss Manos and Scheidt walked in the opposite direction, refusing even to glance at Agent Granville who, of course, had stayed back during the brief encounter and now had to go it alone.

Granville tailed the diminutive suspect to the street and watched as she walked aimlessly, or seemingly so, from Overlook Terrace east on 190th Street to Fort Washington Avenue and on to Broadway. After long minutes of this wandering, Granville sensed this part of the trip might be a decoy. He quickly slipped into a phone booth which gave him a view of the street and so let him keep an eye on his quarry, and called a special FBI number. He gave his location and asked for reinforcements. Then he stepped out and picked up Judith Coplon's trail.

Minutes later Granville spotted the help he was looking for in the person of Agent John R. Murphy who fell in behind Granville as Judith Coplon's second shadow. At 191st Street and Broadway, Granville veered off in another direction and circled around the block. Still more minutes later, Granville came back to stalk the suspect as Murphy peeled off.

At 5:55 p.m. Valentin Gubitchev all at once appeared on the scene. Two agents had followed him from the UN Building to the Heights, but now as they spotted Granville and Murphy nearby, they fell back and let these two agents do the spotting.

As Gubitchev rounded 191st Street into Broadway, he walked toward Judith Coplon—and right past her. Neither gave any sign of recognition. The G-men, expecting something of the sort, split up again, each taking up the trail of a suspect.

For more than an hour, Gubitchev and Judith Coplon wandered the streets of Washington Heights, occasionally passing one another, occasionally walking in the same direction, but never looking at each other directly, never exchanging a glance, never handing anything over, never signaling each other.

It was now apparent the Justice Department girl and the Russian engineer were following an elaborate cloak-and-dagger routine.

Finally, after an hour and more of seemingly aimless promenading, Miss Coplon headed back to the IND subway at 190th Street and boarded a downtown express that ultimately deposited her at the 42nd Street station on 8th Avenue. It was 7:30 p.m. when she climbed the stairs to the busy street, just a block west of Times Square. Agent Murphy had never let her out of his sight on the train ride and he was still stalking her now on the street. But he had no idea where Gubitchev was. Nor Agent Granville.

Miss Coplon headed east on 42nd Street, past the bright blinking lights of the all-night movie houses that illuminate the street into an incandescent brilliance, past the multitude of hot dog stands, pizza parlors, army and navy stores, past the throngs of black-jacketed teenagers who make the gaudy street their constant hangout.

Murphy clung to Judith through the crowds and soon the blinding lights of Times Square burst upon them. Judith Coplon turned the corner into Seventh Avenue where it merges into Broadway, walking into the pulse center of the big city. Here his quarry suddenly slowed her pace, almost ambling along now. The crowds were fairly thick in Times Square because curtain time was approaching in the more than score of legitimate theaters that dot the area. It was easy to lose her in those throngs, so Murphy moved closer.

In front of the Paramount Theater at the corner of 43rd Street, Judith suddenly turned and started back. Murphy stepped into the doorway of a variety store and waited until his prey had passed, then he picked up her trail again. It led around the corner into 42nd Street once more. As Miss Coplon walked west toward Eighth Avenue, Murphy suddenly became aware of Gubitchev. He had popped up about fifty feet behind Miss Coplon and was going in the same direction. Murphy had been about seventy-five feet behind Miss Coplon which put Gubitchev only twenty-five feet in front of the G-man—almost too close for Murphy's comfort.

Murphy turned and looked in desperation for Agent Granville who had had the job of tailing Gubitchev. There was no sign of him. It was up to Murphy now to follow both suspects, who now walked on past Eighth Avenue and headed toward Ninth.

About mid-block, Gubitchev suddenly looked back over his left shoulder, held the glance, then turned his head frontward again. A few paces on, Gubitchev tossed another quick look over his left shoulder, then his right. He straightened again and quickened his pace.

Then, as he drew abreast of Miss Coplon, Gubitchev broke into a run. All at once Miss Coplon began running, too. As Murphy took after them, Gubitchev and the girl sprinted across Ninth Avenue and hopped aboard a downtown bus.

Instead of racing for the bus himself, Murphy darted into a bar-and-grill and phoned the FBI to report what had happened. A radio flash went out immediately to all FBI cars to converge on the bus.

From scattered directions, the unmarked cars gathered speed and headed crosstown, downtown, uptown, all targeting in on the south-bound bus. One FBI car, far uptown, raced along the West Side Highway, an elevated expressway that snakes along the Hudson River shore, and as it neared the scene came to grief—with a flat tire. That put four agents out of action.

But no misfortune overtook the other pursuing cars and within minutes they had the rear of the bus fixed in the beams of their headlights. The trail had been picked up even before the bus had gone ten blocks. And Judith Coplon and Valentin Gubitchev were still aboard the bus, but sitting apart on opposite sides of the aisle. They were still pretending they were strangers to each other.

When the bus stopped at 14th Street, the northern edge of Greenwich Village, Gubitchev and Miss Coplon stepped off. It was 9:05 p.m. and the neighborhood was nearly deserted. For the first time, in the darkness of the quiet street, Gubitchev and Miss Coplon apparently felt it was safe to meet. They stood a few minutes chatting, then walked east on 14th Street and went down into a BMT line subway station.

A train bound for the Canarsie section of Brooklyn pulled in and the suspects scampered aboard. Into the same train went Granville, who had been picked up in one of the FBI cars after Miss Coplon and Gubitchev had given him the slip earlier, and now was again restored as the primary tail.

In the car the couple separated again, taking seats apart from each other. But at the next station, Union Square, they suddenly leaped to their feet and dashed out of the car in what seemed to be perfect timing for their exit. They went out just as the doors were closing. Granville could not get off in time and was forced to ride the train to the next station, where he quickly phoned the FBI command post to report what had happened.

The time now was 9:22 p.m. and for the next twelve minutes the FBI lost all touch with Gubitchev and Miss Coplon. But at 9:34 p.m. they were spotted once more on the east side of Third Avenue near East 15th Street. By now Granville had gotten back and joined the other G-men who had the couple in their sights once more. Again he stalked behind at a discreet distance as the other agents took up obscure positions in doorways along the grimy avenue.

Granville allowed the two to stroll unhampered across 15th Street. All at once the deserted avenue came to life as a stream of cars converged on the area. Just then Granville was joined by Agent Murphy who had brought instructions.

He spelled them out very simply: "We take them!"

Midway between 15th and 16th Streets, on the east side of the avenue, Agent Granville drew up to Gubitchev and Miss Coplon, tapped them gently on the shoulder and said grimly, "I am a special agent of the FBI. You are both under arrest."

Miss Coplon's handbag was seized and examined on the spot. In it the G-men found the very documents the suspect was reported to have taken with her when she left her office in the Justice Department earlier in the day. One of these papers was a two-part memorandum which dealt with: (1) actual Communist attempts to lay hands on the geophones which had been designed to register the destructive force of atomic bombs; and (2) fictitious data that the FBI was using to hire Amtorg officials as informants concerning the Red conspiracy in the U.S. The signature of FBI Director J. Edgar Hoover was on the memo to make it look authentic.

Gubitchev was given a quick frisk to determine whether he had a weapon on him. He was clean. Then Granville went through Gubitchev's pockets and found a plain white envelope containing $125 in $5, $10, and $20 bills. In addition, he had $4.25 in another pocket.

Over their protests, Gubitchev and Miss Coplon were escorted into a car and driven to FBI headquarters in the Federal Building at Foley Square in downtown Manhattan. They were questioned for the next seven hours, during which time both suspects categorically denied every allegation that they had engaged in espionage.

Miss Coplon insisted the meetings the FBI had witnessed—on January 14, February 17, and the last one which had ended in her arrest—were nothing more than innocent get-togethers of a "maiden and man carrying on a romance." She told her questioners she had met Gubitchev in September of 1948, had fallen in love with him, and, until the first rendezvous on January 14 which the FBI observed, was hoping to marry him. That night she learned for the first time Gubitchev could not go through with his promise because he already had a wife. When the FBI saw her raise the newspaper she was holding and gesticulate, Miss Coplon explained, she was actually trying to hit Gubitchev in anger.

Shortly before 3 a.m., the FBI concluded its questioning and notified the United Nations Secretariat to send an attorney to the Federal Building to determine whether Gubitchev was on official duty when taken in custody and hence entitled to immunity. At the same time the prisoners were directed to make efforts to obtain counsel.

Meanwhile, Federal Judge Simon H. Rifkind was awakened and asked to come to his chambers in the Federal Court House to conduct an arraignment.

At 4 a.m. the prisoners were brought before Rifkind. All he did at that juncture was advise Gubitchev and Miss Coplon of their constitutional rights. Then he recessed the proceedings until 11 a.m. to give the couple time to obtain lawyers. When the arraignment resumed at 11 o'clock, Miss Coplon had an attorney; Gubitchev still did not. Judge Rifkind held Miss Coplon in $20,000 bail and Gubitchev in $100,000.

The question came up immediately about Gubitchev's status. Did he enjoy diplomatic immunity?

The answer was provided by an observer at the arraignment, Oscar Schachter, of the UN's legal staff. Schachter said Gubitchev was not on United Nations duty at the time of his arrest and thus did not enjoy immunity against the charges of violating United States laws. In default of bail, Miss Coplon and Gubitchev were both lodged in federal detention pens.

Gubitchev's arrest brought immediate and angry reaction from the Soviets. In Washington, Russian Ambassador Alexander S. Panyushkin called on Under-Secretary of State James E. Webb and demanded Gubitchev's immediate release. Webb told Panyushkin that the State Department was discussing the case with the Justice Department and the UN Secretariat for a final determination.

The next day, Saturday, March 5, Secretary General Lie suspended Gubitchev from his Secretariat post, reiterating that the Russian enjoyed no diplomatic immunity under the circumstances. He said he was going according to the rules which were spelled out clearly in the United Nations headquarters agreement.

Secretary of State Dean Acheson replied to Moscow a week later and sealed Gubitchev's fate by stating that the United States did not recognize the diplomatic immunity claimed for the accused Soviet engineer.

While Judith Coplon was able to go free the day after her arrest, once bail was posted, Gubitchev was not so lucky. No one came forward to put up his $100,000 bond, and he was kept in the Federal House of Detention for fifty-three days. Finally, a Soviet official put up the money—in cash—and Gubitchev was released.

Meanwhile, a Federal grand jury in New York indicted both Gubitchev and Miss Coplon on charges of espionage; Miss Coplon was accused of passing Justice Department documents and Gubitchev of receiving them. Another Federal grand jury in Washington also indicted Miss Coplon, alone, on a charge of stealing those documents from the Internal Security Division.

The Washington trial was held first. It began April 25, 1949, and lasted ten weeks. Miss Coplon swore repeatedly that she had met Gubitchev only because she loved him and that she had three excuses for carrying the valuable government papers: she took them home to work on; she needed them to bone up for a Civil Service examination she planned to take to advance herself in the Justice Department, and she intended to use them as source material for a novel she planned to write that she would call *Government Girl.*

She wept, shouted, and yelled at the trial. She screamed she was being framed and that the Government's case was "so fishy it smells to high heaven." She accused the Justice Department of "engineering" the charges against her to avert congressional criticism of what she termed the department's failure to crack down on Communists.

John M. Kelly, Jr., the chief prosecutor, told the jury of eight men and four women, six of whom were Negroes, that Judy "gave herself —mind, body, and soul—to the Russians." He insisted the Communists had seen beneath her "veneer of innocence and pretty face" and gotten to the "hard core of steel" underneath.

"They found a girl who hated many people and many things and most of all the United States Government," Kelly declared.

The prosecution made much of its contention that during the time Judy claimed she was infatuated with Gubitchev, she had spent successive nights in Baltimore and Philadelphia hotels with a Justice Department attorney, and other nights in his apartment. Judy admitted it but insisted they had not been intimate.

On June 9, the jury returned the verdict: guilty.

Just before she was sentenced, Judith Coplon stood before Judge Albert L. Reeves in the federal courtroom in Washington and declared, "I understand that I can plead for mercy. That I will not do. To me that would be an admission of guilt. I'm innocent! I'm innocent!"

The judge did not agree. The defendant, he ruled, had a fair trial. The evidence was incontrovertible. He found that Miss Coplon's conduct when she met Gubitchev on February 18 and again on March 4 was "such as to arouse the gravest of suspicions." Her pocketbook, the judge asserted, was "literally bulging with highly confidential secrets," most of which referred to suspected espionage agents.

"She is charged with a serious offense," the court declared. "She violated a high trust. She was in a highly confidential position. She attempted to betray the country although she had taken a loyalty oath."

The sentence: forty months to ten years.

Now Judith Coplon faced another trial—with Gubitchev—in New York City. The proceedings got under way January 24, 1950, and they were greatly enlivened by the antics of Judith Coplon's voluble, fiery attorney, Archibald Palmer, who had been twice fined $100 for contempt of court by Judge Reeves in Washington. Palmer stayed out of serious hassles with Federal Judge Sylvester Ryan during the New York trial but fell afoul of his client, who never did get along too well with her lawyer.

Shortly after the trial started, Miss Coplon asked that Palmer be dismissed as her counsel on various grounds which Judith purported had made her lose confidence in him. He was then dismissed by Judge Ryan.

When Miss Coplon failed to select a new lawyer, Judge Ryan named Attorneys Samuel Neuburger, Leonard Boudin, and Sidney S. Berman to defend her. Their contention throughout the trial was that Miss Coplon's association with Gubitchev had been strictly a romantic one.

Gubitchev's attorney, Abraham L. Pomerantz, also claimed that a friendship existed between his client and Miss Coplon, and asserted that the Government's case was largely based on illegal search and seizure and on wiretap evidence.

On March 7, the jury returned a verdict of guilty against both Miss Coplon and Gubitchev. Before pronouncing sentence on Miss Coplon, Judge Ryan lashed out with this denunication:

"You have brought dishonor upon the name you bear; you have brought disgrace and even tragedy upon your family. You have been disloyal to the country which has nourished you, helped you acquire an education and placed in you high trust and confidence. Your country looks upon you with sorrow. You have proved yourself an ungrateful daughter. My observation of you during the trial and my knowledge of the facts convince me that the seeds of disloyalty still find root within you."

The tragedy referred to by Judge Ryan was the death of Miss Coplon's father. The family had tried to keep the news from the elder Coplon who was an invalid. At the time of his daughter's arrest, Coplon was recovering from a stroke. Despite the family's attempts to shield him, he heard of the arrest through a radio broadcast. When his daughter was indicted a second time on March 16, 1949, in Washington, Coplon suffered a second stroke and never regained consciousness. He died on March 29, 1949, at the age of sixty-nine. Miss Coplon was with her father at her home in Brooklyn when the end came. He died in the belief his daughter was innocent of the crime of betraying her country. He actually accepted her explanation that she had merely "borrowed" the secret documents found in her possession for the book she was planning to write.

Judge Ryan imposed fifteen-year sentences on Gubitchev and Miss Coplon, hers to run consecutively. But the tall, square-jawed Judge Ryan literally rocked the courtroom when he turned to address Gubitchev:

"You came here as an emissary of peace; you were accepted among us in the role of a friend; you violated your oath of office to the Secretariat of the United Nations of the world. . . . You stand convicted before the world of betrayal of all human mankind. You, it has been found, have by your acts attempted to destroy the hopes of millions who would avoid war and establish peace among the peoples of the world. And you do that with arrogance and with a smile on your lips and on your face as you stand here before me for sentence, and in defiance of all humanity . . ."

Everyone was expecting Judge Ryan to reel off one final blast at Gubitchev, then send him off in the custody of the guards to do his time in Federal prison. The final blast came, but it was impregnated with a great surprise:

"The Attorney General of the United States and the Secretary of State have recommended that this sentence be suspended and that you be sent out of the country. These officials state that they feel that the best interests of the United States of America and of its citizens will be served by following this course. . . . It is beyond my province to question the reasons for or the wisdom of their recommendation. I shall accept it . . ."

Then Judge Ryan gave Gubitchev an alternative: get out of the country or go to jail.

Gubitchev was delighted inwardly, yet he made a brief stand of it by threatening to fight the sentence. "I want very much," he said, "to clear my name." But the gesture was empty. On March 13, four days after Judge Ryan gave him a choice, Gubitchev advised the Federal court he would be pleased to leave the United States in lieu of doing fifteen years in prison.

Gubitchev also tried in those last hours to have the court rescind its directive that he "never return" to the United States, but U.S. Attorney Irving H. Saypol who had conducted the prosecution was quick in warning that he would permit no "shenanigans," that Gubitchev could accept the terms laid down by the court or else.

Gubitchev did not press his "technical legal reservations" any further and on the 20th of March he sailed for home on the Polish liner *Batory*. He was accompanied by his wife, Lydia, who met her husband dockside and thrust welcoming arms around him. Gubitchev could not return the embrace. His wrists were still manacled—and remained so until the vessel set sail.

Meanwhile, Judith Coplon, out on a total of $60,000 bail, turned to the higher courts for a reversal of her dual sentences. Through her attorneys, Neuburger, Boudin, and Berman, Miss Coplon met a broad-shouldered, sandy-haired, blue-eyed young man who worked as a lawyer in their office. His name was Albert H. Socolov. They were introduced in January 1950, just before her second trial.

On the afternoon of May 29, about fifty relatives and members of the family gathered in the Coplon four-room apartment in Brooklyn to witness a simple, double-ring wedding ceremony, conducted by Rabbi Max Felshin of Manhattan's Radio City Synagogue, in which Judith Coplon and Albert Socolov were married.

Looking radiant and rested, Judith Coplon was hardly to be compared with the tired and angered woman who in March had stood before the bench and listened to Judge Ryan label her a traitor to her country.

Her new husband immediately made it his personal business to clear his wife's name. With Attorney Boudin as the chief ball-carrier,

Socolov masterminded an appeal and achieved the first breakthrough on December 5, 1950, when the United States Circuit Court of Appeals at Foley Square unanimously set aside her New York conviction—even though holding that her "guilt is plain."

The court, presided over by distinguished Judge Learned Hand, ruled that the conviction must be upset because Judith Coplon was arrested without a warrant and that the Government had failed to show conclusively that its evidence did not stem from other than illegal wire-tapping sources.

Although the indictment was not dismissed and the way was left open for retrial, many sources at once conceded that the high court had knocked the props from under the Government's case. The court had found that the incriminating evidence—the Justice Department documents allegedly found in Miss Coplon's handbag—could not be used against her because the G-men had seized them without a warrant. The papers were the crux of the case.

Since then a law has been passed enabling the FBI to make arrests without warrants, but that could not apply in the Coplon case.

Boudin and Socolov then hit the U.S. Court of Appeals in Washington on Miss Coplon's 1949 conviction there. The verdict was upheld but the court said she was entitled to a lower court hearing to determine whether her telephone conversations with her lawyer, Palmer, before and during her trial in Washington had been tapped. If the phones were tapped—a fact conceded by the Government at the New York trial—then, the court ruled, she was entitled to a new trial in Washington.

But the hearing suggested by the Court of Appeals never came off. Instead, opposing sides sought relief before the United States Supreme Court. The Government went in with two motions, the defense with one, both hoping to bring order out of the chaos created by the conflicting Court of Appeals decisions.

On January 28, 1952, the nation's highest tribunal merely added to the muddle by refusing any review. That left everything up in the air, where it has remained ever since.

For more than a dozen years, Judith Coplon, or Mrs. Albert Socolov, has been a free woman while government officials debate and deliberate what they can do with her case which has come to be one of the most celebrated "hot potatoes" in the annals of jurisprudence.

And today Judith Coplon is still a free woman, although she is being continued in the $60,000 bail which has never been returned. Forty thousand of that money, all in cash, was put up for her bail in New York; the other $20,000 was posted through a bonding company in Washington. Not a penny of interest has been earned on that money in all these years.

The indictments against her still have not been dismissed and it is next to impossible to learn when, if ever, they will be dismissed or new attempts made to bring Judith Coplon to trial. The case, a legal nightmare, has passed through four national administrations: Truman, Eisenhower, Kennedy, and Johnson. And still it lingers.

Meanwhile, Judith Coplon, now a matronly mother of four children, spends her time as an obscure housewife, living in a 132-year-old red-brick apartment house in downtown Brooklyn. Socolov bought the house and the family occupies three of the four floors, which they have remodeled and furnished.

Judith Coplon's dark brown hair is still dark brown, but strands of gray show now. Although she is twenty pounds heavier than she was in the early 1950's when she was front page news, she still runs up and down the stairs with plenty of bounce and exudes a surprising middle-age youthfulness.

If you should ask why Judith Coplon has not tried to have the dual indictments dismissed and the $60,000 returned to her and the bonding company, part or all of the answer perhaps lies in the fact that she has those four children. The last thing she wants is to have them find out about their mother's past. Espionage is a hard subject to discuss with youngsters, especially when it concerns their own mother.

Try to talk to her husband about the case, and he says, "I don't want to discuss it. We have cherished these years of privacy we have had . . ."

The years have been private for Gubitchev, too. Nothing of his whereabouts in the Soviet Union has been heard during all this time. If he is still alive, no one this side of the Iron Curtain knows.

3 : Our Eastern Seaboard
Defenses Under a Red Spyglass

THE Gubitchev-Coplon spy case revived a clamor for an investigation of the United Nations that had been demanded back in 1948, when charges of subversion were being hurled about by a handful of congressmen and senators whose tactics were labeled by critics as "incredibly irresponsible and hysterical."

The thunder was sounded off by three State Department subordinate officials of the Visa Division, who gave testimony to a Senate Judiciary Subcommittee in Washington to the general effect that the UN headquarters was being used by Communist countries as a "gateway" to slip hundreds of subversive agents into this country, to roam unwatched under cover of diplomatic immunity.

One witness, William McGrath Harlow, chief of the department's Diplomatic Visa Section, expressed the belief that "every representative of an Iron Curtain country" attached to the UN "is a threat to the security of the United States."

The other two witnesses, Robert G. Alexander and R. Clyde Larkin, also gave testimony to the same general effect—that the security of the United States was threatened by several hundred Soviet and satellite representatives who were using the UN merely as a cover up for subversive activities.

Larkin told the Senate subcommittee that some agents were moving about freely "trying to collect intelligence data of benefit to their own country, as well as for the enlightenment of various groups in this country."

Alexander, a 31-year-veteran of the State Department service and an expert on visa matters, added fuel to the fire by saying the UN was honeycombed with international and domestic Communists.

The charges brought angry reaction from the staff committee of the UN, which unanimously passed a resolution in behalf of the more than 3,000 employees of that time, condemning the repeated spy accusations against the organization. The resolution stated that the "unsubstantiated charges which have been made, and the manner in which they were publicized, unjustly cause damage to the United Nations in general and the Secretariat in particular."

The charges by the three State Department officials quickly prompted Secretary of State George C. Marshall to form a committee of distinguished citizens to look into the matter. The committee consisted of Benjamin M. McKelway, James H. Rowe, Jr., and Marcellus C. Sheild.

After listening to the testimony of the three State Department officials and completing its study, the Secretary's committee reported back that it did not find several hundred persons, or even one person, abusing America's hospitality under UN auspices by spying or conspiring in espionage. The committee was "shocked by the manner in which these serious charges were made." It pointed out that the "irresponsible" statements "produced serious repercussions on the foreign policy of the United States."

They did in truth, too, for the United Nations was injured and doubts were raised abroad about the sincerity of America's support of the great undertaking that was the still infant world organization.

The New York Times commented on the incident: "This episode might not have occurred, and certainly would have drawn less attention, if people's ideas of what constitutes evidence had not been upset by the activities of one or two other congressional committees. We have to guard ourselves but we do not have to go into hysterics in the process."

Although the committee failed to find any documentation in the three State Department officials' charges, the Central Intelligence Agency conducted its own investigation and reported back to the

Senate Judiciary Committee, headed by Senator Pat McCarran (D.-Nev.) that Communist terrorists, wholesale killers, spies, and subversive agents did, in fact, hold jobs with the United Nations and its subsidiary organizations.

Senator McCarran released the contents of a letter from Rear Admiral R. H. Hillenkoetter, director of the CIA, who had investigated a list of one hundred names of UN employees submitted by the Mc-Carran committee.

Here were Hillenkoetter's findings:

a) Thirty-two of the employees were engaged in active work for the intelligence agencies of their respective countries.

b) Twenty-nine others were high-ranking Communist Party officials. And as such, the committee indicated, they must be considered as engaging in subversive activities against the United States.

c) Twenty-one more were engaged in active Communist organization work of an underground or subversive nature outside their native homelands.

d) Fifteen others were not in the CIA's "derogatory information file."

e) The remaining three had definite pro-American sympathies or had shown disaffection with Communist ideology.

Another part of Hillenkoetter's letter to the senators described the pattern of Communist espionage and subversive group operations, listing these specific objectives:

a) Placing agents in strategic U.S. installations.

b) Establishing communications facilities for agents to transmit material, one facet of which is the system of seamen couriers.

c) Checking on Soviet personnel in this country to guard against defection.

d) Dissemination of Communist propaganda and gathering of adverse facts about the United States.

e) Through U.S. immigrant and language groups, sending American currency to Russia, where it aggregates a considerable income for Russian intelligence operations abroad.

f) Maintenance of liaison between Communists in the United States and Russian headquarters.

g) Organization of pressure groups to oppose American legislation adverse to Russia.

Hillenkoetter further went on to describe how Russia went to extreme lengths to select personnel for service in the United States and the UN, and extreme pains to pick diplomats and other officials who would not defect and who would make good spies.

The concern over Red spies in the UN eventually diminished, but with the Gubitchev-Coplon case came a new ground swell of fears and apprehensions about the world organization as a seat for espionage. For the first time, the critics could point to Gubitchev and say, "See, we told you . . . the UN is reeking with Red agents."

The New York *News,* which could look out of its own imposing skyscraper across 42nd Street and see the mammoth 39-story UN structure blotting out the magnificent view of the East River, wrote a bitter editorial about the UN after the Gubitchev-Coplon case. At the time, Congress had not yet allocated the $65,000,000 U.S. loan for the construction of the building on property donated by the Rockefeller family.

> Every precaution should be taken—and put in writing—against letting the UN serve as a spy hideaway and retreat [wrote the *News*]. Congress can force such restrictions, too, if it so desires. That $65,000,000 U.S. "loan" for the UN palaces in east midtown New York has not yet been okayed by Congress—and need not be, as long as the UN is the least bit stuffy about limiting diplomatic immunity.
>
> Or, if Congress should feel like just inviting the UN to take its world HQ the hell out of this country and move them to Geneva, Switzerland, we think that would be even better. It seems a safe bet that, no matter how severely we limit diplomatic immunity, some clever spies, Russian or other, will always be able to make dangerous uses of UN world HQ if they are in the United States.

Needless to say, the United States okayed the loan and the United Nations remained, even though the *News* chose not to be a friendly neighbor.

Before too long, the *News* and other opponents of the UN had something more to cackle about when the Senate Internal Security Committee in Washington touched off a full drive against subversives and Communists in the Secretariat. The storm broke over the UN in mid-summer 1952, when an investigation linked forty Americans in the UN to espionage. Although the scandal pointed directly to Communists and their agents inside and outside the UN, there had been no hint as to which Reds might have been involved in the attempts to subvert the Americans.

The probe led to the dismissal of twenty-nine disloyal Americans and the suspension of eleven others. Several of the latter group turned in their resignations before they could be given hearings.

The highlight of the Senate Internal Security Committee hearing came in early December when Evelyn Thaler, secretary to Konstantin E. Zinchenko, head of the UN's Department of Security Council Affairs, testified. Zinchenko was a Russian.

Miss Thaler told the probers that she had been a Communist at one time, but quit of boredom. The committee praised Miss Thaler for helping spotlight the twenty-nine disloyal American employees at the UN, who were later fired, and praised her for co-operating with the committee as well as the FBI. Observers could only guess whether she hadn't supplied even more vital information at the closed sessions.

At any rate, Miss Thaler's testimony helped focus attention on a strange vacancy that had developed in the august councils of the United Nations. Her own boss had suddenly dropped out of sight, or it just became apparent that he had.

Actually, the vacancy at his desk was noted some months before and it was a matter that had gnawed at Secretary General Trygve Lie. Then around mid-September of 1952, Lie decided to make it his business to find out what had become of Zinchenko.

"What has happened to Konstantin?" was how Lie put it to one of the Soviet Delegation members, Arkady A. Sobolov, when they met for lunch in the delegates' cafeteria shortly after noon on the 13th. Konstantin Zinchenko as Assistant Secretary General of the UN was the highest ranking Russian in Lie's Secretariat and the official who sat in for the Secretary General when he was away from the UN. Lie himself was aware that Zinchenko had gone back to Moscow in June, but he had taken far too long to return.

Sobolov shifted uneasily in his chair as he mulled over the Secretary General's query. Then finally he said with a forced smile, "I have been wondering myself why Konstantin has not come back. I had heard he was ill, poor fellow. Maybe he is still indisposed . . ."

It was about what Lie had expected to hear. It's practically the stock reply one gets from Russian government officials at the UN after one of their number drops out of sight suddenly and mysteriously and in all likelihood isn't coming back.

Lie had heard reports for some time that Zinchenko was ill in Moscow, but like other diplomats wise in the ways of reported Soviet ailments, the Secretary General suspected strongly the illness was mostly diplomatic, and that Zinchenko had seen the last of his days in the U.S. and in the service of the UN.

Of course, if anyone had known what had become of Zinchenko, Sobolov would be the one. For Sobolov himself had held Zinchenko's $22,000-a-year Assistant Secretary post until late 1949 when the Gubitchev-Coplon case had exposed Russia's espionage activity in the UN and brought widespread criticism of the Soviets. Sobolov was then recalled to Moscow and from there had sent word back that "illness" prevented his return. Zinchenko then was assigned to take Sobolov's job.

Sobolov eventually returned to the UN, but he had a reduced rank in the Soviet Delegation. Observers of the diplomatic scene agreed at the time he was very fortunate indeed to have recovered his health.

And now Zinchenko was "ill." But still another element of mystery cloaked the case because, along with Zinchenko, one of his chief aides, Nicolai Skvortsov, also was among the missing and had been for some months. He had taken home leave in April and returned to Moscow. Skvortsov, who had put in three years at the UN, was expected back in a month. But then he applied for an extension of leave on the ground his wife was sick. The request was granted and he was continued on the payroll, drawing a tax-free $8,000-a-year salary with full retirement benefits.

No one at the time when Lie inquired about Zinchenko could attach any significance to the dual absences except to speculate along the usual channels: Zinchenko and Skvortsov had fallen out of the good graces of their government and Premier Stalin was dealing with them in the obvious manner.

Nor was much thought given to the fact that the two Russian diplomats had left the scene right in the thick of the storm over the United Nations in mid-summer when the congressional investigation had linked the forty Americans in the UN to espionage.

In the uproar over the charges against these Americans, a hue and cry rose in Washington and other quarters in this country once more against the UN's Department of Security Council Affairs, the very department headed by Zinchenko, the now missing Assistant Secretary General, where the accused Americans had worked.

There was more than a little significance in this situation because the department at the time was dealing in highly important matters pertaining to the Korean War which was then still raging.

There was also considerable significance to the action Lie had taken against Zinchenko, in early 1952, in denying him access to any reports coming in from the Korean front. Zinchenko had been caught making unauthorized diversions of certain documents dealing with strategy, troop movements, and other military matters concerning UN forces in Korea. There can be little doubt that Zinchenko was feeding the information to Moscow which was actually directing the Red forces fighting against the UN divisions on the battle lines.

Secretary General Lie's quarantine of Zinchenko had the effect of reducing his position on the 38th floor to that of a courier. At that same time, Zinchenko's assistant, Skvortsov, also was restricted, so that he, too, had only limited access to papers and documents dealing with Korea. To say the quarantine contributed to Zinchenko's and Skvortsov's departures would probably not be far from the truth.

Zinchenko had come into his post in 1949 as one of the UN's eight Assistant Secretaries General. When the war broke out in 1950, Zinchenko theoretically became the UN Minister of War, Communication, and Information. That put him in charge of all legal, military, and judicial affairs relating to the subsequent UN operations in Korea. This prize position had been delegated to the Russians at the 1945 San Francisco Charter Conference after Molotov's threats to withdraw from further participation in the world body. Molotov then named Sobolov for the job.

The first weeks of fighting in Korea produced understandable confusion in the conduct of field operations and in reports on activities coming back from the front. The Security Council, which had voted UN intervention to stop the Communist North Korean invasion, stipulated that field commanders make frequent reports to the world organization.

These reports went directly to Zinchenko. In time we were to learn that, in receiving this information himself, Zinchenko in effect was getting information about American and UN troops from a theater of war where the enemy in actuality was being commanded by Zinchenko's own boss, Stalin.

Even before Secretary General Lie suspected what was happening in his own Secretariat, the field commander, General Douglas MacArthur, who headed the U.S. forces as well as those of other nations under the UN banner on the Korean front, had begun to realize what was going on. The North Koreans seemed to have an almost uncanny ability to anticipate MacArthur's battle plans.

The General decided on a new strategy, not on the field but in his reports to the UN. He limited the information to general matters of a non-military nature and kept battlefield and logistic data down to an unenlightening minimum.

MacArthur had a secondary reason for holding back. On more than one occasion he had found the UN Security Council had censored his reports on the course of the war in the Far East. This had pulled him into a temporary feud with Trygve Lie. The General was truly on the spot. He was damned if he sent a full and accurate account of activities because he knew that, through Zinchenko, the information would go right back into the hands of the Communist Chinese and North Koreans. And he was damned if he didn't send the full report because he was committing a slur against the whole UN structure.

It was an unfortunate position for MacArthur. And it soon made trouble for him. Zinchenko, as the UN's Minister of War, Communication, and Information, was compelled to notify MacArthur that he was failing in his obligation to the UN. The complaint was certainly justified, but coming as it did from Zinchenko—he was no longer able to transmit accurate warfront information to the Kremlin because of MacArthur's holdout—the question of the General's actions became academic.

In the exchange of messages between Zinchenko and MacArthur

which followed, a long-distance feud soon galvanized. Zinchenko demanded full reports; MacArthur refused to comply.

Finally in anger over Zinchenko's abuse, MacArthur whipped off a blistering complaint to Secretary General Lie. The General did not accuse Zinchenko of espionage; he merely charged that his reports were being censored by the Security Council.

Zinchenko took this occasion to strike back at the General. The Soviet official called a news conference and acidly denounced MacArthur for "holding out" on military information. This outburst was viewed as an attempt to stir up a row and put UN pressure on the General. But the pressure never developed. Instead, not long afterward Lie began holding closed door conferences with the Security Council—without Zinchenko. It was apparent now that Lie, too, had become aware of Zinchenko's real aims in demanding full battlefield reports. Within a few short weeks the Secretary General directed that henceforth reports from MacArthur must not cross Zinchenko's desk; they were to go directly to Lie.

Lie followed this move with the establishment of a "vigilance committee" which, in effect, went a step further in blacking out Russia's access to all information about Korean UN military activities. Only the committee was allowed to handle the reports from Korea. And— Zinchenko was not on the committee.

Thus Zinchenko was reduced, for all intents and purposes, to the level of a liaison or courier between the Secretariat and the Soviet UN Mission. In subsequent months Zinchenko was seen more and more in the company of his aide, Nikolai Skvortsov, and their comings and goings together began to raise questions about what activity they were engaged in.

The suspicion arose because UN observers had always regarded Skvortsov as a man of mystery. Young and clean-cut, Skvortsov had been the greatest enigma that UN correspondents had ever encountered among Russians who passed through the skyscraper headquarters. He liked to chat with people he knew so as to show off his excellent command of English; he cracked jokes; he was affable. Yet he was severe and aloof and extremely cautious in what he said in conversations with correspondents.

The most curious aspect of Skvortsov's peregrinations was the frequency with which he went in and out of the UN Building. Although his duties demanded his presence inside most of the working day, he seemed to have an inordinate amount of business somewhere outside. Where he went and what he did were questions asked but never answered. At least not in the UN.

But a time finally came when one person in the UN did learn about Skvortsov's mysterious trips, now being made with Zinchenko, his boss. Secretary General Lie got the word from the State Department, and it was that Skvortsov had been trying to subvert a number of Americans into obtaining secrets about America's Eastern Seaboard defenses.

Lie also was told that the man behind the plot was Zinchenko, the Secretary General's own first assistant. Lie was truly shocked. He was cognizant of Zinchenko's clandestine role in the Korean military reports affair, but he never suspected a plot to steal the military secrets of the UN's host nation, let alone through a distinguished delegate of the Soviet Mission such as Zinchenko.

Valentin A. Gubitchev was the first person in the UN to be caught as a spy, but he did not enjoy high diplomatic status. In fact, he had no diplomatic immunity at all. He was merely a staff member. Zinchenko was a top-ranking representative of the Soviet government as well as the United Nations.

Lie was informed about Zinchenko and Skvortsov only a week after the Secretary General had had that lunch with Arkady Sobolov and had inquired about the long-missing Assistant Secretary. Now it became evident to Lie why Zinchenko and Skvortsov had taken their leaves so suddenly and why both were delaying their return to the UN.

Of course, the Soviet Union was aware of the probe into the activities of the forty Americans in the UN who were suspected as Communist sympathizers or spies. Had the Kremlin allowed Zinchenko or Skvortsov to return in the midst of this investigation, the Russians certainly could anticipate their involvement in the inquiry; the Senate Internal Security Committee had already been told in private hearings that the two Soviet emissaries were behind the whole plot.

Zinchenko and Skvortsov had been trying all along to recruit many of those Americans working in the UN as Soviet spies. But the plot never got far off the ground. Alerted to Skvortsov's and Zinchenko's unusual comings and goings at the UN, the FBI put a tail on them early in the campaign. One of the factors that drew this shadow was the discovery that Skvortsov previously had been stationed with the Soviet Embassy in Ottawa at the very time the notorious Sergei M. Kudryavtsev operated in Canada as head of the spy ring which stole our atomic secrets. There was immediate suspicion therefore that Skvortsov might have had experience in espionage and that he was a full-time Red spy; he was now looked upon as the man who may have held the funnel through which our nuclear data passed on its way from Kudryavtsev to the Kremlin.

But these were only suspicions. Before long, however, the FBI's surmises received validating support. Trailing Skvortsov, agents had witnessed his surreptitious meetings with various American UN employees. When these meetings began to attract Zinchenko also, the FBI moved in quickly and grabbed off the Americans, one by one, questioned them, and learned what the Russians were after.

The FBI said Zinchenko and Skvortsov were out to get any information dealing with military and seaport facilities on our Atlantic Coast: the capacity of our naval shipyards in Brooklyn, Norfolk, and Portsmouth; data on the Electric Boat Company yards at Groton, Connecticut, where the United States was about to launch its nuclear sub construction program; statistics about Air Force landing strips at Mitchell Field, Long Island; Andover, Massachusetts; and Maguire Air Force Base in New Jersey; and numerous other closely guarded top-secret data.

But the FBI was always a step ahead of Zinchenko and Skvortsov. No sooner did the Russians select one or another of the American UN employees for a job of espionage than the G-men were on to it. They intercepted the employees one at a time, questioned them, learned what they had been asked to do, and engaged them in a prudent mission of counterespionage.

That there had been some transmission of secrets to the Russians cannot be doubted, because when Congress finally stepped in with its probe and prompted the dismissal of the twenty-nine disloyal Americans and the suspension of the eleven others, there was solid proof to point to their subversive ties with the Kremlin. Yet there was insufficient evidence to show any had committed espionage and so warranted prosecution under the law. Ostensibly they were fired or suspended for merely associating or being seen in the company of Russia's emissaries, which was certainly enough to raise serious doubts about their loyalties to the United States and to the UN. While there never was real evidence that any of the Americans actually had transmitted secrets, the FBI believes some of them did, although it has never been able to prove it. Most of the witnesses pleaded the Fifth Amendment, which in itself was grounds for dismissal.

Only when the plot crystallized and the FBI had proof of Skvortsov's and Zinchenko's attempts to subvert the Americans in hand did FBI Director Hoover notify the State Department, which in turn alerted Lie, who was given a first-hand rundown on the spy scandal in his midst.

Of course, there was little Lie could do then against Skvortsov and Zinchenko, for they were back in Moscow. Actually, the FBI wanted Lie to do nothing. Both Skvortsov and Zinchenko had notified the Secretary General of their intentions to return as soon as they had conquered their respective bouts with "illness." The United States wanted them back to pick up the strings of their espionage activities on the chance that they would lead the authorities to other spy contacts. So Lie went along with the plan.

But when September passed into October and Skvortsov and Zinchenko both continued to stall about their return, Lie was convinced the Soviet Government had gotten wind of what was suspected of the two diplomats even though their names had never been mentioned at the congressional hearings.

Early in November, Lie finally sent a note to Skvortsov in Moscow, informing him he had been dismissed. No note was sent to Zinchenko. Inasmuch as he enjoyed high diplomatic status, Lie wanted to avoid an "incident." Moreover, it was becoming increasingly apparent that Zinchenko would never return, for nothing had been heard from him for several months.

It wasn't until December 13 that an announcement of the UN spy scandal was made to the public. It came when the United States Delegation at the UN called reporters to a conference and broke the news with this statement: "The United States Government has notified the United Nations that Mr. Nicolai Skvortsov has attempted espionage activities. The United States has also indicated to the United Nations that such conduct is in its opinion a clear violation of his status as an international civil servant. Pending UN action, the U.S. Government has taken steps to deny a visa to Mr. Skvortsov, who is now on home leave."

It made no mention of Zinchenko in the announcement, which significantly had come only a few hours after a three-man judicial advisory committee had completed its study of the "disloyal" employees at the UN and submitted a report to Lie. In effect, the jurists recommended disciplinary action against foreign nationals accused of subversion and dismissal of disloyal American UN employees.

This was the beginning of what ultimately became in the months ahead a full drive against subversives and Communists in the Secretariat.

The public was never told that there was a direct tie between Zinchenko and Skvortsov and the forty Americans in espionage. You are reading it here for the first time in its natural order of evolution.

There is a little more to tell.

Zinchenko's vacant chair in the Secretary General's office and in the council halls of the UN remained unoccupied through the rest of 1952 and for the first half of 1953, and the FBI always was on the wait for his return so it could see where his trail in espionage might lead.

Then unexpectedly on July 1, almost a full year after Zinchenko's departure, a new Assistant Secretary General came into the post. He was Ilya S. Chernyshev, and he was sent here from Moscow on the heels of a note of resignation Lie received from Zinchenko.

As Chernyshev stepped into the job vacated by Zinchenko, the new Assistant Secretary had to face the deep-seated suspicion that had begun to gnaw at many Western diplomats in the UN—that a Russian diplomat could not be expected to play a neutral role such as the rules required of UN employees, not even someone on the diplomatic level.

Chernyshev, former deputy director of *Tass,* took the pledge of allegiance and signed the oath of loyalty to the world organization, but his word and signature had far less meaning now.

The story of Konstantin Zinchenko would not be complete without a brief postscript on his ultimate fate.

As suspected, Zinchenko had fallen out of the good graces of the Stalinist regime and had been shipped off to a prison camp in one of the last purge campaigns before Stalin's death. He remained a political prisoner until the post-Stalin rehabilitation procedures enacted by the new government.

Zinchenko first reappeared in June, 1955, when he joined the staff of the Soviet English-language magazine *News* as a foreign affairs commentator. And his first article was a tirade against the United States which he accused of systematically flouting the United Nations. Among other things, he charged us with violating the UN resolution against war propaganda, obstructing Soviet disarmament proposals, bypassing the Security Council, and making the UN a "cold war battlefield."

By contrast, Zinchenko declared that the Soviet Union always had firmly upheld the Charter. He neglected to mention his old sidekick, Nicolai Skvortsov who, like himself, had fallen down in his role as a spy for the Soviet Union while serving as Zinchenko's chief aide. And he failed to comment even in passing about Soviet espionage activities in the UN.

Two years later, Zinchenko moved up another notch when he was appointed head of press service on a newly formed State Committee for Cultural Relations with Foreign Countries.

This committee's existence was described in a dispatch from *The New York Times* correspondent, Max Frankel, in Moscow this way: "The Soviet Union looked at its Western window today and saw an Iron Curtain. The fabric appeared to be Western, the Government said, and it appointed a committee to haul it down. The committee at once pleaded with Western correspondents to help haul . . ."

Today Konstantin Zinchenko still serves in that post. The continued absence of so prominent and talented a diplomat from public functions of the Soviet Foreign Office and the lack of an assignment in the Foreign Office to this day indicates that he still is not out of his difficulties with the Kremlin.

But he's still better off than Nicolai Skvortsov.

Nicolai has not been heard from since early 1952, when he left the U.S. with the hot breath of the FBI panting on his back.

4 : The Sperry Bombsight— A "Bargain" at Six Thousand

THE year was 1952 and it had suddenly become very warm for April, even in Washington, but it wasn't the hot sun that bothered the assistant naval attaché in the capital. Rather, it was a feverish fright which had swept over the Russian Embassy.

In the painstaking business of espionage, the margin of safety one believes he possesses is rarely measurable, and for one reason or another, the Embassy decided its own margin had narrowed to the danger point in the case of a man we shall call Frederick Timsford.

Tall, distinguished-looking, with a massive head on broad, rugged shoulders, Frederick Timsford was an engineer at a large electronics plant on Long Island. All of six feet two and a bristling two hundred and forty pounds, Timsford looked more like a lineman for the New York Football Giants than a spy. Actually, Fred Timsford was not a spy—he was a counterspy.

His role as double-agent was incited by his recruitment into the ranks of Soviet subversion during the early part of April, 1951, in New York City, even while the last unmelodious strains of the Gubitchev-Coplon case were still echoing in a groaning symphony of travail and trial for its participants.

The forty-one-year-old engineer had attended a small gathering of his company's employees in the Astor Bar in Times Square. The occasion was simply to enjoy a pleasant night on the town—a brief cocktail hour, dinner, then a Broadway play. It would break the monotony of their daily rigors at the plant and their nightly suburban routines at home with wife and children and the ever-recurring chores of spring-feeding the lawn, mending window screens, putting out the garbage.

As is their habit sometimes when they gather around a table weighted with cocktails, engineers—like other professional people—have a tendency towards loquaciousness. This group would not have been incongruous in some other bar where loud talk is part of, or indeed is, the atmosphere. But in the quiet, dignified limits of the Astor, the heady conversation attracted some attention from the red-coated captain, yellow-jacketed waiters, and the customers around them whose tête-à-têtes were being conducted in quiet whispers.

But most of the attention seemed to come from one customer in particular, a short, stocky man with blond hair and the sort of aquiline good looks that you could compare with a Soviet medium T-34 tank. He was sitting alone at a table for two in the second aisle from the window on the West 44th Street side. The engineers occupied a string of tables along the window where a long leather seat runs from the front to the rear of the bar.

The laughter, the gaiety, the kibitzing did not seem to do anything more than attract this man as the group downed their drinks and called for new rounds. Certainly he wasn't annoyed by the clarion-voiced group. He sat virtually unconcerned, dwelling meditatively over his own goblet.

Just before 7 p.m. the levity suddenly diminished at the engineers' table. All at once someone had brought up an engineering problem he had encountered at the plant. The gathering quickly plunged into a serious discussion of its solution. From jovial men on the town they had quickly reverted to the calculating, slide-rule, methodical men that their profession had made them.

Just as suddenly, almost automatically, the blond man sitting opposite them seemed to freeze, then to concentrate on the discussion across the aisle. The topic was on the operation of a radar unit under development for cargo ships. The man listened intently, his eyes now riveted on the speaker, Frederick Timsford, who had edged into the center of attention by providing pertinent details which proved he had the answer to the problem.

The short, stocky onlooker so absorbed in the discussion was eminently qualified for the role of listener. He had the credentials for it, both by training and by avocation.

This was Aleksandr Petrovich Kovalev, Second Secretary of the Soviet Delegation to the United Nations, a graduate of the Soviet School for Espionage and Sabotage in Moscow.

For approximately two dollars and forty cents—the price of two cocktails—it was a night well spent for Kovalev. From that night on, Frederick Timsford was his daily target. He would stalk him from his home in Freeport, Long Island, to the plant not very far from his home, to some of the better restaurants on the Island where Timsford occasionally dined with his wife and children, to the intermittent cocktail sessions at other gathering spots that Timsford and his engineer friends patronized.

Kovalev studied Timsford's style of clothes, his house, his family, his habits, all in a calculated effort to assess his target's wants and needs, and, through that knowledge, his vulnerability.

In time, Kovalev decided that, like so many suburban husbands and home-owners, Timsford was in bondage to the banks for his mortgages on house and car, to the department stores, to the supermarkets, the liquor store, the lumber yard, the lawn nursery, the dentist, the doctor, and a dozen others who extend the one commodity the contemporary male apparently cannot exist without—credit.

And having reached this conclusion from his steady observation, Kovalev went the next logical step and reasoned Timsford needed money. It was on that basis that Kovalev made his approach to Timsford.

First came the casual, almost accidental meeting on the evening of April 26, 1951, in a Lake Success restaurant where Timsford had gone after work for a drink or two at the bar. He was alone. Kovalev took the stool beside Timsford. He introduced himself. He said flatly that he was Alex Kovalev, the Second Secretary of the Soviet Delegation.

"I drop in here once in a while," Kovalev said. "We have our estate nearby at Glen Cove, you know."

Timsford was suddenly alerted to a memory. He turned back

a few weeks to the gathering at the Astor. He recalled sitting there with his back against the wall in the bar and talking to his co-engineers. There had been a blond-haired man at the table across the aisle who had suddenly begun to listen to what Timsford was saying about the radar device. Timsford had noticed this sudden attention to his technical exposition on the problem that had been brought up by one of the other engineers. And he had lowered his voice when he became aware that the man was listening in because, after all, he was discussing a matter that dealt with a sensitive technical development still under wraps at the plant.

Timsford's most outstanding asset was his photographic memory. He could even recall that the stranger at the table that night at the Astor had had a second cocktail before getting up and leaving. And he had not forgotten the face.

It was the same face on the man beside him now at the bar in the Lake Success restaurant. It was Alex Kovalev's face.

Why did this high-ranking Russian delegate from the UN seek him out, Timsford wondered? Was it his discussion of the radar unit that had prompted the Soviet official to meet him in this casual way, a chance encounter that was not really accidental at all? Was there a plot, Timsford asked himself?

Whatever the motive, Timsford was determined not to let on that he had taken notice of Kovalev at the Astor Bar. Timsford would act dumb. He would wait and find out what the Russian was after.

"What kind of work do you do?" Kovalev smiled as Timsford offered to buy the Russian a second drink.

"Oh, I'm an engineer."

There really was no point in hiding his identity, Timsford reasoned. The Russian probably knew enough about him to detect any false statement he might make.

"Isn't that a coincidence," Kovalev said. "I am an engineer, too. But I am not doing very much in that line now. Mostly diplomacy these days at the United Nations."

With the surprising discovery that both were engineers, that each had the same field of interest as the other, Kovalev suggested they get together again.

"I have never met an American engineer before," Kovalev said as if he had discovered one of the Seven Wonders. "What do you say we have dinner together some night next week?"

Timsford responded as though he had read Kovalev's master script. Certainly he'd meet his newly made acquaintance. How about Wednesday night of next week?

Timsford said nothing to anyone about his encounter with Kovalev. The following Wednesday night he kept his dinner date with the Soviet emissary at the Tower Clock Restaurant in Roslyn, not far from Lake Success.

There was nothing subtle in Kovalev's approach when he got down to business in the middle of the meal.

"I am not going to try and fool you, Fred," Kovalev began. "I know a great deal about you. I know that you are greatly in need of money. I am prepared to pay you considerable amounts."

Timsford somehow concealed the shock he felt, perhaps because he expected the Russian to make precisely this kind of an offer. Yet Timsford had not anticipated such an undisguised approach. He had always given Soviet espionage agents more credit for craftiness.

"You are to supply us with certain information we need on the Sperry bombsight, but that is not all," Kovalev whispered as he munched on a celery stalk between mouthfuls of roast beef au jus and mashed potatoes, the same course ordered by Timsford.

"We also will need certain data about Navy equipment and ships, cargo ships—and radar."

Timsford glanced apprehensively at Kovalev across the table.

"Suppose . . . suppose I get caught," he asked in an air of pretended fear that would have done justice to the acting talents of Sir Laurence Olivier. "You know I could be sent to the electric chair. Look at the Rosenbergs . . ."

Just a month ago, in the Federal Courthouse in New York City, Julius and Ethel Rosenberg had been sentenced by Judge Irving R. Kaufman to pay for their crime of passing America's atomic secrets to the Soviets. The penalty was death.

"It's a very big risk," Timsford complained quietly.

"We will work something out to make it impossible that you can be suspected," Kovalev interrupted. "Your risk will be very little—but the money, very big."

Timsford was playing a role and, even without training or advice from the FBI, he was magnificent at it. When dinner was over, he was in Kovalev's hip pocket. Or that is what Timsford wanted him to believe.

As he shook hands and promised to meet Kovalev the following Saturday for "instructions," Timsford was positive now that the whole thing wasn't some kind of nightmarish gag and that Kovalev was, in fact and in the flesh, a genuine Soviet spy.

Thirty minutes later, Timsford was home in Freeport. He greeted his wife and children, then went straight to his den. He closed and locked the door after explaining to his family that he had some important drawings to study. Then Timsford did the thing he knew he had to do. He telephoned the FBI.

At 10:15 p.m., two FBI agents drove through the block and past Timsford's ranch-style home, then circled around and repeated the cruising procedure. They were first making certain that no one was watching Timsford's house, that no Red agent was on a stakeout to detect any unusual activity after Kovalev's proposition had been made to the engineer.

Then, when they were satisfied that the coast was clear, the G-men parked their car a short distance away from Timsford's house and walked to his front door. Timsford admitted them and showed them into the den.

There behind the locked door the G-men listened to Timsford's recapitulation of the events that led up to tonight's offer by Kovalev. And there, too, the FBI agents outlined in detail the instructions Timsford must follow.

Kovalev would have to be watched by the FBI. He would be shadowed by FBI observers whenever he met with Timsford, whether in a restaurant, a bar, or anywhere else. And Timsford, too, would have a shadow when he was away from his work or his home.

But for Timsford himself there was a more delicate, extremely sensitive plan to follow. The FBI would have to have accurate reports on where meetings were to take place, what codes, if any, were agreed upon, and what information Kovalev was after.

The FBI—and Timsford—would have to learn, if they could, what other persons were involved. The Government's counterplot against

"There is nothing really wrong, but we must change procedures because those are the orders," replied Kovalev in a polite but severe tone when Timsford tried to pry from him the reason for the switch.

Timsford was somewhat taken aback by the new method of transmitting data which Kovalev outlined to him. The counterspy was no longer to deliver raw documents or even copies of them. Henceforth he must commit everything to microfilm which, in case the heat is on, is an easily disposable object.

"Just touch a match to it and—poof!" Kovalev advised as he oriented Timsford on how to get rid of the evidence in a pinch.

"Tell me this," Timsford said. "What do I use for a camera?"

"This," Kovalev smiled, reaching into his pocket. He pulled out a small camera of German make that was no larger than a pack of cigarettes. "You will take all the information down on this."

When the meeting was over, Timsford headed to Felice's Restaurant at Old Country Road and Post Avenue in Westbury, about twelve miles out on Long Island from Lake Success. And there in the bar he met his two FBI contacts as had been arranged beforehand.

Timsford, whose retentive powers were described as "almost in the realm of the supernatural," gave the G-men a verbatim and detailed account of his conversation with Kovalev earlier that evening:

KOVALEV: You will take photos with this camera, but you will not develop the film yourself. You will place the undeveloped film in a black paper wrapper, then encase it in a rubber covering. After that you will insert it into a beer can for us.

TIMSFORD: And what do I do with the beer can?

KOVALEV: You will dispose of it in Glen Cove, not far from our Mission's estate.

TIMSFORD: How will I let you know I have something for you? Just phone as I have been doing?

KOVALEV: No, that is out. No phoning. No more personal contacts. You must signal us.

TIMSFORD: Smoke signals, like the Indians?

KOVALEV: I am not joking. This is serious business. You were the one who expressed fear of getting caught at the beginning, remember? So pay attention and don't be funny. This advice I am giving you is intended to give you the greatest degree of safety you can expect in the kind of business we are doing.

TIMSFORD: I'm sorry, Alex. I'm listening. You said you wanted me to signal.

KOVALEV: That is right. You will signal in this way. When you have film to deliver, you are to park your car on West Ninetieth Street in Manhattan. Use the north side of the street. There is a fireplug just in from Central Park West. Park your car there on any Wednesday morning and remain there from nine thirty to nine thirty-five. You are not to leave the car.

TIMSFORD: Is that all?

KOVALEV: No. In your car you must have a red package. Any kind of package with red wrapping which we want you to put in the back so it can be seen through the rear window.

TIMSFORD: And then?

KOVALEV: Now that we know to expect something from you, we will be prepared. That night you are to go to Glen Cove. You will drive out on Northern Boulevard and then turn left on Glen Cove Avenue. Drive along Glen Cove Avenue until you see a stone wall on the right side of the avenue. There will be a hole in the wall slightly beyond a telephone pole. The pole will have two faint white bands painted on it. When you see the hole, place the beer can in it. But remember this. It must be placed there between ten and ten fifteen at night. No earlier, no later. We have studied the location and that is the safest time.

TIMSFORD: Is that it?

KOVALEV: There is more. After you have placed the beer can in the hole in the wall, drive into the village of Glen Cove and then retrace your route to the Golden Slipper and drive to the parking lot. Time it so that you reach there by ten forty to ten forty-five. Park your car in the lot and stay in the car until eleven o'clock. Then you can leave. But—and this is very important—you must have the red package still showing in the back window of the car. In that way we will know that you left the material for us in the wall.

TIMSFORD: I've got that straight. But how will I know you made the pickup? Suppose something goes wrong? Say some kids come along and pull the can out of the wall. Who tells me?

KOVALEV: It is your job to check this out, and we have thought of a way. On the following day, you are to go to the Continental Restaurant on Flatbush Avenue Extension near the Long Island Railroad

OUR EASTERN SEABOARD DEFENSES UNDER A RED SPYGLASS

Konstantin Zinchenko of the Soviet Union accepts congratulations of countryman Yakov Malik on appointment as Assistant Secretary General of United Nations. Other delegates, including Mrs. Eleanor Roosevelt, form receiving line to welcome Zinchenko. Date was October 25, 1948. Four years later—after a bitter feud with General Douglas MacArthur, who accused the Russian of feeding UN Korea battle plans to the Kremlin and Red Chinese—Zinchenko quietly slipped off to Moscow, one step ahead of FBI which found he was mastermind in a plot to recruit 100 American UN employees in Soviet espionage.

". . . AND THEY SEEMED LIKE SUCH NICE, QUIET PEOPLE"

Their neighbors in New York City's suburban-like borough of Queens had no suspicions about Ivan Dmitrievich Egerov, a Russian national working as personnel director in UN. But FBI caught him and his wife, Alexandra, in role of inter-city couriers transmitting U.S. missile and military secrets. Here Egerov (in doorway) and wife leave Federal Building after arrest. But they escaped prosecution as spies when State Department traded them for two Americans imprisoned in Soviet Union.

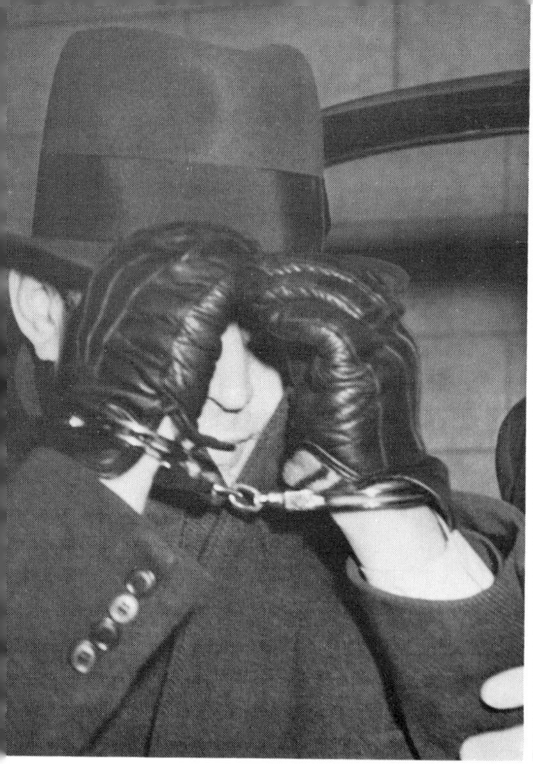

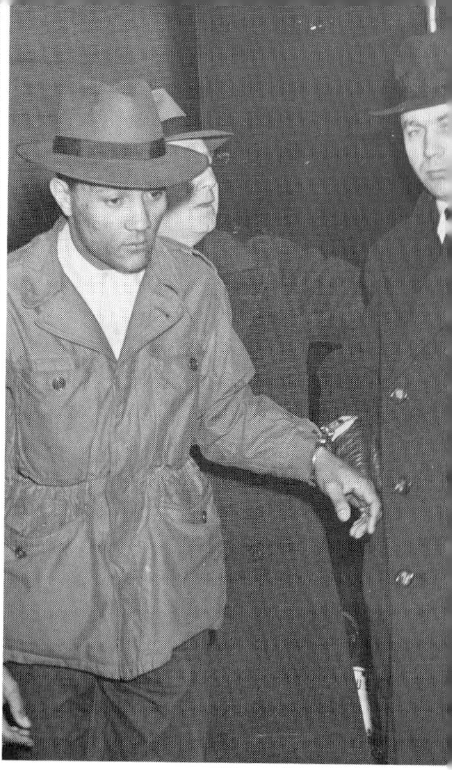

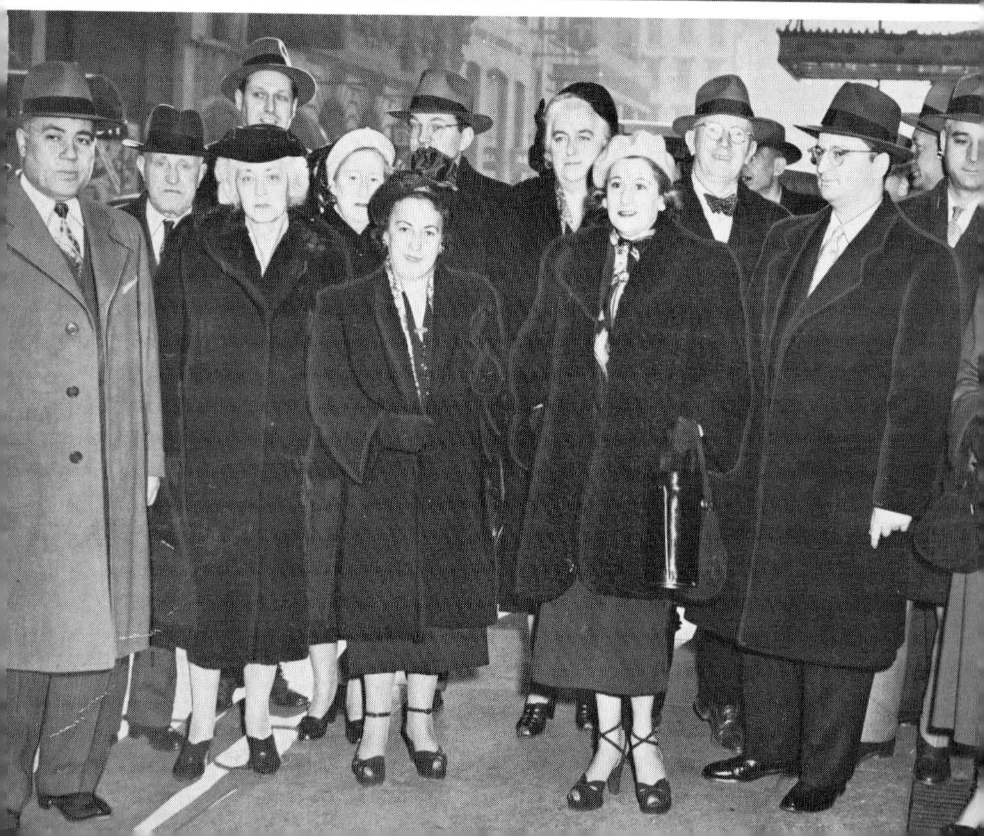

VALENTIN GUBITCHEV—

THE FIRST UN SPY

First case of espionage to sprout from United Nations involved Valentin Gubitchev, Soviet engineer who helped design UN skyscraper headquarters. He conspired with Justice Department girl Judith Coplon in stealing confidential FBI information. Photo top left shows bashful Gubitchev in undiplomatic pose after arrest. At top center he is being brought into Federal Court for trial with Judith Coplon. Jury (bottom left) found both guilty of espionage but Government let Gubitchev go home. Judith then won freedom on legal technicality and married her lawyer, Albert Socolov (top right), who holds first of their four children. As they sail for homeland (bottom right) Gubitchev's wife still manages smile despite testimony that her husband romanced Judith.

THE RED COLONEL AND

FBI Agent Fred Peck, posing as U.S. Army Colonel whom Soviets recruited in East Germany to steal military codes from Fort Leavenworth's staff school, is shown in remarkable series of photos taken with hidden FBI telephoto camera. Sequence beginning top left shows Peck paying cab fare on Madison Avenue and 86th Street in Manhattan where he has rendezvous with Soviet contact. Film strip next shows Colonel Maksim Martynov.

OUR GENERAL STAFF SCHOOL

Soviet member of UN Military Staff Committee, waiting, checking watch, then getting first look at the American "Colonel." In film at right the "Colonel" looks at the time, again walks by Martynov who pretends no recognition. But in last two enlarged sequence shots, Martynov makes approach (top) and finally speaks prearranged code words. Diplomatic immunity saved Martynov from our laws, but he was ordered out of country.

Premier Nikita Khrushchev still could hide anger with a smile back in 1960. He has just come out of Soviet UN Delegation Building in New York City to condemn U-2 spy plane incident over Soviet territory. Arrow shows face of Igor Yakovlevich Melekh, chief of Russian Section in UN Secretariat, agreeing with boss that spying is outrageous. Insert shows Melekh's full face—after FBI arrested him (see photo right) and German-born illustrator Willie Hirsch (wearing glasses) for attempt to steal maps of Chicago's defense installations. Melekh and Kirill Sirgeevich Doronkin (bottom), another Soviet employed at UN who was in on plot, were sent back to Moscow. Hirsch was deported later to Czechoslovakia. At right Melekh and family cast last look at U.S. from liner *Bremen*.

A
KHRUSHCHEV
VISIT

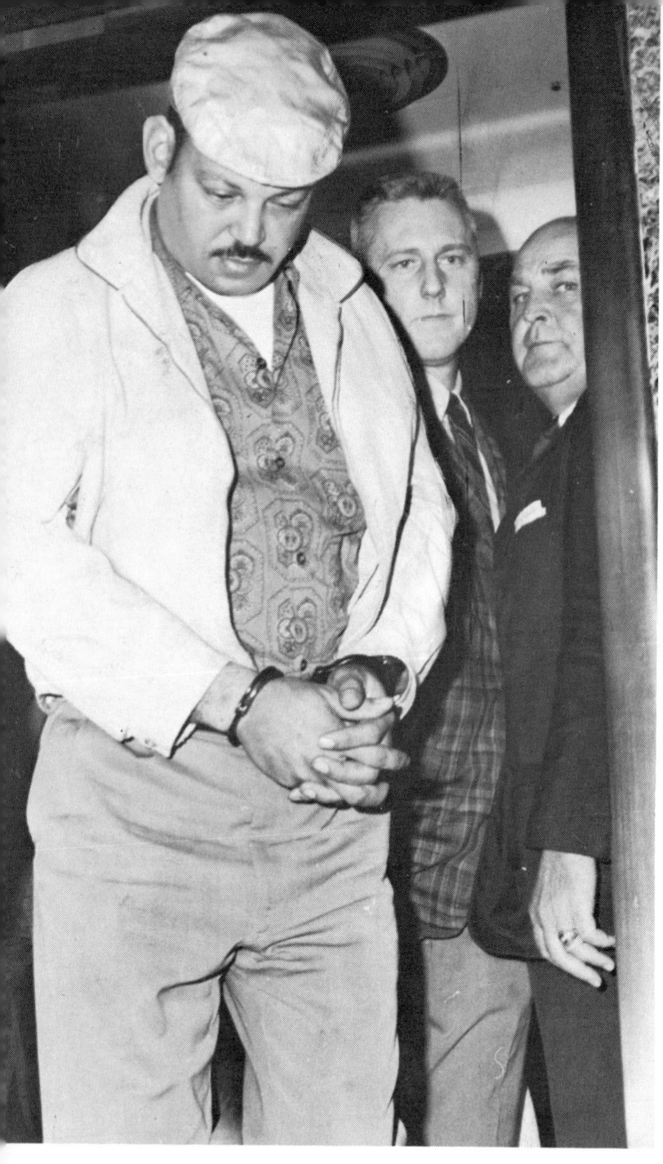

THE UNITED STATES SAILOR

WHO FELL FOR THE LINE

Shame and desolation mask face of Nelson Cornelius "Bulldog" Drummond after arrest for stealing and selling NATO and Navy secrets to Soviets for $22,000. First and only Negro in American history convicted for espionage, Drummond escaped electric chair but received life imprisonment. His Soviet contacts, Evgeni M. Prokhorov (top right), a Second Secretary at UN, and Ivan Y. Vyrodov (bottom right), a Third Secretary, were protected by diplomatic immunity which was their passport back to Russia.

him get into a blue Dodge and drive away. Then he came back into the restaurant. The other agent was at the directory stand. The first FBI man walked over and looked at the page the other agent was pointing to. It was Page 700. And the word "Manhattan" at the top of the page was, indeed, underlined.

Then the operative who had found the mark in the book reached into his pocket and pulled out a photograph he was carrying. It had been distributed to the agents working on the case.

"Yes," he said to the other agent, "that was Kovalev."

This procedure continued into the summer of 1952, a period which saw Timsford go through the routine—and it was routine after a while—six times in all. It was always the same—parking on West 90th Street on any given Wednesday morning, the red package in the back window, the microfilm wrapped in black paper and protected with its rubber covering inserted in a beer can, the drop in the stone wall, the inconsequential drive into Glen Cove, the trip back to the tavern parking lot, the wait, then the trek home and the telephone call to the FBI to report, "Mission accomplished." And in Brooklyn, the assignment of a different team of operatives each time Timsford delivered was to wait in the restaurant for a Soviet agent to come in and make his notation in the Manhattan directory. A different team of agents because Kovalev—and it was Kovalev every time who marked the book—could have recognized his watchers.

By the end of September, 1952, the markings in the directory reached Page 750, denoting that six deliveries of information and data had been made by Timsford and received by the Russians.

For his efforts up to this time, Timsford had been paid a total of $3,500; this included the money he had received in Washington. There is an added touch of the cloak-and-dagger that applies to the way the counterspy was getting his money for his work in the Glen Cove hole-in-the-wall operation. Since he had been told there would be no more personal contact, Timsford had to rely on another method which would get around the ban on face-to-face meetings with Kovalev.

This procedure was simple enough. On the day following each delivery of microfilm, a Thursday, Timsford was to drive to the tavern in Lake Success where he had met Kovalev and go in for a drink. Then he would come out and drive home. By then he would have his money. It would be in an envelope under the car floor mat in the front. While Timsford was having his drink inside, someone from the Soviet Mission was putting the money in the engineer's car.

In every case, it was Kovalev who was spotted doing this by the G-men shadowing him.

On October 5, Timsford returned home from the plant and found a letter waiting for him. It was marked "personal." Timsford's wife, however, was not one to regard any delivery by the U.S. Post Office with any high degree of exclusivity. At least, not where it concerned herself and her husband. Her attitude, common to a few wives, was that "what's mine is his and what's his is mine."

"Honey," she trilled as Timsford came through the door. "When did you ever do a favor for a Captain Olson? Why you never told me that you performed any services for a ship . . ."

Timsford, as he explained it later with a slightly red face to the FBI, felt the floor under his feet quiver just a mite as a cold sweat swept his body.

"Oh, that's something I had to do for the company," he stammered, trying to manufacture a believable story. "They had sent me to check on the radar equipment on Captain Olson's ship a couple of months ago . . . I just forgot to tell you."

"But," his wife interrupted, "why did Captain Olson write to you at home? Why didn't he send the letter to the office? And why did he mark it 'personal'? My goodness, there's nothing personal in this letter. It's just a thank-you note. I don't understand it . . ."

It took another desperate few minutes to allay his wife's suspicions or, if not that, at least her curiosity. Timsford told her that Olson wanted to write to him sometime when he was steaming back to New York so they could have a drink together.

"He took a liking to me," Timsford said casually. "You know how these Swedes are. You're a Swede, don't forget."

As Mrs. Timsford headed for the kitchen to begin supper, Timsford took the letter with considerable apprehension still churning inside him and went to his den. And there he read it.

"Dear Fred," it began. "I want to thank you again for all you did on the ship for me when we were docked in New York. We are sailing this afternoon and I am writing to let you know again how much I appreciate everything. I want to see you again and I hope it will be very soon."

The letter was signed with a typed signature: Captain Olson.

The receipt of such a letter, postmarked in New York, had the greatest significance in Frederick Timsford's dealings with the Soviet espionage ring. He had been advised in Washington by the man who called himself Victor Ustinev that if he should ever receive such a letter, signed by Captain Olson, it was a signal that he was wanted in the capital for a personal encounter with his contact there. The time of the meeting was to be at 10 p.m. two days after the date on the letter, October 4, 1952, and the place was the Men's Bar in the Mayflower Hotel.

Timsford notified the FBI immediately about this development.

Two days later, October 6, Timsford left work early and caught a train at Pennsylvania Station which brought him into the capital shortly before 9 p.m., in plenty of time to make the meeting.

Timsford knew as he walked into the dimly lit Men's Bar in the Mayflower that G-men would certainly be staked out in the place, although he didn't know who they would be or where they would be sitting. Ustinev, or whatever his name was, would know nothing.

Timsford had been instructed by the FBI to arrive early, ahead of his Soviet contact, and to hold the table until Ustinev arrived. Timsford may have suspected, although he didn't indicate so, that the two men who seated themselves at an adjoining table shortly after he came in might very well be FBI agents. He had the same passing thought about three other well-dressed men who walked in minutes later and sat at another nearby table.

At any rate, Timsford felt comfortable. He wasn't certain but he had a gnawing suspicion that he might have been found out by the Russians and that this meeting could be the payoff, a payoff that could even come in bullets, although that isn't the way the Reds do business in this country. It's too dangerous to risk killing a man they suspect of a double cross, especially an American citizen. They are better off just dumping him as an agent and latching on to someone else. This way there is no blood on their hands and they are far less likely to risk a head-on clash with the FBI.

Whether they considered it or not, if they entertained any thoughts of violence against Timsford or, for that matter, upon anyone else working as a counterspy for the FBI, killing that man would have the same effect in bringing down the full force of the Bureau as it would were an agent harmed.

Actually, Timsford need not have even given a thought to the possibility that the Soviets were wise to him or that they were dissatisfied with his work. If anything, as Timsford was to learn from Ustinev once he arrived and had taken his place at the table, his work was being received with only the greatest satisfaction by the Reds.

"We have gotten nothing but compliments from home since you have been helping us," Ustinev said with gleeful satisfaction as he ordered a drink for himself and another round for Timsford. "But, as I told you before, there are things we must watch. And one of these is the possibility that we will get down to a routine that will be noticed by someone. That is why I have called you here. I want to shift the recognition signals which Alex Kovalev gave to you. It is not much of a change, but it is enough to assure us that nothing will go wrong."

One of the two men who had taken the table beside Timsford's shifted slightly in his chair and continued to sip his drink. They were strangely silent, these two men—and for good reason. They did not want to blur the conversation at the next table with their own voices; every word being spoken by Timsford and the Russian agent was going down on tape. The man had just shifted in his chair because the tape recorder he had in the specially sewn, extra-large inside pocket of his jacket was pressing uncomfortably against his chest.

Ustinev plotted the new "recognition signals," as he called them.

"From now on, after you drive away from the fireplug on West Ninetieth Street, you are to cross Central Park West and enter the Transverse Road, southbound. You will note to your right as you drive along that there is a traffic light stanchion about one hundred and fifty yards beyond your point of entry into the park. Look carefully and you will see the number twenty-seven is stenciled on the stanchion. When you observe this, look down at the base. If you see a banana peel lying there, then you will know that not only have you been seen by our contact, but also that we are prepared to pick up the material you have ready for us."

Then Ustinev stressed and re-stressed a point. "If you do not see the banana peel, do not go to the drop that night. It means that something is wrong. You will have to wait until the following Wednesday, or perhaps the one after that. Or you may receive another 'Captain Olson' letter from me."

Timsford was tempted to tell Ustinev that another such letter to his home might well blow the whole plot to the high heavens, but he had second thoughts about this. He had not been advised by the FBI to discuss this incident of letter-tampering by his beloved wife, and Timsford was a man who did only what he was instructed to do. He kept his mouth shut.

On October 15, back in New York once again, Timsford followed through with the new procedure and drove into Central Park after parking at the fireplug for the required fifteen-minute waiting period.

Just as the Soviet agent in Washington had said, a stanchion holding up a traffic light stood on the Transverse exactly one hundred and fifty yards beyond the entrance. Timsford looked closely and spotted the number "27" stenciled on the pole, a marking placed there by the Department of Traffic to facilitate the locating of lights reported out of order by the patrolman on the beat.

And at the base—a banana peel.

That night Timsford drove out to Glen Clove and deposited the first of several newly requested microfilm reproductions of important data concerning the Sperry bombsight. One of the nation's most closely guarded military devices, this is an "eye" that provides our Air Force bombers with a vastly greater accuracy than the Norden bombsight that had gained such wide fame and acclaim in World War II.

Again, as in all previous instances when Timsford delivered data to the Russians, the information was supplied by the FBI. And it was all so carefully doctored that there would be no way for the Soviets to know it was not accurate information until they had actually begun to develop the unit themselves. And this they could not do until they had acquired all the design information for the various components that go into the bombsight; so complicated is this procedure that it could well have taken years before they had assembled all of it. Then and only then would they realize that they had been taken on a good old-fashioned Yankee sleigh ride.

Timsford delivered additional information on the bombsight on three later occasions during November and the early part of December.

It was after he had made his last drop, on December 3, that Timsford received instructions to provide the Soviets with something extra —a certain electronic device used in military aircraft. The unit, of course, cannot be purchased on the open market. The only way it could be gotten would be for someone like Timsford to steal it from his own plant.

Timsford had received the word that the Russians wanted this device in a pencil-scrawled note that had been left in the envelope with his payoff for the last delivery. He found the envelope in the usual place under the floor mat of his car parked in the lot outside the Lake Success restaurant.

He found $1,000 in the envelope—$500 for the last microfilm delivery with data on the bombsight and $500 for the purchase of the electronic device. This latter unit sells under contract to the Government for about $75. So the Russians must have been quite desperate to get their hands on it.

This could have proved a hot potato for the FBI in its effort to string the Russians along in their dealings with Timsford. His failure to deliver the device, which the Russians must have known Timsford could pilfer from his plant, would pose the threat of ending the engineer's usefulness to the Reds and bring a cessation in their dealings with him.

But the FBI quickly solved the problem. The Department of Defense came to the rescue by providing an early model of the electronic device, one which had proved extremely faulty in operation. The specifications of this model, actually a laboratory prototype, were vastly changed in the units that finally were turned out on the production line.

The Russians didn't know this when they took delivery and probably never found out until they had gone to the trouble and expense of building the unit in one of their own electronic plants in the Soviet Union.

By then, of course, it would seem entirely possible that they might have sent Aleksandr Petrovich Kovalev up in a plane to test the unit's airworthiness. And if all did not go well, it is unlikely that any Soviet official would mourn Kovalev's unfortunate mission.

For, to bring this case to a rapid conclusion, Kovalev had to undergo the ignominy of being exposed as a spy by the State Department. It happened on February 3, 1954, when Ambassador Henry Cabot Lodge had the occasion to present the first of many such notes in his long career in the UN which advised the Soviet Union that one of their people had been caught in the act of spying. And in this case it was Aleksandr Petrovich Kovalev.

He was declared persona non grata, and a week later, on February 10, he sailed aboard the *Gripsholm* for home.

And Frederick Timsford?

He was given the heartfelt thanks of the FBI.

Fred Timsford received no monetary emoluments from his own country for his long and perilous role in counter-espionage. But he was pleased anyway. After all, he had collected $6,000 from the Russians for a lot of worthless information and material.

Fred Timsford was ahead of the game, and so was the FBI, thanks to him.

One strange aspect hangs on this case. No announcement about Kovalev's involvement in espionage or about his deportation was made until May 23, 1960—six years later. And then it was revealed in a list of fifteen Soviet officials who had been declared persona non grata in the past seven years because of their involvement in espionage, a list that the United States had prepared for disclosure before the Security Council in defense of Soviet charges growing out of the U-2 spy plane incident over Russia.

Here, reprinted from the official State Department text, is all that was revealed about the Kovalev case at that time, which is all that has ever been said about it since.

ALEKSANDER PETROVICH KOVALEV:

Kovalev arrived in the United States October 8, 1950, as a Second Secretary of the Soviet Delegation to the United Nations. In the course of his stay in the United States, Kovalev arranged to receive undeveloped microfilms of materials of intelligence significance at a drop area in New York City. The recruited agent was told to park his car in a designated area in New York City at a designated time and to place a package wrapped in red paper therein so that it could be seen through the rear window in the event material was to be passed. An additional signal by way of marking a telephone directory in a New York restaurant was perfected to indicate to the agent that the material delivered to the dead drop was picked up. Material of intelligence significance was left by the recruited agent in the New York dead-drop area and it was retrieved by Kovalev. The agent was given $500 to purchase an electronic device for delivery to the Soviets, an additional $500 in payment for delivery of a microfilm reproduction of portions of a manual dealing with an automatic steering device for ships. Kovalev was declared persona non grata by the Department of State for his actions in this case on February 3, 1954, and he departed the United States February 10, 1954.

That was the end of the announcement. The facts are identical to ours—except that we also have the full story in all its detail.

Moreover, we can now reveal what wasn't known of one of Frederick Timsford's early Washington encounters with the assistant naval attaché who called himself Victor Ustinev.

That meeting the night of October 6, 1952, in the Men's Bar at Washington's famed Mayflower Hotel had provided the G-men with their opportunity to tear the mask from the agent's face as he sipped his vodka martini and instructed Timsford about new "recognition signals"—the banana peel.

The two men at the one table, as we have already related, were Federal agents who took a recording of the conversation between the Russian attaché and the American engineer.

Timsford's suspicion about these two men was well founded. Timsford also had an idea that the three other men who had taken another table nearby were also agents. He was right about them, too. And one of those agents had the job of photographing the entire scene at the little table occupied by Timsford and the Russian.

When the photos were developed in the FBI darkroom, it was child's play for the bureau to trace the real identity of Victor Ustinev.

The picture of the man seated with Timsford matched the photo in the State Department files of an assistant Soviet naval attaché named Igor Aleksandrovich Amosov.

Amosov was given his deportation orders the same day as Kovalev —February 3, 1954. Amosov made a quicker departure than the UN-based spy, leaving four days later, on February 7.

The FBI had broken up the Kovalev-Amosov spy operation, but they could not rest on their laurels. Already another case of espionage was beginning to burgeon in the United Nations.

5 : The Red Colonel and
Our General Staff School

EVEN before the thunder of the Kovalev-Amosov case had subsided, the FBI was collecting evidence against still another Russian spy suspect, Maksim Martynov, a member of the UN Military Staff Committee, the organization that has no apparent real or useful purpose other than to deter the formation of a permanent UN military force.

Word had been flashed from West Berlin of a fantastic Soviet proposal to obtain United States army intelligence manuals at the General Staff School at Fort Leavenworth, Kansas. An American army colonel, whom we must identify only as Frank S. Pilgrim, had been broached with the proposition in August, 1954.

A 39-year-old career man, Colonel Pilgrim had been stationed in East Berlin since the end of World War II, and his time had come for a well-deserved furlough in the States. Not that the colonel had been given no annual furloughs, but he had preferred to spend those leaves visiting countries in Europe. His departure from his post in Germany now was to be permanent, since he had also received orders to report to Leavenworth for a new tour of duty after his leave expired.

It came as no surprise to Colonel Pilgrim when he received a phone call at American Headquarters in West Berlin the morning of August 12 and found the party on the other end of the line was

Aleksei Vladimir, a colonel with the Russian garrison in East Berlin. Pilgrim and Vladimir had been quite friendly. They had met often to discuss official matters dealing with the border situation between East and West Berlin, and out of these get-togethers grew a social relationship that brought them back in each other's company for dinner in various restaurants on both sides of the divided city.

This particular call, the morning of August 12, 1954, was strictly social.

"I have heard that you are leaving us," Colonel Vladimir said with a genuine tone of regret. "I feel terrible. We have worked well together."

Colonel Pilgrim said he was sorry that his stay in Berlin had to come to an end. He had enjoyed every day of it, but he was now very anxious to get back "and see what the States look like."

He then mentioned casually that his next post would be Fort Leavenworth.

"I'll help draw up some manuals from my experience with you fellows so that our Intelligence people will be better able to keep tabs on Soviet activity," Pilgrim said jocularly.

"How about lunch?" asked the Russian colonel. "I would like to see you once more before you leave."

The invitation was accepted. Five days later, on August 17, Colonel Pilgrim drove across the border into the Soviet sector and met Vladimir near the Unknown Soldier's Tomb. He parked his jeep and joined the Russian officer in a Soviet staff car that was waiting nearby.

"We are not going to a restaurant," Vladimir informed Pilgrim as the driver started out. "You are coming to my place. I have a special lunch prepared. This is my way of showing you my friendship."

The Russian colonel's quarters occupied the first floor of a spacious three-story stone dwelling on a tree-lined street about a ten-minute drive from the border.

A young Russian who worked as a houseboy for the colonel opened the door and admitted the host and his American guest. As they walked into the living room, Pilgrim encountered a heavy-set stranger about as tall as he was himself—six-feet-two—who sprang from the arm chair he had been occupying and walked with anxious but lumbering steps toward the two men who had just arrived.

Dressed in a dark blue business suit, the man smiled broadly as Colonel Vladimir took care of the introductions. The civilian was introduced as Arkady Vostok, a "good friend." He spoke good English although with a pronounced Russian accent.

The houseboy served the meal in the dining room and the conversation at the table was nothing spectacular. They talked about conditions in Berlin, about women, the weather, then hopscotched on to other subjects. Finally the houseboy approached Vladimir and whispered in his ear.

"Oh, no," the colonel said with surprise. "No coffee?"

Vladimir jumped to his feet. "Gentlemen, I will go to the store myself and bring some coffee right away." Without another word he hurried out of the house, leaving Pilgrim and Vostok to carry the conversational ball themselves at the table.

Vostok immediately cocked an eye at Pilgrim. "I suppose you will be happy to return to the United States. Will you be spending any time in New York City?"

"I expect to," Pilgrim said, gazing at his questioner with curiosity. "Why do you ask?"

Vostok smiled into a glass of water he was sipping. He put the glass down and looked up at Pilgrim. "I would like to meet you there. You see, you have an opportunity to make a lot of money. I have something in mind . . . very secret, mind you. It should be to your liking. It won't be much trouble . . ."

Pilgrim took the suggestion with the pretense that he was turning it over in his mind. His training in G-2 told him at once that he was dealing with a Soviet agent who was trying to recruit him for some clandestine purpose. His training also told him that he must not back away from the suggestion.

"What's on your mind, Vostok?" Pilgrim said, interest bubbling in his voice. He leaned forward to show genuine curiosity.

"I am after the manuals the Army puts out—the intelligence manuals used in the training at the General Staff School . . ."

Vostok spoke bluntly. Pilgrim smiled silently for a moment, then pushed his chair back. He got to his feet and walked around the room as if pondering the enormity of the proposition. Actually, he was trying to look like a man who would betray his trust, to make it appear believable to the propositioner that he was accepting the offer.

"How much money?" Pilgrim demanded, patting his pocket to signify his willingness if the price was right.

The Russian looked pleased. "You do not have to worry. It will be well worth your effort. What is important now is to arrange a time and place to meet in New York." He got up and walked over to Pilgrim who was standing at the window.

"I am going to try to make it to New York by October fifteenth. We will meet at the northeast corner of Madison Avenue and Eighty-sixth Street. Shall we say at four that afternoon?"

Then putting a friendly hand on Pilgrim's shoulder, Vostok grinned. "I may not be able to get there myself, but someone else will take my place if I am not there. Let us arrange signals. You are to wear civilian clothes and you must come alone. If the weather is cold, you will wear a topcoat or overcoat. But underneath you must wear a tweed jacket. You will stand at the corner a few minutes, then look at your watch. Then you will be approached. Someone will say to you, 'Didn't we meet in Spechstrasse, Berlin?' You will reply, 'Yes, I lived at Number Nineteen.' Then you will know you are dealing with the right party—and so will we."

After listening intently to Vostok's instructions, Pilgrim asked what manuals he was supposed to get.

"Whatever ones have been published," Vostok said somberly. "We are paying you high. We will have to receive our money's worth. We want the latest . . ."

Pilgrim grinned at him. He was trying to conceal the shiver of excitement he felt, the trembling anticipation of getting back to American Headquarters and reporting the Soviet plot to his superiors. Even as he spoke, he envisioned himself delivering the manuals to the Soviet agent in New York—and then providing him the surprise of his life when FBI men closed in and made the arrest.

"If I or someone else does not meet you on the fifteenth, or if you yourself cannot make it then, we will get together at the same location on the twenty-fifth, same time," Vostok said.

Then he recited six additional alternate dates for Pilgrim in case any of the previous ones were not productive. The dates were spaced on the days of the following months falling on the 15th and 25th in each instance.

"Is it all clear to you, Colonel?" Vostok asked.

Pilgrim nodded. His face was enigmatic. "It's all very clear."

A moment later the two men turned at the sound of a slamming door. Colonel Vladimir, the host, was back, a package under his arm. "I got it," he smiled triumphantly. "What a difficulty it is to get a good brand of coffee. That is why I went myself. The Russian Army's influence works wonders on these Berlin grocers. I have gotten the best South American coffee."

By the time coffee was served, Vladimir, Vostok, and Pilgrim were ensconced in the soft upholstered chairs of the living room discussing world affairs and other matters, none of which remotely approached the subject the Russian civilian had broached to the American military man.

When it was time to leave, Pilgrim and Vostok parted with a brisk handshake.

"It was a great pleasure, indeed, to get to know you," Pilgrim said.

"The pleasure was all mine, Colonel," smiled Vostok with a significant wink.

Colonel Vladimir drove his American counterpart in the staff car back to his jeep at the Unknown Soldier's Tomb and the two officers from opposite sides of the Iron Curtain shook hands in a warm farewell. At no time did Vladimir mention Vostok to Pilgrim. It was as though Vlarimir had no part in the deal, or at least he made no effort to show an awareness of it.

Back at American Headquarters in West Berlin, Colonel Pilgrim promptly reported his experience of that afternoon in East Berlin to his superiors in G-2. He gave them a play-by-play account of the entire conversation with the Russian who called himself Arkady Vostok. Later the colonel sat with an artist and helped him prepare a sketch of the man who had propositioned him to steal the Army School's intelligence manuals.

Three weeks later, Pilgrim left Berlin for New York. He landed at Idlewild Airport and was met, according to plan, by FBI agents who had been alerted to the plot by the Army. They drove Pilgrim to the Hotel Commodore, next to Grand Central Terminal on East 42nd Street, where the FBI had arranged for the colonel's stay in a large suite.

The G-men told Pilgrim that as a necessary part of the scheme they were to live with him and accompany him wherever he went for the next week to ten days. They did not explain quite clearly why this was pertinent to the investigation, and the colonel didn't ask. But all during that period, during which the G-men questioned Pilgrim intensely about his career in the Army, his family background, and a great many other personal details, the officer's curiosity mounted. From time to time he asked his questioners about their tactics.

"It's part of the preparation for the case," he was told. Nothing more. Pilgrim was edgy by the end of the tenth day. He couldn't understand what the agents were after. He began to wonder whether he himself wasn't suspect. Finally, just as his patience had frayed, he was let in on the mysterious doings.

"We've been studying you all this time, Colonel," he was told. "Now we know everything about you. Exactly what anyone who has ever been acquainted with you might be expected to know about you. And, just as importantly, we have studied your walk, your posture, the way you sit, your mannerisms, your habits, your way of talking. You see, Colonel, you aren't going to keep that appointment with Arkady Vostok or any other Soviet agent. Your double will deal with these boys now."

Surprise and disappointment were mingled in the expression on Pilgrim's face. Surprise—because he never suspected the FBI had made that close a study of him; disappointment—because he had counted on being in on the "kill." But Pilgrim readily accepted the FBI's reasons for preferring to handle this case in their own way, and his disappointment soon left him when he got a glimpse of the man the FBI picked to impersonate him. He was the colonel's spitting image—same height, same weight, same build, same dark brown hair, blue eyes, large hook-like nose and receding chin, same ruddy complexion, same severe look.

There were only two differences in their appearance. The FBI agent, Fred Peck, was a few years younger than Pilgrim and lacked Pilgrim's bushy, dark brown mustache. But a makeup man flown up from the Bureau in Washington soon took care of both.

The next several days, Peck and Pilgrim spent ten to twelve hours a day together as the agent sought to capture every detail of the colonel's personality. Painstakingly Peck worked at the impersonation, refining, polishing, until at the end of a week the two were literally mirror images of one another.

October 15 finally came and Peck was ready. But his bosses decided to play a waiting game with the Russians. If Pilgrim—played by Peck—showed up for the first appointment, he might seem too eager and, to the Russians perhaps, too suspect.

But other agents were ready to scout the locale at Madison Avenue and 86th Street to see if the Russians indeed intended to go through with the rendezvous. The agents staked out the neighborhood well in advance. Days before they had made arrangements to occupy second- and third-story quarters in nearby buildings which would give them vantage points for observing the action on the corner below. But more than mere observation posts for FBI agents with high-powered field glasses, these hidden positions were to serve as vantage points from which 16 mm. movie cameras would record the activity on the sidewalk through powerful telephoto lenses.

This was the first time a long-distance camera, employed by the FBI to catch Red agents in acts of espionage, was to trap a Soviet United Nations diplomat enjoying both the immunity that goes with the position and U.S. hospitality in an attempt to steal American secrets. It would not be the last. Previously, in the case involving Soviet Naval Attaché Igor Aleksandrovich Amosov, still cameras had been successfully employed indoors to record his meeting with Frederick Timsford in Washington.

At 4 p.m., ten FBI agents were in their places, hidden behind carefully curtained windows and also posted on the street in various disguises—laborers and other industrious workers scurrying along the street pretending to be busy with one chore or another. One agent was inside a wine and liquor store at the very corner where the meeting was to take place. He was sweeping the floor, with one eye trained on the street to observe what was going on.

The appointed hour passed and there was no sign of a man answering the description of the Russian who had told Colonel Pilgrim to meet him at this corner on this date. The G-men had sketches of the Soviet agent, Arkady Vostok, but did not spot anyone who looked like the drawing. At the same time, no one else took a position at the corner to await Pilgrim's arrival.

However, during their period of observation, the FBI agents recognized three men who made their presence in the neighborhood conspicuous by strolling back and forth repeatedly, as if they were look-

ing over the area. The agents on the stakeout recognized these recon-
noiterers. They were staff members from the Soviet Mission to the
UN.

For something like twenty-five minutes, the trio coursed over this
corner, individually and together at various times, as if eyeing the
situation, perhaps looking for Colonel Pilgrim, to see if he had kept
his end of the bargain.

Shortly before 4:30 p.m., the Russians hailed a taxi and drove
away. The FBI packed up its binoculars and telephoto-lensed
cameras and left the scene, too.

On October 25, the date of the second rendezvous, Agent Fred
Peck, by now a master of the art of walking, talking, and looking like
Colonel Pilgrim, was ready. Peck arrived at the scene at 3:57 p.m. A
cab dropped him off at the southeast corner. He stepped out of the
taxi which had stopped at the bus stop and paid the driver through
the open window of the front door. He then crossed 86th Street to
the northeast corner and took his place at the designated spot in front
of the liquor store. Inside the store, an FBI man again wielded a
broom. Across the street, other agents strolled leisurely along with
one eye on the mustached Peck standing alone with his hands in his
overcoat pocket. Two more FBI men passed by in front of Peck. Up
in the windows, still more agents were ready once again with binoculars and long-range cameras to "shoot" the scene.

At 4:01 p.m. two Russians from the Soviet Mission were spotted
crossing 86th Street. The cameras rolled. The men looked at Peck as
they approached. But that is all they did. They cast a long, searching
glance at him and continued on their way. They gave no sign of
recognition. And Peck pretended not to see them. He simply followed
through with the pre-arranged signal worked out with Vostok, which
was to glance at his wristwatch on his left hand.

The Russians went to the end of the block, turned, and strolled
back. Again they gazed searchingly at Peck, then moved on. They
crossed 86th Street and disappeared.

At 4:30, when it appeared that the Russians would not try to make
contact with Peck, the FBI called off the stakeout.

"What could have gone wrong?" Peck wondered. "Do they see
through my disguise?"

That was a possibility, but it was too far-fetched to believe that the

Russians, who ostensibly had never seen the real Colonel Pilgrim, would spot the perfectly disguised G-man as an impostor.

There was nothing to do but wait until the next date—November 15.

Again, as before, Peck arrived in a cab which deposited him at the bus stop. Again, as before, Peck paid his fare through the front window, and as he did he cast a quick glance to the opposite corner. Now he had a feeling the rendezvous was going to come off. He spotted a tall, solidly built figure in a dark blue overcoat and black fedora hat standing erect at the northeast corner, back against the wall of the liquor store. His hands were folded behind his back. He looked from side to side now and then to glimpse pedestrians passing by.

"This may be it," Peck told himself as he waited for the traffic light to change. Then he crossed over and walked slowly past the man standing on the corner. Peck did not look at him. He kept his glance straight ahead. But from their observation posts, the other FBI men saw the tall man in the dark blue coat turn and stare fixedly at Peck as he strolled by. Several G-men peering through binoculars recognized the man at once.

"This is the real thing," one of the agents said. "They've sent the big boy out on this one. A military man."

It was Maksim Martynov, the Soviet member of the UN Military Staff Committee. Martynov, in brief, was a 38-year-old colonel in the Soviet Army and had been in the United States as a representative of his country on the military branch of the UN since 1949.

Peck walked to the end of the block at 87th Street, then came back down Madison. As he strode along, Peck kept one important identifying feature of Colonel Pilgrim's very much in mind—his bearing. Peck had to walk erect, shoulders back, as years of military training had taught Pilgrim to do.

Passing again, at a slower gait, almost a hesitant walk, Peck turned and shot a glimpse at Martynov. The Russian's eyes met Peck's. Martynov's lips opened slightly as if he were going to speak. But he apparently decided not to. Peck walked on and paused about ten feet away. As he stood there, he glanced back at Martynov, who was gaping at the undercover agent. Peck waited a few moments, then took a step forward, raised his left hand, and looked at his watch. At the same time Peck took out a small paper packet that was stuffed in his right-hand coat pocket.

Martynov's eyes were attracted to the packet. He continued his studied gaze of the tall, military-like figure, then apparently made a decision. He approached Peck.

"Colonel, didn't we meet in Spechstrasse, Berlin?" he said in a broken English heavy with a Russian accent.

Peck smiled. "Yes, I lived at Number Nineteen," the American colonel's impersonator replied.

Martynov extended his hand. "My name is Schultz. I have been looking forward to this meeting, Colonel." Then he turned and studied some of the passersby, men and women hurrying by, some mothers wheeling buggies on their way to air their children in nearby Central Park. Martynov appeared to be bothered by the congestion. "Shall we take a ride?" he suggested.

Peck didn't want to lose the FBI observers who were recording the meeting for posterity. "I'd prefer to take a little walk," he suggested. "I've been doing so much traveling lately that I need to stretch my legs."

"Fine, Colonel," Martynov replied. Peck pointed toward Central Park, a block to the west. "Shall we go where it's nice and peaceful, Mr. Schultz?" he said. Martynov nodded.

As they crossed Madison and walked along 86th Street to Fifth Avenue, then to the opposite side where the Park began, Martynov almost immediately asked Peck about his "assignment" to obtain the intelligence manuals from Fort Leavenworth.

"I did not get them yet, Mr. Schultz," Peck said apologetically. "It's not that I encountered any trouble, but a thing like this takes a little time. I don't think it will be much longer."

Martynov then plied Peck with queries about the intelligence activities of the army, asking about the size of its staff, the posts where its personnel were stationed, the amount of training they received, whether they worked with the Central Intelligence Agency, and many other matters concerning intelligence operations. Peck answered every question. He didn't give the correct answer each time, for the FBI had anticipated the line of questioning the agent would be subjected to. His replies had all been carefully rehearsed. Some answers were correct. They had to be, because the FBI knew that the Soviets would spot a wrong answer to certain questions. But Peck gave nothing of value away. His job was to stall Martynov, to bring him back another time when he would be still more anxious to receive the intelligence manuals.

Yet Martynov's anxiety showed even now. "Look, Colonel," the Russian blurted. "I want to get those documents at all cost." Martynov stuffed a roll of bills into Peck's hand—twenty-five ten-dollar bills. "This is just for your expenses," the Soviet officer smiled. "When we receive the package from you we shall pay you the big money."

Peck suggested to Martynov that they meet at the same time and place the following January 25. "Agreed." Martynov grinned. They shook hands and parted.

Peck showed up on time for his next meeting with Martynov. The other FBI agents again were stationed at the windows with their long-distance cameras, while others strolled past the two men as they greeted each other on the street corner. Martynov appeared pleased at seeing Peck, who was carrying a briefcase.

"You have it, Colonel?" he asked anxiously, eyeing the briefcase.

"I have it," Peck said. "Shall we walk to the Park?"

"No," Martynov said firmly. "Let us go somewhere else, out of the way."

Even as the evening darkness lowered, the FBI's supersensitive film and lenses followed the two men and recorded in perfect detail every movement they made on their way across to the south side of 86th Street and into the Hotel Croydon's small, richly paneled bar where the cocktail crowd was just beginning to gather. Martynov led the way to a corner table.

A waiter came over and took the order; Martynov asked for a vodka on the rocks, Peck a whisky sour. As the waiter walked away, Martynov whispered, "Don't raise your voice—tell me, did you get what I want?"

Peck gave the Russian an affirmative nod. "In here," he smiled, running his hand over the briefcase he had placed at his left on the floor.

Martynov's eagerness was overpowering. He reached down to grab the briefcase. Peck pulled it away. "Not yet," he said. "Let's talk about the money."

Peck was bidding for time. In a few minutes, the time was right. By then several patrons had entered the bar and seated themselves at tables near the two men. The Russian eyed the patrons with a probing eye and he seemed to acquire a measure of uneasiness over their presence.

"Look," he finally said, "let's get out right now. I don't like this place."

Peck reached for the briefcase and placed it in the center of the table. "Mr. Schultz," he said to Martynov, "this is for you. Take it."

Martynov seemed surprised. He put out his hands to take it.

As he did, two conservatively dressed patrons at separate tables rose in unison and glided quickly across the floor to the table. Peck's motion with the briefcase had been their signal. Now peering down in the bar's dim amber light, they each flicked open a leather case and displayed their identifications as agents of the FBI.

Martynov's eyes darted at the men and past them to the doorway beyond, but he saw instantly there was no chance to escape. Instead, he summoned a scowling indignation and cried, "What are you doing? I am a diplomat. I have immunity. You cannot touch me."

He plunged his hand into his suit's breast pocket and fumblingly spread out his diplomatic credentials. There was nothing the FBI men could do.

"All right," said one of them. "We can't hold you. Get out. But you know what this means. You'll be out of America in a week."

The agents cleared a path for him as Martynov got up from his chair and stormed out the door. Reluctantly the three FBI men watched him board a bus heading downtown in the direction of the Soviet Mission to the UN.

The FBI sent its report on the case to the Attorney General and the State Department. On February 21, 1955, the United States Government declared Martynov persona non grata and five days later the Soviet spy left for home.

Once again the FBI had effectively thwarted an insipient Soviet espionage operation stemming out of the UN. But just as surely as one case was over, another would begin. And by the following year the FBI was wading through the mire of not one but three new episodes involving Soviet conspiracy at the UN.

The first of these dealt with a case which achieved nationwide headlines. It was the defection of nine crewmen aboard the Soviet tanker *Tuapse* who had fled their ship after it had docked in San Francisco. The crewmen had said they did not want to return to Russia and asked for asylum here. It was granted.

But then, on April 7, 1956, five of the nine crewmen abruptly left their United States asylum for Russia. They departed so swiftly that American officials had no opportunity to question them.

An effort by immigration authorities to interrogate the five at Idlewild Airport was thwarted by Arkady Sobolov, head of Russia's United Nations delegation, who told the officials that the seamen did not want to answer any questions.

Their sudden redefection and swift departure for Russia under a Stalin-like atmosphere of secrecy and oppression raised speculation that the five were being blackmailed into returning to the Soviet Union, possibly through threats against their families. At the same time, it triggered a Senate investigation into the whole sphere of Soviet UN activities in the United States.

The episode evoked similar concern from the State Department, which promptly ordered the ouster of two Soviet diplomats, and sharply rebuked the high-ranking Sobolov but did not call for his expulsion. State also dispatched a sharp note to the Kremlin demanding that the Soviet Government instruct Sobolov and his staff to stick strictly to their United Nations functions in the future.

The note said that Sobolov insisted on intervening during a departure interview with the seamen conducted by immigration officials at Idlewild. It said Sobolov did this "despite the presence of an accredited representative from the Soviet Embassy in Washington."

Testimony presented to the Senate Internal Security Subcommittee in mid-April was to the effect that the Russians had overstepped their UN functions and engaged in activities outside their official capacities.

Rebuked with Sobolov in the State Department's note were two members of the Soviet Delegation, Aleksandr K. Gurynov, an attaché, and Nikolai Turkin, the third secretary of the Soviet Delegation. Charging that Gurynov and Turkin had behaved in a particularly objectionable manner, the note stated that the two exceeded "the scope of their official capacities and thereby abused the privilege of their residence."

Although the U.S. expelled both Gurynov and Turkin, in reality the expulsion only applied to Gurynov, because Turkin had accompanied the five seamen back to Russia.

The Soviet Union put in the popular disclaimer and objected to the charges made against the three diplomats. But they made no attempt to have the State Department reconsider the expulsion order against Gurynov.

To reporters at the airport, Gurynov himself had seemed remote from the hub of Soviet supervision during the episode with the seamen. He had remained starkly inaccessible behind a wall of six beefy Soviet UN employees, and precisely what his role was in the crewmen's redefection has never been made clear. And, of course, Gurynov himself wasn't saying.

Actually, observers at the airport who later testified before Senator Eastland's subcommittee said that the mastermind behind the seamen's alleged kidnapping was really Konstantin Pavlovich Ekimov, First Secretary of the Soviet Mission to the UN. Although Ekimov's name was never raised in the State Department's note, he was generally described as "the man in charge at the airport."

Why the State Department didn't take steps against Ekimov remained a mystery—for the time being. As it turned out, Ekimov's immunity from U.S. action against him was short-lived. His day would come before the year was out.

Meanwhile, Gurynov departed for Russia aboard the *Queen Mary* on the following May 9th. Leaving in good spirits, he played host at a brandy party for some thirty guests in his cabin-class stateroom.

"I'm very glad to be going home," he blithely said as he sipped his brandy. "I'm going back to the motherland."

"What about the Senate probe into allegations that the five seamen were kidnapped?" asked a newsman.

"Nonsense," the smiling Russian declared with a wave of his hand. "I had no relations whatsoever with this case. I was just one of many friends who spoke to the boys returning to the motherland. I was just seeing them off."

The *Queen Mary*'s smokestack had barely dipped beyond the horizon, figuratively speaking, before another Soviet UN diplomat was ordered expelled from this country, and again the issue turned on blackmail.

As a result of the seamen's incident, the Senate stepped up its inquiry into allegations of Soviet harassment of Russian refugees in this country. Information was reaching the Senate Internal Security Subcommittee and its chairman, Senator Eastland, that Soviet UN personnel were using blackmail and applying other pressures on the refugees to force their return to their homeland.

It is legal for Soviet Embassy officials in Washington to contact former Russian citizens in this country, but a Soviet diplomat or employee at the United Nations is prohibited from doing so since such action is consular in nature.

One of the key witnesses among the refugees testifying before the Eastland subcommittee was former Soviet Army Captain Michael Shatov, who at the time was living in New York. On June 13, 1956, just two months after the alleged kidnapping of the five seamen, he told the probers under oath that two ranking Soviet diplomats at the UN had brought terrific pressure on him to return to Russia. Although his testimony was never made public, it was indicated the Russians were trying some sort of blackmail scheme to force his return.

He flatly accused Soviet Second Secretary Rotislav E. Shapovalov and Aleksei Petukov, a technical aide, of applying the pressure. Senator Eastland forwarded the results of the Senate inquiry to the State Department, and two months later, after satisfying itself that the allegations were true, State ordered Shapovalov's expulsion and warned that Petukov would be declared persona non grata if he persisted in undiplomatic activities.

Shapovalov was expelled, the State Department revealed, because he had made "direct contact with Russian émigrés in this country." Petukov, director for Asia and the Far East of the UN Technical Assistance Program, drew the minor penalty because there was no proof he had made any direct contacts, although his overall involvement in the scheme was undisputed.

The morning of September 12, 1956, found Shapovalov, his wife, Ada, and their six-year-old daughter, Ludmilla, aboard the luxurious *Queen Elizabeth*, ready to sail with the outgoing tide. In a brief shipboard interview, through an interpreter, Shapovalov called ex-Soviet Captain Shatov a traitor, said that America was a good country, Americans a good people, then concluded sadly that "at the same time there are in America some people such as Senator Eastland who don't like Russians being here."

The bells of justice for Konstantin Pavlovich Ekimov, so silent the previous April when witnesses branded him as the mastermind in the seamen's alleged kidnap plot, finally tolled in December, 1956.

The brilliant Red ringleader, officially the First Secretary of the Soviet UN Delegation, became the third high-ranking Russian to sail for his homeland under a State Department expulsion order growing out of testimony before the Senate Internal Security Subcommittee. And, like Gurynov and Shapovalov before him, his ouster was again linked to the Soviet Union's intense effort at coercing Russian refugees back to their native land.

But in Ekimov's case, the coercion took a new twist in that it involved the forced return not only of a Russian émigré but also of his Philadelphia-born baby daughter, a full-fledged American citizen.

So ominous was the case that Republican Senator William E. Jenner of Indiana, in his role as acting chairman of the subcommittee during Senator Eastland's absence, remarked gravely: "This is the first time that the Soviet Union has attempted to assert its sovereignty by force over a United States citizen in the United States."

The strange case which startled all of America unfolded in September, 1956. It began when Aleksei Chwastov and his American-born daughter, Tanya, two-and-a-half years old, approached a case worker for the Church World Service in Philadelphia in early September and told of the coercion certain Russians in this country were applying to get him to return to the Soviet Union—and to take Tanya with him.

The Church World Service interviewed Chwastov in Philadelphia and again in Newark, New Jersey, and then satisfied that he was in fact being intimidated, notified U.S. Immigration officials. Chwastov was brought to New York City on Thursday, September 27, for still another interview by immigration and refugee officials, and this time, strangely, he announced that he would return to Russia "on my own." His charges of coercion, he said, had all been a "misunderstanding."

To Roland Elliott, immigration director of the Church World Service, the organization that had sponsored Chwastov's entry into the United States in 1951, the refugee's sudden reversal rang false. He told Chwastov he was "free to go or stay," but to think it over for a night before giving his final answer.

Casting about for a safe place to keep Chwastov for the night, Elliott hit upon the refugee's own church, the Russian Orthodox, and by evening a church representative had taken Chwastov and Tanya under his wing.

Chwastov and Tanya had been living alone in Philadelphia. Tanya was an illegitimate child born in Philadelphia, July 12, 1954, to Chwastov and Elena Romanow who later became Mrs. George Dieczok and settled in Detroit.

Chwastov had good reason to fear the Russians. His two brothers had been slain by the Communists and Chwastov himself had several times been imprisoned and tortured by the Red government as a political prisoner. He was toiling in a slave labor camp in Austria when freed by the United States troops at the end of World War II.

Having weighed his decision for the night, Chwastov told the Church World Service and the immigration officials the next morning that he wanted to remain in America if he could be assured that he and the baby would be safe from Communist agents.

Chwastov and Tanya were moved into a rooming house on New York City's West Side, where they were supposed to stay until Monday, October 1, when the church representative would take the refugee and his daughter upstate and get him a new job in Richfield Springs, New York.

But the plan never materialized. Sometime during that weekend, Chwastov and Tanya vanished from the rooming house and weren't seen again until they appeared at dockside on the morning of Wednesday, October 3, prior to the sailing of the *Queen Mary*. Chwastov refused to say anything except to affirm in glum monosyllables that he had changed his mind and was returning to Russia of his own free will. Chwastov and Tanya were hustled aboard the big liner and placed in their tourist cabin, while three Russians intercepted U.S.

immigration officials who had hoped to question the refugee more fully.

One of the Russians was a burly three-hundred-pounder never identified. The second was Fedor F. Solomatin, attached to the Soviet Embassy in Washington. The third was—Konstantin Pavlovich Ekimov.

For nearly an hour, the three Russians engaged immigration officials in a spirited argument on Tanya's American or Russian status. The argument was inconclusive and the trio joined Chwastov and Tanya in their cabin. A short while later, an unidentified immigration agent found them and attempted to block their departure until Tanya's status was cleared up. Solomatin objected to the inspector's authority and the inspector left temporarily to call his superiors for instructions. When he returned to the cabin, it was empty.

He hastily called for aid, and a few minutes later three other immigration men joined him in a search of the ship, which by now had slipped away from its pier and was heading toward Quarantine. When the ship passed Quarantine and left the harbor heading for the open sea, the immigration men had to leave and ride a Coast Guard launch back to shore to report their failure.

When the *Queen Mary* arrived in Southampton, Chwastov and Tanya were bundled off to the Soviet Embassy in London where they were safely detained beyond the reach of U.S. officials. In the meantime, Tanya's mother, who by now had married George Dieczok, tearfully journeyed to London in a desperate attempt to block her daughter's departure for Moscow through the English courts. But she learned to her heartbreak after a brief legal skirmish that the case was outside the court's jurisdiction.

A few weeks later, Tanya and her father were taken behind the Iron Curtain and have not been heard from since.

Back in the United States, the State Department assembled all the facts in the perplexing case, and on October 29 it ordered Konstantin Pavlovich Ekimov expelled from the country.

Senator Jenner called Ekimov's part in the forced return of Chwastov and his infant daughter a "reprehensible act." Jenner also demanded the ouster of Fedor Solomatin, but under the consular laws of the country the Soviet Embassy official in Washington was technically within his legal rights in interceding in the Chwastov affair.

The case drew wide publicity both in the United States and abroad because of the child and the emotional impact her plight had on people everywhere.

While Ekimov was preparing to leave, Immigration Director Elliott, appearing before the Senate Internal Security Subcommittee to plead for tighter immigration laws, spoke movingly of the Chwastov case and said it was typical of thousands of others in the United States.

"The action of Soviet representatives here," he said, "is contrary to the best interests of our country and the safety of those who have fled persecution from the very forces which now seek their return."

On a cold, wintry December day in 1956, five weeks after he was declared persona non grata, Konstantin Petrovich Ekimov walked up the gangplank of the *Queen Mary* for the first leg of his journey home. He and five Russian associates carried his bags.

The longshoremen had refused to touch them.

6 : The Friendliest of All Russian Spies

THE Marine Firebrand Corporation is a fictitious name and so is that of Richard Simmons, a tall, graying individual with a military bearing, who is the sales engineer of the firm. But only the names are disguised to protect the innocent dupes in one of the classic cases of how the Soviets, employing blandness and subtlety, sought to obtain secrets from an American momentarily caught off guard.

The date is early June, 1955, and Simmons is in his office in lower Manhattan giving dictation to his secretary. Suddenly they are interrupted by the receptionist's voice coming over the intercom.

"Mr. Gladkov from the Soviet Mission to the United Nations wishes to see you."

Simmons was not surprised. He had been expecting a visit from the caller since they met at a cocktail party some weeks before.

"All right, Miss Jones," Simmons said. "Send him in."

The door opened and instead of one there were two men, both smiling as they walked in. The shorter of the two—heavily built, about five-foot-six and one hundred, seventy-five pounds, with gray eyes and balding blond hair, approached Simmons—shook hands, and said, "So glad to see you again."

This was Boris Fedorovich Gladkov whom Simmons had met at the cocktail party. The engineer did not know much about Gladkov, for their first meeting had been brief. He knew Gladkov was attached to the Soviet Mission at the UN but was unaware in what capacity.

But during their conversation at the party, Gladkov had learned a few things about Simmons—particularly the fact that he was an executive with Marine Firebrand, a company noted for its advances in turbine engines both for commercial and military vessels. Gladkov suggested at the time that he might drop in sometime and discuss the possibility of buying some turbines for export to the Soviet Union. Simmons had thought the Russian was merely making conversation.

Now, in his office, Simmons was to learn Gladkov had not been talking idly. After introducing his companion as Victor Rudenko, whom he described as "an associate," Gladkov commented about the rainy weather, about his lumbago which was bothered by the dampness, and engaged Simmons in a brief, friendly chat about the luxuriousness of his office and its decor which was Swedish modern. Then Gladkov came down to cases.

"Since the last time I spoke with you," Gladkov said quietly, "I have discussed your new marine turbine with my government. They have instructed me to begin negotiations with you for the purchase of several."

Simmons was surprised the Russians knew enough about the turbine to seek an order and he asked Gladkov about it.

"We read your brochure and the printed specifications are quite impressive," the Russian replied. "Our government believes the turbines can be used very satisfactorily in some of the new ships we are building."

Gladkov did not explain how he obtained the brochure, but it was a document that had been widely distributed by the company in its sales campaign.

Simmons shook his head. "I'm sorry I didn't explain this to you at the party when you brought up the subject," he said politely. "You see, our company is bound by a strict government rule against doing business with the Soviet Union or any . . . er . . . satellite country. I hope you understand this is not my policy . . ."

Gladkov laughed. "You Americans . . . so suspicious. Why, I am not here to buy atom bombs. I'm only looking for a simple new type of turbine for our commercial vessels. Do you know we have bought them from other American firms? All we must arrange to clear the deal is an export license, which I'm certain the Government will grant."

Simmons felt stupid. Of course, he had never dealt with a Soviet customer before and had never had occasion to face up to the machinery involving a sale to Russia. He had just felt that the turbines his company produced could not be sold to the Soviet Union.

"If what you say is true," Simmons said apologetically, "I will stand corrected. I will check on it immediately."

Gladkov took out his card and handed it to Simmons. "This is where you can reach me when you have word," he said.

The other Russian, Rudenko, who had not spoken yet, now broke into the talk. "You are a hunter, Mr. Simmons?" Rudenko was standing at the far wall admiring the picture of a large deer that Simmons had bagged.

"Are you a hunter, too?" Simmons asked curiously.

"Oh, no, I am not," Rudenko replied. "But Boris—well, he is one of the good ones. He has a sharp eye behind a deer rifle."

Gladkov smiled at the compliment. "Don't build me up too much, Victor," he said. "Mr. Simmons doesn't have a bad eye if he can fell a deer like this one. Look at that aim—right through the eyes." Then he turned to Simmons and said, "Who knows, maybe one of these days we can go out and try to bag a couple of deer, eh?"

Simmons nodded condescendingly. He figured the suggestion was just idle chatter. "Maybe so," he smiled. He shook hands with his Russian visitors, watched as they left, then returned to his desk. His mind played with the visit, wondering what to make of it. Well, he mused, it would certainly make good dinner conversation when he got home. It's not every day he talked to authentic Russians.

Later that day Simmons checked through the legal department of his firm and with other sources and found to his surprise that there was no prohibition against selling the commercial type turbine to the Soviet Union. He promptly phoned Gladkov.

"So I was right, eh?" Gladkov chided good-naturedly. He told Simmons that he would notify his superiors about the availability of the turbines and wait to receive orders to negotiate directly for their purchase. He suggested that the Soviet Government might want to buy six turbines "as a start." It would take a few days for a reply.

Simmons heard nothing from the Russian for the next couple of days. By week's end he had all but forgotten the incident. Thus it came as something of a surprise when, in mid-August, nearly two months later, his secretary's voice cut across the intercom in late morning and announced a visitor, a Boris Gladkov. Would Mr. Simmons see him?

"Yes, of course, send him in," Simmons replied. As he waited, Simmons' thoughts turned back to the earlier discussions with Gladkov and his desire to buy the company's turbines.

When Gladkov, whose somewhat ruddy complexion and rugged features also suggested fondness for the outdoors, entered the office, the two men shook hands and Simmons immediately said lightly, "Well, Mr. Gladkov, whatever happened to the turbine business? Has somebody underbid us?"

"No, no, not at all, my dear Mr. Simmons, nothing like that," the Russian replied in good English just barely tinged with an accent. "As a matter of fact, I've had my hands tied. I can't do anything without clearance from back home. It will come, I'm sure. You should know the red tape when our two governments are involved."

Then Gladkov moved toward the wall. "Actually, this is simply a social visit. I was intrigued by this picture of you with the deer." Gladkov looked at the framed photo admiringly. "I thought possibly we could have lunch together sometime soon. Maybe we can swap some hunting stories, and perhaps you will tell me where to find that kind of deer."

The two men agreed to meet at the Harwyn, one of New York's smartest supper clubs, at noon the following Monday. When the hour neared, Simmons walked the three and a half blocks from his office to the restaurant and found Gladkov already there, waiting at the bar.

The two men greeted each other cordially. "Come," Gladkov said, swallowing his cocktail and putting the glass on the bar. "I have a fine table for us."

Simmons and Gladkov seated themselves in the crowded dining room and after a round of martinis ordered sirloin steaks. As the waiter walked away, Gladkov settled back in the chair and said, "I must confess you Americans do have remarkable food."

After a moment of idle chatter, Simmons tried to satisfy his industrialist's curiosity. "Have you heard from your government yet about the turbines?" he asked.

Gladkov waved his hand. "No, no, my friend. Let's not talk business. Let us enjoy our drinks and our meal. And let us get to know each other better."

An adept conversationalist, Gladkov swung into one amusing anecdote after another as he described his life in Russia, his family, some innocuous incidents about his experience as a Soviet diplomat. He seemed to like to dwell on his family. He had a lovely wife, he said, from a village in central Russia who had gone to medical school but quit before she became a doctor to marry him.

"Yet, it is a shame she is not a physician, but I must say her training comes in very handy when either of our two little boys get sick." Gladkov talked a while about his time in the Red Army during World War II and modestly described some of the battles he was in as a Soviet ski trooper.

In turn, Simmons skimmed over his own personal history and then asked Gladkov, "How do you like the United States?"

"Oh, I like it very much," Gladkov answered. "I find Americans quite friendly and pleasant to be with, although we Russians, too, are famous for our hospitality and friendliness."

Gladkov chatted on lightly, saying how he enjoyed the great variety of goods that American stores offered for sale; he was particularly impressed with the vast number of automobiles that crowded the streets and highways.

"We don't have nearly that many," he said, then added with a smile, "but give us time."

The steaks, both ordered medium rare, slowly vanished as the two men talked. And then the coffee and apple pie came. The talk turned to hunting. Gladkov's enthusiasm was genuine. He spoke glowingly of the great bear and elk that roamed the thick woodlands flourishing in the north central region of the Soviet Union near Gladkov's home village of Novorossisk.

Expertly he described the rifles, shotguns, and ammunition he used on various hunts. He admired most American weapons but thought possibly the Russian equivalent of our .30-.30 was a bit superior, and he had some reservations about the quality of some of the game birds found during the one or two outings he had in the Adirondacks earlier in the year.

"Too scrawny," he quipped.

Gladkov did most of the talking. And Simmons, for his part, was content to listen. He found it an unusual and stimulating experience to be so close to someone from a land that in many ways was a tantalizing enigma to him and to most Americans.

Only once did Simmons try to probe Gladkov's mind on the great political issues dividing their two nations. But Gladkov resolutely avoided politics.

In answer to Simmons' passing reference to the Hungarian Revolt, Gladkov said simply, "I think that there is possibly some misinformation among Americans about it." And then he quickly skipped to another subject.

In all, they sat, talking and eating, for a pleasant hour and fifteen minutes, then it was time to leave. Gladkov paid the check.

As they walked toward the exit, Simmons felt the need to reciprocate Gladkov's generosity. He casually remarked that he was having a party at his home that weekend, and perhaps Gladkov might find time to stop by.

It was meant simply to be a courtesy gesture, but to Simmons' mild surprise, Gladkov seized on the invitation quickly and accepted, saying, "May I also bring my wife? It is not often that she gets the chance to see and talk to Americans."

It was a typical suburban split-level party that Gladkov and his wife encountered when they arrived the following Saturday night. About thirty persons, appropriately well-dressed men and women, were standing about in clusters in the living room, den, and patio of the Simmons' $32,000 home on Long Island's North Shore. Most of them engaged in the animated conversation that frequently characterizes such parties.

They had been told that a genuine Soviet diplomat would be there and they were at their sophisticated best. Nor, once the Gladkovs fell into the rhythm of the party, did they disappoint anyone. They were excellent guests. Gladkov brought along a bottle of vodka and presented it to Simmons, saying it was "the very best of Russian spirit." Everyone sipped a little of the vodka and toasted the visitors.

Gladkov accepted the toast modestly and began mixing with the guests, many of whom were executives in industry or fairly high-placed officials in government.

Mrs. Gladkov, a reserved woman, spoke sparingly under the handicap of the language problem. But her husband immediately became the hit of the party. A clever conversationalist, he held everyone's attention as he spoke of his own experiences, particularly about hunting. But frequently, and almost unnoticeably, he shifted from monologue to dialogue as he asked questions of the other guests—what their names were; where they worked; what they did. To each male guest, Gladkov presented his personal card, and in nearly every case, he received the other's business card in return.

All in all, the party was a huge success, largely because of Gladkov's presence. More social engagements between the Russian diplomat and Simmons followed.

As the weeks wore on, the two became increasingly closer friends, hunting together, attending Broadway plays with their wives, dining out, and even taking the subway up to Yankee Stadium to see the New York Yankees play the strange and incomprehensible game of "beezball." Gladkov took a particular liking to Yogi Berra. "He looks like my brother Stanislaus," he would chuckle.

The two men clearly got along well together and seemed to find one another interesting. Gladkov liked to talk but he also knew when to stop and listen. He drank, but not excessively. He always paid his share of bills, and sometimes more. He spoke intelligently of current trends in medicine, science, the arts. He had a scholar's knowledge of Tolstoi, Dostoevski, Jack London, Mark Twain, and Theodore Dreiser.

By the end of summer, Gladkov had become assimilated into the fabric of Simmons' social life. Then on a morning in late September, Gladkov unexpectedly reintroduced a subject that had long been forgotten—the marine turbines.

"We've received word from Moscow at the Soviet Mission that we can begin negotiations," Gladkov said. "I think that the order will be substantial. Is there any way you can expedite matters?"

The suddenness of the contract talks startled Simmons.

"The whole thing had completely slipped my mind," Simmons said. "Frankly I don't know where things stand. I'll have to check. Give me a day or two."

"Of course," said Gladkov. "By the way, have you put out any new literature about the turbines?"

Again Simmons said he would have to check.

Two days later, Gladkov and Simmons met for lunch at the Harwyn Club, and this time Simmons had with him several new pamphlets and a new, rather lengthy technical paper on the turbine.

"You can look these over, but they don't amount to much," Simmons said. "Just some material we've put together to promote sales. We haven't done anything new in research."

"That's quite all right. I'm sure these will be very interesting and may help sell my bosses on placing a bigger order," the Russian said.

That ended all business talk as the conversation reverted to more general subjects.

A week went by and Gladkov appeared in Simmons' office and requested some fairly widely distributed literature about turbines manufactured by rival companies. Simmons had his secretary dig into the files and gave Gladkov the material.

On another occasion about three weeks later, Simmons furnished Gladkov the names of several engineers in his plant and also the names of a few members of his engineering society that Gladkov wanted for "file purposes."

Gladkov and Simmons continued to see each other for lunch or at social gatherings during the ensuing weeks. Then suddenly the Christmas holidays were upon them and Simmons was plunged into a rush-order period at the company. Not that marine engines and turbines are part of Yule giving, but it just happened to be a busy time.

On New Year's Day, Simmons and his family went to Bermuda for a vacation. When they returned three weeks later, Simmons phoned Gladkov but got no response at his home. An inquiry at the Russian Mission to the UN brought the answer that Gladkov and his family had returned to the Soviet Union for a vacation of their own.

Simmons did not see Gladkov again until the end of February when the Russian telephoned his American friend for a luncheon date, explaining then that he and Mrs. Gladkov had returned to Novorossisk for a visit with their families. Gladkov was particularly happy to have seen his parents again. "They're getting older, you know," he sighed. "They won't have many more years."

For the next three or four meetings nothing technical came up in their discussions and when it did it was almost as an aside.

"You're just the person to help me," Gladkov said one day over coffee. "My old friend Yuri Malinovsky is having a problem. You're the man to solve it. Yuri is an engineer back home. He's doing some work for his company on plans for a turbine. He needs some advice."

As though from memory he recited the technical problem involved, then asked Simmons if he would write some suggestions for Yuri.

Simmons took out a diagram he had in the portfolio he had brought with him to the restaurant. It was a much simplified version of the marine turbine that Gladkov was negotiating to buy from Simmons' firm. Simmons turned the diagram over and dashed off the solution to the problem Gladkov had posed.

Gladkov pocketed the sketch and chatted with Simmons a while longer. The men made a date to get together the following weekend at a resort hotel in the Catskill Mountains, about a hundred miles upstate. Then the Russian picked up the tab, $17.25, left a $20 bill on the table, and the two departed.

By now it was late April and spring was at its luxuriant zenith. Rich green carpetings of grass covered the flower-sprinkled countryside of Monticello and a bone-warming sun hung golden in the sky as the two men walked leisurely along a winding, wooded path late that Saturday afternoon. The talk at first was casual—more about hunting, what the ladies had planned for the evening, the weather.

But something seemed to be disturbing Gladkov. Simmons noticed it and finally asked, "Is there anything wrong, my friend?"

"No, not really. But I keep worrying about my friend Yuri. This is an important job for him and he seems to be having one problem after another. I wonder . . ." He fell silent.

"Is there anything I can do to help?" Simmons asked.

"I'm sure you could but I don't think it's fair. After all, you are a busy man. But maybe we can find some way." Gladkov hesitated a moment. Then he said, "Why . . . why don't you help out as a consultant . . . a paid engineering consultant? I'll be happy to absorb the cost . . ."

"Why, Boris, I'm surprised at you," Simmons said. "My company wouldn't stand still for that! But . . . I'll be glad to help out Yuri without charge. I'll be doing it for you because you are my friend."

Gladkov gave Simmons a pound on the back and thanked him.

Later that day Gladkov and Simmons headed to a pond stocked with trout and pike and lazed a quiet two or three hours in a rented rowboat. That evening the two couples drove to an Italian restaurant nestled in the heart of the so-called "borscht belt" and dined heartily of baked clams, veal scallopini, and chianti. They took in the night-club act in their hotel and managed, as comfortable friends so often do, to get slightly lightheaded by evening's end. They slept over at the hotel that night and, after breakfast the next morning, left for New York in Simmons' car.

In their ensuing meetings, Gladkov always managed to relay some new problem his friend Yuri was encountering to Simmons, and Simmons, the older, more experienced, engineer, would either solve it on the spot or ask for a day or two to gather the necessary information, which he always managed to obtain.

The two men held to their agreement that Simmons would receive no consulting fee since he did not accept the status. But as the problem-solving became more complicated and almost a ritual part of any evening they spent together, Gladkov insisted that he at least reimburse Simmons for any expenses his American friend incurred.

On one occasion it was for several trade magazines Simmons had to buy, another time Simmons made several long-distance calls to engineer friends, arranging contacts for Yuri when he had other technical problems to clarify. The sums were never great, but they were always offered promptly—and accepted.

As the sessions became more frequent, Gladkov began asking for more complicated, more detailed information. Yuri, he would say, needed data unavailable to him back home on gears, generators, condensers for naval vessels, and even—on one occasion—certain general information concerning atomic submarines.

At no time did Gladkov ask for classified information or in other ways try to breach U.S. security. But Simmons nevertheless suffered some fear that the inoffensive favors he was doing for his friend would be misinterpreted if they became known to his firm.

As a result, Simmons, although absolutely convinced he was doing nothing wrong, established a somewhat clandestine process of passing along the needed information to his Russian friend from the UN.

When Simmons suggested the need for such discretion, Gladkov laughingly agreed, saying, "Any mystery novel reader would appreciate this, you know. The classic way to pass material is called 'the drop.' Yes, we can work something out."

The details of the first and subsequent "drops" varied, but they followed a general pattern. Here is a typical one:

Simmons left his office at 6:05 p.m. on a Tuesday and rode the BMT subway to Union Square where Broadway and 14th Street cross. He went up to the street and walked east to 15th Street and First Avenue—a rendezvous area made popular in espionage some years back by Judith Coplon and Valentin Gubitchev—then swung northward until he spotted Gladkov's 1955 red Ford sedan parked at a meter on the east side of First Avenue, between 17th and 18th Streets.

The car was unoccupied. Simmons walked up to it confidently as though he were the owner, opened the right-hand door nearest the curb, and climbed in. He pretended to be looking for something in the glove compartment, but he was actually placing an envelope under a blanket on the car's front seat. Once the envelope was tucked in its hiding place, Simmons continued the charade of hunting through the glove compartment, pretended to be unable to find it, and left the car, walking southward on First Avenue at a brisk pace as though he suddenly remembered where he left the object he was looking for.

Simmons almost enjoyed what he came to call "the game." It added an element of thrill and excitement to his relationship with the Russian diplomat, and yet, of course, as Simmons thought of it, the whole thing was entirely innocent.

On a day in the middle of June, 1956, Simmons met Gladkov for one of their more or less regular Wednesday lunches and as the Russian UN delegate entered, his friend noticed a sprightlier bounce to his walk. He seemed to be excited about something.

"Dick, my friend," Gladkov said. "Let me congratulate you. I finally heard from home and we want your turbines. It's definite. They've looked over your specifications and want to increase the order now to twelve. This should be a fine feather in your cap."

Simmons modestly acknowledged the congratulations and the two men ceremoniously shook hands on it. During lunch they discussed possible shipping dates, export requirements, and the other details. And Simmons promised to have his sales and legal departments work these out and draw up a contract of the sale within the following week.

By Tuesday, the contract was drafted. The amount Simmons' company was to receive was substantial. In every respect the contract seemed to be mutually profitable to both sides. The turbines were in Simmons' plant in the metropolitan area and could be shipped immediately. The contract was mailed to the Soviet Government.

Ten days later Simmons and Gladkov had dinner together. Gladkov announced the news immediately.

"They're satisfied back home. Very satisfied. They aren't asking a single change in the contract."

His superior in New York, he said, would sign for the Russians in a day or so and Simmons' company could expect a check promptly. Then Gladkov fell to eating his dinner and for some inexplicable reason sank into a strange quiet.

After several minutes Simmons felt obliged to ask, "Is something wrong?"

Gladkov looked up. His face was grim.

"Dick," he began hesitatingly, "can I ask you to let me have the specifications for the [classified] turbine. My superior would like to see them before he signs the contract."

Simmons stared across the table at Gladkov. The American engineer was bewildered by the request.

"I can't do that," he said finally, with an edge of astonishment in his voice. "That's a different turbine completely. Our contract covers the commercial type. What you're asking for is classified information. You're asking for specifications on a military turbine. I couldn't possibly give you what you want unless you were cleared by the State Department in Washington. And you know you couldn't get such clearance."

"I know," Gladkov said meekly, as though suggesting he was doing nothing more than performing an unpleasant errand for someone. "Look," he pleaded, "we've been good friends for a long time now. I'm sure you can help me out."

Gladkov now suggested that the whole deal might fall through if he didn't supply his government with the classified data.

Simmons toyed with his fork in silence as he appeared to ponder his friend's request.

"I'll have to let you know," he finally murmured. "I can't say anything more about it now."

Simmons went home that evening, his mind a spinning kaleidoscope of doubts, worries, and fears. He slept a troubled sleep that night and woke up the next morning still seized by anxiety. He drank a cup of coffee for breakfast but refused any food. At precisely thirteen minutes after eight o'clock, he abruptly rose from the table, walked to the kitchen telephone, and dialed the New York number of the Federal Bureau of Investigation.

For the rest of that morning, afternoon, and late into the evening, Simmons gave a full account of all his dealings with Gladkov. Slowly, methodically, through expert questioning of FBI agents, every gap and hole in Simmons' story was filled in until the G-men had what amounted to a finely woven tapestry of the relationship and every known fact connected with it between Richard Simmons and Boris Gladkov, beginning with the very first meeting at that cocktail party in late May, 1955, more than a full year ago, and ending with the previous day's disturbing dinner, when Simmons finally realized that he'd been a tool in a far deeper and infinitely more insidious operation—espionage.

As the FBI agents reconstructed the case, they recognized an all too-familiar story. Scores of times before they had heard other innocent dupes unfold, sometimes too late, their stories of friendship and favors with members of the enemy camp.

Simmons' case was almost a classic example. Here were two men, a Russian diplomat in the service of the UN and an American industrialist, meeting across what amounted to an international chessboard in a game in which the Russian wrote the rules, held all the pieces, and directed all the moves. His adversary did nothing, really, but pick up the pieces and slide them across the board like an automaton, ignorant of the rules, of the stakes involved, unaware that he was even playing the game. He never had a chance.

Gladkov was a legally accredited diplomat charged with carrying out the legitimate business of his government on these shores. In that capacity, he enjoyed, though with some restrictions, the freedoms of an open and democratic society. But Gladkov was more than an emissary in the political arena. He was also a Soviet KGB agent and had been specially selected and trained in Russia for espionage work in the United States.

His "chess" opponent was, it is true, an intelligent, well-educated

man, but he was absolutely devoid of any skills in espionage or counterespionage, and was further handicapped by the fact that nothing in
his healthy, democratic background bred those suspicions that are
second nature to the professional spy.

Unknown to Simmons, he had been thoroughly investigated and
personally sized up by the Soviets long before he met Gladkov at the
cocktail party. They knew who he was, how much authority he
wielded, even what his hobbies were. They could have decided upon
Simmons as a man worth nurturing for any of several reasons.

A Soviet agent might have met him at a party a year or two before
Gladkov ran into him and discovered his huge fund of technical
knowledge. His name might have been gleaned from the business
pages of *The New York Times* or the *Wall Street Journal*. It could
have come up at an engineers' convention in Atlantic City. They
might have spotted it in a trade journal.

The purpose of that first visit to Simmons' office by Gladkov and
Victor Rudenko, the aide who dropped out of the picture once it
became clear that Gladkov had established the necessary rapport with
Simmons, was to scout the American executive in greater depth than
had already been studied, and see if he was worth developing.

Obviously from the Russian viewpoint he was.

Not everyone passes the test. If an American indicates hostility, the
Russians will more than likely drop him. But anyone who appears
friendly—and most Americans do—is considered a definite possibility.

What followed was almost Chapter I in any espionage manual.
Gladkov established a common interest—hunting. Then came the inevitable social follow-up contacts. Once the friendship was solid—
and the Russians will spend months and even years abuilding if the
prospect seems sufficiently promising—the innocent pleas were made
for bland, plainly inoffensive material and information: "to help Yuri
back in Russia."

At this point, the money offer is always advanced and usually accepted because it is always negligible and seemingly justified. In Simmons' case, Gladkov paid out exactly $1,550 during their year-long
relationship.

Speaking about such emoluments as are proffered by the Russians,
FBI Director Hoover once said: "Money is one of the most effective
recruitment weapons. The Soviets have money and will spend it

quickly and in sizable sums if they feel they will benefit. . . . The acceptance of money gives the Soviets a dominant hand, which is part of their strategy. Even gifts such as vodka, caviar, and books are designed to put the businessman under an obligation."

At some point, usually after money or some other material inducement has been accepted by the American, the Soviets have to take a gamble. The risk eventually must be taken. The Russians will listen to unimportant peripheral information and sometimes even appear eager for public source information, but the prize catch is to break through the inner secrets of business, government, and the military.

It becomes the moment of truth for the Soviet spy and his whole future and, indeed, even his life may depend on the outcome.

In the Richard Simmons case it came when Gladkov asked for the technical specifications of a classified marine turbine. Other men might have succumbed to the arsenal of pressures the Soviets had imposed on him by now, but Richard Simmons was made of sterner stuff. The security of his country was paramount over all other considerations. Thus, his call to the FBI.

The FBI moved swiftly. Simmons had blown the whistle on the plot in mid-June. On June 22, 1956, based on Simmons' detailed and, in some cases, documented account, the State Department declared Boris Fedorovich Gladkov persona non grata for engaging in "activities which were highly improper and incompatible with his status as a member of the Soviet Delegation to the United Nations."

He left New York on July 12, 1956, and returned to Russia. His mission had ended in failure.

In this one instance, the Soviet danger was eliminated before any real harm was done. But the FBI was certain of one thing—that somewhere another Boris Fedorovich Gladkov was already at work on another Richard Simmons.

7 : Land, Sea, and Now Our Air Secrets

THE spy cases sprouting out of the United Nations in 1956 did not end with the ouster of Turkin, Gurynov, Shapovalov, Ekimov, and Gladkov. This was a hectic year in the annals of espionage, one which brought on the exposure of a bumper crop of Red agents.

A half dozen UN-based Russians were tapped by the State Department as spies during 1956. There had never been so many cases in one year before—nor since.

There is no way of knowing whether the Russians were particularly industrious in 1956 or if they were more careless in their movements. It must remain one of the mysteries inherent in subversion, which in itself is a baffling profession.

If it proves nothing else, each case does exhibit the vulnerability of Kremlin agents. None can know, despite his knowledge and training in this crafty art, when he will become enmeshed in one or another of the bizarre twists that inevitably bring a plot to steal our secrets to the attention of the law.

There are many heroes in the relentless crusade to expose the enemy endangering America's security and defense; and the paladin in this spy adventure we are about to relate is Henry Farmer, a simple, hard-working family man living on Long Island and employed as a draftsman with one of the large aircraft companies out there.

Actually the name Henry Farmer is fictitious, as was Fred Timsford and Richard Simmons. The FBI has never released the names of the actual persons for their own protection. But they are being protected from different fountainheads of trouble. Timsford's identity is kept under wraps for security reasons alone. That reason also applies to the anonymity given Farmer, but in addition this man needs protection from the possible ramification of the seeping distrust and stigmatism that could accrue to him.

For Henry Farmer is a man who unwittingly came close to contributing to the Communist cause before awakening suddenly from a nightmarish experience which brought him face to face with reality. His haste to bare the whole story of how he was taken in, and his willingness to make amends, earned him both forgiveness and well-deserved privacy.

Henry Farmer's work at the aircraft company, which we, of course, will not name, was important so far as it went. But as happens so often, the salary wasn't enough for his needs. Farmer earned $8,500 a year and found it hard making ends meet. He had a family, children, and a heavy mortgage on a new house. This is a weakness that espionage agents seek to find in their recruits, as we have said.

Henry Farmer decided that he must acquire an additional income and the best way he knew how was to put his talents as a draftsman to work in his spare time. To that end he solicited part-time employment by placing an advertisement in the classified section of a New York City newspaper in the early part of December, 1955.

It was gratifying for Farmer to receive an almost immediate response.

The name Victor Petrov meant nothing to him and it had no greater significance once Farmer got talking with the man who phoned him about a job. Farmer detected the accent but he wasn't certain of the man's nationality. Just in passing, he thought the man was of Slavic or Russian origin.

Petrov told Farmer that he wanted some drawings traced and asked about his fees. After a brief conversation, the caller said he'd let Farmer know.

Ten days passed. On January 15, just as Farmer and his family were sitting down to dinner, the phone rang. Farmer answered it.

"I am Victor Petrov," the caller said. "I want to see you, Mr. Farmer, about some work I would like to have done."

Farmer invited him to his home, and in less than an hour, Petrov was at the door.

Farmer, greeting the man who responded to his ad, found a sturdy-looking individual who stood about the same height as himself, five feet nine inches, but who was somewhat heavier, about one hundred eighty pounds. His brown hair had premature strands of gray that seemed to reflect the color of his eyes. His face, almost olive-toned, appeared to be that of a man in his early thirties.

Farmer ushered the visitor to the living room and offered him a drink, which he accepted. It was Scotch on the rocks.

"Well, Mr. Petrov, what can I do for you?" Farmer asked, sitting next to his guest on the sofa.

Petrov wanted to learn first about Farmer's qualifications and experience. He asked questions politely and with tact. Farmer answered readily, explaining almost immediately his connection with the large aviation corporation, which he named.

The name acted like a magic word. Petrov instantly showed an absorbing curiosity and interest in the draftsman and his work.

"It is simply a stroke of luck that I ran into you," Petrov remarked enthusiastically. "You are just the man I have been looking for, someone to provide me with diagrams for airplanes."

Bewilderment seized Farmer at once. He thought Petrov was referring to sketches of planes either in production or on the drawing boards at the aircraft plant where the draftsman worked. If so, he was sorry but he couldn't possibly do that.

"Oh, no," Petrov laughed. "I simply want you to make drawings of whatever is readily available. You know—the designs that appear in magazines and other air publications."

Petrov then identified himself as a translator employed by the United Nations Secretariat, but he did not bother to add that he was a Soviet national. Farmer, who was reluctant to ask, assumed, as he had on the phone when he first heard Petrov speak, that he might be Czechoslovakian, Yugoslavian, or perhaps—Russian.

Petrov told Farmer that his purpose in having the tracings done was for a sideline job he held as a translator for some foreign countries.

One of these accounts, he said, was a toy manufacturer who was producing authentic scale-model submarines, ships, tanks, automobiles, and planes. He said the firm was too small to afford a full-time draftsman.

"And besides," as Petrov put it, "your American designs are so much better than what they can get on the Continent."

That was why he had come to Farmer—to provide drawings on a part-time basis.

"I am willing to pay you at the rate of two dollars and fifty cents an hour for your time," offered Petrov.

Farmer rather liked the offer but he had some reservations about copying plans or drawings of actual planes, which, he suggested, was larcenous since it infringed on copyrighted or patented designs. But Petrov dismissed that argument.

"It's done every day," he chuckled. "The companies don't mind it as long as we don't build the real thing. In fact, it makes them happy that someone is promoting their product among the children. It builds up prestige and good will for the companies."

Petrov then pulled out a recent issue of an aviation magazine from his leather portfolio and turned to a page containing the diagram of a U.S. Air Force single-seater jet fighter.

"I want you to copy this for me," Petrov said. "Is it a deal?"

Farmer consented. He told Petrov he would have it ready in a few days and the two parted on a firm handshake. On the way out, Farmer invited him to come back some evening for dinner with his family; the draftsman's wife and children were shopping at the supermarket this evening.

"I will be happy to join you," the departing guest assured Farmer. "Maybe very soon."

Even as Petrov walked down the front steps, thoughts about the assignment coursed through Farmer's head. Why, he asked himself, did Petrov want him to copy something out of a magazine that already was available in the very form required for the production of a toy. True, Petrov said the company had no draftsman and he had also instructed Farmer to draw enlargements of the design which could be translated into templates. At the same time, Petrov asked Farmer to reduce the scale drastically from feet to inches for application to the production of the plane as a toy and not the real thing. Yet anyone who had taken high school mathematics could have worked out the new figures, while the pilfering of the design itself and its enlargement to the required dimensions could have been accomplished via any inexpensive enlargement process on a photo-copy machine.

The thought of easy spare-time money then came into Farmer's thoughts and quickly chased out whatever confusion coursed through his head. By the time his wife returned from the market and joined him in the living room, he was bubbling with eagerness to tell her all about this first spare-time assignment that would pay him $2.50 an hour.

Farmer quickly plunged into his first extra-income job. He worked on the drawings the next few nights at home and then received a call from Petrov. Since Farmer was ready to deliver the finished sketches, he invited the client over to the house the next night.

That evening Farmer took Petrov to a corner of the living room where Farmer had a desk and showed the Russian the sketches he had prepared.

"Marvelous," Petrov remarked exuberantly after looking them over. "Just what I wanted. Perfect. You are a master draftsman."

Then digging into his portfolio again, Petrov took out another aviation magazine and turned to a page with a design for a different fighter plane. He showed it to Farmer and asked him to reproduce that model. Again it was a simple routine of merely duplicating design and reducing scale.

It was child's play for Farmer, virtually an insult to his intelligence and his talent as a draftsman. But the five crisp ten dollar bills that Petrov put in Farmer's hand for the time he had put in on the design just delivered were perfect palliatives for any indignation he might have entertained about the plebeian nature of the work—and a good argument to end his wife's nagging about working at home. There was no question in Farmer's mind that he had found a gold mine in Petrov. He was determined to satisfy and asked no questions.

"I can have it ready in four or five nights," Farmer volunteered eagerly, resolved now more than ever that he was going to please this high-paying client.

"That will be fine," Petrov said with a glow of satisfaction. "I will call you in a few days to find out if they are ready."

Actually, a week went by before the Russian phoned. Farmer had the sketches ready and asked Petrov to come over the next evening. Again Petrov was delighted with Farmer's sketches and again he provided the draftsman with an issue of an American aviation magazine to copy an airplane, this one a bomber. The assignments continued.

Then, in late February of 1956, Petrov came to the house on one of his regular visits and, sitting at Farmer's desk, he noticed the previous November's issue of an aviation monthly the draftsman subscribed to. Petrov picked up the magazine and leafed through its pages. Then he suddenly stopped and studied a design for a military plane that was being developed by a West Coast firm.

"I wonder," Petrov asked, "could you send in this reader's reply card to get more information about this airplane? I think some of my accounts might be interested in a later model like this one."

Farmer felt no qualms about doing it. He filled the card out on the spot and said he would mail it first thing in the morning.

"I will save you the trouble," Petrov smiled, taking the card. "I will mail it tonight." That night Petrov gave Farmer still another design to copy.

In early March, Farmer had a call from Petrov who invited the draftsman to have dinner with him in a neighborhood restaurant. Farmer agreed and they met at the corner of Roosevelt Avenue and 77th Street in Jackson Heights, Queens. Petrov had not indicated why he wanted to meet Farmer away from his home, but as the two men munched on their food in a nearby restaurant, they began sailing into a new savanna of companionability that had not been achieved at any of their many gatherings in Farmer's home. They were soon discussing considerably more mundane matters than drafting—politics, religion, and friends.

That last area seemed to interest Petrov the most. He dwelled on the subject of Farmer's friends at length, asking about them in various ways. As Farmer later recalled, Petrov had an insatiable curiosity about what people the draftsman knew at the aircraft plant, what jobs they held, and his extent of friendship or acquaintanceship with them. Farmer harbored no hesitancy in discussing his fellow employees. He spoke freely and truthfully about them. Well freely, anyway. In trying to make an impression on Petrov, Farmer may have gone overboard in tossing around a few names of key figures at the plant as close friends when at most they were merely executives he knew just in passing.

At any rate, the evening was a huge success so far as Farmer was concerned. Not only did he develop what he viewed as a deep camaraderie with Petrov, but he also came away with the idea that his client had a new and high respect for his importance at the plant. This was certain to continue the part-time work that Petrov had been giving him.

Before parting, Petrov presented Farmer one more plane sketch to trace. Then he suddenly seemed to remember something.

"Did that material from the magazine come yet?" Petrov asked.

Farmer said it had not arrived but would let him know as soon as it did.

In late March, the two met again in the same Jackson Heights restaurant. The information about the plane in production on the Coast had come and Farmer turned it over to Petrov who was enthusiastic about it.

The talk once more reverted to the pattern of the last meeting, centering on the people Farmer knew at the aircraft plant. Now Petrov was exhibiting curiosity about their incomes and their financial straits. When Farmer mentioned that one of the engineers, a man who worked on aircraft methods and design, was in a money jam and was himself looking for part-time work, Petrov's face lit up.

"I think I can help him," Petrov offered almost eagerly. "I have something big in mind, but it is too soon to talk about it. I will let you know. There will be a lot in it for you, too."

For the moment, Petrov had another problem. "I have a client in Austria who has been using the sketches you have been making. He has a very small plastics company and at night he has been going to the university to work on his doctor's degree. He needs some of the latest literature and pamphlets from your company to prepare a thesis. Can you help? Can you get them out of your company's library?"

"Sure," Farmer laughed. "That's a cinch. We distribute that literature to all our clients. No problem."

There was another fifty-dollar drafting job for Farmer before they parted, and there was also payment for the information that Farmer had obtained from the magazine.

"I am going to be paid by my client for this, so there is no reason I shouldn't pay you for your trouble," Petrov said, putting twenty-five dollars additional in Farmer's hand.

On their next meeting in the same restaurant, Petrov had come prepared to talk about his "big deal." But nothing was said until after dinner when Petrov suggested they take a walk. Petrov seemed to know the neighborhood better than Farmer and led the way along 77th Street to Broadway, then along 78th Street to a small park.

"Here's a good place to sit and talk," Petrov said, stopping at a bench.

Despite several drinks before and after dinner, Farmer had the presence of mind to be shocked when Petrov began discussing his "big deal."

What Petrov now proposed was a treasonous scheme to obtain classified or top secret information about military aircraft in production at the plant on Long Island.

"I can't do a thing like that," Farmer blurted in protest. "I can go to jail for something like this. So can you . . ."

Petrov grinned and patted Farmer on the hand indulgingly.

"You need money," Petrov said knowingly. "I have plenty of money to pay you. Not the kind you have been receiving from me, but really big—in the thousands. You have a family to raise, a big mortgage around your neck, debts to pay. I can put you on easy street."

Then, gazing intently into Farmer's eyes, Petrov whispered, "Don't give me an answer now . . . think about it. I can wait. But not too long. I will have to go to someone else . . ."

Before they got up to leave, Petrov took out an envelope and put it on his lap. "Take this," Petrov said, pushing it toward Farmer. "Open it later when you are thinking about my proposition."

Farmer reached out and palmed the envelope. Later, at home, he found it contained one hundred dollars. That night Farmer thought about Petrov's offer. He didn't breathe a word of it to his wife and, as he later revealed, he "didn't sleep all night, worrying about what could happen to me and my family."

In his stupor he had failed to ask Petrov what he was going to do with the information. Yet Farmer had a good idea it would not be going to any of his toy manufacturing clients. Such data as Petrov was asking wasn't required in building toy planes. As the United States Air Force was to tell us, this information would have been an excellent guide to the Russians in determining the status of our air-craft development.

The next day Farmer was at his wit's end with worry. He needed money badly, but his conscience told him that this was not the way to get it. He was not going to commit treason. While he was not yet certain that Petrov was a spy, Farmer had ample reason now to sus-pect the worst of his benefactor.

Could Petrov be a Russian spy?

The thought sent a chill through Farmer. Trembling at the idea that he had conceivably been suckered into a Red espionage trap, Farmer decided to see the FBI. He called the New York City office and asked for an appointment "to discuss a very urgent matter." He was told to come right in.

It was Saturday and Farmer did not have to work that day. He kept his date with the FBI in the afternoon. The meeting with the G-men lasted several hours, during which time he told in detail every step of his relations with Petrov and of the drafting jobs he had been given to do. Meanwhile, a quick check on Petrov's name told the FBI what he had neglected to inform Farmer—that he was a Russian.

Farmer's story had a familiar ring to the FBI, which at that mo-ment was still in the midst of the investigation into the case involving Boris Gladkov's attempt to weed out classified information on a mili-tary-type turbine from Richard Simmons. But the similarity was not as great. Petrov had not gone to the lengths that Gladkov had in building up a friendship that encompassed a complete circuit of social events. Petrov had merely been a guest in Farmer's house, had done the draftsman a good turn by providing him with spare-time work, but had never gone to the trouble of building up the closely knit association that was inherent in the other case.

But the story Farmer told did have an almost exact parallel in a case the FBI had worked on a few months before when another American, Sidney Hatkin, an Air Force economist, had inserted a classified advertisement in a newspaper for work. Hatkin was desperate for employment; he had been suspended for a year at the time as a suspected security risk.

A Soviet Embassy employee in Washington, Vladimir P. Mikheev, who saw the ad, got in touch with Hatkin and asked him to gather some aviation statistics. Unlike Farmer, suspicion gripped Hatkin at once and he went to the FBI.

The story broke in the newspapers prematurely and the adverse publicity prompted the Russians to put Mikheev on a fast plane back to Moscow, where he has remained ever since. The Kremlin acted so swiftly that it spared the State Department the trouble of preparing a formal note of protest and a request for Mikheev's recall. For his own quick enterprise in alerting the FBI, Hatkin was restored to a non-sensitive Air Force job.

Because the case involving Petrov and Farmer had gotten far more involved, it was handled differently. After baring everything about his dealings with Petrov, Farmer was instructed by the FBI to "play along." He was told to meet Petrov again and to find out precisely what information and date he was seeking. Farmer agreed to play the dual agent.

The FBI already knew a great deal about Petrov, as it does about most Russians at the UN. It was known that he lived in an apartment house at 110 West 96th Street on Manhattan's Upper West Side. With him was his wife Vladilena and a six-year-old son, Alexei. Petrov was also known to be thirty-one years old, he had come to the UN from Moscow on February 17, 1953, and was holding down an $8,000-a-year translator's job in the Language Section.

So far as the FBI was concerned, there was no question Petrov was a spy. That called for certain moves. G-men were assigned to watch Petrov, and a tail also was put on Farmer.

The following week, Farmer met Petrov in the Jackson Heights restaurant which, by this time, had become the central rendezvous for their transactions.

"Can we do business?" Petrov asked after settling down with Farmer over cocktails.

"Yes," Farmer replied matter-of-factly.

Unknown to Farmer and Petrov, their meeting now was in the process of being preserved for posterity. Seated at a table nearby were two FBI men pretending to be in deep conversation and oblivious to the goings-on about them. The agents made a good pretense of looking like a couple of businessmen unwinding at the end of a difficult day. But one of the agents had a miniature camera concealed in his jacket and managed to photograph Farmer and Petrov at their table in various poses.

One photograph, it was later revealed, showed Petrov pulling out a large printed sheet. This was a published chart concerning the physical specifications and flight characteristics of United States military aircraft. The chart contained a number of blank columns, indicating that specific information relating to certain airplanes could not be released publicly in the interest of national defense.

"I want you to get me the figures for these missing blanks," Petrov murmured to Farmer.

Farmer said he himself did not have access to those figures, but that the engineer he had mentioned at their previous meeting—the one who worked on aircraft methods and designs and was in a money jam—might very well be the man to supply the missing data.

"Good," Petrov smiled. "I do not want to deal with him. I leave it in your hands. You come to terms with him. I will pay you. The price is two thousand dollars. You can split with him any way you wish . . ."

Later that evening, according to pre-arranged plans, Farmer met the G-men in a diner in Long Island City not far from Jackson Heights and turned over to them the chart Petrov had given him.

The agents gave Farmer his orders which were: "Stall." They wanted to prolong the negotiations for as long as possible, to see how anxious Petrov was for the information and also to observe what other espionage activities he might be involved in.

The days became weeks and the weeks passed. Summer finally came and Farmer still had not delivered the chart back to Petrov with the data. But their meetings continued. Always Farmer came prepared with a good excuse for the delay, an excuse that had been framed by the FBI and drilled into Farmer at long briefing sessions.

Petrov's patience appeared at last to be wearing thin. His exasperation reflected in his voice finally one day in mid-August when he complained to Farmer at their favorite restaurant: "Now listen, this can't go on. You are taking too long to provide me with the figures. I must have them by next week or the whole deal is off. This is my final word."

Farmer could see that Petrov would not be strung along any further. It was obvious that he had to produce the document by the following week or admit failure and put an end to the negotiations with the Russian. But that decision was not in Farmer's province. The FBI was calling the signals and it was up to them to say what Farmer must do. He reported back what Petrov had said.

The FBI's instructions to Farmer were brief but explicit: "We will let you know what to do. Let us know if he calls you in the meantime."

All the delay over the months was engineered by the FBI to give its agents opportunity to observe Petrov, in the expectation he might betray himself in other espionage endeavors. But he did not attempt to suborn any other American. It appeared his primary goal was to obtain the airplane data he was after from Farmer.

The FBI felt finally that Petrov would not lead them to other conspiracies. As it was, all the evidence that was needed to make a case against Petrov was in hand. The findings were forwarded to Washington with the recommendation that the game they were playing with the Russian come to a halt, since it promised to serve no useful purpose to prolong it.

FBI Director Hoover studied the evidence and concluded that the field office had the right slant. He turned the case over to the Attorney General, who decided that the evidence against Petrov, while solid and indefensible, was not sufficient or worthwhile to warrant his arrest and prosecution. The case against Valentin Gubitchev, who, like Petrov, did not enjoy the diplomatic immunity held by some of the other Russians caught in espionage, was far stronger and yet he managed to escape punishment in the end. What chance would the Government have against Petrov with the relatively thin skein of evidence they had on him—a published chart of physical specifications and flight characteristics for United States military planes which wasn't even in his possession now, and, of course, a document that in itself was not incriminating since it was something that anyone could obtain. The crime would have been committed had Petrov succeeded in obtaining the data and figures for the blank boxes on the chart which he had asked Farmer to get. But Farmer had gone to the FBI and the FBI never allowed Farmer to deliver the secret information.

Moreover, Petrov held the trump card. He had the "spy trade" working for him, a pattern of operation that was now beginning to shape itself more and more, and which, in later years, would come to be regarded as the only way to deal with Russian spies: give them back to the Soviets in exchange for one of our people who had been accused in Moscow of espionage. To make a circus out of Petrov's arrest, to put the Attorney General to the trouble and expense of prosecuting, when in the end it would be nothing more than a perfunctory performance, was not only wasteful and time-consuming, but ridiculous. Reality must be faced with reality.

So, since it did have the goods on Petrov anyway and because his conduct was not in accord with the UN Charter Agreement, the Attorney General decided to put the matter into the State Department's hands with the recommendation for the Russian's ouster.

The State Department agreed and transmitted its decision to James J. Wadsworth, deputy United States delegate to the United Nations in the absence of his superior, Henry Cabot Lodge, Jr., the U.S. Ambassador, who was in California at the time.

Wadsworth wasted no time putting the case against Petrov on the 38th floor desk of the Secretary General. Sitting behind that desk was Dag Hammarskjöld who was getting his baptism in the field of espionage as practiced in the UN by Soviet nationals employed as civil servants.

Hammarskjöld proved no less a foe of Charter violators than Lie. After studying the testimony against Petrov, Hammarskjöld drew up the order for the Russian's dismissal from the Secretariat. That order went out on August 24—but not fast enough.

Petrov had already taken his leave. Without waiting for a formal discharge, the Russian translator, his wife, and son made a hurried departure from their apartment the day before, although the rent was paid through September, and had taken a Scandinavian Airlines plane out of the country, with Moscow as their destination.

It was never made clear whether Petrov had advance warning that he would be unmasked as a spy and that Hammarskjöld intended to dismiss him. But it was learned that Petrov called in "sick" on August 22, just as Hammarskjöld was beginning to look over the case Ambassador Wadsworth had brought to him. And the Soviet translator did not show up for work the next day, either.

His rushed travel arrangements were said to have been made without United Nations' aid, and a Soviet spokesman denied his delegation had helped pave the way for Petrov's hurried departure.

"We disclaim any knowledge of him or of his activities," the Soviet spokesman stated.

Despite this denial, the FBI, which had a tail on the spy, spotted Russian UN representatives at New York International Airport bidding adieu to Petrov and his family as they boarded the airliner for home.

The Petrov case was stamped closed soon afterward with a terse announcement from the State Department that no further action through the United Nations was necessary, and that as far as was known, no United States co-conspirators were involved.

The United States UN Delegation also issued a statement saying that Petrov's dismissal had been ordered on the basis of evidence that he sought to get "information vital to the security and defense of the United States."

The bare details of the case and a generalized description of Petrov's subversive activities were made public in Washington by Assistant Attorney General William F. Tompkins who headed the Justice Department's Internal Security Division. In telling of the long and fruitless espionage effort, Tompkins asserted that "at no time had Petrov succeeded in getting any classified information."

Tompkins also made it clear that Farmer was not involved in security charges. His intent in running the advertisement that had attracted Petrov's attention was simply to provide Farmer a source of extra income in his spare time. Farmer, whose loyalty was beyond question, continued to work at his job at the Long Island aircraft plant.

And he continued to seek part-time work in his spare time by running ads in the very newspaper that had caught Petrov's eye. But he has been a lot more careful in picking his outside employers after this experience.

And what of Petrov?

Nothing was heard about Petrov after his departure until a brief dispatch was filed from Moscow by United Press International on June 19, 1961. It read: "Three more local Communist Party officials have been fired in Soviet Premier Khrushchev's drive to weed out inefficient and dishonest bureaucrats, it was announced yesterday. The Communist Party newspaper, *Pravda,* said Yaroslav regional Party Secretary B. Barinov was released from his job 'for not insuring leadership.' *Pravda* said two other officials—bureau member Alexandre Borisenko and Party Secretary Victor Ivanovich Petrov—were relieved."

If one were to attempt to evaluate what the future could hold for Petrov, about whom no word has come here since that UPI dispatch, one must consider his failure first as a spy at the United Nations, then his downfall as a Communist Party official.

It might even be safe to say that Petrov, having run the gamut of washouts, has been committed to history and that there is nothing left but his ignominious past and that somewhere on some wall in some Siberian salt mine is etched his epitaph:

VICTOR IVANOVICH PETROV—FAILURE. R.I.P.

8 : Vice President Nixon
Lets a Spy Out of the Bag

THE sky was growing dark, and ominous granite clouds swirled in from the West, dimming the afternoon light. A curtain of violet shadow hung over Main Street as it did over the rest of the city that September 18, 1959. Apart from the threat of a downpour, the broad thoroughfare was busy with passing cars and pedestrians who seemed to ignore the menacing weather.

Neither did anyone appear to pay attention to a brown two-and-a-half-ton delivery truck, devoid of all lettering or identifying features, as it cruised slowly along Main Street. The man behind the wheel spoke like a ventriloquist, virtually never moving his lips. His thin young face was somber, his eyes more alert than most drivers'. He was trying to watch not only the weaving threads of traffic but also the files of pedestrians coursing back and forth on the sidewalks on both sides of the street.

The man driving the truck had a job to do. So did the other two men to whom he spoke so furtively now and then. They were riding in the back, unseen from the street. These three were FBI agents on an important mission on Main Street in Springfield, Massachusetts. In fact, this was the most important moment in the FBI's three-month investigation into a plot by a Soviet political affairs officer at the UN to steal designs of cryptographic machines used in intelligence work by the U.S. Army.

The first rumblings of the conspiracy were heard in late June of that year when a 22-year-old ex-college student phoned the FBI office in Springfield to report he was being harassed and pressured "to commit treason against my country" by a Russian whom he knew only by the name of George. Agents were sent immediately to the caller's home in the outskirts of Springfield.

They found a pleasant, intelligent, level-headed young man who has been identified to the authors by the pseudonym of Robbie Rostak. Beside him, when he answered the door, was a young, dark-haired girl, no more than eighteen or nineteen, whom Rostak introduced as his wife. The agents were shown into the living room which was sparsely but tastefully furnished. The couple had been married less than a month.

"We're still waiting for some of the furniture to arrive," the bride apologized. She offered the agents the settee, then she hurriedly fetched two folding bridge chairs for herself and her husband.

"Gentlemen," Rostak said slowly, drawing in a sharp breath as he sat stiffly in his seat. "I would like to see your identifications again, please." The FBI men had flashed their credentials at the door, but Rostak and his wife had hardly glanced at them.

The G-men again pulled out their leather cases containing the FBI identity cards and passport-size photos. Rostak eagerly got up and this time closely examined the proof that gave the two men title to belief and confidence.

"I am scared," Rostak said defensively. "I'm not sure whom to trust. This matter I called you about has bewildered me. I haven't been able to sleep or eat. My stomach is in a knot . . ." He went back to his chair.

One of the FBI agents said, "Just relax now. You are in good hands. Let's hear your problem. Forget all your worries and get it all off your chest."

Rostak grinned and his wife almost laughed with relief at the reassuring words.

"Where shall I begin?" Rostak asked, rubbing his hands almost impatiently.

"Right at the beginning," the agent said with a look at his watch. "We have all the time that it will take you to tell us the whole story. We're here to help you."

It was 6:30 p.m. as Robbie Rostak began the recitation of his encounter with Soviet plotters. Here is the gist of Rostak's story:

In the latter part of August, 1958, Robbie Rostak was discharged after two years in the army that included a tour in Korea in intelligence communications. After arriving home, he took advantage of the G.I. Bill to further his education and enrolled in a college near his home.

At school he met some foreign-exchange students who somehow stirred his interest in language study. His thinking was influenced particularly by one of the group, who became a close friend and advised Rostak that he could receive far better training in language studies at a foreign university.

"He told me that I had the qualifications to merit a scholarship," Rostak related. "He suggested that I try the University of Mexico."

The University did not tender him a scholarship, but the zeal to pursue his study in a foreign land prompted Rostak to leave his college and go to Mexico City. His first objective was to learn to speak Spanish, which he thought would make the University more receptive to his next application for scholarship. Rostak concentrated intensely on mastering the language and in about four months he had acquired a high degree of fluency in both writing and speaking. But he still could not afford the tuition fees.

About that time he heard that the Russian Embassy in Mexico City was offering college scholarships to qualified and deserving foreign students. Without any reservations or second thoughts, Rostak said, he went directly to the embassy to inquire about the scholarship program.

"As I got to the embassy," Rostak said, "a man was coming out. I asked him in English whom I could see about scholarships the Soviets were giving for study in Mexican colleges. But the man didn't understand English. Then I talked to him in Spanish. Still he couldn't understand me. So then I tried Ukrainian . . ." Rostak interrupted the narrative to explain to the FBI agents that his ancestry was Ukrainian and that he spoke the language flawlessly.

"The stranger understood me now and said that he could help me. Without taking me into the embassy, he asked me to meet him at four o'clock that afternoon in front of the Reforma Hotel."

Rostak went to the hotel a few minutes before the appointed hour and waited. Promptly at 4 p.m. a chauffeur-driven car wheeled to a stop in front of the hotel and a man in the back summoned the youth to him.

"Are you the young man interested in scholarships?" Rostak quoted him. When he said he was, the man invited him into the car. This was not the same person whom Rostak had met outside the embassy. The youth made no attempt to ask why his first contact didn't keep the appointment; he concluded that this was procedure, that the man who had met him now was the one to deal with about the scholarship.

As it turned out, he was the man. But his offer, over drinks at a café to which the benefactor and the chauffeur took Rostak, was not to the University of Mexico.

"They talked about scholarships that the Russian government was offering to a university in Moscow. They made the suggestion after they had brought up the fact that I had spoken to the other man in Ukrainian. I told them that my parents came from the Ukraine. That is when they became extremely interested in me. They invited me to meet them the following day."

On that day, Rostak said, the two Russians took him forty miles into the country for a picnic. They had brought a basket of assorted Russian food and picked an isolated spot at the grassy edge of a woodland at the base of a high-sloped valley that Rostak had never seen before nor since.

"They talked to me about the beauty of the land and how it compared with Russia," Rostak continued. "Then the conversation turned to scholarships. As the chauffeur served the food, the other man, who told me his name was George, took out some forms from his pocket and asked me to fill them out. He told me it was strictly routine procedure, that the forms were a necessary requirement in applying for a scholarship."

The questions were routine: name, address, date of birth, education, employment, and military service. Rostak answered the last question by stating that he had served about a year in Korea and that he had been assigned to intelligence communications. The Russian made a note of this fact on the back of the questionnaire.

After the picnic, the Russians drove Rostak back to Mexico City and dropped him off at his place of residence, a small hotel. George told him that if the Soviet Government was favorably disposed to granting him a scholarship, Rostak would be notified to that effect by letter. The signature, he was advised, would be simply "George."

A month went by without a word from the Soviet Embassy. Then a letter arrived at Rostak's hotel. It was a brief message on plain stationery, saying, "Everything is all right." It was signed "George." But after that, he heard nothing more and at the end of May, Rostak decided to return home. Rostak by now had met his future bride, a beautiful native of Mexico City. She had grown impatient with his indecision about school or matrimony. Rostak decided on matrimony and married the girl in the Mexican capital. Then the young couple left for his home in Massachusetts.

But no sooner had they arrived than his mother told Rostak that "a man named George has been telephoning you constantly." Several days later, on June 5, "George" phoned again and found Rostak at home. The Soviet scholarship had come through for him, Rostak was told. He could attend the University of Mexico. But there were a few details to discuss. Could Rostak meet George in front of the Capital Theater at Main and Pynchon Streets? Rostak kept the appointment.

As he approached the theater, a man walked up to Rostak and introduced himself as "George." But it was a different George than the Russian he had met in Mexico City. They went in this George's car to a tavern and sat at an out-of-the-way booth which George selected. Rostak tried to save the man's time by telling him at the outset that he was not sure he was still interested in a scholarship to the University of Mexico, that he was married now. In fact, he and his bride were all packed and ready to leave on their honeymoon, an auto trip to New York City.

"That's when he made his pitch," Rostak told the FBI men who were listening to his story. "George asked me whether I didn't think I could do something for my country. I was amazed at the question. I told him that I had done something for my country—I had served two years in the army. He said he didn't mean America, but the Ukraine. That was a shock. I told him that the Ukraine was not my country. That my parents had come from there. I said I was born in the United States and this was the only country I knew.

" 'That is not so,' he told me. 'You are still considered a Ukrainian because of your ancestry.' I tried to argue with him but he cut me off by saying there were some very important people he wanted me to meet. 'Since you'll be in New York,' he said, 'let us meet in St. James Park in the Bronx. It is opposite Morris Avenue.' Then he proceeded to give me detailed instructions on how to get there and what to do.

"First, he didn't want me to bring my wife to the park. Secondly, he wanted me to leave my car in Manhattan, take the subway to the Kingsbridge Station in the Bronx, then walk to the park. Finally, he reeled off a code that I was to follow in making contact with the people who were waiting for me. I was to be met by a stranger who would approach me and say, 'Have you seen George lately?' I was to reply, 'Yes, I saw him in Mexico City.'

"Next this fellow asked me to repeat the instructions. I did. He made me give my word that I would keep the appointment which was for two o'clock the following Saturday. I said I would be there. But I said it only to get him out of my hair. I didn't like all the secrecy and I began to be suspicious about the whole deal with their scholarships."

Rostak and his wife went on their honeymoon but stayed clear of the Bronx except when they passed through that borough on their way to the city and on their way home eight days later.

Rostak said it came as no surprise when he got home and had a call from George expressing disappointment over his failure to show up for the meeting with the "very important people." George then asked Rostak to meet him in Springfield on June 25. Rostak kept the date, which was in the same tavern they had visited on their previous rendezvous. In the meantime, Rostak and his bride moved out of his parents' home and settled in their own apartment.

"And this is why I called you," Rostak told the FBI men in a voice suddenly growing tense. He sat back stiffly in his chair, arms locked around his angular frame, eyes staring sightlessly down on the floor. He had been composed until now and had told of his encounters with the Russians in an even, equable tone, but it seemed that the stress of what he had still to say was beginning to reach him. It was the most important part of his story, the reason why he had summoned the FBI to his home.

"It happened yesterday, gentlemen," Rostak said, lifting his head to face the FBI agents squarely. "George asked me to go to Washington and get a civilian job in the Defense Department. He said that I had the qualifications because of my experience in intelligence communications in the army to get employment as a cryptographic machine operator. I had happened to mention to the George who had taken me on that picnic in Mexico that I had worked on the army's cryptographic setup when I was in Korea.

"I told him sternly that I had no desire to go to Washington nor to get a job in the Defense Department. But he got angry. He slammed his fist on the table and said, 'Now, listen to me, young man. We have this background sheet on you—the one you filled out in Mexico City. It has your signature on it. We don't want to hold it against you, but it won't sit right with your own government if they know you signed up for a Russian scholarship. You know how suspicious they are about people who are too friendly with the Soviets.'

"Then he started to give me a long spiel again about my Ukrainian ancestry and how I owed my people something. He played on my sympathies and told me that I would be doing something for world peace if I followed his advice." Rostak shook his head in dismay. "How did I let myself get so involved?" he commented sadly.

His listeners assured him he had more than atoned for any wrong he might have done by calling the FBI. But what else, they wanted to know, did the Russian named George want from Rostak? So far it was a big buildup. Where did it go from there? Why was Robbie Rostak so frightened?

"George took out a note pad. He said, 'You have more than a year of experience with the cryptographic machines. I want you to take this book and put down in it everything you know about those machines. I want diagrams of the machines—all your knowledge about them.' When he was through, I sat stunned and silent for a long while and he kept staring at me. Finally he said, 'Will you do it?' By then I had made up my mind. I managed a smile and said I would do it. But what I really meant was that I was going to do what I had decided in my mind—call the FBI."

The agents who had taken the story down in a verbatim transcript gave Rostak some immediate instructions. He was to keep the appointment with George. Try to arrange the meetings in the open—anywhere that the FBI will have an opportunity to watch. "Even if it has to be indoors, try to pick a public place, like the tavern, where we are in a position to observe without attracting attention . . ."

There were other instructions, specific advice on how to handle himself in his conversations with George or any other Russian who might try to deal with him. All of it was comforting reassurance that Robbie Rostak had nothing to fear anymore.

"Thank you, gentlemen," he said as the agents bade him and his wife goodnight. The time was 10:55 p.m. It had taken four hours and twenty-five minutes to relate his story to the FBI and to listen to their instructions.

Ten days went by before Rostak again heard from George. As he had promised to do, Rostak agreed to meet the Russian. Then he notified the FBI.

"He asked me if I had prepared the sketches," Rostak told the agent on the phone.

"We have them partly ready. We will have someone bring the notebook to your house tonight."

The next day Rostak kept his appointment with George. They met at the corner of Main and Hampden Streets where George was waiting in a car. Close by, the two FBI agents who had gone to Rostak's house were watching the corner from their own car. They saw Rostak enter the Russian's auto and followed at a discreet distance as they drove away.

The Russian tooled his car through the crowded downtown streets out to the city limits and northeastward in the direction of the picturesque Hoosac Hills, the lesser range of mountains east of the Berkshires. The trip extended along the narrow, winding macadam highway skirting the valley of the Connecticut River, and then veered up a steady incline through Mount Tom State Forest that took them to the top of 1,200-foot-high Mount Tom.

There George escorted Rostak to a low stone wall where they sat to talk. His first words were about the notebook. In the car he had asked Rostak if he had it. Rostak had reached for his inside jacket pocket to indicate the answer. George said to leave it there, that he could not look at it while he was driving. Now, in the quiet splendor atop Mount Tom, the Russian asked to see the book and the plans Rostak had prepared on the cryptographic machines. The young counterspy handed the notebook over. George took it with an eagerness that was clearly apparent to the two FBI men who remained in their car in the parking lot from which they had a commanding view of the rendezvous. One of the agents also had a movie camera and was grinding out some footage that would later prove enlightening, if not surprising, when it was developed.

George skimmed through the pages of the notebook with the quiet, studied look of a man who had a technical understanding of the drawings. After he had pored through the dozen or so pages that had been prepared for this occasion, George spoke in a sharp, impatient voice.

"You haven't done too much here. I expected that you would have much more than just the exterior designs. These don't tell anything." He was plainly annoyed.

But Rostak had been forewarned to expect the complaint. "It just can't be done this soon," he said with a shrug. "You seem to think that I invented the machines. I have to work at this carefully. You do want accurate work, don't you . . . ?"

"Oh, yes, yes," George broke in urgently. "Accuracy above anything. If you need time, take it. By all means . . ."

"Then," Rostak said quietly but adamantly, "please don't put the pressure on me. I need time. You will get it."

It was just what he was supposed to say in a situation such as this.

George offered Rostak a cigarette and flicked his lighter for both of them. They seemed to reach an impasse in the conversation for a moment, but Rostak was ready for the next move by the Russian. He had been alerted by the FBI about the probable turns the meeting could take.

George looked at Rostak with a somber expression and said firmly, "Robbie, I want to urge you again to try to get that job in Washington. You will be doing something for world peace. Can you understand that?" And before Rostak could reply, George injected an incentive that he hadn't previously mentioned—money.

"How much?" asked Rostak, his face lighting up just as if the FBI had turned on the switch.

"One to two thousand dollars a month," the Russian replied as nonchalantly as if it were a ruble.

Rostak nodded approvingly. "That sounds very interesting." He smiled into George's eager waiting eyes.

The Russian extended his hand. "It's a deal, then?"

"Yes," Rostak said with an animated nod. "For that kind of money I am willing to do all I can for world peace!"

They drove back to Springfield and George dropped Rostak off at the corner of Main and Hampden. "I will be in touch with you," the Russian said.

Then he handed Rostak the notebook. "You take this," he directed, "and work up those sketches that I want. Until the next time . . ."

He threw Rostak a short salute and drove away.

That 16mm. film, shot in Kodachrome, was a breathtaking spectacle of the scenic Connecticut River Valley and of the well-known peaks of the Hoosac Mountains such as the gentle Mount Holyoke and the taller Mount Toby. The background faded into a raw purple haze that obliterated the distant Berkshire range rising in its majesty to the imposing heights of famed 3,400-foot Mount Greylock, the tallest point in the entire state of Massachusetts. But the camera had not been focused nor trained with any deliberation upon the beauties of the region. These were purely a fringe benefit accruing to the man who took the pictures.

What he was after came out in clear, unmistakable perspective—the face of Rostak and, more particularly, of George—at their meeting atop Mount Tom. The lines of George's face, the deep-set furrows under his brown eyes that gave the appearance of a man older than his thirty-two years, his light brown hair, his thin and rigidly expressionless lips—all came out as distinctly as if Leon Shamroy had filmed him in a close-up on a Hollywood sound stage. In fact, only the sound was lacking.

Clips from the film were rushed to the FBI's New York City office. It was a painless routine to establish what the agents in Springfield had long suspected. George was not George by any angle his countenance revealed on film. Full face, right profile, left profile, George was not George but Vadim Aleksandrovich Kirilyuk, a political affairs officer employed by the Department of Trusteeship and Information from Non-Self Governing Territories, a division of the United Nation's Secretariat. And, of course, a Soviet citizen.

The FBI's brief sketch of Kirilyuk pulled from its files revealed this background: Born 4-1-28 at Vinnitsa, Ukraine, Russia. Height, six feet; weight, 200 pounds; hair, brown; eyes, brown; build, heavy; married; smokes.

This information added nothing to the case. But the FBI didn't need to know anything more about Kirilyuk now. Now it was just a matter of giving the Russian a little more rope to fashion the noose which would lift him out of the UN and swing him aboard a fast plane or ocean liner back to Moscow.

That opportunity presented itself on September 18, 1959, the dark and ominous day that had brought both the threat of thunder squalls and the FBI in droves to Springfield, to administer the *coup de grâce* to this latest Soviet spy discovered nesting in the arboreal safety of the UN.

In stark contrast, at this very hour—3:45 p.m.—at the UN itself, Soviet Premier Nikita Khrushchev was advancing to the podium to speak before the General Assembly about finding a means to stop mankind from backsliding into an abyss of war. This was the dramatic highlight of Khrushchev's historic American goodwill tour which had evolved out of President Eisenhower's personal invitation to the Premier to visit this country.

As the undistinctive brown panel truck coursed its way along Main Street that dreary late-summer afternoon, the two agents in the back were being kept apprised of developments both by their driver and a radio that was broadcasting instructions to them from FBI headquarters in Springfield. The agents also had their own peepholes drilled in the panels of the truck to afford them a view of the sidewalks on both sides of the street and an opportunity to take some important additional footage on their motion picture cameras poised on both sides of the truck.

The truck made four passes along a seven-block stretch of Main Street, starting at 3:30 p.m. Each time it came to the end of its designated patrol area, the driver made a lazy U-turn at a corner and eased his way back over the route.

There was no activity until 3:45 p.m. when the driver of the truck broke a long silence and coughed into a handkerchief. This was a feint to alert the agents in the back. He reported to the others that their man was on the west side of the street, walking away from them. He spoke behind the cover of his handkerchief drawn over his mouth.

The agent had spotted Kirilyuk, the man better known to Rostak as George. Rostak himself had been summoned by Kirilyuk the night before to meet him in town, but the method chosen by the Russian was different than any procedure he had used in the past. It was almost a throwback to the modus operandi of Aleksandr Kovalev in his dealings with Frederick Timsford in the attempt to obtain the Sperry bombsight data. But, instead of a red package in the back window of his car and instructions to look for a banana peel, Robbie Rostak had been told to arrive at Main and Hampden in a taxi, to alight at the corner, stand there for five minutes as if expecting to meet someone, then head over to Railroad Street and wait in front of a restaurant for his contact who would be George—actually Kirilyuk.

The FBI knew of the plan because they had been apprised of the instructions telephoned to Rostak the night before.

As the truck passed him, Kirilyuk was walking at a lazy but steady pace toward Hampden Street. The cameras whirred silently, recording his presence in Springfield and recording his every move.

The agents manning the truck noted Kirilyuk turning from time to time and peering over his left shoulder to the other side of the street. His gestures prompted his watchers to search the east sidewalk to see what curiosity was commanding Kirilyuk's attention. They soon found the attraction—a short, stocky man with broad shoulders, wearing a dark blue suit, like Kirilyuk, and walking with the same slow, casual gait.

The second camera was quickly swung into action and captured this stranger in a movement that seemed designed as a countersurveillance. That is, he was there to determine if Kirilyuk was being watched or trailed by anyone. This stranger, later to be identified as Leonid A. Kovalev, an associate of Kirilyuk's at the UN, did not even cast an eye at the truck, so prosaic was its appearance.

The FBI crew pressed along the street until it had gained a short distance on the two Russians, then double-parked in the middle of the next block as if the driver had a delivery to make. Presently the two men passed and kept going until they had reached the corner of Hampden Street. Then, as Kovalev crossed over and strolled further along Main, Kirilyuk ambled to a clothing store off the corner and stood in the shadow of the entrance. The FBI agents manning the truck had a clear, unobstructed view of the activity.

A few minutes later, at 3:55 p.m., a cab screeched to a stop at the corner and out of it emerged the tall, angular, youthful counterspy, Rostak. He went through the motions of paying the driver, but it was all exhibition. The driver, garbed in cabbie's hat and provided by the Springfield Police Department with all necessary appurtenances to establish his identity as a hackie, was actually an FBI man. To make it look more real, the agent handed Rostak change before he left the cab to keep his appointment with the Russian agent.

From the cover of the clothing store doorway, Kirilyuk or, more familiarly, George, watched Rostak as he stood on the corner for the length of time he was instructed to wait. Following orders like a private in the army, Rostak maintained his vigil, with his feet planted slightly apart on the sidewalk, craning his neck in pretended search for someone he was expecting. He never saw Kirilyuk in the darkness of the doorway.

Several claps of thunder rumbled out of the leaden sky but Rostak seemed to ignore it. He carried on the ruse for the prescribed five minutes, then turned and walked toward Railroad Avenue and the restaurant George had named for their rendezvous.

Seeing the coast clear, Kirilyuk left his place in the shadows and proceeded to the restaurant where he found Rostak waiting. He shook hands warmly with the young American, then took his arm and led him into the restaurant.

Rostak and the Russian sat at a table near the entrance. It was obvious Kirilyuk had no intention of asking for the notebook containing the more refined sketches of the cryptographic machines in the restaurant. The sketches were ready. They had been carefully—and erroneously—prepared by army experts. Rostak had the notebook in his inside pocket and offered to hand it over to Kirilyuk. The latter shook his head.

"No, no," he said heavily. "Not here. Later. Did you bring your car like I asked you?" Kirilyuk had told Rostak the previous night to park his car in a block east on Hampden Street and then to walk three blocks further east and let a cab bring him to the rendezvous. The Russian said this was a way "to make certain we are clean," meaning there was no tail on them.

After downing their sandwiches and coffee, Kirilyuk paid the check and got up. "Let's go to your car," he commanded.

As they walked out of the restaurant, two of the FBI men who had been riding in the back of the truck, strolled leisurely along Hampden Street in the vicinity of Rostak's car. They were there to observe the next episode in the clandestine drama.

The other Russian, Leonid Kovalev, had now dropped out of sight.

Actually, a team of G-men followed him to a nearby hotel where he sat in the lobby to await Kirilyuk who arrived there a short while later. Then together they went back to New York.

But first, Kirilyuk and Rostak went to the car. The FBI had anticipated that the Russian would ask his American victim to drive to some other locale. As it turned out, that was Kirilyuk's plan.

"Let's take a little spin," he said.

Rostak switched on the ignition. The motor coughed once, twice, three times, then lapsed into an agony of silence. "Damn it," Rostak complained with a pained expression, "it's that miserable distributor again."

Rostak had taken care of the distributor to make certain the car wouldn't budge when he came back to it. The FBI had arranged their observation teams in key positions along the street to continue their compilation of evidence against the Russian, and they didn't want the car to move from that spot.

Kirilyuk was forced to alter his plans. He fell into deep concentration for a moment, trying to decide on what to do. Finally he made up his mind.

"Let's see the book right here," he said anxiously. "But be careful. Don't let anyone see you taking it out. Slip it down on the floor over the transmission."

Rostak removed the book from his pocket and placed it down on the hump on the floor between himself and the Russian. Kirilyuk's hand, steady as a rock, thumbed methodically through it. He barely looked at the first dozen or so pages; he had seen those before. He was interested in the new, intricate patterns he had asked for, the interior designs of the cryptographic machines. There were about fifteen new pages of sketches. Kirilyuk examined each design scrupulously, his body tilted sharply so he could read the notebook in the out-of-the-way and awkward position.

"These are excellent," Kirilyuk finally blurted exuberantly. "But there is a lot more. When will you have the rest?"

"A few more weeks," Rostak said with a studied air of exasperation. "This isn't easy, you know."

"Yes, yes, I realize," Kirilyuk placated. "You are doing very nicely, very nicely!"

Rostak then glanced at the Russian with a look of concern. "You know, George, this is a dangerous thing I'm doing. If I get caught, I'll be holding the bag . . ."

"You need not fear," Kirilyuk assured him. "Remember, there is nothing to be nervous about. The biggest and most powerful country in the world is behind you."

Even as the FBI agents walked past, their eyes on Kirilyuk, he resorted to his grandest boast. "My dear boy, it's impossible for you to get caught. We'll take care of you, no matter what."

Almost as an afterthought, Kirilyuk reached down and tore the pages with the cryptographic machine designs out of the notebook, folded them twice, and put them in his inside jacket pocket. Then he turned to Rostak and advised him on a new method for passing such information in the future.

"Whenever you bring me something, put the pages in a newspaper. Tear out the pages from the notebook and put them in the inside of a rolled-up newspaper or magazine which you can hand over."

Then Kirilyuk offered his hand to Rostak. "Until the next time, good-bye."

Kirilyuk got out of the car, slammed the door, then stuck his head through the open window. "I am sorry to leave you this way. I hope you don't have too much trouble starting the car. That's the trouble with these American-made machines—very undependable."

The case had now reached a point where all the evidence amassed against Kirilyuk left no doubt of his involvement in espionage. It was forwarded to the Attorney General for review. Then on it went to the State Department.

But a change in procedure was followed in this case. There was no immediate announcement of Kirilyuk's activity as a spy. The United States tactfully decided not to embarrass the Soviet Union in light of the Khrushchev visit which was being hailed as the first real thaw in the Cold War. President Eisenhower decided to keep the news of this case from the public for the time being.

But very quietly Ambassador Lodge went to Secretary General Hammarskjöld with the facts developed by the FBI. After studying the case, Hammarskjöld advised the Soviet Delegation to the UN that Kirilyuk had to go. On January 10, 1960, without any fanfare, without any parting shots at the United States, without a word, Kirilyuk, his wife, and their two young children slipped away from these shores for the last time.

It wasn't until May 18 of that year that the world learned about Vadim A. Kirilyuk, and then the word came in an announcement more dramatic than that of any previous spy case.

No less a personage than Vice President Richard M. Nixon made the disclosure while on a visit to Buffalo, New York. Nixon was compelled to reveal the plot in the wake of the furor created by the downing of Francis Gary Powers and his U-2 spy plane over Russia. The Vice President named Kirilyuk and told briefly how the Russian had tried to obtain the drawings of the Army's cryptographic machines.

Six days later, on May 23, Ambassador Lodge formally went before the UN Security Council and handed over the list of fifteen Soviet officials who had been declared personae non grata in the past seven years because of their espionage activities.

Kirilyuk's name headed that list. Like all the others, Vadim Kirilyuk was now safely out of the country. Like the others, he had failed to obtain the sensitive information he had sought which would have given the Kremlin a better insight into the workings of our intelligence procedures.

But already other UN-based Soviet agents were working on other Americans and the next target was Chicago. The Russians decided they wanted data on that area's rocket and aerial defenses.

The assignment went to a burly, graying Russian UN Secretariat employee named Igor Yakovlevich Melekh . . .

9 : A Khrushchev Visit

THE story of Igor Yakovlevich Melekh begins on the sidewalk in front of the Soviet Mission to the UN on the afternoon of September 29, 1960.

"I condemn spying and will not tolerate it . . ."

The words were spoken by a short, pudgy man with hanging jowls and a red face—Nikita Khrushchev.

Reporters furiously scribbled down his translated words in their notebooks. The occasion for Khrushchev's appearance was to spout a big head of steam about a matter that had been grating him for several long months—the U-2 spy plane incident.

This was Khrushchev's second visit to this country in a year. It was the last thing the world expected of him after his denunciation of the United States, his destruction of the Paris Summit Conference, and the ultimate affront, his cancellation of President Eisenhower's visit to Russia.

Khrushchev hadn't come to New York this time as a state visitor. He was there as head of the Russian Delegation to the UN for what resembled a summit session on the Congo, world disarmament, and other international crises.

Khrushchev's appearance required hasty maneuvers by our State Department because of the great embarrassment he had caused us by ranting over the U-2 plane Francis Gary Powers had crashed deep in Russian territory on May Day, 1960. The United States did not offer the Soviet Premier the red carpet it had laid out for him on the earlier, historic state visit here which took him across the breadth of the land.

The orders went out this time: Keep Nikita pinned down to Manhattan Island.

But the Soviets protested the limitation on their leader's travels, and the State Department lifted the restriction slightly, allowing the Red Premier to spend weekends at the Soviet Delegation's retreat at Glen Cove on Long Island, thirty miles east of the city.

The curb on Nikita's travels and movements occasioned some weird scenes, especially during the press conferences. On weekends, for example, he met reporters at the gates of his delegation's rambling Long Island estate. On weekdays in New York City he talked to the press at the front door of the Soviet Delegation's headquarters on East 67th Street.

Every day Khrushchev came out and talked to the throngs of reporters massed at the entrance, expatiating on a wide range of subjects, cracking jokes, sometimes insulting the United States, often snapping barbs at President Eisenhower, and occasionally sniping on the delicate issues about United States aerial reconnaissances over Soviet territory.

The afternoon of September 29 was not especially different from the other days of Khrushchev's stay. Khrushchev was particularly vociferous about American espionage activities. He was wound up and clearly angry as he condemned spying.

That was one difference in the press discourse. The other was in the gathering of newsmen around the portly Kremlin dictator. The ranks of the press had inconspicuously increased by two this day. Only a trained observer who had taken a daily poll of reporters at Khrushchev's conferences would have noticed the added starters.

Actually they were not reporters, these two. They were FBI agents who might have looked like newsmen. But they were not there to keep tabs on Khrushchev. Their mission was to maintain strict surveillance over the balding, somber-faced man with the hooked nose, slitted eyes, and dark brows standing next to the Premier and shaking his head in agreement with what Khrushchev was saying.

This was Igor Yakovlevich Melekh, the 47-year-old chief of the Russian Section of the UN Secretariat, a man who had come to the

FBI's attention some weeks before when the FBI learned the Russians were seeking aerial photographs, as well as maps, of the Chicago area.

What was there about Chicago and its environs that prompted the Soviets to seek out such data?

The FBI learned that the Russians were out to locate the positions and placement of our military and defense installations in that area so as to provide the Soviets information for bombing targets, data for Russian bombers and for Russian intercontinental ballistics missiles firing ranges to be used in case of war, or in case the Russians decided to pull a Pearl Harbor.

In a free country like ours, of course, aerial photographs are available to the public and can be bought in almost any well-stocked book store or from a commercial map maker.

The Soviets are fully aware of this and through the years they have been taking full grip on this easy-to-get information. The FBI knows the Reds have gathered immense quantities of aerial photographs of many areas of the United States.

Yet this is not the only interest or target of Russian espionage agents, as the preceding chapters of this book have indicated. But aerial maps are a major scope of Soviet intelligence.

As FBI Director Hoover has told us: "Soviet agents for three decades have engaged in extensive espionage against this country, and through the years have procured a volume of information which would stagger the imagination. This information includes a vast number of aerial photographs of major U.S. cities and vital areas which have given the Russians the product of aerial reconnaissance just as surely as if Soviet planes had been sent over the country."

Most significantly, the Russians have not been content merely in grabbing publicly available data. They have even gone so far as to rent planes and fly over critical "target" cities in the United States and have taken their own photographs.

One such case involved Leonid Igorovich Pivnev, an assistant air attaché stationed in Washington, who previously had traveled extensively throughout the country and obtained a number of available aerial photographs of various areas.

On May 3, 1954, Pivnev hired a Washington photographer to fly over New York City in a rented plane and take photos not commercially available. He specified the scale he wanted, the altitude to shoot from, and gave the photographer exacting orders on what pictures to take. Pivnev wanted the photos to show vital port facilities in New York Harbor, industrial plants, and military installations including the strategic Brooklyn Navy Yard. For all this, he offered the photographer seven hundred dollars.

But the FBI got on to Pivnev. He was declared persona non grata and returned to Moscow on June 6, 1954. However, the exposure of this Soviet plot did not stop the Reds. They went right on collecting aerial photographs of major cities and vital areas of the country.

As the FBI became more aware of the Soviet's increasing activity in this systematic program of espionage, the State Department sent a note to the Soviet Ambassador that restricted certain types of data to Soviet citizens in the U.S. Among the banned items were aerial photographs, except those which "appear in or are appendices to newspapers, periodicals, technical journals, atlases, and books commercially available to the general public."

The Soviet response to the restrictions was typical of their philosophy. They circumvented the ban by subverting Americans to buy aerial photographs and even to steal maps for Russia.

Soviet spying in the United States always has been brisk, as we have shown so far, but, except for 1956, it probably was never more so than in the early spring of 1958. At that time, the FBI learned that the Russians had set out to obtain aerial photographs of military installations in the Chicago area and a set of maps pinpointing the metropolis's defense sites. Until then the Soviets had been unable to put their hands on satisfactory area maps of Chicago which would give them so-called "bomb target" areas.

Their desperation to obtain these became apparent in a sudden flurry of feverish activity in that direction, when a Soviet agent began making overtures to a Chicago man who had access to the secret data sought by the Reds.

The man, who has never been identified by the FBI, reported the proposition to the Bureau's Chicago office. He told the G-men he had been offered "big money" if he could obtain the data for the Soviets. He said he didn't know the man who approached him, but that the man had said he would get in touch again.

"I told him," the informant said, "to give me time to think it over. I needed the time to report it to the FBI and see what I should do."

The G-men regarded this development as a ten-strike. Now the next step was to find out who the espionage agent was. The FBI induced the Chicagoan to become a double agent, a role involving him in a highly dangerous game of deceit. He would pretend to be in need of money and willing to let himself be corrupted by the Russians so they could get what data they wanted. And at the same time he was a full-fledged FBI counterspy.

And so began one of the most involved and dangerous cloak-and-dagger operations in the annals of Russian espionage in the United States. It was to become a cat-and-mouse game in which the FBI would scamper from Chicago to the UN in New York, and to a number of other cities in a two-and-a-half-year pursuit that finally led to Igor Yakovlevich Melekh, the man who had stood on East 67th Street and Park Avenue behind Premier Khrushchev.

But it all began with the Soviet's man in Chicago.

The FBI got a quick break. Not many days after this man had contacted the Chicago man, he called again to find out if they could do business. This time the FBI was watching. And they later learned his identity. His name was Willie Hirsch, a 52-year-old German immigrant.

Acting as Melekh's representative, Hirsch laid it on the line for the double agent. The Soviet spy wanted up-to-date maps showing Chicago's port facilities, industrial plants, defense installations such as anti-aircraft gun emplacements, and other military information vital to the aerial defense of Chicago. He also wanted maps of the same critical "target" areas.

The double agent, now called Agent X by the FBI, did not set a price, nor did Hirsch talk money. Instructed in advance by the FBI on how to deal with Hirsch, Agent X haggled, which is what a man not too desperate, yet in need of money, would do. Agent X was a respectable businessman in reasonable financial straits, and he had to act the part.

So a price was not agreed upon. Agent X was to let Hirsch know later what he must pay. Agent X said he had to engage others in the clandestine operation and he could not know what price they would ask. And it was left like that until the next meeting.

Hirsch seemed confident that he had made a good contact. His confidence would not have been so great had he known that from the moment he met Agent X, he was a marked man. The FBI, diligently digging into Willie Hirsch's background, learned that he made his home in a $225-a-month four-room apartment on the fifteenth floor of a fashionable 20-story building at 30 Fifth Avenue, in the Greenwich Village section, known as Cambridge House. The apartment was just a block north of Washington Square Park. Hirsch had only to look out his window to see the Washington Arch, a replica of the Arc de Triomphe in Paris, erected in honor of one of the nation's great patriots, the same George Washington who led the "Rabble in Arms" in Revolutionary War days.

The FBI also learned that Hirsch was using an alias, John Gilmore; the FBI found, too, that he had been living in the building nine years; that he had a wife, Ruth, and a stepdaughter, Susan, eleven years old, who lived with him.

Hirsch, so the FBI had discovered, worked as an illustrator for medical journals and publications under the Gilmore name. He was, furthermore, a sick man. He had a heart condition and ulcers and was a diabetic. Several times in the past, the FBI was told, Hirsch had been carried out of the building to an ambulance and rushed to a hospital when one of his various ailments gave him trouble. Further inquiry into the records of the U.S. Immigration and Naturalization Service disclosed that Hirsch had come to the United States as a boy from Germany and never had bothered to become a citizen.

Now the FBI had all it needed on Hirsch. Any other information, particularly and most importantly on his spy activities, would be obtained by shadowing him. As the days wore on, Hirsch, a short, stocky, graying man with a moon face and sagging jowls who wore horn-rimmed glasses and bow ties, stuck to a routine that did not suggest he was engaged in espionage.

Invariably he carried illustrations, which apparently he had prepared in his home studio, to various medical publication offices. This procedure could have been dismissed as routine and harmless.

Then one day the pattern changed.

Hirsch subwayed to midtown and met a man on a street corner not far from the United Nations Building. The stranger was somber-faced, had a hooked nose, narrow eyes, and dark brows. His suit had the lines of European tailoring. The conversation was brief. Then Hirsch and the stranger parted.

The latter's trail went a most surprising course, directly to the UN.

The G-men could not violate the ban against crossing the line into the UN, but they had other ways at their disposal of learning that the stranger was employed upstairs in the Russian Section of the UN Secretariat's Languages and Meetings Service, as chief of the section.

By then, of course, the FBI knew who the man was: Igor Yakovlevich Melekh. Now the FBI realized that the plot to steal the Chicago photos and maps was being directed by the Soviets from the UN.

The FBI kept tabs not only on Willie Hirsch but on Igor Melekh, too. During the next few months, over the summer of 1958, Hirsch and Melekh met frequently. Then Willie Hirsch went back to Chicago to meet the American counterspy, Agent X, to talk about the data the Reds were seeking. The routine repeated itself several times in that period.

Every meeting was designed by the G-men to prolong the negotiations between Hirsch and Agent X for psychological reasons. The FBI was certain the longer Agent X stalled the more anxious the Russians would become and the better chance there would be of other Red spies unknown to the G-men at the time entering the negotiations.

By late October, however, Willie Hirsch informed the Chicago contact that he would have to produce the photos and maps or the deal was off. Coached by the FBI, Agent X said he might be ready to act, but he promised nothing.

On October 23, FBI agents under the direction of Harvey G. Foster, the special agent in charge of the New York City office, trailed Willie Hirsch, now accompanied by Igor Melekh, to Pennsylvania Station where they boarded a train for Chicago. Two G-men quickly arranged with the Pennsylvania Railroad for a sleeping compartment right next to the one shared by Hirsch and Melekh. Sound detectors and recording equipment took down every word the spies spoke in their room. Their destination, of course, was a meeting with Agent X.

At this meeting, Hirsch introduced Melekh as the "big man in this deal." Melekh demanded that Agent X produce the secret data immediately or no deal. The counterspy, still stalling for time, agreed. But he must have money.

Melekh took out a roll of $20 bills and handed them to the Chicago man. It amounted to $200. Before leaving, Melekh and Hirsch promised another payment, but they demanded to see some action.

Nearly a month passed without further meetings, although they kept in touch by phone. Hirsch would call Agent X periodically, urging haste. In his conversations he would say "Gypsy" wanted action. "Gypsy," of course, was really Igor Melekh, the Soviet UN employee.

Meanwhile, as Hirsch and Melekh were shadowed back to New York, an interesting development came about in the offices of the Chicago FBI which quickly became significant.

A second Chicago man called and said he had been approached by a Soviet agent to procure aerial photographs and maps of the Chicago area. He wanted to know what to do.

The Soviet spy system had now reached out to another American citizen. It was clear to the FBI that the Russians were making a double effort to get the photos and maps. Their desperation was showing.

The FBI immediately recruited the second Chicago man as a counterspy. Reputable and well-to-do like the first counterspy, Agent X, this citizen was designated Agent XX to protect his identity.

Agent XX said he had been contacted by a Russian who identified himself only as Kirill and had been given implicit instructions on what photos and maps were wanted. But there was one catch: they had to be delivered at once or no deal.

The FBI made arrangements for Agent XX to get such documents. Then he sat back to wait the Russian agent's phone call with further instructions.

Days later Kirill called and was delighted that the photographs and maps had been obtained so swiftly. He instructed Agent XX to drive to New York and meet him at the New York Central Railroad's parking lot adjacent to the station in Scarsdale, a small, wealthy community in Westchester County just outside New York City.

The date was November 15, 1958.

Notified by Agent XX of the rendezvous, the FBI assigned special agents who posted themselves in key places near the parking lot.

It was exactly 6 p.m. when Agent XX reached the station in his car. He drove to the designated area to keep his scheduled meeting with the Red agent, who still was a mystery man to the FBI.

At 6:05 p.m. a dark Chrysler sedan pulled into the parking lot and entered a stall at some distance from where Agent XX was parked. A woman and a man got out. But the woman remained beside the car and only the man walked over to the Chicago man. He introduced himself as Kirill.

Agent XX opened the trunk of his car, a gray 1959 Buick Electra 225, and took out a paper-wrapped package.

"Here are the photographs and maps you wanted," he told Kirill.

The Russian took the package and handed over an envelope containing bills of large denomination. (The amount has never been revealed by the FBI.)

As the G-men watched from their observation posts, the Chicago man and the Russian spy and the woman with him got into their respective cars and drove away. One group of G-men followed protectively behind Agent XX while another trailed the Soviet agent and the woman.

Kirill drove to New York City and what turned out to be his home. The next morning he drove to work—at the United Nations. The FBI identified him as Kirill Sirgeevich Doronkin, film editor of the UN's Radio and Visual Division in the Department of Public Information. The woman with him had been his wife Irina.

Kirill's efforts were not destined to win him the Order of Lenin. His booty was so much worthless paper.

Evidently the Russians discovered this very quickly, for the very next day the Soviets were back at it in full swing with the first team of Willie Hirsch and Igor Melekh trying to get their hands on the real maps and photographs.

Melekh himself phoned Chicago and told Agent X, the first counterspy, that the time had come to deliver. This was the tip-off to the FBI that the Soviets knew Kirill Doronkin's maps and photographs were not the real thing.

Instructed in advance what to say, Agent X told Melekh he was ready but needed just a little more time and money. Melekh ordered the counterspy to come east and meet him at a designated location in Newark, New Jersey, across the Hudson River from New York City.

They met and the counterspy received another two hundred dollars, all in 20's, and was told the balance of the money would be paid upon delivery of the photos and maps. No date was set, but Agent X assured Melekh he would hurry it up as much as he could.

As it was at all other meetings, G-men watched from nearby hiding places. Everything seemed to go off smoothly except for one unexpected development.

To the G-men's amazement, Melekh was being shadowed by a man they knew was not one of J. Edgar Hoover's operatives. They knew that because they knew Melekh's shadow. His name: Kirill Sirgeevich Doronkin.

The FBI understood at once.

Because Doronkin had turned up with phony pictures and maps, the Russians knew the FBI was on to him. The Russians also correctly reasoned G-men were following Doronkin.

Thus by sending Doronkin out to loll about as Melekh and Agent X held their rendezvous, the Reds were using Doronkin as a "safety" man for Melekh, which meant that if the latter should be followed, the known Red spy trailing behind at a distance would serve as a decoy, drawing the FBI men away from Melekh. Beyond that, Doronkin was to tip off Melekh in case the FBI closed in suddenly, to prevent Melekh's arrest or even identification.

But there was something Doronkin, Melekh, and their bosses didn't know. The FBI already had Melekh's number, too.

The FBI continued to keep tabs on the Russian spies. Nothing of importance happened until mid-January of 1959. Then Melekh, the UN Secretariat employee, called their operative, Agent X, in Chicago and asked if he was prepared to deliver. Agent X was ready. He had finally obtained the necessary photos and maps sought by the Soviets, he said. Actually they were photos and maps doctored by the FBI to reveal no critical defense installations in their precise locations. But they were prepared with painstaking effort, the idea being to deceive the Reds into believing what they didn't believe of the photos and maps that their other spy, Doronkin, had delivered—that these were legitimate. It could take months, perhaps years, before the Soviet Intelligence system determined the inaccuracies in the doctored documents.

A rendezvous was arranged in the Fulton Street subway station of the IRT line in Brooklyn. Agent X came east by train for the meeting with Melekh. The date was January 17, 1959. The time was 5:30 p.m.

With subway trains roaring in and out of the station almost drowning out their conversation, Agent X handed over a package containing the photos and maps and Melekh put an envelope into the counterspy's hand. The envelope contained five hundred dollars, again all in 20's. Hirsch, the German illustrator who had started the negotiations with Agent X, wasn't in on the final payoff.

The transaction on the subway platform ended all negotiations between the Russian spies and either Agent X or Agent XX.

But that was not the end of the FBI's activity. A tail was kept constantly on Melekh and Hirsch as well as on Doronkin, although the latter's value in espionage was certainly lost so far as the Russians must have been concerned. They knew our intelligence agents were onto him, and they were probably expecting it when they were asked a short while later to send Kirill Sirgeevich Doronkin back to Moscow. The Soviet Mission to the UN protested as it always does, but in the end Doronkin went back. That was March 11, 1959.

That left Melekh and Hirsch to contend with. Since they had been so successful in their dealings with Agent X, the FBI reasoned that the Russians still had confidence in them and might send them out on new assignments. Weeks, months, a year passed. Melekh and Hirsch did not once appear to be involved in another plot. Melekh continued to work at the UN, Hirsch as an illustrator on the outside.

The State Department and the Justice Department finally decided that there was no point in keeping the strict and unrelenting surveillance over Melekh and Hirsch. It could be years before they were given another espionage assignment. Possibly, too, the Soviets detected the phoniness of the maps and photos of Chicago's defense and military installations, and realized that here also the FBI was wise to them.

The wheels of justice were quickly put in motion. On the early evening of October 27, 1960, FBI agents moved out and took both men into custody at their respective homes in New York City. The particular date was chosen because a Federal grand jury in Chicago which had listened to all the evidence in the case presented by an assistant United States attorney had returned indictments against

Melekh and Hirsch, as well as against the now-departed Doronkin. The true bill specified espionage involving "conspiracy to obtain information pertaining to our national defense for transmittal to Soviet Russia."

Melekh, the Russian Secretariat employee, was seized in his $200-a-month, two-and-one-half-room apartment at 333 West 86th Street, where he lived with his wife, and their two small children, Marina, two and Mikhail, who was just six. When the FBI swooped into the apartment, they interrupted a gay birthday party for Mikhail. Several other children who lived in the building, all sons and daughters of Russian delegation employees, were attending the party.

Melekh was taken downtown to the FBI's headquarters where he came to a dramatic confrontation with a man he knew quite well, a fellow spy named Willie Hirsch, who had been similarly picked up in his own apartment.

Residents of both Melekh's as well as Hirsch's apartment buildings were stunned to learn they were spies. Neither had worn a slouch hat with downturned brim over the eyes nor a trenchcoat with upturned collar as the storied spies do to mask their identities.

They simply hid behind the best disguise of all—respectability.

After their stopover at the FBI's Manhattan offices, Melekh and Hirsch were whisked further downtown to Foley Square for arraignment in the chambers of Federal Judge Lloyd McMahon.

The Federal Courthouse loomed a ghostly white in the glare of television and newsreel lights that were turned on the two accused spies as they arrived in a black FBI sedan.

Head bowed, Melekh, in brown trousers, white shirt, brown tie, and brown gabardine coat that gave him a closer appearance to a spy than ever before, made his way from the car. Ignoring the hordes of reporters and photographers pressing around him, he sullenly climbed the long flights of courthouse steps with FBI agents holding him firmly by each arm.

He was followed by Hirsch, who was clad in a blue suit, white shirt, blue and white tie, and gray topcoat. His heavy jowls bounced like Jello as he stepped from the car and made his way up the steps behind Melekh to the courthouse. He, too, ignored the newsmen.

They stood stolidly as Judge McMahon read the charges. When the court asked them if they had anything to say, Melekh spoke.

"Generally I understand the nature of this charge, but . . . I protest the way my arrest has been done. I have been arraigned since 7
p.m. and they wouldn't let me finish my talk on the phone."

Judge McMahon asked, "Have you a lawyer to telephone? You
may use my phone."

The prisoner replied, "It will be very difficult to get one tonight."

Judge McMahon then said, "In this country we do not keep people
against their will nor from getting counsel."

United States Attorney S. Hazard Gillespie, from the New York
District, then told the court, "He has had ample opportunity to
obtain counsel since the time he was taken in custody. A recommendation was made in Chicago for bail of twenty-five thousand dollars each. But as United States Attorney for this district and mindful
of the responsibility placed upon my office to produce these people
before the court in Chicago, I ask for seventy-five thousand
each . . ."

Gloria Agrin, an attorney who had been summoned for Hirsch,
gasped audibly.

Gillespie continued, ". . . subject to change which may be made
in Chicago later."

Miss Agrin then said in an indignant tone, "I raise serious objections to this bail. You might as well have said two million dollars."

Judge McMahon replied, "It seems to me that in view of the serious nature of the crime charged, and the fact that ample opportunity to consult with counsel is available, and to be sure that he himself
is available, I will set bail of fifty thousand . . ."

The judge added, "Each."

The prisoners were then taken to the Federal House of Detention
for the night.

In the next few days there were several surprising developments,
and they all came from the Soviets.

First, an official from the Soviet Delegation marched into court,
plunked down the $50,000 bail to spring Melekh. He was startled to
have the money turned down.

It seemed that the cash, brought to court in a suitcase, belonged to
Nicolai Reznichenko, chief of the Soviet Consular Division. And because Reznichenko had diplomatic immunity, U.S. Attorney Gillespie

feared the Government might not be able to seize the bail or hold Reznichenko responsible if Melekh jumped back to Russia.

As this and other cases we have covered always show, the Russians are quick to disown nationals of other countries caught in acts of espionage for the Soviet Union. Thus it was not surprising when they failed even to lift a little finger in Hirsch's behalf. All their efforts were in behalf of Melekh only.

The day after Reznichenko's money was refused, U.S. Commissioner Earl N. Bishop was approached with a request for Melekh's release. This time it was the Russian's wife, Irina, who had been furnished the $50,000 by the Soviet Embassy. Bishop finally granted Melekh his freedom when his wife swore she would inform the Government "at once" if Melekh made plans to leave the country.

To prove the tender of bail, Attorney William Kleinman, who had been retained by the Soviet Embassy to represent Melekh, took a worn, brown attaché's bag and turned it upside down on Commissioner Bishop's desk. Neatly packed $10, $20, $50, and $100 bills cascaded out to a round pile of $50,000.

That afternoon Melekh was released from jail with the restriction that he could not leave Manhattan, and if he so much as sought sanctuary in the United Nations or any embassy where the United States did not have jurisdiction, his bail would be forfeited. He also was ordered not to enter piers, railroad trains, or terminals, nor make any move, actual or implied, to leave the city.

When Melekh left the Federal House of Detention, he had no comment, not even a word about his accused sidekick, Willie Hirsch, in the dangerous game of espionage they had played. Hirsch still was behind bars, and, for the Russians, a forgotten man.

While removal proceedings were being awaited before Melekh and Hirsch were taken to Chicago to be arraigned on the espionage indictment, Soviet officials in New York and Moscow wailed loudly about the arrest of their delegate.

Tass, Khrushchev's official news agency, screeched about the United States jailing Melekh "unlawfully and provocatively."

At the United Nations, one Soviet delegate demanded that Secretary General Hammarskjöld arrange for Melekh's release and end "this shameful act," his arrest. Another said the arrest had been contrived by Allen W. Dulles, then head of the Central Intelligence

Agency, to justify the United States' U-2 spy plane flight over Soviet territory which had created so much furor in Moscow and was made much of here by Khrushchev when he visited the UN.

But the Soviet Union was rudely rebuffed in Melekh's case because he did not fall into the category of a diplomat. Melekh had the dubious distinction of being the second Soviet member of the UN staff to be arrested; Valentin Gubitchev was the only other one in all the years of Red espionage perpetrated against the United States from the world body's home base.

The U.S. attorney in Chicago set about in earnest to prosecute Melekh and Hirsch until word reached him from the Justice Department asking for a postponement in any action. Not long after, in a surprise move, Attorney General Robert F. Kennedy requested the court to give Melekh his freedom, provided he returned to the Soviet Union.

Melekh agreed. He was released, and on April 8, 1961, he left the country.

Of the three spies exposed by the FBI, Doronkin and Melekh, both Russians, managed to elude punishment. Only Hirsch, the German, was left to face the music.

But not for long. Some weeks later the case against Willie Hirsch was dropped. He went free because the charges against him could never stand up in court once the charges against Melekh had been dropped. Hirsch's part in the spy plot was deeply intertwined in the acts and conspiracies of Melekh.

But Hirsch did not get off lightly at all. The U.S. Immigration and Naturalization Service stepped in and ordered his deportation to Germany. On July 21, 1961, before formal proceedings were started, Hirsch and his family sailed "voluntarily" for Germany, en route to Czechoslovakia where asylum had been granted them.

During the intricate behind-the-scenes activity that led to Melekh's release and return to Moscow, many newspapers throughout the United States strenuously objected to the kid-glove treatment accorded the Soviet spy.

The criticism prompted President Kennedy to comment on one specific charge that had been leveled—that the charges against Melekh had been dismissed because there was a connection with the Soviet Union's release of the American RB-47 fliers who had been shot down over the Barents Sea on July 1, 1960. Kennedy said there was absolutely no connection.

Officials later explained that the case had been called off for several reasons, but largely in the hope it would make things easier for the United States to intervene on behalf of Americans who got into trouble with the Soviet Union in the future.

To be sure, a number of Americans have been in trouble in Russia since, by being arrested and accused of spying. And they have to a man all been released after only brief detainment.

It would almost seem that we have come to a sort of unwritten agreement with the Kremlin. An agreement which says: "We'll catch your spies and you can catch ours, but let's swap them when all the screaming and shouting dies down."

10 : Satellite Espionage—
Murder Czech Style

THE high, sharp clatter of leather heels on marble floor echoed nervously down the long antiseptic third-floor corridor of the United Nations Secretariat Building.

Someone was in a hurry.

In a dozen offices lining both sides of the hall, the weathered faces of UN correspondents snapped up at the unfamiliar sound. Ordinarily the third floor in the Secretariat Building is reserved for the working press and the UN's own press information service. Except for the times when a major news story is breaking, the corridor is usually a sea of calm.

The sea was never calmer than on that extremely dull afternoon of June 16, 1961, and that, perhaps, is why the sudden flurry of footsteps exploded so intrusively into the newsmen's idle reveries.

Within moments they were out of their seats and satisfying that hallmark of their trade—their curiosity. A few peered out into the lengthening corridor to see a slim figure in black dart into one of the rooms commonly used for press conferences by UN officials.

Without delay most of the press corps ducked into the room behind him and found to their surprise that the darkly clad intruder was a minor liaison officer from the Czechoslovakian Mission to the UN making an extremely rare appearance on the third floor.

Rare, because Czechoslovakia almost never had anything to say directly to the press. Russia did all of Czechoslovakia's talking.

Rare, too, because the Czech official was of such a minor rank that no one, including correspondents who had been there for ten years or more, knew his name. Nor would he disclose it despite queries from a half dozen correspondents.

His name, he said, didn't matter. He was there simply to distribute a statement from his government. Would each correspondent please take one and read it?

The Czech moved around the room passing out the mimeographed handout and then in another staccato outburst of leather on marble, he swept down the corridor and was gone.

Alone in the conference room, the correspondents took a minute or two to digest the contents of the two-page document and then were dashing for their telephones and filing the opening stanzas of what later became another celebrated case of Communist espionage at the UN.

In a writing style as dry as the Sahara, the Czech statement accused United States intelligence agents of attempting, by coercion and threat, to enlist a certain Miroslav Nacvalac as a spy against his own government of Czechoslovakia. Nacvalac's name was familiar to most of the correspondents. He was in no way a diplomat of the first magnitude, nor was he a flamboyant personality. But he held the relatively important post of Counselor for the Czechoslovakian Mission to the UN and, as such, was occasionally in the public eye at the UN.

The Czech document went on to state that United States Intelligence had sought Nacvalac's services on the assumption that he was in a key position to "observe, participate in, and report secretly on the clandestine activities" not only of the Czechs but of all Iron Curtain delegations at the UN.

The story was moderately good for a dull afternoon. The UN correspondents reported it completely, although realizing their day's work was only beginning. There would be more coming, and soon, because their experienced eyes told them that the real reason for the extraordinary appearance of the Czech official on the third floor was actually to beat the United States to the punch. What tipped the correspondents was the last paragraph in the press announcement. It stated with calculated underplay—and almost as an afterthought—that after failing to enlist Nacvalac as an espionage agent, the U.S. had branded him a spy and ordered him expelled from the country.

The correspondents' hunch proved right. The Czech announcement beat the American version by precisely one hour.

The United States put its own case on display with an announcement from UN Ambassador Adlai Stevenson that Nacvalac not only was guilty of espionage, but had tried to hire an American citizen of Czech descent to spy on U.S. military establishments.

The Ambassador's statement was brief and devoid of specifics, but the Iron Curtain countries nevertheless sent up a screeching howl of protest over America's countercharges.

The Communists denied Nacvalac was a spy and reiterated with blustering invective their original claim of U.S. attempts to turn the Czech into a traitor against his own people.

For three days the United States—and the world—listened to a crescendo of denouncements from the Soviet camp, then dropped a small A-bomb of its own. Nacvalac was not simply a spy, the United States said, he was the chief of the entire far-reaching network of Czechoslovakian espionage in America.

Actually, the Czech and U.S. announcements had simply brought to an eruptive climax a sinister cloak-and-dagger episode that was three years abuilding. It had its genesis in Nacvalac's arrival at the UN as the Czech diplomat in charge of his delegation's budgetary affairs. He did nothing to attract suspicion to himself. He moved about inconspicuously, was seen at the correct Iron Curtain gatherings, occasionally chatted amicably with his new Western friends at the UN.

He was always prompt and displayed the tidy, precise mind of an accountant. Everything about him was methodical. He was in his Czech Delegation seat before meetings began, never leaving until the conferences were over, even if it meant missing lunch or being late for a dinner engagement.

When Nacvalac, tall, dark, and young-looking for his thirty-six years, drew the UN assignment in the summer of 1958, he had behind him a spotless record of Communist loyalty. Moreover, he seemed to be perfectly trained for work in the Czech diplomatic corps. An early journey for the Czech Government took him to Moscow, where he learned to speak Russian fluently. As he progressed, his talents took him to important Communist "listening posts" in Vienna, and by the time he reached the UN in New York, he had added fluent German and English to his diplomatic arsenal.

He adapted to New York life easily. He dined out frequently with his petite wife, Hana, and often entertained Iron Curtain colleagues in his comfortable apartment a few steps off Park Avenue. As Third Secretary of the Czech Delegation, he appeared to be less dependent on his official income than others of his rank. His sons, Miroslav, Jr., eight, and Ivan, ten, attended the private school reserved by the Soviet UN Mission for children of Iron Curtain citizens serving on the UN staff.

In all outward appearances Nacvalac led an exemplary life.

But he had come to the United Nations for a purpose and before long was immersing himself in his real work—espionage. In the end, that proved to be his undoing.

Nacvalac was a graduate of the Soviet School for Espionage and Sabotage. Like many Europeans, he had a contempt for American counterespionage. He rated only the British and French intelligence services as worthy of his respect. But respected or not, the American agents were on his trail virtually from the moment he set foot on our soil.

Thus it was that the United States could pinpoint the exact date—November 3, 1958—that Nacvalac stepped into the case that blew up in his face at the UN on a dull June afternoon two years and seven months later.

It began when Nacvalac left the Czech Delegation on Madison Avenue on that November 3rd afternoon, presumably on Soviet instructions, and met a contact at a rendezvous point near the New York Stock Exchange in the heart of Wall Street. The contact was Karel Hlasny, a Czech-born, naturalized American stationed as an instructor in the Army Language School at Monterey, California.

At this point Nacvalac had only a superficial knowledge of Hlasny gleaned from certain correspondence Hlasny had sent to the Czech UN Mission. Hlasny's sweetheart was still in the Old Country and he was trying to bring her over. He had asked the Czech UN Mission to help secure an exit visa from Czechoslovakia. In Nacvalac's trained espionage mind, Hlasny seemed a prime candidate for undercover work. The deal Nacvalac was trying to set up was a simple quid pro quo. Hlasny could have the exit visa in return for certain information.

The two men met on the sidewalk outside the Stock Exchange and repaired to a nearby restaurant for a late luncheon. In the course of it, Nacvalac dangled the promise of the exit visa for Hlasny's girl friend and extracted a promise of cooperation from the young Czech expatriate.

Nacvalac had no specific assignment in mind for Hlasny yet but said he'd be in touch with him soon. The master spy spelled out a code by which they would keep in contact and arranged for the next meeting. By the time lunch was over, so were all the preliminaries. The men shook hands and went their separate ways.

The next meeting took place in Los Angeles two months later, on January 11, 1959. The time had come for Nacvalac to put his new recruit to work. Measured against the scale of international espionage, the assignment was rather elementary.

It was Hlasny's job to collect information on certain regional military projects, information that was, although Hlasny didn't know it, actually available from public records. The purpose, of course, was to test Hlasny's loyalty and to break him in for more important tasks in the future. Hlasny delivered to Nacvalac's satisfaction.

The next assignment was to provide Nacvalac with the names of people selected by the Army to study Slavic languages and to hunt out and report any character weaknesses they betrayed, whether any were drunkards, homosexuals, and the like—all of which could be invaluable for blackmail purposes later if necessary. Nacvalac sealed the bargain by handing Hlasny six hundred dollars in $5's, $10's, and $20's.

Once again Hlasny performed his assignment faultlessly, but on May 27, 1959, in a meeting between the conspirators in Monterey, Hlasny presented his own demands: there would be no more "co-operation" until his sweetheart joined him in America.

All further meetings between the two were suspended for three months until the attractive young woman arrived in the United States in mid-August. Then Nacvalac promptly informed Hlasny that it was now his turn to produce.

Though still contemptuous of American counterintelligence, Nacvalac realized he was dealing with a novice and decided to change the locale of their get-togethers. Instead of meeting in Monterey as they had been, the conspirators now agreed to hold their next rendezvous in the Milton Kreis Restaurant near Geary and Powell Streets in San Francisco.

The date of the meeting was November 14, 1959. Hlasny drew another minor assignment and received five hundred dollars in payment.

The two men continued to communicate with each other by code but did not meet in person until three months later when they once more rendezvoused in the San Francisco restaurant.

The principal reason for the long delays in the in-person tête-à-têtes was Nacvalac's need to function also at his UN post in New York City three thousand miles away. Absence of any great duration from the Secretariat office could attract suspicion. The delays had nothing to do with another circumstance that Nacvalac knew nothing about.

The Czech spy, though full of contempt for the United States and playing his brand of espionage as carefully as he knew how despite his disdain for our own agents, was totally unaware that Karel Hlasny throughout all their secret negotiations was and had been working with the FBI and faithfully reporting every detail of his surreptitious dealings with Nacvalac.

During 1960, Nacvalac met Hlasny three times all told—in March, August, and November. Each time Hlasny furnished the Czech with military information he had sought but which had first been cleared by the FBI.

There was another meeting between the two, supposedly their last. This was in San Francisco on January 21, 1961, when the Czech paid Hlasny two hundred dollars for what Nacvalac believed to be "classified" information relating to details about certain Army projects in California. Again, all the material turned over to Nacvalac had first been cleared by the FBI. Nacvalac then gave Hlasny a miniature camera and instructed him to use it in the future in his espionage work.

"You will hear from me about what we want you to do next," Nacvalac told him. Then he returned to New York.

For the next four months Nacvalac made no further overtures to Hlasny. Then came a day in early June. The FBI office in New York received an anonymous phone call.

A male voice with a Slavic accent whispered, "You have a good chance to enlist the services of a valuable Czechoslovakian emissary to the UN. He is fed up with his country's system and he has indicated an interest in discussing the possibility of defecting and remaining in the United States. He can provide you with a lot of information . . ."

The FBI agent who took the call asked for the name.

"Miroslav Nacvalac is the man. Look up his status at the UN and you will see."

The G-man wanted to know where he could get together with Nacvalac; it was not beyond the agent's suspicion that the man he was talking to was Nacvalac himself. That's an old Iron Curtain tactic employed by agents who have begun to feel their usefulness to the motherland has taken a nosedive; foreign agents on the Soviet payroll, such as Nacvalac, often look for a way out when they suspect they have fallen from grace, whatever the reason. So, very plausibly, Nacvalac might have heard rumors winging around the UN lounge that he was through or even have sensed that his usefulness was at an end by the changed attitudes of his Russian superiors, and a fast exit into the protective arms of the FBI and asylum in the United States was a far better fate than a plane trip home to Prague where the cruelties of the established order would await him.

The voice on the phone made it clear Nacvalac wanted to talk business, and if the FBI wanted to listen it could send its men to the Gripsholm Restaurant at 324 East 57th Street at lunchtime on Tuesday, June 13. The FBI agent quickly consulted his superiors. Harvey G. Foster, the agent-in-charge of the New York office, gave the order: "Keep the date."

Two G-men were assigned by Foster to rendezvous with Nacvalac. But they did not go alone to the meeting. They took along a former military attaché in the Czech Embassy in Washington, Frantisek Tisler, who was to serve for the FBI as the go-between. Tisler had become disenchanted with Communism, quit his post, and asked for asylum here. Prague immediately labeled him an embezzler, and sought to recall him to Czechoslovakia. The U.S. refused to accept the charges and granted Tisler asylum. Moreover, Tisler knew Nacvalac.

At the restaurant, the G-men and Tisler found Nacvalac sitting at an out-of-the-way table chatting with a guest. Tisler pointed out Nacvalac. One of the FBI agents walked through the dining room, crowded during the lunch hour with some sixty patrons, and stopped at Nacvalac's table. The G-man slipped his hand in his jacket pocket, pulled out his identification, and flashed it to the two men at the table.

"I'd like you to leave," the agent politely told the Czechoslovakian emissary's companion. "There is some business we would like to discuss with Mr. Nacvalac."

Without a word, the man rose and left the table. The second G-man and Tisler walked over and sat down with Nacvalac and the first agent who had taken the departed guest's chair. The FBI later learned that the man who had just left was an American economist from Connecticut who had been invited to lunch by Nacvalac, presumably to be a witness to the G-men's visit.

Nacvalac did not enter into any kind of discussion that even remotely suggested his intention to defect or to serve this country as a double agent. It soon became apparent to the FBI men that Nacvalac was enjoying a vague pleasure out of having brought about the meeting with "American intelligence agents," as he called them. He had nothing really to say. He seemed ill at ease and his conversation was rambling and weary, without order or sense. He spoke about his beliefs and his devotions which were strongly pro-Communist, yet he espoused a certain begrudging admiration for the capitalistic system. He commented obliquely on issues hanging fire in the General Assembly, at intervals pausing to ask the G-men and Tisler for their views on the issues.

Neither espionage nor the mention of Nacvalac's defection was brought up by anyone during the hour and a half that the meeting lasted. During it, Tisler seemed the most uneasy. It had been his understanding that he was wanted there to pave the way for Nacvalac's defection. He was bewildered.

Not the G-men, however. They saw an ulterior motive through the smokescreen of Nacvalac's reticence, although they couldn't equate it precisely to the ultimately startling turnabout the case would take in the UN when the Czechs issued their charge that the United States had attempted to recruit their man to spy on his own people.

Three uneasy days passed at the UN after the Czech announcement, as correspondents scrounged around for new angles to give them fresh leads on the story. Just as it began to appear that this latest spy thriller was destined to go into limbo, with only the formality of Nacvalac's ouster left to provide the next and final development in the story, the UN press corps was treated to a hearty surprise.

It came on June 19 when none other than Miroslav Nacvalac himself trudged into the UN lounge for the first time since the respective charges and countercharges were issued by the Czech and American delegations. A score or more eager correspondents quickly surrounded Nacvalac, who appeared to relish the magnetism of his new-found status.

Nacvalac was in fine vocal fettle. He launched a rambling tirade against the United States, painting a pernicious mosaic of FBI efforts to recruit him into the ranks of the "American counterespionage machine." He reviewed the luncheon meeting in the Gripsholm Restaurant and identified the two agents who had accompanied Tisler as "Mr. Mack" and "Mr. Jack." He said they accosted him on their own volition, that he had not sought them out.

Nacvalac's platitudes were followed that night by stiffly worded broadsides beamed by Moscow and Prague radios against "American gangsters." Among other charges, the Communists revived the U-2 spy plane incident and, with *Pravda* and *Izvestia* joining in the thunder of condemnation, bellowed that the Nacvalac case demonstrated clearly that the United States held nothing sacred, not even the Charter principles binding the UN together as a protector of small nations.

Irrelevancies continued to fuddle the issue as Soviet and Czech diplomats stumbled over each other in their haste to deliver notes of protest to Secretary General Hammarskjöld.

The thunder boomed steadily louder over the next two days and then Nacvalac advanced to the fore again to issue a new statement. He challenged the State Department to present just one shred of evidence to corroborate the charges that he had met Karel Hlasny in San Francisco—or anywhere else. Nacvalac blandly denied he had ever set foot in California.

"They are liars and they cannot prove it." He said it almost with a snarl.

That was June 18; the time—shortly before noon. Nacvalac's statement was flashed to Washington. An hour later, a press attaché in the State Department summoned capital reporters to his office for what he termed "an important development."

"This, gentlemen," he said, "should end Mr. Nacvalac's frantic denials."

He distributed to the reporters a set of photographs. They were pictures of the outside of the restaurant at Geary and Powell Streets in San Francisco, and they showed in a dramatic, clear sequence Karel Hlasny entering the eatery, followed a few feet behind by another man.

The other man, big as life in the photos, was Miroslav Nacvalac.

"Fake!" protested Nacvalac. "The pictures are doctored."

Next morning the Soviet Delegation was gripped by a new spirit of righteous belligerence for the downtrodden diplomat. Truculently they demanded sharp intervention by Hammarskjöld against the United States. They threatened to invoke Article 21, which provides for an international tribunal of three arbitrators, to resolve the case. Moreover, the Soviet Delegation summoned all neutrals and the Afro-Asians in particular to condemn the "imperialist travesty by the colonialist powers who run the UN."

Six days after the spy case burst into headlines and had engendered the animosity and bickering that had gone unabated for that period, the State Department put its foot down. In a note to the Czech Delegation, it demanded that Nacvalac leave the country in the next twenty-four hours or he would be arrested and summarily deported by our own authorities.

At exactly 10 o'clock of the following morning, June 23, Miroslav Nacvalac, his wife, and their two children arrived at Idlewild Airport to board an Air France jetliner for Paris, en route to Prague.

The branded Soviet spy was grim and unsmiling. Anger still crossed his face. He took one final swipe at the United States, declaring; "I'm being forced by blackmail and pressure to leave this country and my important post at the United Nations. I blame this terrible crime on American gangsterism."

Nacvalac flicked a cigarette ash off his smartly cut Fifth Avenue suit and turned to shake hands with Soviet and Czech delegates who had come out to the airport to see him off. Then, taking his wife and children, he mounted the ramp and disappeared into the plane.

Miroslav Nacvalac, a smart satellite spy who arrogantly despised America's intelligence system, was on his way home a failure, a victim of his own system's audacity.

Czechoslovakia managed to keep out of the FBI's hair for the next seventeen months. Then, on October 19, 1962, the Czechs, the FBI, the United Nations, and the police of three states were once more shoulder to shoulder in the newspaper headlines.

It was 10:10 a.m., October 18, a Thursday, when New Jersey State Trooper Stanley Dutkus of the Clinton Barracks, saw a 1962 Cadillac sedan zoom by his cruiser parked on the shoulder of Route 22 near Intersection 69, outside Clinton in Hunterdon County. Route 22 is a main link between New York and Harrisburg, Pennsylvania.

Dutkus quickly set out in pursuit of the speeding car. In seconds, he was blazing along with siren screaming at eighty miles an hour.

The Cadillac paid no heed to the trooper behind. The driver kept pouring on the speed—90, 100, 105 miles an hour. Dutkus noted the New York license of the car, DPL-41. He knew it was a diplomatic plate, but he doubted that a diplomat was crazy enough to drive as wildly as that. He thought the car might have been stolen.

Stepping on the floorboard, Trooper Dutkus managed to squeeze all the speed he could out of his Pontiac until it was tearing along at 110 m.p.h. He pulled abreast of the speeding Caddy in an attempt to force the driver to the side of the road. But the man behind the wheel swerved to the outside and tried to run the trooper off the other side of the road.

It was a close call for Trooper Dutkus, who managed to slow down and avoid a tragic collision. As he fell behind, he grabbed the phone and radioed Clinton Barracks for help. He gave the direction of the pursuit and flashed word of the attempt by the driver to crash his car into the police vehicle. Then Dutkus once more tried to overtake the Caddy, only to have the driver veer menacingly toward him again. Dutkus decided to play it safe and stayed on the fleeing car's tail.

About three miles ahead of the chase, State Trooper William Howie was at a truck checkpoint on Route 22 when the alert from Clinton crackled over the air. Howie hurried out to the center of the road and looked east in the direction from which the fugitive car was reported coming. Seconds later he spotted a black car in the distance barreling down the highway, another right behind. It was the Caddy with the police cruiser tearing toward him.

Howie raised his hands and waved frantically in an attempt to flag down the oncoming car. But the driver kept coming. Without letup on his speed, he bore down on the trooper. Howie leaped to one side, out of the path of the car. As it roared by, the trooper raced to his own cruiser and joined the pursuit.

Traffic ahead slowed the first trooper, Dutkus, and he fell behind the Caddy which ignored the other cars on the road, zipping and zigging around them as it went. As traffic thinned again, Dutkus drew nearer and so did Howie, who then spurted ahead and tried to force the fugitive car to the side of the road as Dutkus had tried to do unsuccessfully twice before. Once again the Caddy's driver resorted to the turn-in tactic at high speed and drove Trooper Howie off.

The chase now was rapidly approaching the two-lane Phillipsburg–Easton Bridge spanning the Delaware River to Pennsylvania. Both troopers had radioed their difficulties back to headquarters and orders were flashed to the bridge police to set up a roadblock.

Wooden barriers were spread across the highway. As the Caddy approached the barricade, it slowed down for the first time to about 40 m.p.h. Holding that speed, the driver slanted his car as he reached the barriers, hit them at an angle, and plowed through. The troopers followed past the debris of splintered lumber strewn on the highway and stayed on the fugitive's tail as he put on a new burst of speed going into Pennsylvania.

Trooper Dutkus finally put on a tremendous burst of speed of his own that shot him past the Caddy. In front now, he tried to slow down the big car. But Trooper Howie radioed from behind the warning that the Caddy was trying to ram Dutkus' car from the rear. Howie accelerated to get away from the Caddy. The speed went back up to 110 m.p.h. And the driver was still trying to ram Howie with the Caddy—at 110 m.p.h.

Suddenly there was a sickening screech of tires. The driver of the Caddy seemed to lose control. His car swerved first, then careened to the edge of the road and mounted the gravel shoulder. In the next instant, amid a cloud of dust raised by its spinning wheels, the out-of-control Cadillac crashed through a wooden guard rail, plummeted down a ravine, and disappeared from view.

Troopers Howie and Dutkus braked to a halt, leaped from their cars, and raced down the side of the hill. The car, its wheels still spinning, had overturned and come to rest on its roof. Smoke was pouring from the engine and its gas tank was ablaze.

Howie hurried to his cruiser to fetch a hand fire extinguisher. When he got back, Howie was amazed to see the driver—he seemed about thirty-five to forty, stocky, and brown-haired—on his stomach, resting on his elbows inside the car. In his right hand he was holding an automatic. With his left he was pushing a clip into the gun.

Just then two more troopers' cars arrived. These were Pennsylvania State Policemen. Corporal John E. Uditis of the Bethlehem Barracks was one of them.

As the senior trooper on the scene, Uditis spotted the danger and yelled to the New Jersey policemen to get back. Howie and Dutkus quickly climbed the hill.

"The man's crazy," Howie told Uditis.

"I'll say he is," Uditis replied. "You fellows cover me," he ordered; then, his own revolver in hand, he went down to the overturned car.

Exercising caution, he drew slowly toward the car. The driver now was smoking a cigarette with his left hand. His right was out of sight. The fire in the gas tank had burned itself out. The overheated engine was still smoldering but no longer posed a threat.

"Take your hand out . . . take your hand out slowly," Corporal Uditis commanded.

The man in the car, who seemed uninjured despite the turning over in the crash, calmly went on smoking. Uditis again ordered him to show his right hand. But the man puffed on his cigarette and stared blankly at the trooper.

Turning for a split second to the other troopers on the hill, Uditis shouted, "Bring me a sledge hammer to break the window."

As he snapped his head back, Uditis saw the driver's gun hand move, bringing the automatic into view. An instant later, the gun was being pointed at the trooper.

Uditis saw the danger. He squeezed the trigger of his service revolver. A shot rang out. The man in the car winced. The bullet struck him in the shoulder. For several seconds he seemed dazed and hurt; then all at once he appeared to relax.

Finally, he raised the automatic to his own temple—and fired.

As the driver slumped into unconsciousness on the "header" of the overturned car, the other troopers scampered down the hill and helped Corporal Uditis pry open the door.

An ambulance was summoned. The comatose driver was borne on a stretcher up the hill and rushed in the ambulance to nearby Easton Hospital.

At the scene the troopers looked over papers they had removed from the victim's pockets before he was taken to the hospital. To their astonishment, they found the man who had given them all their difficulties was a diplomat. His identification showed he was Karel Zizka, forty, an attaché of the Czechoslovak Mission to the UN.

In the car, police found one hundred rounds of .38 caliber ammunition scattered about, a roll of three hundred dollars in American money, and an empty bottle of imported Russian vodka.

Word was quickly relayed to New York City police, who went to the Czech Mission at 1109-11 Madison Avenue near 83rd Street in Manhattan, to report the episode of the errant diplomat to superiors. The blinds around the mission building at that hour, shortly before noon, were strangely closed. The patrolmen were greeted at the door by a tall, well-dressed man who identified himself as Antoni Nenko. He said he was an aide.

When the patrolmen determined that Nenko knew Karel Zizka, they told him what had happened and the hospital he was in.

"Thank you very much," Nenko said stiffly, betraying unusual nervousness. The policemen then left.

Meanwhile, back in Easton Hospital, Zizka's life was teetering on the precipice of eternity. Physicians found that the bullet he had fired into his temple was lodged in his brain. Emergency surgery was required to save his life. The operation would have to be performed at St. Luke's Hospital in neighboring Bethlehem.

Shortly before noon, just as the policemen were breaking the news about Zizka to the Czechs back in New York, the patient was taken by ambulance to St. Luke's where he underwent a two-and-a-half-hour brain operation. Afterward, physicians reported his condition as critical and gave him little hope to pull through.

Even as Zizka was being wheeled out of surgery to a private room in the hospital, the reception hall downstairs was buzzing with nervous chatter that none of the hospital personnel could understand.

It was Czechoslovakian, and doing the talking were three Czech emissaries, Dr. Zdenek Pisk, Dr. Frantisek Teliicha and Antoni Nenko, all of whom had sped to Bethlehem after receiving word about Zizka.

In New York again, police were able to dovetail an earlier episode into Zizka's wild flight across New Jersey and Pennsylvania highways.

It all started around 7:30 a.m. when Zizka's Cadillac ran into a 1955 Plymouth sedan at 86th Street and First Avenue. The damage was slight, but the Caddy did not stop. The owner of the Plymouth saw the Caddy hit his car, took down the license, DPL-41—DPL stands for diplomat and means its driver cannot be ticketed—and reported it to police.

Minutes later Patrolman William Myers of the Safety Enforcement Squad received the call on the air and spotted the Cadillac at 92nd Street and York Avenue where it had stopped for a red light.

As Myers drew close, the light changed to green. The Caddy spurted forward. Suddenly a Buick loomed ahead. The driver behind the wheel of the Caddy—Zizka—lost control and ripped into the side of the Buick.

Patrolman Myers hopped out of his radio car and went to talk to Zizka.

"I am in a hurry," the Czech said curtly. "I am on my way to Idlewild Airport. I am a diplomat. I have diplomatic immunity."

Myers knew the score. He could not hold Zizka, nor even ticket him. So the patrolman made notes and waved the car on. Then, in accordance with departmental policy, he routed his report so it would reach the Czech Mission.

The errant car was not spotted again until it whizzed by Trooper Stanley Dutkus and started the chase that ended with Zizka's crackup in the ravine and his suicide attempt.

The mysterious flight and actions of the Czech diplomat stirred everyone in the United Nations Building. Rumors quickly spread through the third floor that the real story was not the chase in Jersey and Pennsylvania but right there in New York.

Someone had heard someone say that there had been a murder at the Czechoslovak Mission Building on Madison Avenue.

The rumor spread and raced like wildfire. The Czech Delegation was besieged by inquiries. Polite smiles, firm denials met every such inquiry. But by late afternoon, Milos Vejvoda, counselor of the Czech

Mission, was compelled to come out and read a statement at the Mission's headquarters. From the first-floor foyer he addressed himself to a gathering of newsmen.

> After the reports of the inexplicable behavior of Mr. Zizka, and about his firing at a state policeman, the members of the mission and the families became suspicious that Mr. Zizka's wife has not been seen since the morning.
>
> When she did not answer the telephone and knocking of the door, the door of their flat was opened by force. Mrs. Zizka was found dead in the bathroom, and the flat was in a terrible state and was partly demolished.
>
> On the table [was] a report by Mr. Zizka, explaining that he killed his wife and that he will commit suicide.
>
> According to all persons who have known them, the Zizka family life was happy and quiet, and this tragic happening can only be explained by a sudden mental breakdown.

The Zizkas, Vejvoda went on to say, had two children, a girl, eighteen, and a boy, fifteen, both in Czechoslovakia. He stood cool and impassive as he read his statement and answered a few questions tossed at him.

"Yes," he admitted, "the body is still upstairs."

In contrast, a somewhat more emotional peripheral account came a while later, after police arrived on the scene, from Miss Rita Myatt, a Canadian-born resident in an apartment house at 48 East 83rd Street, opposite the Mission.

Miss Myatt said she had been restless and awake during the wee hours of the morning and, as she put it, "I heard a woman scream about five times at about four-forty. So I got up and took a cold drink from the Fridge. I didn't see anything, but it was terrible. She was screaming blue murder."

This was a statement from a woman living across the street. Didn't anyone living right in the Mission itself hear Mrs. Zizka's screams?

"I have said what there is to say," Vejvoda snapped, adamantly refusing to answer further questions.

Shortly before Vejvoda had read his statement to reporters, Dr. Jiri Hajek, the Czechoslovak representative at the United Nations, had taken the precaution to phone Police Commissioner Michael J. Murphy downtown at Police Headquarters on Center Street. It was 5:30 p.m. and Murphy was about to leave for home.

Dr. Hajek was trying to be brief. He merely wanted to report a murder, the murder of Karel Zizka's wife, Vera, also forty.

"But you need not concern yourself," Hajek told the Commissioner. "We have the situation in hand. We will ship the body back to Prague."

Murphy, who has a peculiar idea that murders in New York City ought to be investigated by his own department, politely asked for a few details. He was given the barest. The victim, Hajek informed the Commissioner, was found Thursday morning in the three-and-a-half room apartment on the third floor of the Czech Mission. It appeared she had been bludgeoned to death. A Russian physician, Dr. Anna Cernyseva of the Soviet Union Mission to the UN, was summoned and pronounced the victim DOA (dead on arrival).

"We still must conduct an investigation," Murphy said firmly when he was told that he could not probe the murder. Dr. Hajek insisted that the Mission was "inviolable" because of the diplomatic immunity it enjoyed.

"We merely called you as a courtesy," Hajek told the Commissioner.

But Murphy, who comes from tough Irish stock, wouldn't take no for an answer. Finally Hajek yielded and gave his permission to police and other authorities to see for themselves what did happen.

Dr. Milton Helpern, the city's chief medical examiner, was permitted to enter the Mission shortly after 6 p.m. With him came Assistant District Attorney Gerald Fogarty, Police Deputy Chief Inspector George Gallagher, and Assistant Chief Inspector Edward W. Byrnes. They were the only officials allowed into the forbidding eight-story stone building that houses the Czech Mission to the UN and which was now a house of murder.

The killer, according to Hajek, was the victim's husband, Karel Zizka, who himself now lay closer than ever to death. Hope that he might even live until morning had been given up at St. Luke's; nevertheless, physicians continued to fan what little flame of life was left in the Czech attaché's body.

Dr. Helpern was permitted to examine Mrs. Zizka's corpse. Clad in a blue silk nightgown, the body still lay on the floor in the bedroom.

The face was a fright. The skull had been crushed and blood covered every portion of the face.

From a hasty examination that he was allowed to conduct there, Dr. Helpern determined that the woman's skull had been broken in several places by blows from a hard object. He also found that there was a bullet wound in the left temple and several knife punctures in the chest.

No gun was found in the apartment, the Czechs told police, but they pointed to a blood-caked wooden meat-tenderizing mallet and suggested that was the weapon probably used as the bludgeon.

A look around the apartment revealed a terrifying tapestry of violence and death. The rooms were a shambles, with the kitchen and dinette awash in liquor from smashed gin, whisky, wine, and vodka bottles, and splattered with food. On the kitchen tablecloth was a message scribbled in pen in large block English letters: "I went probably mad and so goodby, goodby."

Nearby in a stamp album was scrawled: "I have killed her to death —wife—goodby, goodby."

Dr. Helpern turned to Counselor Vejvoda and asked for permission to remove the body for autopsy to Bellevue Hospital's morgue.

"I am afraid you cannot do that," Vejvoda told the medical examiner. "You have no jurisdiction here. This is foreign territory . . ."

Vejvoda had the upper hand. There could be no argument. The Czech Mission's building was a diplomatically immune island of Communism in the middle of Manhattan, and now more than ever a house of mystery, not only to the people in the neighborhood but to the authorities who had gone there to look in on a murder they were not allowed to investigate.

As the lawmen and Dr. Helpern left the forbidding Red outpost in the center of the city, the heavy brocade curtains on the doors were hastily pulled, shutting out any view left to the outside world.

"It's a strange thing," commented Inspector Gallagher as he and the other officials were surrounded on the sidewalk by reporters who had not been allowed entry to the Mission except for those brief few minutes in the foyer when Vejvoda read off his prepared statement on the murder. "The minute you step inside that door, you are in Czechoslovakia."

Within the hour, a hearse from the I. Weil Sons, Inc., funeral home pulled up in front of the building. Three men carried a canvas body-stretcher inside. About fifteen minutes later, the door opened and the three men came out lugging the stretcher with Mrs. Zizka's blanket-covered body. They placed it in the hearse, then drove away.

At police headquarters and at District Attorney Frank S. Hogan's office, reporters besieged officials for an explanation. Was there to be no investigation of the murder? Why?

The answer was "no." Diplomatic immunity and all that, you know.

Moreover, it was stated, Zizka himself, if in fact he was the killer, could not be prosecuted. Nor even arrested. He would be protected by a full diplomatic immunity against prosecution if he lived.

Diplomatic immunity extended to Zizka in his status as a member of the staff of a delegation to the United Nations under the agreement entered into between the United States and the UN on June 26, 1947.

This pact covers four principal categories of representatives of member nations: ambassadors or ministers plenipotentiary; resident members of their staffs; persons designated in the United Nations Charter; and such other principal resident representatives of members to a specialized agency or members of their staffs.

It was the same law that protected all the other diplomats whom we talked about in the preceding chapters—the Russian diplomats who spied here and got off scot-free. And now a satellite diplomat had committed murder.

"No police action is planned," Inspector Gallagher finally informed the press. "There are no charges to be made. The incident occurred on foreign territory. We have no jurisdiction. There will be no autopsy. The body will not go to the morgue. We understand that the body will be flown to Czechoslovakia for burial sometime tomorrow."

"Who do *you* think is the killer?" one reporter wanted to know.

"We were told it was the husband," Gallagher said. "We have only their word. That's all."

The next day the scene of greatest interest shifted once again to Bethlehem where surgeons had managed miraculously to keep Karel Zizka alive through the night. But it was a losing battle. Zizka, who never regained consciousness after firing the bullet through his temple, succumbed at 10:20 a.m.

The three Czech delegates who had arrived at St. Luke's the previous afternoon had remained overnight and were on hand to begin making arrangements for the body's shipment to New York. But the Lehigh County coroner, Dr. Clayton Werley, declared that the body could not be removed before an autopsy was first performed.

Dr. Teliicha, who was First Secretary, and Dr. Pisk, Second Secretary, both of the Czechoslovakian Embassy in Washington, and Nenko, Third Secretary of the Czech Mission in New York, all violently opposed the autopsy.

"That's orders, gentlemen," Dr. Werley said firmly. He had already discussed the matter with the Lehigh County district attorney and the State Department in Washington.

"I am advised, gentlemen," Dr. Werley went on, "that diplomatic immunity ends at death and that it is perfectly legal and proper to determine the exact cause of death."

Dr. Werley then went ahead with the autopsy and made his ruling: suicide.

Afterward, Zizka's body was released to the Czechs. A hearse arrived a while later and took the body back to New York. It reached the city in late afternoon just as the wife's body was being put aboard an Air France airliner at Idlewild for the flight back to Prague. About two hours later, Zizka's body was taken in a casket to the airport and was flown home on another Air France trans-Atlantic plane.

A Czech spokesman at the UN announced that night: "There will be no further discussion of the case. It is closed so far as we are concerned."

And in that atmosphere of conspiratorial secrecy, the Czech Mission wrote "finis" to the case of Karel and Vera Zizka, a case of murder and suicide.

But it did not end precisely on that note. Newspapers in New York City and others around the country wrote steaming editorial criticism of the Czech Delegation, then dwelled at length on the abuse of diplomatic immunity as practiced by members of Iron Curtain countries.

At the UN, many an eyebrow was raised and many questions were asked.

Why did the Czechs go to such lengths to prohibit a decent inquiry into the crime?

Was Zizka a Red agent?

We have repeatedly seen espionage machines in foreign lands liquidating agents caught in one act or another of treachery. Such killings can often be disguised as suicides or accidents.

What was it in Zizka's case?

Is it conceivable that Zizka was ordered to murder his wife, the wife he supposedly loved so much, according to Milos Vejvoda? Is it possible that his wife had committed some act of treachery and Moscow wanted her out of the way?

And is that the reason Zizka went berserk—because he was forced to kill the woman he really loved?

Or did he simply lose his head during a marital squabble, slay her in a fit of anger, then take his own life in remorse?

Who can say now? Who can know? The Czech Delegation to the UN cloaked the case in so much secrecy, perhaps on orders from the Soviet Mission, that the facts in the case were effectively smothered.

If there was anything more to it than what we've told you, diplomatic immunity performed a noble service for the Czechs in obliterating the efforts of police to unearth all the facts.

Needless to say, the law regarding diplomatic immunity has not been altered. Murder can still be committed as easily as espionage in New York City or anywhere else in the United States. And the killer can feel free to escape punishment, just as the spy does. All he needs is diplomatic immunity.

There is one consoling aspect to this hair-raising episode of the Czechoslovakian diplomat. It was the first case of murder involving a delegation to the United Nations and the only one up to now.

Yet the morrow could dawn on a new case of Iron Curtain murder in the UN. It will probably have the very same ending.

11 : The Soviet War-of-Nerves
Plot Against the United States

IT was warm, sunshiny, and perfect flying weather at Havana Airport on the afternoon of October 3, 1962, as a jet airliner, bearing the bright colors of Cuba but patently of Soviet origin, roared down the runway for the takeoff.

A small group of government officials and six Russians, headed by Alexei Alekseyev, chief of the Latin American Section in the Foreign Office at Moscow, waved politely from the field as the jet with its thirty passengers picked up speed and nosed into the bright blue sky on a northerly course.

When the plane had disappeared from sight, the contingent at the airport returned to their offices in Havana, but only to learn they were wanted back at the airport. Mechanical trouble had forced the plane to return.

Repairs were made within the hour and the six stiffly correct and uniformed Russians, along with the Cuban officials, saluted the departing passengers and marched off to their waiting cars as the plane this time streaked up to 30,000 feet en route to its destination, New York, with its thirty passengers, headed by Osvaldo Dorticos, Cuba's puppet president.

The plot to blow up a large area of the eastern seaboard of the United States was about to be put to its acid test. It had been many months in planning and it was now up to one man among the thirty aboard that plane to launch the terrible holocaust upon the United States.

He was Roberto Lazaro Santiesteban y Casanova, a 27-year-old Havana-born saboteur who had been drilled and trained in the terror school the Russians had recently established just outside Havana.

The hope, of course, was that the sabotage would severely damage the United States, but not provoke it into a full-scale nuclear war with Russia.

The Kremlin, well aware of the arsenal of U.S. nuclear and rocket might it would face in a war, must play it "safe." Yet by steering clear of a hot war, the Soviet Union can still advance itself toward the goal of world domination by subtle and covert means, those cold war weapons and devices so capable of wearing down the enemy through attrition and corruption of national morale. Espionage and subversive agitation, designed to reduce the vigor, vitality, and stability of an enemy nation, are two of the Kremlin's weapons. Sabotage, which can ruin a country physically, is another in the Reds' cold war arsenal.

So far as sabotage goes, no nation in the world has exerted more time nor greater energy than the Soviet Union in attaining the know-how to put this destructive force to work. Not only have the Russians mastered the technique of sabotage themselves, but they have instructed satellite nations in its uses, as they have Cuba.

On the wings of the plane bearing Roberto Santiesteban y Casanova that warm afternoon of October 3, 1962, rode Soviet hopes for the success of the first real test of its sabotage virtuosity against a major power, the United States. The Russians felt comfortable and confident about the plot for they were not directly involved in its execution. Only the Cubans could be blamed. Yet we have since learned that the Central Intelligence Agency has obtained unimpeachable evidence against Moscow, showing its cyclopean hand in the plot.

By the time the jet reached New York's Idlewild Airport, it was dark and cold. But the promise of success for the incredible band of conspirators seemed as bright and thermal as the sun burning on the other side of the world that October Thursday.

The plane landed and was guided to a special berth at the airport where security and police precautions protected President Dorticos from the boos and shouts of exiles who had come to protest his arrival.

Formalities were brief. Squinting through his thick-lensed eyeglasses in the white light of popping flashbulbs and brusquely ignoring reporters' questions, Dorticos hurried to a limousine at the head of a small fleet of autos waiting for the party. Dorticos was anxious to be on time for a dinner date with Andrei Gromyko at the Soviet UN Mission. In fact, it was Gromyko's doing that brought Dorticos to New York.

Some days before, Gromyko implored Khrushchev to send either Castro or Dorticos to the UN to salvage some Russian prestige out of the slap administered by President Kennedy when he threatened to take action to stop the positioning of Russian troops and nuclear rockets on the Caribbean island, action which, on October 21, had led to a blockade of Cuba.

Kennedy's bold stand and the immediate support he received from the Organization of American States had put the Russians on the spot. Their prestige in the eyes of the whole world was at stake. The President had given Khrushchev an ultimatum: get the troops and rockets out of Cuba, or else . . .

From the Kremlin, the order went to Havana: "Send Dorticos to New York to see Andrei Gromyko."

The order also went out: "Send Santiesteban Casanova to execute the sabotage strike."

It had been three years in the making, this plot, and now the time had finally come.

The beginning was in 1959, even as Fidel Castro paraded behind the facade of a "liberator" of the Cuban people. After Castro surged into power on the crest of an impassioned revolution that overthrew the hated Fulgencia Batista regime, he began at once to carry out the secret directives from the Kremlin that were designed to transform the Caribbean nation into a Communist state.

To build this Soviet beachhead in the Western Hemisphere into a Soviet base for military and subversive pressures upon all Latin America, Castro had to be hitched openly to the Moscow droshky which would lead Cuba full circle into the Communist orbit.

Khrushchev designated his wily Armenian deputy, Anastas I. Mikoyan, to the job of harnessing Castro. And Mikoyan, the traveling salesman of the conspiracy, knew just what to do. In Havana, he and Castro signed a vital trade agreement, thus laying the economic foundation for Russia's subsequent, inevitable political take-over of Cuba. Later, when he returned to New York, Mikoyan faced a packed press conference at the UN and laughed off all suggestions that he had ulterior motives in Cuba, and that the trade pact was merely a cover-up for other more grandiose designs.

But evidence of direct Russian intervention in Cuba soon began accumulating. Cuban exiles and foreign correspondents, lucky to get out of Havana with their lives, periodically reported an ominous influx of Russians—silent, high-cheeked men in square-cut suits, accompanied by women whose bearing was so military-like they looked almost like soldiers in dresses. And instead of pocketbooks, the women always seemed to carry mysterious-looking locked briefcases.

In retrospect now, the chronology of events from 1960 through 1961 testifies graphically to the systematic Sovietization of Cuba in that brief time span. Cuban exiles and experts on Russia had repeatedly voiced warnings in the United States about the Soviet build-up, but nothing was done to prevent or arrest it except an occasional declaration by the United States that we would not tolerate any violation of the Monroe Doctrine.

The clamor grew loudest after Mikoyan, back in Moscow now, delegated Alexei Alekseyev to leave the Latin American Section in the Foreign Office and proceed to Havana and organize the second stage of the Soviet take-over.

Alekseyev took scores of "advisers" with him, people who gradually displaced Cubans in key positions in the Castro regime. These Russian "advisers" also were instrumental in filling many executive positions by advancing Cuban Communists who had until now remained discreetly out of the public's eye.

As Alekseyev thus tooled the engine for Cuban Sovietization, he also built into it the added horsepower needed to drive the Communist droshky into other Caribbean and Latin American lands when the time became ripe.

But primarily his aim was the United States, chief target of the Soviet–Cuban military build-up that was about to begin.

By the time Alekseyev left the summer heat of Havana and returned to the cooler precincts of the Kremlin, Fidel Castro and his brother, Raul, were deep in Khrushchev's pocket. The Soviet Premier had only to give the word now to begin the next stage in the conspiracy—the *coup de grâce* of sabotage against the United States.

For this phase, Khrushchev handpicked a henchman seasoned to the core in the webs and wiles of espionage, sabotage, and subversion. He was the man who headed the Soviet spy ring in Canada in 1945 which gave Russia the secrets of splitting the atom and the know-how to build atom bombs, secrets and know-how filched from the United States while it was still in the stupor of World War II.

The man was Sergei M. Kudryavtsev, an unprincipled Kremlin agent who had served his apprenticeship in espionage in the *Tass* office during Hitler's days in Berlin.

Once again now, Kudryavtsev sallied forth from Moscow to the Western Hemisphere with the rank of ambassador. The sweltering weather of Havana gripped the Russian's porky frame uncomfortably, but he found instant pleasant relief in the air-cooled luxury of the Soviet Embassy, where the kingpins of the Communist conspiracy network in that part of the world had gathered for a briefing on the mechanics of the sabotage plot against the U.S.

Kudryavtsev's job was twofold: he had to cast a blanket of agents over Latin America; and he had to prepare the first direct action against the United States, sabotage that was calculated to grate on American nerves and instill consternation and panic in strategic areas of the East Coast. Immediately afterward, if all went well, the plot was to be extended to other vital areas of the country.

Those fortunate enough to have lived in America during World War II would have difficulty understanding the rapacious effects of what the Germans so aptly describe as *nervenkrieg*. Hitler's propaganda minister, Dr. Joseph Goebbels, refined this insidious weapon to a fine art. The Russians copied and improved on it with assiduous skill.

Britain withstood the Nazi bombings of London and other cities valiantly. But in 1944, the heroic nation buckled a bit under the impact of the V-1 and V-2 rockets, those terrifying weapons which splintered and shattered large areas of the British Isles. Even to this day, it isn't difficult to speculate on Britain's fate if Hitler had had the deadly missiles a year or two earlier.

It is entirely possible that the nerves of those courageous people would have cracked, for a war of nerves is a poisonous weapon. Like opium, it creeps into the nervous system dose by dose until it brings on physical and moral collapse.

Sergei Kudryavtsev was deeply versed in this psychology of the *nervenkrieg,* for he had been the very master of subversion who, for a time, had run the Soviet network of espionage and sabotage in West Germany. He knew how to contrive dangerous incidents, plan involved undercover projects, and take advantage of every situation in bringing an assignment of terror to a successful conclusion.

In Cuba he could operate freely and without cover, an unusual experience for him. Cuban Communists who journeyed to Caribbean and Latin American lands as agents found Kudryavtsev had a keen perception of their special problems. They went on their missions much the wiser for the advice and direction he imparted.

His own special problem was to plot the initial move against the United States. To help him put over his scheme, Kudryavtsev had at his disposal the services of the Communist Party of the United States. But, to be sure, whatever role the Party was to play would, as always, be a subordinate one. The Kremlin has never regarded American Communists sufficiently "reliable" to be trusted with important duties. Traditionally, Moscow looks to this country's Communist Party for subordinate help, such as providing information—the thankless, dirty, and dangerous job of legwork.

Kudryavtsev also could rely for a limited amount of help upon the Soviet Embassy in Washington.

But his real preparation base for the *nervenkrieg* against the United States was the Soviet Mission to the UN. In that adjunct of the Kremlin in New York City, Kudryavtsev had at his disposal a ready-made springboard from which to launch the sabotage blows dictated by Moscow.

By June, 1962, after receiving guidance relayed from Moscow through the UN command post, Kudryavtsev had the blueprint ready. It was clear that the ringleader responsible for the execution of the terror and sabotage in the New York area must be someone who could work under a protective shield that would render him virtually immune to detection. And he would need unfettered freedom to circulate at will in the target area.

There was only one logical candidate for the job—someone who could operate out of the UN's Cuban Mission which enjoyed immunity from the travel restrictions laid down for certain other Communist or satellite delegations.

Kudryavtsev realized that the man he would finally pick to lead the sabotage ring into its orgy of destruction must be assigned to an inconspicuous post in the Cuban Mission and that he be granted authority to employ trusted aides. The Mission thereby would be used as the base of operations, serving both as the channel of communication with Havana and as supply depot for whatever the terror drive would require.

At the UN, too, the ringleader of the Cuban sabotage team would have the benefit of all the experience and advice that was at the fingertips of the Soviet officers on the UN Mission staff. It would be a terrible oversight of the Russian espionage network's capability to presume that the Soviet military men at the UN had not mapped out a detailed target area long before the Soviet-Cuban plot was hatched.

In their plan we must recognize that they knew precisely what public buildings, railroad terminals, bridges, tunnels, and defense and military installations had to be destroyed for their *nervenkrieg* to be most effective.

Now that we know about it, Kudryavtsev's program for the destruction of our East Coast facilities leaves little doubt that he had the kind of guidance which can come only from a highly skilled, clandestine, psychological-warfare planning and operational unit like the Soviet military staff at the UN.

Although Kudryavtsev had organized and started his saboteur training program in a "terror school" just outside Havana, he never finished the job. At the beginning of summer, 1962, Khrushchev grew impatient with his own grand design to convert Cuba into an unvarnished Soviet military and political beachhead. The aging Kudryavtsev was not capable of handling this assignment, so back to Havana went Alexei Alekseyev, the architect of the Cuban take-over.

Alekseyev lost no time paving the way for the arrival of the advance guard of Soviet troops and "technicians" who would install the dreaded nuclear warhead rockets and missiles.

In time, historians will record how much prestige and ground in the struggle between the free world and Communism was lost by Khrushchev and gained by President Kennedy in the subsequent showdown which led to the withdrawal of the missiles and warheads and the reduction in the body of 17,000 Soviet troops which had occupied the island by the late summer of 1962.

Suffice it to say, however, that Khrushchev failed to panic or intimidate America. But in October of that year he was still trying, and the key instrument in the war of nerves was still the sabotage plot against the East Coast.

With the canny Alekseyev now running the show in Cuba, the time had come to draft the leader for the attack on the U.S. The man who would lead the team of saboteurs on their mission had to come from the band of terrorists being drilled and readied in the "terror school" on Havana's outskirts. And when Alekseyev studied the records of the students, he settled inevitably on the one who had shown the greatest talent for terror, Roberto Santiesteban y Casanova.

A little man of twenty-seven with crinkly black hair, Santiesteban was furnished with a diplomatic passport which identified him as an attaché at the Cuban Mission to the UN. When he passed through the gates at Idlewild Airport that night of October 3, 1962, with President Dorticos, the furtive-eyed Foreign Minister Raul Roa, and the other Cubans who had come up from Havana, hardly anyone among the greeters from the Soviet and Cuban Missions to the UN seemed to pay even the slightest attention to Santiesteban.

The inconspicuous little man walked briskly to one of the cars in the fleet that had come from the city to pick up the planeload of Cubans, and in a blink of an eye, he had vanished into the night with the rest of the entourage.

That was the last we saw of Santiesteban until six weeks later when he was ready to execute the lessons he was taught in the "terror school."

During all those weeks in New York, Santiesteban had huddled for hours on end with the Soviet military staff until he was thoroughly briefed on what targets he was to sabotage. The whole list had been laid out for him: Macy's department store, Grand Central Terminal, subway stations, New Jersey oil refineries . . . the works!

Time bombs would be planted in a specified critical location at each of the installations so as to cause the maximum devastation and loss of life.

It was precisely 10 o'clock of Friday night, November 16, when Santiesteban stepped out of the doorway of an apartment house on once-fashionable Riverside Drive skirting the Hudson River. It was nearly freezing and Roberto Lazaro Santiesteban y Casanova drew up his collar to protect himself against the icy winds blowing in off the river.

This was the moment. He was on his way to carry out the first ignominious assignment in the Soviet-Cuban plot to blow up vital areas of the eastern United States.

12 : The FBI Nails
the Cuban Saboteurs

ROBERTO LAZARO Santiesteban y Casanova was but one of several conspirators behind the scheme to unleash the Soviet-designed Cuban terror against the New York metropolitan area's 16,-000,000 residents. Santiesteban had laid out the plan for the others—the people he had chosen with Soviet UN military staff approval—to carry out the wholesale destruction.

As he walked along Riverside Drive heading for his official diplomatic car parked fifty feet down the street, Santiesteban stopped suddenly under the glare of a street lamp and glanced at a piece of paper he had pulled from his pocket. It held only an address: 242 West 27th Street.

This was his destination, the rendezvous point for Santiesteban and two other conspirators who would galvanize the wave of terror against the citizenry. At that address, his two handpicked accomplices were waiting. They had arrived hours earlier to prepare for the big strike. They were on the sixth floor of this grimy, unkempt commercial building in the heart of Manhattan's renowned Garment District. The 27th Street block between Seventh and Eighth Avenues is probably a classic example of the dinginess and decrepitness of this particular area of New York City. Except for the magnificent ultra-modern edifice that is the Fashion Institute of Technology directly across the street from No. 242, the block is a monotony of smoky brick structures, four to fourteen stories tall, housing an assortment of fur cutters, dress manufacturers, coat makers, and dealers in sundry other apparel goods.

As it happened, the occupant of the sixth floor of 242 West 27th Street was a manufacturer of costume jewelry, one of the chief sidelines of the garment industry. The owner of the business was José Garcia Orellana, a 42-year-old Cuban national who had been doing a modest trade with dress firms in the area, supplying them with ornaments and jeweled accouterments that go on dresses.

A hand-lettered sign on the translucent glass of the firm's only door was the lone clue to the nature of the business conducted inside. The sign read: MODEL-CRAFT COSTUME JEWELER MANUFACTURERS.

Although it was Friday night and the vast garment district was bathed in the darkness of weekend inactivity, the offices of the Model-Craft jewelry concern's loft were strangely and inexplicably busy. Lights burned brightly and two figures moved stealthily within.

One was José Garcia Orellana himself; the other was a younger man, Marino Antonio Esteban del Carmen Sueirro y Cabrera, another Cuban national who was in Garcia's employ as a "salesman." Or, at least, he had been posing as such. Actually, neither man was interested in costume jewelry—certainly not on this Friday night of November 17, 1962.

Other business was on their minds at this moment, the business of sabotage. Before them in the center of the loft was a large five-shelf, six-foot-high safe, its doors ajar. Garcia and his 22-year-old "salesman," Sueirro, stood before the vault eyeing it contents. What held their gaze was the collection of explosives and incendiaries stocked in the safe.

These were the devices that the Cuban saboteurs were going to employ in their nefarious scheme to blow up the refineries, department stores, public transportation, and other targets marked for destruction by the Havana-Moscow Red axis.

Garcia and Sueirro had waited long for this moment and now they had very little time left. Within minutes they expected to be on their way, ostensibly to target No. 1, the multimillion-dollar petroleum complex of the Humble Oil and Refining Company plant in Linden,

New Jersey. This vast sprawling empire lies some ten miles from Bayonne down the western shore of the Arthur Kill, the body of water separating New Jersey and Staten Island.

In from the sea each year come millions of barrels of crude oil from all over the world to feed the oil-hungry metropolitan area. Giant tankers and barges tie up in the Kill. Hoses swing out. The crude oil flows into the "cat plants" and is "cracked." Out through a maze of color-coded pipes into acres of tanks flow, in turn, gasoline, heating oil, industrial fuel oil, alcohol, naphtha, jet fuel, kerosene, lighter fluid, anti-freeze—the host of products that heat, power and provide amenities for our way of life.

The catalyst plants towering into the sky look like mountainous Christmas trees at night, ablaze with lights. Oil is an around-the-clock industry.

If the plot hatched by the Cuban saboteurs were to come off as planned, they would have to get inside the plant. Could they? What protective and security measures did the company have in force to guard against the danger of sabotage?

Fortunately, this was a time that Humble and a number of other refineries along the Jersey shore had just recently initiated a program of intensified security. What prompted it was the devastating saboteur strike at the refineries in Venezuela in October at the height of the Cuban crisis. It was strongly suspected—if not proven—that Cubans were responsible for the havoc wrought upon the Venezuelan plants, and the refineries in Jersey were quick to realize the potential danger to themselves.

Their first step was to triple and quadruple the police forces which patrol the endless acres of refinery grounds. At Humble, the head of plant protection, stocky, broad-shouldered John Hoff, fifty-five, wasted no time in beefing up his force. He ordered three radio cars and twenty pickup trucks on around-the-clock patrol from the instant the first explosion echoed up from the Venezuelan oilfields.

Hoff also ordered every inch of the eight-foot, barbed-wire-topped cyclone fence surrounding the 1,600-acre plant and its maze of pipes and tanks checked for holes and breaks.

"We're ready for anything," Hoff said confidently after issuing orders to one hundred and sixty key men on his force to maintain vigil.

Hoff also cautioned Humble's thousands of employees: "Be alert and report if you see anything even remotely suspicious. Don't make physical contact with strangers. Call headquarters at once."

"Headquarters" for plant protection was a radio-control room, a nerve center that picks up flash reports of everything that happens throughout the refinery. In organizing his stepped-up protection plan, Hoff also established a tie-in with the Linden police and the security task forces at the other two Linden refineries, Texaco and Cities Service.

Presumably they were ready for the Cuban saboteurs, even though they had no idea when or how they might strike, if at all. And yet the time was so perilously close. Perhaps only an hour or two away.

How could the saboteurs, even with the lessons taught them in the "terror school," begin their destruction against the plant when security alert was so high?

A look inside the vault at the Model-Craft Costume Jeweler Manufacturers on West 27th Street told the story. It virtually bulged with the familiar crenellated or pineapple-type hand grenades, large non-fragmenting cylinders of TNT detonators, incendiaries, and a whole variety of other weapons of destruction.

On the bottom shelf were all the instructions the saboteurs would need to arm and deploy the weapons in their strike; precise rules on how to spread devastation and death, even with around-the-clock guards on duty.

For example, the booklet bearing instructions on the arming and use of the detonators and incendiaries gave these suggestions:

> The detonator, because it is shaped like a pencil, will fit into a slot at the side of the incendiary proper; the latter itself is a smooth black package (about the size of a packet of four cigars) and can be concealed in the inside jacket pocket or other good hiding place without creating suspicion.
>
> Do not attach the detonator to the incendiary while you have it on your person. This process is done only when you are at your target. That is when you affix the detonator—and then push the button.
>
> The incendiary is timed to go off in approximately an hour to an hour and fifteen minutes. But before that, at exactly ten min-

utes after the detonator is depressed, the incendiary will burst into flames for about ten minutes . . . The actual explosion will not occur until the full cycle has passed . . .

Drawings, diagrams, and sketches were contained in the leaflet which showed exactly at what parts of tanks, trains, stations, buildings, and even ships the incendiary should be placed for "maximum destruction and vulnerability."

The text of the leaflet was in English and French, which suggested that the Cubans, and in all likelihood the Soviets, had obtained these weapons of sabotage from some holdover surplus stockpile that might have belonged to the French Underground during the Resistance in World War II.

There was no literature on the use of the hand grenades, but it wasn't necessary. Although very destructive and dangerous, a grenade is, nevertheless, a relatively simple device. The saboteurs could employ this tool as a last resort in the blow against the refineries. In effect, if they could not get inside the barbed-wire fence and past the security patrols, they could hurl grenades over the fence at the tanks and pipes with every reasonable chance of causing a fracture or a break which, in turn, would touch off a devastating explosion and fire.

The Cuban saboteurs had overlooked nothing.

Even as Garcia and Sueirro waited for Santiesteban to reach the office on West 27th Street, other Cuban agents at that very moment were preparing to move out and make simultaneous "death blow" strikes against the greater metropolitan area.

As Santiesteban consulted the scrap of paper in his hand now to familiarize himself with the address he was heading for, the man who was Garcia's "salesman" hurriedly left the sixth-floor loft, went downstairs, got into his car, and drove crosstown to Third Avenue and East 24th Street where he met a woman. The scene was less than ten blocks from where Judith Coplon and Valentin Gubitchev had come to the end of their trail more than a dozen years before.

The time was 10:25 p.m. and the woman Cabrera rendezvoused with was olive-skinned, pretty, and young. She was American-born Ada Maria Dritsas, twenty-six, of 204 East 25th Street. Her occupation was teacher and recreation supervisor at a social center called the Hudson Guild, 436 West 27th Street, two blocks from the loft building where the explosives and incendiary devices were stored.

Ada was waiting on the corner and when Sueirro drove up and parked at the curb on Third Avenue, Ada walked over, opened the door, and got in beside the driver. Sueirro turned off his motor and blacked his lights. There in the darkness, the two spoke quietly.

Subdued, too, was the conversation in another part of town at that precise moment. The scene for this colloquy was a comfortable, neatly furnished apartment in a building at 265 West 71st Street where over coffee José Gomez Abad, twenty-one, and his wife, Elsa Montero de Gomez Abad, twenty, were soberly discussing a plan to spread death and destruction in New York City itself.

Gomez and his wife were also part and parcel of the total Cuban-Soviet conspiracy. Like Santiesteban, they had one thing going for them that the others did not—diplomatic immunity, a wonderful escape hatch for a spy or saboteur if he should get caught. They had come to this country in the guise of employees of the Cuban Mission to the UN.

A pert, dark-eyed beauty, Elsa Montero had arrived in New York City on August 28, 1961. Fluent in English, Elsa was assigned to operate the switchboard in the Cuban UN Mission, a job which requires a trustworthy person. Elsa was just such a person, for she had been one of the staunchest supporters of Fidel Castro back in Havana. As a teenager, Elsa had fought with rifle and bayonet in the Revolution which overthrew Batista. Her assignment to the Cuban Mission was a token of Castro's gratitude to a loyal subject.

That same gratitude had gone out also to Elsa's husband, José, although at the time Castro sent him to New York, December 14, 1961, Gomez Abad had not yet met the woman who would become his wife. As a teenager, too, Gomez Abad had also carried a rifle and a belt of grenades strapped around his middle and trudged into the cities and towns to fight the hated Batista soldiers.

Mustached, curly-haired, and almost handsome, Gomez Abad joined the staff of the Cuban Delegation on his arrival from Havana. Although he held minor rank, he was noticed around the UN's corridors and cocktail lounges as a man with far greater freedom and much more spending money than befits the commonplace attaché listed in the delegation roster, as he was, on the third rung from the bottom. That wasn't smart of Gomez Abad, for that freedom and spending power have been in the past the great betrayers of an otherwise good agent.

Let us say here and now that Gomez Abad became a man to watch. As events will show, Gomez Abad had come to the UN as a key agent of Cuban espionage activity and purposely was placed in an insignificant category to give him the elbowroom needed to engage more effectively in the underground work that was his real mission.

José met Elsa soon after he arrived in New York and they fell in love and married. It cannot be doubted that he was alerted beforehand to Elsa's own importance in the Cuban conspiracy; and now with marriage they became partners in everything they had to live for. Now they could—and did—work as a team. Elsa, on the switchboard, could eavesdrop on conversations and detect any turncoats disloyal to the Communist masters in Havana; José, in turn, with his freedom to roam New York as he pleased, could round up the likely candidates for the team Santiesteban would need when he finally arrived in the city to launch the sabotage-and-terror plan.

It was, in fact, Gomez Abad who had things in readiness for Santiesteban. Gomez Abad was the one who found custom jeweler Garcia and salesman Sueirro and recruited them as key figures in the sabotage plan. He liked what Garcia and Sueirro offered.

Garcia and Sueirro both had extensive backgrounds in pro-Castro organizing activities in New York City. Both belonged to the "Movimiento del 26 de Julio" or 26th of July Movement, the basic group on which Castroism has been built. It was on July 26, 1953, that Fidel Castro led an attack on Batista forces at Santiago. Seventy of 165 attackers were slain, and the revolution-bent doctor was sentenced to fifteen years in prison. He was subsequently freed in an amnesty and deported to Mexico. From there he returned to lead the revolution which overthrew the Batista regime.

Garcia and Sueirro had not only frequented but were officers of the Casa Cuba Club, one of the most notorious gathering places in New York for Castro sympathizers. Sueirro was treasurer and Garcia president of the club located at 691 Columbus Avenue on Manhattan's West Side. It was in this club that the plot to hijack American airliners and fly them to Cuba was hatched, but the New York City police, acting on the FBI's information, raided the club and thwarted the plot.

The two candidates for the sabotage ring also were active in the affairs of the Fair Play for Cuba Committee, which, because of its attitude on the Cuban controversy, had come under the scrutiny of the Senate Internal Security Subcommittee in 1961.

And now Garcia was already recruited into the ring and at this precise moment, 10:25 p.m., he was waiting alone in his sixth-floor office for the arrival of Santiesteban.

Santiesteban by now had folded the piece of paper he had consulted for directions to Garcia's place downtown, and had begun to walk toward his car. The wind was still blowing briskly from the river all along Riverside Drive.

At Third Avenue and East 24th Street, Antonio Sueirro Cabrera and Ada Maria Dritsas may not have felt the chill of that wind as they sat in their car, but they were impelled suddenly by an urgency to breeze along. Wherever it was they had to go, the time had come. Sueirro turned on his headlights and started the motor.

Up in the apartment shared by the Cuban Mission's newlyweds, José Gomez Abad and Elsa Montero de Gomez Abad, that same imperativeness to move on started them toward the door of their apartment. They turned out the lamps and, with José leading the way, came out of the apartment into the lighted hallway.

Incredibly now, although none yet knew of it, each participant in the Cuban sabotage plot to destroy our eastern seaboard had for weeks before begun to head into the center of a massive web, a web painstakingly woven by the Federal Bureau of Investigation. And at this very minute—10:25 on the night of Friday, November 16—the web was fully spun. The time had come to close in on every one of the plotters.

The deserted sidewalk along Riverside Drive, where Santiesteban walked toward his car, suddenly sparked to life as a half dozen G-men issued forth from the shadows of building doorways, emerged from alleyways, sprang from behind parked cars, and in quick formation formed a ring around the Cuban saboteur.

"What you want?" Santiesteban cried excitedly in his broken English as fire flashed from his angry eyes at the sight of what he surely must have guessed was the law.

"FBI," said one of the agents curtly. "We want you to come along with us."

Unknown to the Cuban conspirators, the FBI had greatly increased its vigil of Cubans in this country, particularly in the New York and Florida areas, because of the grave deterioration of U.S.–Cuba relations. The Cuban Mission to the UN had become the prime target of FBI surveillance. And from this outpost the G-men were able to detect the first signals of the sabotage plot almost from the moment it was conceived. Then it was simply a matter of baiting the trap—and waiting.

The words of the FBI man had barely been uttered to this first of the Cuban saboteurs trapped, when Santiesteban lurched, grabbed the G-man around the throat, and hurled him backward. Then, before the other agents could move against the Cuban, he dug his hand into his pocket, pulled out a wallet, and from it took a piece of paper.

With a seemingly practiced smooth, swift motion, he rammed the paper into his mouth and began to chew it. But one of the G-men lunged at Santiesteban and knocked him off balance. The others closed in and took a grip on him. The first agent took hold of Santiesteban's jaw and with the help of another G-man extricated the saliva-soaked paper.

The paper contained a formula for a highly secret, powerful explosive that was to be used in the sabotage operations. Its mixture constituted five volatile ingredients that included nitroglycerine, phosphates, and soda.

Santiesteban wasn't going to give up without a fight, even though the secret formula had been seized. Cursing shrilly in Spanish, he hurled punches and kicked high in a furious attempt to escape. But the six G-men were too much even for a man as wild as Santiesteban. He was subdued, but in the process he had suffered bruises and cuts on his face and left eye which later prompted him to protest "brutality methods" by the FBI. Luckily for Santiesteban, he never pulled the fully loaded automatic Mauser he was packing in his inside jacket pocket.

There was no violence elsewhere as other G-men moved in simultaneously to close the ring against the rest of Santiesteban's saboteur team.

Antonio Sueirro Cabrera and Ada Maria Dritsas were seized on their corner before the driver could release the brake and shift into drive. Things happened so swiftly there on Third Avenue that not even the few passersby at that late hour had any idea what was happening. No less so, perhaps, than Antonio and Ada who were so overwhelmed by the sudden appearance of agents around their car that they sat staring blankly in stunned silence.

There were G-men to the left and G-men to the right, and without a single wasted motion, they had the door on either side of the car opened and the two suspects by the arms. Just as swiftly, they packed them into an FBI squad car and headed uptown to the FBI's regional headquarters at 201 East 69th Street, where Santiesteban also was being taken.

At that very moment, too, José Gomez Abad and Elsa Montero de Gomez Abad had stepped into the hallway and were in the process of locking their door when, like the others, they were stunned and speechless as FBI men broke from cover under the stairwell and surrounded the pair.

The words, "You are under arrest!" spoken by one of the G-men prompted a sharp and sarcastic rejoinder from Gomez Abad after he had recovered from the initial surprise of the entrapment.

"How you going to make it stick?" he snapped. "We have diplomatic immunity—you know that?"

"Just come along with us," replied the agent. The husband and wife saboteur team were escorted downstairs and, like the others, taken to FBI headquarters.

Only one member of the sabotage ring was yet to be accounted for. But time had run out on José Garcia Orellana, too, and inexorably he was being sucked into the trap of his making.

When the door of his office on West 27th Street opened suddenly, José might have been expected to believe Santiesteban was arriving a few minutes early. But spies and saboteurs work on a split-second schedule, and if Garcia Orellana had thought Santiesteban had just come in, he could not be much credit to his profession. As it turned out, he wasn't.

"So early, Roberto?" called José from the vault where he was sorting hand grenades into neat piles along the fourth shelf.

But the ear-splitting silence followed by the sudden and hurried shuffling of several pairs of feet prompted José to wheel around in stark astonishment. The surge of five neatly attired men in overcoats and guns in hand told José the jig was up even before one of the agents announced crisply, "FBI. You are under arrest."

As two agents put handcuffs on Garcia Orellana, the other three G-men examined the vault. In addition to the grenades, detonators, and incendiaries, they found two pistols, three loaded pistol clips, and a quantity of TNT. More grenades and detonators were found secreted in an old 42-inch fluorescent lighting fixture that was tilted against a wall. The G-men uncovered the material under the curved hood, hidden in with the wiring and transformer.

Garcia, who had arrived in the United States in 1941 and became naturalized by virtue of service in the army during World War II, was hustled downstairs, and he, too, was taken to FBI headquarters.

The FBI had carried out its crackdown so efficiently that not a word about the arrests was heard until the next morning.

The official announcement came jointly from the U.S. Mission and the FBI at 11 a.m. and it pointed to a sabotage and terrorist plot of staggering scope, a plot that bore all the earmarks of careful masterminding and preparation by experts in possession of both the resources and secret channels of information essential to the success of the mission.

Except that they hadn't counted on the effectiveness and efficiency of the FBI.

The sheer audacity of the scheme to blow up installations paled even the infamous design of evil aimed at America by Hitler who personally had approved a plan to land Nazi saboteurs on U.S. soil by submarine in June, 1942. German U-boats had landed eight men in rubber life rafts on the East Coast—four at Amagansett, Long Island, and four in Florida, but a tip to the FBI had led to a quick roundup of the would-be saboteurs before they could carry out their assignments. Six were executed within two months; the two others were sent to prison.

Immediately following the joint announcement of the arrests of the Cuban saboteurs, the U.S. Mission to the UN summoned correspondents to inform them that a note of protest had been delivered by Ambassador Stevenson to the Cuban UN Delegation and to Secretary General U Thant. The United States demanded that José Gomez Abad and his wife, Elsa, be recalled immediately to Havana. Both were accused of active participation in the sabotage and terror conspiracy, and were specifically named as the ones who supplied the explosives and incendiaries to the ring.

The evidence of this was the address found on some of the packages in which the contraband came, 155 East 44th Street, the home of the Cuban Mission to the UN.

Stevenson's note sidestepped the customary diplomatic niceties and went straight to the point, saying: "José Gomez Abad and Elsa Montero de Gomez actively participated as co-conspirators in a plot against the security of the United States. Their activities are a gross violation of their status as members of a permanent mission to the UN. The U. S. Government considers this criminal activity a most flagrant abuse of the privileges of residence. The permanent mission of Cuba is requested to effect the immediate departure of Jose Gomez Abad and Elsa Montero de Gomez from the U.S."

Carlos Lechuga, the Cuban Ambassador to the UN, pilgrimaged hastily and dutifully to U Thant's office to protest in pain against the "grossly unfair accusations" by the U.S. Thant was busy elsewhere. But an aide listened politely. Lechuga then faced the correspondents, aired his outrage, then stalked out of the UN Building.

Soon Moscow Radio was protesting that the U.S. was harassing Cuban nationals in this country with "trumped-up" charges of sabotage. It accused the U.S. of trampling on the sanctity of treaty agreements with the UN by making Cuban diplomats scapegoats of its propaganda hate campaign against Castro.

Pravda and *Izvestia* joined shortly after and Havana Radio added its protest by calling the arrests "a Yankee maneuver to offset the recent arrest of a United States Central Intelligence agent in Cuba who tried to blow up a mining installation . . ."

The Cubans also raised an outcry at the arrest of the master saboteur, Roberto Lazaro Santiesteban y Casanova, but it was a weak protest by contrast to the complaint lodged in the case of the Gomez Abads. It seems Santiesteban had indeed arrived on a diplomatic passport, but the State Department had held up his papers in processing them for reasons it did not reveal. Thus Santiesteban, technically and legally, could not claim to enjoy diplomatic immunity.

Three days later, on Tuesday, November 20, Gomez Abad and his wife unobtrusively boarded an Aeronaves de Mexico jet bound for Havana via Mexico City. They were returned home under the protective cloak of diplomatic immunity.

Meanwhile, Santiesteban, Marino Antonio Esteban Del Carmen Sueirro y Cabrera, and José Garcia Orellano were put in jail; Santiesteban was held in $250,000 bail and the others in $100,000 each. Maria Dritsas, the teacher who was with Cabrera in the car, was released after extensive questioning. Authorities said she had no hand in the plot, nor even knew about it. She had merely met Cabrera "socially," it was explained.

On Wednesday, November 21, the trio was indicted by a Federal grand jury in New York for sabotage and conspiracy, and also was accused of having acted as unauthorized agents of a foreign government.

After the hearings in court in which all three entered "not guilty" pleas, the case quickly seemed to be forgotten. Nothing more was heard about the Cuban saboteurs for the next four months, except for one unconfirmed report that Attorney General Robert F. Kennedy had visited Santiesteban in the Federal House of Detention in New York City to discuss a "trade" with him. At the time the Government was negotiating with Cuba for the release of U.S. nationals and others involved in the calamitous Bay of Pigs invasion. There had been talk, too, that besides the drugs and medical supplies that Castro was seeking in the exchange, he also wanted release of the three saboteurs.

On April 22, 1963, the release became a reality. The three Cubans were given their freedom to return to Cuba. Along with them, the Government threw into the bargain a fourth Cuban prisoner, Francisco "The Hook" Molina del Rio, a Fidel Castro supporter who accidentally killed a 9-year-old girl, Magdalena Urdaneta, of Caracas, Venezuela, during a shooting fray with anti-Castro Cubans in a New York City restaurant in 1959. At the Federal Government's request, New York Governor Nelson A. Rockefeller commuted Molina's sentence of twenty years to life, "with the express condition that Molina del Rio be deported and never again re-enter the United States. If he does so, he is automatically deemed an escaped convict and compelled to serve the balance of his sentence."

The prisoners' release was granted on the ground "that the State Department had suggested to the Department of Justice that it would be in the national interest if the three defendants were released."

There was a provision that Santiesteban and Sueirro leave the country immediately. No stipulation was made in jeweler Garcia's case. But Garcia, who had become a naturalized citizen because of his service in the U.S. Army, elected to go to Cuba with his wife, Josephine, and their two daughters, aged twelve and seven years.

On the night of April 21, Santiesteban, Sueirro, Molina, Garcia Orellana and his family were taken under guard to Idlewild Airport and escorted aboard an Immigration Department plane bound for Florida; they were transferred there to a Cuban airliner that took them back to Havana.

In the aftermath of the prisoners' release, it was learned that Castro had brought up the names of the prisoners during discussions with James B. Donovan, the New York attorney who had worked the Abel-Powers swap and was then negotiating for the release of the Bay of Pigs invaders. Donovan, who since then has gone on to become president of the New York City Board of Education, reported the conversation to officials in Washington. It was then decided to release the three saboteurs and the killer of the little Venezuelan girl.

Special circumstances dictated Molina's release. But in the case of the saboteurs, once again, the United Nations with its built-in protection became the shield and the umbrella under which Communist espionage agents and terrorists can function and do function with immunity in this country.

In the aftermath of the FBI's quick work in smashing the sabotage ring and the disclosure of its existence by Ambassador Stevenson, a great public cry of rage was lofted against the Cuban UN Mission. Angry throngs milled truculently at the Mission's doors and demands rang out everywhere that the Cuban UN emissaries be summarily deported. Less drastically, some newspapers urged that travel restrictions be imposed on the Cuban UN representatives as they are on UN delegates from the Soviet Union and satellite nations. Even General John B. Medaris, retired chief of the Army Space Program, lent his weighty voice to the appeal.

In the end, the same travel restrictions applying to Soviet bloc countries were imposed on the Cuban Delegation. But under the sanctuary of diplomatic immunity, New York remained as fecund as ever for espionage and sabotage activity.

As the liberal New York *Post* editorialized: ". . . unfortunately, for every group exposed, it is reasonable to assume another may be escaping detection.'"

13 : Soviets "Buy" the GOP Candidate

ELECTION posters such as these were tacked on wooden telephone poles, pasted on cast-iron street light standards, strung on traffic stanchions, and displayed prominently in hundreds of locations in the Howard Beach section of Queens during the fall of 1962, a time when a particularly vigorous political campaign was being waged in that area of New York City.

Richard A. Flink, a mere twenty-seven years of age, was matching youth and ambition against his rival's maturity and experience. As a Republican, Flink was also fighting upstream against a strong current of Democratic voters who comprised the political power in the 12th Assembly District. Yet Flink was eager and determined to unseat the incumbent assemblyman, J. Lewis Fox.

Flink had one thing going for him that Fox did not—Flink's campaign was being financed, in part, by the Soviet Union.

Incredible as it may appear, two Russian employees at the United Nations had managed to work their influences on this young Republican political hopeful until they were certain he was on their side and convinced that he was going to toe the line of Communism in subtle but substantial ways once he was elected. For this they contributed a total of three thousand dollars toward his expenses in the Assembly race, and Flink took the money willingly, even eagerly.

But Flink's acceptance of the three thousand and his assurance to the Reds that he would espouse Kremlin propaganda in speeches he delivered before various organizations did not constitute a traitorous act. For Richard Flink was definitely not a traitor at all, but a patriotic American who, as the FBI has put it, made a notable contribution in aborting the first known attempt by UN-based Soviet agents to infiltrate the nation's politics.

Richard Flink was born in 1934 to parents who, although immigrants, had been in the United States many years; his father came from Staraya Russa, Russia, in 1906, his mother from Vienna a few years later. After Richard, there was a girl, Yvette. The parents eventually moved into a comfortable apartment at 245 West 107th Street on Manhattan's upper West Side, home for Richard Flink for a good many years of his life.

Richard attended Public School 165 on 109th Street between Broadway and Amsterdam Avenue, achieved a superior scholastic standing that won him admittance to highly rated Stuyvesant High School. He graduated with honors, was accepted by Brandeis University in Massachusetts. In 1955 he received his degree, came back to New York, then enrolled at New York University Law School at Washington Square. He went to live in the Law School dormitory at 33 Washington Square West, opposite the college. As a student, he worked part time in the New York office of U.S. Attorney S. Hazard Gillespie.

By 1959 Flink had his law degree and prepared to take the New York State Bar examination in June of that year. With a friend, whom we shall call Joseph Seldrich, Flink crammed for the exam. He studied at the NYU Law Library on the Square along with Seldrich, a graduate of Amherst College and Harvard Law School.

It was a day in late June, 1959, when Seldrich mentioned to Flink that he had been to the New York Coliseum to see the Soviet Trade

Commission Fair, and while there had met one of the officials, a Vladimir Orlov, the head of the exposition's literary section.

"He heard so much about Greenwich Village," Seldrich told Flink. "He wants to come down and be shown around."

Flink knew the Village well. He had lived, those years at NYU, in its very midst. He knew every section, every landmark, every place of interest in that world-renowned community which adjoins Washington Square.

"Will you show Orlov around?" Seldrich wanted to know.

"Certainly," agreed Flink without a second thought. "Bring him down."

The following week Seldrich escorted Orlov to Washington Square and Flink took them on a tour of the Village. When it was over, Orlov couldn't thank Flink enough.

"You must come up to the exhibit and see some of the interesting things we have in my country," Orlov said. Flink agreed he would, and as a courtesy Orlov gave him passes.

The young law student told of his meeting with Orlov and the Russian's invitation to the Soviet exhibition at the Coliseum to a young man whom we shall identify as Milton Chernik. Chernik, another of his friends, was at once fascinated by Flink's encounter with the Russian.

"Why don't you invite him to my cocktail party?" asked Chernik. "I think the crowd would enjoy meeting someone from the Soviet Union."

Flink said he'd ask. A few days later he went to the Coliseum, met Orlov who greeted him warmly, and was given the red carpet treatment as he was taken through the Soviet exposition to view a fashion show, an agricultural demonstration, several scientific exhibits, and a literary display which Orlov himself had charge of. Then Orlov introduced Flink to another Soviet fair official, Gnadi Beckerov.

Flink ultimately tendered Orlov the invitation to the cocktail party at Chernik's apartment three nights hence.

"I won't be able to go myself," Orlov apologized. "But perhaps Gnadi can attend." He turned to the other Russian.

"It will be a pleasure," Gnadi Beckerov smiled.

Arrangements were made to meet after the exhibit closed the night of the party. That was at 10 p.m. On the appointed evening when

Flink went to the corner of Central Park South and West 59th Street, just across from the Coliseum in Columbus Circle, he found Orlov waiting. But not alone. With him was another Russian who was introduced to Flink as Yuri A. Mishukov, a translator in the UN Office of Conference Services.

"Is it all right if Yuri comes along, too?" asked Beckerov.

Flink said that would be just fine. The party was in an apartment in the Peter Cooper Village housing development in the east 20's. But Flink soon found himself in an embarrassing situation. The guests at Milton Chernik's party appeared to take a sordid delight in ridiculing the Russian visitors. They criticized the Soviet Union's political philosophies, poked fun at Premier Khrushchev, and, in general, made the Russians' visit an unpleasant experience. Because he felt responsible for their plight since he had brought them there, Flink stepped into some of the arguments in the role of an arbitrator. His friend, Joseph Seldrich, was also at the party and he, too, sided with Flink in mediating some of the more heated discussions.

The party ended around midnight. Flink and Seldrich accepted Beckerov's offer of a ride home. Mishukov went along. Flink was dropped off first at the NYU dormitory, then Seldrich was taken home.

Flink heard nothing more from the Russians as he waded into his bar exams, passed them, and became a lawyer. Flink then left his student-attorney job at the U.S. Attorney's office and began the ritual familiar to most young men about to launch their careers, the ritual known as "pounding the sidewalks." But for Flink, a personable, easy-going type with an imposing six-foot-four, 210-pound physique, his job-hunting days were neither long nor unpleasant. Within a couple of weeks he landed a position with Bass & Friend, a law firm at 342 Madison Avenue in Manhattan.

It was now well into the summer of 1959, and despite his new job, Flink decided he'd be able to take on the additional burden of studies for an advanced law degree, his master's. Accordingly, he continued to live at the NYU dormitory while he carried out his twin responsibilities as attorney and student.

With his days and nights filled with work, studies, and now frequent dates with a pretty brunette who would soon become Mrs. Lois Flink, summer swept by and September was soon upon him.

Yuri Mishukov, the Soviet UN employee, chose that month to re-establish contact with his young acquaintance from the party of that previous June, and on a morning just beginning to be tinged with the crispness of autumn, the Russian phoned Flink at the dormitory and suggested they meet over lunch.

Flink talked cordially to Mishukov, but the telephone call actually puzzled him. He wondered idly why the Russian wanted to see him again, yet agreed to the luncheon date, more out of curiosity than anything else.

The two men met at the reception desk on the first floor of the UN Building, then repaired to the delegates' dining room on the fourth floor.

Mishukov was the very embodiment of the good host. As Flink recalled the incident later to these authors, the jovial Soviet welcomed him to the UN, spoke a while of its gargantuan operations and of his own job as an interpreter, and all in all seemed in absolutely relaxed good spirits. The conversation was light, interesting.

"He told me about his family and asked me questions about my family," Flink recounted. "He wanted to know where I went to school, what I studied, what my interests and aims were. He seemed very interested in me as a person. I answered him and, of course, asked him about himself—you know, the same sort of questions. He was quite friendly through it all.

"Then he inquired about my political beliefs, whether I was a Republican or a Democrat. He seemed interested in the fact that I'd worked in the U.S. Attorney's office. I told him I'd done mostly corporate work there and he wanted to know when I left and why, and if I liked it there and a lot of things like that. There was nothing cagey or underhanded about him. It was all open talk and entirely sociable."

After lunch, the two parted with some vague remarks about seeing each other again. It was now mid-afternoon and Flink started walking west on 42nd Street toward Grand Central Terminal and the IRT subway. But as he strolled in the waning afternoon sun, he began reflecting on the entire incident.

Why, he wondered, had Mishukov called him? Could there be anything sinister behind it?

Flink thought a while and tried to dismiss the idea. Yet something kept nagging at his thoughts and, as he reached the subway, the bright, affable young attorney decided on the spur of the moment to talk it over with a good friend at the U.S. Attorney's office, Assistant U.S. Attorney Arthur Savage, who had been Flink's immediate superior in his days there as a student attorney.

Savage listened while Flink unfolded the events in their proper sequence. At the end of his recitation, Flink asked: "Well, Art, what do you think?"

Savage gave some thought to the question before replying.

"I'd say it's a little funny, all right, but I don't see anything, well, diabolic in it. Still . . ."

"Still what?"

"Still, I think to be on the safe side we'd better call the FBI about it. They'll know how to evaluate it. They can tell you better than I what to do."

Savage made the call. An agent listened while Savage filled him in on Flink's experience with the Soviets. The FBI man suggested that Flink meet him outside the NYU dormitory the following day at noon.

The agent easily recognized the towering, rugged-looking Flink. He introduced himself and then escorted the young attorney across the street into Washington Square Park. The sprawling green oasis in the center of one of the city's great cultural and business hubs was a-swarm with NYU students, with a scattering of bearded beatniks, with elderly Italian-speaking neighborhood residents from the large Italian-American settlement in the Village, and with dozens of young children from the new high-rise apartments sprouting throughout the area. The FBI man and Flink found a bench on the quieter west side of the park, and Flink, with occasional questions and prodding from the agent, recapitulated the entire episode with the Soviet officials in detail. The G-man took some occasional notes.

"What should I do?" Flink asked curiously after he had told all there was to relate.

"If he calls again and makes another date, meet him," the FBI man advised simply.

"And then?"

"Just let us know what happens. Call from a pay phone . . ."

Marveling somewhat at the crisp, economical way of the FBI, Flink departed not quite sure what was happening to him, uncertain of what lay ahead, but above all curious and determined to see it all through wherever it led.

Flink waited with high anticipation for Mishukov's next summons even though he had no guarantee there would be one. But there was; it came about ten days later.

"How about lunch?" the now familiar voice asked after the preliminary greetings. Flink agreed readily.

"At the reception desk again," Mishukov said, "and then we'll go up to the lounge. All right?" That was just what Flink wanted.

They met a few days later, during the first week of October. Flink, as he had been instructed to do, cleared the meeting with the FBI.

At lunch, Mishukov was cordial, in good spirits, filled with light, small banter. Flink matched Mishukov's mood and loquacious animation. But as the conversation continued, Flink noticed the tenor changing.

"He began to seek out my feelings about Russia," Flink recalled later, "and to find out if I was sympathetic to Khrushchev. He asked me what I thought about his recent visit to the United States and his talks with President Eisenhower. He tried to find out in general my feelings toward Soviet-American relations. I didn't indicate one way or another too strongly how I felt because I was keeping in mind the advice I'd gotten from the FBI that I had to play up to Mishukov. Personally, I had very strong anti-Soviet feelings because of their anti-Semitic policies."

Mishukov's conversation now ranged over much of what they'd talked about at the earlier luncheon. He again touched on the kind of work Flink was doing now and what he had done when he was working in the U.S. Attorney's office.

Flink restated that his assignment in Foley Square had to do for the most part with corporate law and matters dealing with such institutions as the Department of Commerce, the Small Business Administration, and the Business Advisory Council.

Mishukov finally asked Flink what his real ambition in life was. Flink replied, "I've been thinking about entering politics." According to Flink, "Mishukov's antenna went up with that."

The Russian asked what kind of politics.

"Well, I'd be interested in the City Council, or perhaps the State

Assembly, at first," Flink admitted with a trace of modesty. "You know how it is in politics—you have to crawl before you can walk."

Mishukov was visibly excited as Flink talked on about his political aspirations. "Good, good! Are you taking any steps toward doing anything about it?"

Flink said he hadn't yet, that he was still just thinking about taking that direction into politics. But, as Flink remembered, Mishukov emphasized again how marvelous he thought the idea was and urged Flink to "get on with it."

The luncheon ended on the same friendly note as the first one had, with Mishukov repeating his invitation for another date sometime soon.

After leaving the UN, Flink walked west on 42nd Street to Fifth Avenue and entered a public pay phone. He dialed the FBI and spoke to the same agent he'd met in Washington Square Park. This time, after hearing Flink's account of his last conversation with Mishukov, the agent asked the young attorney to hold on while he summoned his superior to the phone. The incident, it appeared, was escalating into something a lot more serious. Flink went over the subject matter once more in detail and again received instructions to continue his meetings with Mishukov and to report them back to the FBI promptly.

Over the next four months, he met Mishukov regularly, often dining with him at the United Nations. But Mishukov soon began suggesting a variety of restaurants, and they went to such places as the Brass Rail in Brooklyn, Patricia Murphy's Candlelight Restaurant in Yonkers, and other famed Manhattan landmarks such as Scott's, Churchill's, the Beer Pub on Third Avenue, the Long Bar, and Figaro's all-night coffee house in Greenwich Village.

In February Flink completed his studies for his master's degree in law and left the dormitory at NYU to go and live with his parents in upper Manhattan. A month later he told Mishukov at one of their get-togethers that he planned to marry his 22-year-old fiancée in June. Mishukov congratulated him heartily and wished him luck and happiness. Together they drank a toast to the upcoming wedding.

All the while, of course, Flink was in constant touch with the FBI, reporting fully on each meeting he had with the youthful Soviet translator. And with each report Flink became increasingly puzzled about Mishukov's motives. Where was it all leading? So far, across nearly a full year, their relationship had been entirely social, and, from the FBI's considered point of view, entirely proper. Was there nothing more to it?

Flink was still puzzled by the whole aspect of the Russian's aggressive friendship when Mishukov made what Flink considered the first move toward something that brushed against the edge of impropriety.

"He told me that his translator's job was only temporary," Flink related to the authors. "He said he was hoping for a bigger job, something with a diplomatic rank. And to prepare himself for it, he said, he was taking post-graduate work at a Russian university. He asked if I could help him with his thesis which dealt with 'American enterprise.' Specifically, he wanted information about why the Business Advisory Council was no longer with the Department of Commerce. He asked for several Department of Commerce pamphlets. He wanted certain specific information about the Commerce Department's dealings with American businesses. From the material he wanted, I knew he was familiar with the Commerce Department's functions. Since I had worked in the U.S. Attorney's office and my job dealt mainly with the things he was asking about, he thought it would be easy for me to get the pamphlets and the other information."

After checking with the FBI and getting clearance, Flink did exactly as Mishukov asked. He obtained the information and printed material the Russian wanted and delivered it all to him. Then nothing was requested of Flink for a while.

In June, 1960, Richard married Lois in West Hempstead, Long Island, and the young newlyweds set up house in the rambling Lindenwood Gardens Co-operative Apartments in Howard Beach, Queens. Their apartment was at 155-24 84th Street.

Soon afterward, Flink left Bass & Friend and entered a law partnership with Edward Kaplan at 160 Broadway in downtown Manhattan, but he continued, nevertheless, to have those occasional luncheon or dinner meetings with Mishukov.

As the months went by, Flink again was confronted with occasional requests for information that would help Mishukov with his "thesis," but the Soviet visitor was now prodding Flink more and more to enter politics. It became, in fact, his favorite theme.

And then during the winter of 1960, Flink joined the Lincoln Republican Club in Ozone Park, a nearby community in Queens. After a few months, Mishukov's questions began targeting in on Flink's club, the people in it, the political structure of the community, the backgrounds of certain politicians and officeholders.

"He asked a lot of questions about the organizations of various state and federal agencies, too," Flink later reported, "and how to go about applying for membership."

About this time, Mishukov offered Flink some legal work to do for the Soviet Mission, involving the lease for the new building the Russians had purchased on East 67th Street, which was to become their new home.

Flink, to be sure, would be paid for his work. And, as promised, he was. The first payment was $200. When it was turned over to Flink, he was asked to put his signature to a receipt for the money. Flink signed.

"Now they figured they had me hooked," Flink told us. "With the receipt, they could force me to do more work for them, or use it to ruin me if I failed to co-operate with them."

No such hazard really existed, since Flink had been working closely all along with the FBI.

Additional legal work Flink did for the Russians brought him a total of another $300, and with each payment Flink signed a receipt.

By the spring of 1962, Flink, with his outgoing personality, his natural good looks, his quick wit, his youth, his pretty wife usually at his side, his high intelligence, had matured into a potential, if not eminently acceptable GOP candidate for the State Assembly from the 12th Assembly District.

All this while, however, Flink was struggling with a problem at home. He had told Lois even while she was his fiancée that he was in some kind of undercover work for the FBI and that it had to do with the United Nations and espionage, but he never explained it further to her, not even after they were married.

Lois was naturally curious but, more than that, she was becoming increasingly nervous and worried about her husband's continued association with the Russians.

Mishukov finally asked Flink point-blank if he was going to run for office. Flink said he would like to, but that he didn't know if he could afford to finance a campaign, particularly a dynamic campaign such as would be required against an incumbent Democrat in a Democratic stronghold.

"I just don't know if I'll be able to scrape up enough money for it," Flink informed Mishukov. "I'll have to do some deep thinking about it."

Mishukov put his hand on Flink's arm and patted it affectionately.

"We may be able to help," Mishukov said, eyeing the young attorney closely. "Just work on it—get the nomination."

The FBI also appeared to favor Flink's candidacy, but for another reason. It wanted to see just how far the Soviets would go in "helping" him attain the goal they seemed to have their sights set on.

Flink's magnetism and other attributes landed him the nomination in June of 1962 and he embarked at once on an underdog campaign to wrest the Assembly seat from J. Lewis Fox.

At his next meeting with Mishukov, on June 19, the Russian hit the young politician with the very proposition the FBI had been anticipating.

"My superiors," the Russian said softly, "have decided to help finance your campaign."

And as he spoke, Mishukov pulled from his pocket a thick wad of crisp ten dollar bills, adding up to one thousand dollars.

"This is to start you off," he said. "But there is a condition . . ."
Mishukov reached into his attaché case and withdrew a book. It was Nikita Khrushchev's political treatise, *For Victory in the Peaceful Competition with Capitalism.*

"Read this," Mishukov advised firmly. "You'll get an idea on our thinking."

Then Mishukov laid down the rules of the game. He told Flink that he was to espouse the Red line whenever he could in speeches on housing, welfare, state and federal aid, on trade with the Soviet Union, and in a dozen other areas of social reform and political thinking.

Furthermore, Mishukov ruled, Flink was to provide more detailed information on government agencies, politicians, and most of all—the developing ideology of the Republican Party and its practical application by the GOP's national high command.

"We want to see particularly the monthly newsletter sent out by your Speaker of the Assembly [Joseph A.] Carlino from Albany . . ."

In late June, Mishukov met Flink in Longchamps Restaurant in the Empire State Building and told him that his UN assignment was over, that he was leaving for Moscow. Flink had expected this. Mishukov had given no hint of his impending return to the USSR, but the FBI had warned Flink to expect the well-known "switch" soon. Now that the preliminaries were over, Mishukov would be replaced, the FBI said, by a "stronger" man, someone considerably higher than Mishukov in the Communist Party councils.

Mishukov told Flink his new contact would be Yuri V. Zaitsev, a 38-year-old political affairs officer in the UN Department of Political and Security Council Affairs.

Twice during July—on the 10th and again the 31st—Zaitsev met Flink. On each occasion he gave the campaigning young politician a brand new package of one thousand dollars in ten dollar bills for his campaign expenses. Each time Flink had to sign a receipt.

By the middle of August, however, the pressure was beginning to build unbearably for Flink and for his wife. Flink was finding it virtually impossible to run on a Republican ticket and keep the Russians happy by harping along Communist lines, a position he always managed to avoid taking. Yet he never knew who was in the audience checking to see whether he was doing what he was being paid by the Russians to do.

On August 18, 1962, Dick Flink went to the FBI and told them it was impossible any longer to play a double agent. He wanted to devote his full energies to a genuine campaign for the State Assembly without the burdensome yoke that his contradictory double life had lowered on him. The masquerade, he announced reluctantly, would have to end. The FBI agreed. Flink was directed not to respond to any further Soviet contacts.

Then on September 15, much to Flink's surprise, Attorney General Robert F. Kennedy exposed the entire plot and the bizarre three-year split existence led by the young attorney.

From Washington, Kennedy disclosed the fantastic plot in detail and gave it its due importance by labeling it the first known attempt by the Soviet agents at the UN to infiltrate American politics. At the same time, he praised the tough, demanding double role played by Richard A. Flink, a young man who, for three years, had been an adroit counterspy performing a deft and patriotic piece of work for the FBI.

Simultaneously Ambassador Adlai Stevenson delivered a note to the Secretary General's office, declaring the now-departed Mishukov and the still-present Zaitsev personae non grata. Zaitsev left within two days.

At Richard Flink's home, Lois, by now the mother of a 14-month-old daughter, sighed with relief.

"It was an incredible experience," she said somberly. "I'm glad it's over." Then, smiling, she quipped to reporters, "You don't know how hard it is for a woman to keep a secret for three years."

As for Richard Flink, the undercover work and the furious political campaigning he did for the State Assembly, together added up to the most exhilarating experience of his young life.

He was up late into the night on Election Day, 1962, and, with his child in bed, his wife at his side, the Russians gone, and the praise of the Attorney General still vibrating in his ears, Flink watched himself lose the election to the favored Democratic incumbent.

Flink felt badly, even though he had known the odds he was bucking. But he also was aware of a deep satisfaction and pride, for he had made a vital and patriotic contribution to his country.

Richard A. Flink was a winner—even in defeat.

14 : The United States Sailor
Who Fell for the Line

NELSON CORNELIUS DRUMMOND dislikes his nickname, "Bulldog," but it doesn't make much difference any more. He's simply "Drummond" when anyone wants to talk to him, and there aren't many who do. Even in prison, even among the dregs of society, even among killers, rapists, degenerates, kidnappers, and thugs of every description, everyone despises a traitor.

"Bulldog" Drummond moves like a gray solitary phantom these days in the caged microcosm of New York's Federal House of Detention* that has been his world since August 15, 1963, when a Federal jury found him guilty and a judge sentenced him to life imprisonment for what the court termed a "most awful crime," the "heinous" crime of conspiring to spy against his country, of selling highly secret documents to the Soviet Union even while he was wearing the proud uniform of a U.S. Navy yeoman.

When he cadges an occasional cigarette, when he stands in line for meals, when he turns out each morning for work and retires in the silent evening to his cell, Bulldog Drummond tries desperately to win

---

* Drummond was confined to the Federal House of Detention pending outcome of his appeal. If he loses he will be transferred to a Federal penitentiary to serve out his life sentence.

some sign of friendship from the other prisoners, but his plaintive, almost whining appeals are uniformly turned away by everyone.

Perhaps that more than anything else—the shame, the confinement for life, the loss of citizenship, the private nightmares in the dead of night—perhaps more than all these the total rejection by his fellow man is Nelson Drummond's greatest punishment. And it all began, he tries to tell everyone, it all began, really, so innocently . . .

It was in London in 1957, while Navy Yeoman 1/C Nelson Cornelius Drummond, a tall, 27-year-old, husky Negro, a native of Baltimore, Maryland, was stationed in the British capital as an administrative clerk at the U.S. Naval Base. He worked in the section that housed classified papers dealing with electronics equipment, weapons systems, and other technical data pertaining to U.S. and NATO military defenses.

Even then, Drummond was something of a paradox. His service records bore out what his superiors already knew of him: that he was an average sailor with no outstanding qualities to set him apart from others. But once he stepped out of uniform he became something of a hustler, a shifty type, fast with money, a gambler, a little too fond of whisky, an angler always looking for an easy buck. After several months in London, he'd run into considerable debt and had become an easy mark for the Soviet espionage agents who prowled the gray, quiet city for potential recruits. The Russians routinely keep a close watch on military personnel stationed on a foreign land, and it was inevitable that Drummond's carousing would draw their attention.

The story of how he was launched into his career as a traitor was told to the FBI by Drummond after his arrest for espionage in the fall of 1962. Whether or not it was precisely how it happened, no one can really say. But it was part of the evidence presented at his trial, part of the testimony Drummond gave.

It happened on a London street sometime in the latter part of 1957, when a man approached him while he was on a pass from the U.S. Naval Base. The stranger seemed to be well aware of Drummond's background or else he had some idea of the sailor's current greed for money. He offered Drummond two hundred and fifty pounds—approximately seven hundred dollars—in cash to obtain him a Navy commissary pass so he could purchase foods and other articles at the base where the supply was plentiful and the prices reasonable. The tender of so much ready cash struck a responsive chord. Drummond promised to get the pass for the stranger. He took the money, he said, and all he had to do was show his identification card and sign a receipt for the money.

Drummond was unable to get the commissary pass. When he told his benefactor this, he was given a hard time, threatened, then finally given an alternative to compensate for the money he had taken—and spent. That alternative was espionage.

Drummond was invited to the Soviet Embassy in London where he met several of the aides. They were hospitable to him. They wined and dined him. Played up to him. And invited him back. Before long, Drummond's benefactor revealed himself as a colonel in the Soviet Army. He began instructing Drummond on the kind of data he was to obtain from his base. Drummond delivered to the colonel, who also proved to be the Soviet's payoff man.

Then, in early 1958, Drummond was warned by the Soviet colonel that he was facing an investigation by the Office of Naval Intelligence. "But it has nothing to do with your relations with us," he was comforted.

Actually, a naval counterintelligence officer had happened to spot Drummond talking to one of the Soviet Embassy aides. The Office of Naval Intelligence, however, conducted its probe in a very discreet manner. It brought Drummond in for questioning about a purported affair he was having with a married English girl. The Russians, who appeared to have a pipeline to the base, evidently heard that this was the matter under investigation. But the questioning by the counterintelligence officers covered a great deal more of Drummond's activities in London. The answers he gave were not satisfactory. However, he was allowed to think that the probers had given him a clean bill. He was even administered a lie detector test which was actually designed to determine his loyalty. He passed this, although the warning he had had from the Russians might have prepared Drummond to a degree that enabled him to cope with the questions of the inquisition. At any rate, from this day on, Drummond was a marked man. Intelligence kept him under constant surveillance.

The Russians at the Embassy had no further assignments for him after the investigation, but soon after took a renewed interest in the sailor—when they learned he was being transferred to the Newport

Naval Base in Rhode Island. They told him bluntly that he would spy for them.

If we had not already seen the incredible inroads the Soviets have been able to make in espionage operations in the episodes we have already recited, it would probably be far more shocking to know they were willing to continue their relationship with Drummond and to recruit him for espionage in the United States, despite the fact that he had come under the shadow of an investigation.

Before boarding ship in Southampton for his return to the U.S., Drummond rendezvoused with one of his Soviet contacts. He was given fifty pounds—about one hundred and forty dollars—plus a black bag and a single cufflink with a horse-head design. His instructions were that, on the first Saturday of the month after his arrival, he was to go to New York City and there, at 9 p.m., he was to walk south on Seventh Avenue from 125th Street. He was to hold the bag in his hand and wear the cufflink in his lapel.

He was told that a man would approach him and ask, "Can you show me the way to the Savoy Ballroom?" He was to reply, "Yes, I will show you the way." Undoubtedly the rendezvous in Harlem was chosen by the Russians because Drummond was a Negro.

Accordingly, Drummond did as told when he got to New York, and he was actually met by an unidentified Soviet agent on Seventh Avenue near 116th Street in early April, 1958. The agent discussed monthly meeting dates with the sailor, at which time he would provide him with "instructions on what we want you to do and how to do it."

Drummond traveled down from Newport once a month to keep these dates, and received four hundred to five hundred dollars at frequent intervals as he began to deliver documents he pilfered from the Navy's files. His meetings with his Soviet contact were generally held in the vicinity of Seventh Avenue and 121st Street.

Although he had been under that cloud of suspicion from his first association with Soviet people in London, Drummond was assigned as administrative assistant to the officer in charge of Mobile Electronics Technical Unit 8. The assignment was consonant with his still officially spotless service record—and that was how Naval Intelligence wanted it.

Drummond settled down professionally in his new job and carefully learned everything about it: the nature of the documents, how they were routed among the Navy brass, what signatures were necessary before they could be requisitioned, whether they were photographed, where they were filed, how they were accounted for, how long they could be removed from their places before they were missed.

Once he had learned the routine and devised ways of getting the data out of the base in a seemingly effortless style, the mechanics of his treasonous sideline became a mere routine for Drummond. And a profitable routine.

The first conclusive evidence of Drummond's dealings with the Soviets on this side of the Atlantic came toward the beginning of 1960. At this time Drummond had begun to show an affluence highly inconsistent with his yeoman's status. His net service pay, after deductions, totaled a mere $120.95 a month. Yet he was able to toss money around recklessly on women and whisky.

His behavior pattern also showed a change. He was carving a reputation in private life as a wastrel, a gambler, and an all-around troublemaker that brought him afoul of the law again and again.

On May 20, 1960, he was arrested for reckless driving. The following September 13, he was seized in a dice game raided by police, and the very next month he was charged with lewd, wanton, and licentious conduct involving a woman. He was placed on six months' probation. Less than a year later, on September 13, 1961, he was arrested for assault after punching a man in the eye, then was arrested again for fighting on September 2, 1962. He was again placed on six months' probation. At the same time he was fined ten dollars and costs for using obscene and indecent language.

Through it all, Drummond retained his important responsibilities at the Newport Naval Base as administrative assistant to Lieutenant Lawrence H. Carter, who was in charge of Mobile Electronics Technical Unit 8.

In the meantime, Drummond met and married his wife Lucille. Nothing was more surprising to the FBI shadowing Drummond than to find that his mysterious source of income was suddenly plying him with extra-large portions of "long green," as he called it. There was one helping that was big enough to enable him to buy a tavern, the Havana Bar and Grill at 12 Oak Street, just outside the Newport Naval Station. Drummond put his wife to work in the bar during the day while he was at the base, and then went there himself at night to tend bar. Although it was a honky-tonk, the tavern did a thriving business. Mostly sailors from the base and their dates patronized it. But on weekends, when a small orchestra played there, couples from town drifted in for drinks and dancing.

FBI agents also dropped into the Havana Bar and Grill once Drummond took it over. They could be found now and then at the bar for beers that many times were served by Drummond himself with the casualness and eclat of a professional tavern owner. The G-men prepared detailed reports about their visits there and made special note of certain patrons who were unmistakably Europeans. The FBI watchers noticed that Drummond always conversed with these strangers off at a quiet end of the bar.

Despite the mounting evidence that Drummond was solidly in the employ of the Soviet spy system, he was deliberately kept in his sensitive post at the naval base. And for good reason, for his feeling of security in his apparent espionage activity was preserved and given the opportunity to lead the FBI to the big game. At the same time, his access to the important naval documents, plans, and classified papers made Drummond better "bait" for the Soviet agents and shaped up a sort of guarantee that they would not abandon him before the FBI had the necessary evidence to close in. The FBI had to know who was dealing with Drummond, who was providing him with his ready cash. And they had to catch them in the act.

There was a measure of risk in this scenario for, in allowing Drummond to continue in his sensitive post at Newport, the peril always existed of giving up highly secret information to the enemy. Many of the documents, which in part were manuals on electronics maintenance, could enable a foreign power to evade or neutralize the latest detection devices and to penetrate anti-submarine and anti-aircraft systems on United States warships.

For example, so-called countermeasure equipment described in one manual for detecting radar signals was part of a family used throughout the Armed Forces. Other manuals to which Drummond had easy access dealt with maintenance of the latest anti-submarine weapons systems for two classes of destroyers, and still another manual was on aircraft bombs, fuses, and associated components, with appropriate information disclosing the capability and vulnerability of the system.

The FBI's intensive study of Drummond's modus operandi ultimately brought it to the conclusion that his main contact was in New York City. His periodic visits there served to betray him; it seemed that Drummond always came back from New York with large sums of money.

The first important lead to Drummond's big contact in New York came on August 13, 1962, when a team of FBI agents trailed him from Newport to an apartment house at 400 Central Park West at 100th Street, which overlooked Manhattan's Central Park. The agents shaping Drummond's shadow on this hegira were Thomas P. Selleck, Jr., Arthur K. Dowd, Jr., Frederick V. Behrends, Robert C. Puckett, Charles T. Weiss, and Joseph Palguta. It was quite a team of bloodhounds. The FBI was determined finally to break up the conspiracy.

The G-men learned very quickly that Drummond visited apartment 12-R, leased to Vadim Vladimirovich Sorokin and Vladilen V. Klokov, both of the Soviet Mission to the UN. This was an interesting discovery.

The FBI knew that Sorokin, who was a third secretary, had left the United States in May, 1962, and Klokov, who also was a third secretary, departed in November, 1961. Sorokin never tried to return here, but Klokov did. However, he was denied a permit to re-enter the U.S. because the Russians had failed to explain large amounts of electronics equipment forbidden as export to the Soviet Union which Klokov had purchased from an American businessman.

The FBI arranged its own observation post in the building to determine who the new tenant was. An apartment down the hall with a mirrored door peephole provided the G-men with an excellent view of 12-R. And pretty soon they knew that the new occupants of the apartment were two other Soviet Mission diplomats, Evgeni Mikehailovich Prokhorov, thirty-one, a second secretary, and Ivan Y. Vyrodov, thirty-eight, a third secretary.

In the days and weeks to come, the FBI accumulated a wealth of information about Prokhorov and Vyrodov, who seemed to be spending considerable time away from the UN, a great deal of it in Drummond's company. The Soviet diplomats were trailed during the third week in August to Fall River, Massachusetts, where they were seen making a pickup from a "drop," a rusty pipe in a park in that city Earlier that day other agents had followed Drummond to the park and had seen him put something in the pipe drop. Although it is a relatively hard and fast rule of the FBI not to disturb data that is left at a drop, in this case the agents made an exception. Drummond was well on his way back to his base, while the Soviet agents were still en route to the scene.

The FBI found the documents left in the rusty pipe contained data concerning summaries of work in progress on ships of the Atlantic Fleet. These were taken right out of the files in the office where Drummond worked. The papers were imbedded in the hollow of two magnetic containers which held fast to the inside of the rusty pipe. The agents put the documents back as they found them, then watched from a distance through binoculars as the Russians made the pickup.

A week later, the same two Russians journeyed by New York, New Haven & Hartford Railroad coach to East Providence, Rhode Island, where they again made a pickup of classified naval secrets, this time a manual dealing with the capabilities of an electromagnetic interception system that functions beyond the range of radar. The document was hidden by Drummond under a flight of wooden stairs at an abandoned station of the rail line.

Once during August and twice in early September, Drummond also was trailed to New York and was seen entering the Soviet Mission headquarters at 136 East 67th Street. Each time he spent no more than a half hour inside the building, and when he left, he was alone.

Then came September 28. The FBI was ready to move in on Drummond and what appeared to be a specific team of Soviet agents. By now, too, the FBI had conceived of a novel way to lay some traps for Drummond. Arrangements were made with Drummond's commanding officer at Newport, Lieutenant Carter, to install a silent burglar alarm in the office where the yeoman worked which could give a signal in a nearby room when the door to the unit office was opened. In addition, the FBI placed hidden TV cameras in the office which would give a view of both the area around the file cabinet where the secret documents were kept and Drummond's desk. The cameras were linked to a closed-circuit monitoring screen in the same nearby room as the burglar alarm.

After the installations, three FBI men—Selleck, Dowd, and Behrends—were assigned to spy on Drummond.

On the late afternoon of that September day, Drummond's actions in and around the office aroused Lieutenant Carter's suspicions, prompting his tipoff to the three agents who were close by for the surveillance. Carter said he thought Drummond might be getting ready again to "lift some documents out of the file cabinet."

At 5:20 p.m. by the time on his wristwatch, Agent Selleck sneaked into Drummond's office in Mobile Electronics Technical Unit 8 and secreted himself behind a bookcase. Before that, he removed some books to provide himself with a sighthold to observe the activity in the room.

About six minutes later, Drummond entered, went to the cabinet, unlocked it, took some papers, and went to his desk. He was temporarily out of Selleck's sight now, but not from the view of the other two agents who were watching the performance on the monitor in the other room. They saw Drummond extract some papers from a three-level mail box on his desk and place them along with those he had taken from the file into a leather carrying case. Then he left the office. For the record, the agents had shot some stills of the scene depicted on the monitor.

Agent Dowd then whisked himself away from the monitor and dashed to his car. He drove to a spot on Route 138 just outside the base and took up a position there, according to plan. Minutes later, Drummond whizzed by in his 1962 blue Pontiac sedan. He was wearing a brown leather jacket and a maroon baseball cap. Dowd followed.

The trail led downstate into Connecticut. Dowd stayed behind Drummond until Old Saybrook, then peeled off the highway as another agent, Robert Puckett, took over. Puckett stayed with Drummond as he went onto the Connecticut Turnpike and didn't let him out of his sight until they hit Greenwich, just short of the New York State line. Then another G-man, Palguta, followed the suspect as he breezed into the next state past Port Chester, Rye, Harrison, Mamaroneck, and as far as Larchmont where Drummond turned off the highway.

Meanwhile, there was other activity in Manhattan. The G-men

staked out at the Soviet agents' apartment at 400 Central Park West, spotted Prokhorov and Vyrodov taking hurried leave. The time was 10:30 p.m. FBI cars were waiting downstairs to follow the diplomats, whose departure at this late hour signified that they were up to something.

Among the agents who formed part of this tail were Weiss and Dowd who had sped back to New York after completing his assignment of tagging behind Drummond on his way down from Newport.

Agent Puckett, who was the last FBI shadow on Drummond, was still with the sailor. By now, Drummond had driven to a diner on the busy Boston Post Road in Larchmont, entered its parking lot, cut his motor, turned off his lights, and remained behind the wheel in what was a sure sign that he had come this far to rendezvous with someone. Puckett radioed his position and other agents, including Behrends and Selleck, headed for the location.

The FBI would soon see what it suspected already. Drummond was waiting for Prokhorov and Vyrodov. The Soviet agents' trail led up the West Side Drive into the Henry Hudson Parkway, then the Cross-County Parkway, Hutchinson River Parkway, and to the Larchmont exit. Then on to the diner. They reached there at precisely 11:47 p.m. in their 1961 black Buick Electra hardtop sedan.

Vyrodov, who drove, stopped the car in the lot in a stall about twenty-five feet from where Drummond was parked. Vyrodov then got out and went into the diner. Prokhorov sat alone in the car for about five minutes, then left and walked over to Drummond's Pontiac. He opened the door on the right hand side and got in beside the sailor.

The G-men allowed five minues to go by. Then they converged in a body upon the trio. Selleck, Dowd, Palguta, and Behrends surrounded Drummond's car and ordered the sailor and Prokhorov to get out. They were utterly astonished at the stark development and both emerged from the car, bewilderment markedly apparent on their faces.

"What's this all about?" demanded Drummond when he had finally gathered his presence of mind.

"A matter of espionage, Mr. Drummond," replied Behrends as he frisked the sailor.

SOVIETS "BUY" THE GOP CANDIDATE

A cheery hail and hello is offered by Richard L. Flink at Republican reception in Buffalo before opening of 1962 GOP State Convention. Behind him in crowd is smiling U.S. Senator Jacob K. Javits. Flink, a candidate for State Assembly, received $3,000 in "campaign contributions" from Soviet espionage agents who wanted him to spout Communist line. What Russians didn't know though was that Flink had alerted FBI to the plot and was working as counterspy. One of conspirators, Yuri Mishukov, a translator at UN, left country before Government exposed brazen scheme. Other agent, Yuri V. Zaitsev, a UN political affairs officer, was declared persona non grata and returned to Moscow.

First case of satellite espionage involved Czechoslovakia's Miroslav Nacvalac, a counselor for his country's mission to UN. Shown here in official FBI photos taken with concealed long-range camera is Nacvalac going to Milton Kreis Restaurant at Geary and Powell Streets in San Francisco for rendezvous with Karel Hlasny, a Czech-born naturalized American and instructor at Army Language School in Monterey, California. Nacvalac told Hlasny he could have his sweetheart brought to America from behind Iron Curtain if he supplied classified information about Army projects on West Coast. Hlasny revealed conspiracy to FBI, Nacvalac denied all, said he'd never been in California. Photos made him a liar and put him in another pose (below) that is now familiar ending to UN cloak-and-dagger chapters—diplomatically immune Nacvalac, wife, and children board plane for Prague.

SATELLITE ESPIONAGE . . .

MURDER

CZECH STYLE

Once more Czechs at UN figure in headlines in 1962 when State Troopers pursue Cadillac with diplomatic license plates across New Jersey and Pennsylvania highways at 110 mph speeds. Caddy finally goes out of control in Easton, Pa. (see map), plummets down ravine, and overturns. (Chase extended from A to B.) Driver, apparently unhurt in crash, pulls gun when troopers try to take him and shoots self in head. Papers in pockets show he was Karel Zizka, attaché of Czechoslovak Mission to UN. When police checked back at Mission they learned Zizka's wife had been murdered—bludgeoned, shot through head, and stabbed in chest. Notes left in apartment indicated Zizka killed her but authorities were not allowed to investigate fully because Mission is diplomatically immune island. So with aura of mystery cloaking case, Mrs. Zizka's body is carried out of Mission to funeral home for shipment back to Czechoslovakia by plane. Body of Zizka, who died hours later in hospital, also was flown home. To this day there is question about whether Zizka killed his wife during quarrel—or was ordered to take her life.

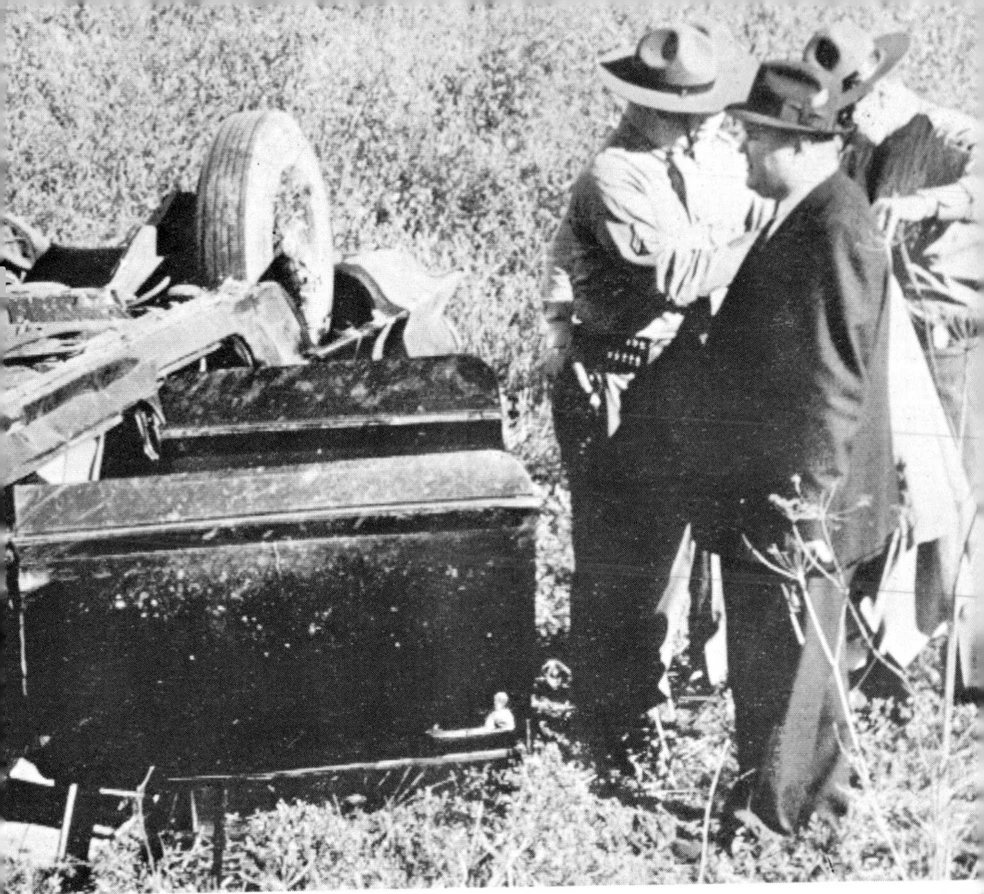

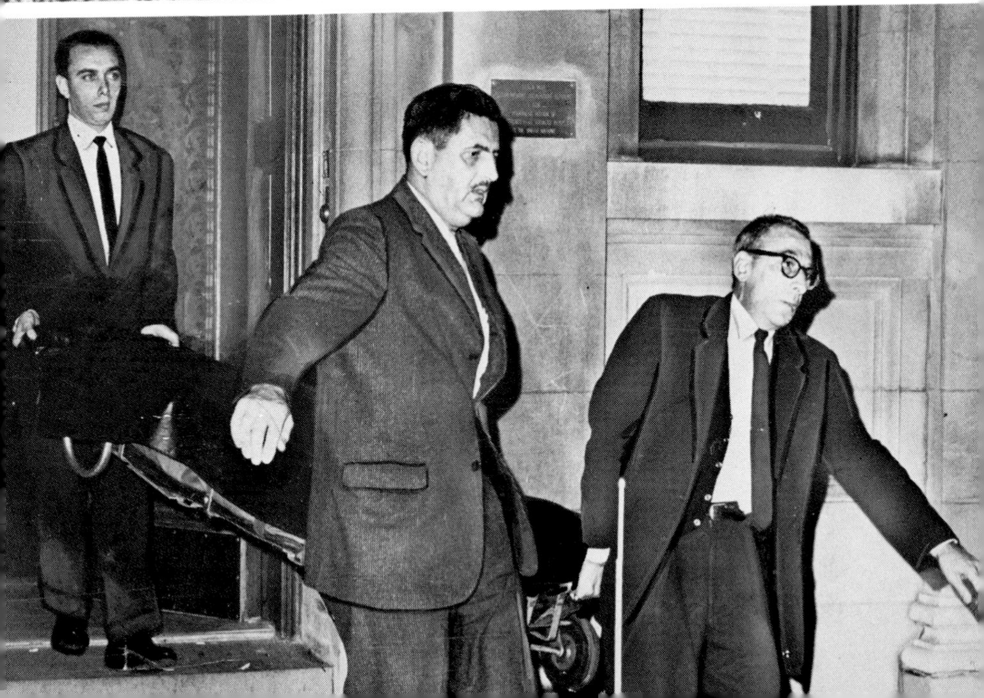

THE ELECTRONICS ENGINEER

American-born electronics engineer John William Butenko is camera shy as he is escorted (above) from FBI headquarters in Newark, N.J., after arrest for passing classified information about Strategic Air Command to Soviet UN Delegates Gleb A. Pavlov (left) and Yuri A. Romashin (right). A fourth conspirator was Igor A. Ivanov (top right), a Russian citizen employed as chauffeur by Am-

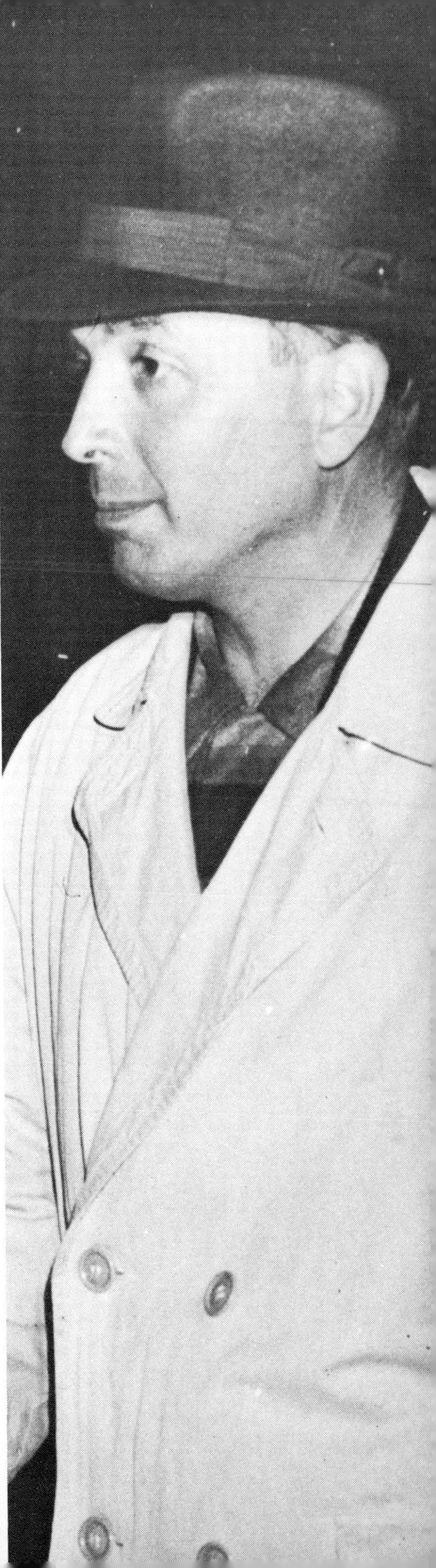

...ND THE RUSSIAN CHAUFFEUR

...org, Soviet trade agency in U.S. Pavlov and ...omashin, thanks to diplomatic immunity, were ...eleased and sent back to Moscow. But Ivanov, who ...idn't enjoy diplomatic privileges, and Butenko ...were tried for espionage and convicted. Butenko, ...who lived in palatial Tudor-style home (below) in ...Orange, N.J., was given 30 years, Ivanov 20. But ...Ivanov was released in bail pending appeal.

The United States was shocked into new awareness of Communist danger in November, 1962, when it learned of monstrous Soviet-designed Cuban sabotage plot against New York metropolitan area's 16,000,-000 residents. Conspirators planned to blow up rail terminals, subway stations, department stores, oil refineries. But FBI stepped in at 11th hour and seized plotters. In photo at top left is mastermind, Roberto Santiesteban Casanova, who flew up from Havana with Castro's puppet president Osvaldo Dorticos as decoy, to unleash horror. Other plotters included José Garcia Orellana (bottom left), Cuban national who stored explosives for the destruction in his Manhattan costume jewelry firm, and Antonio Sueirro Cabrera (seated at right in car), who worked for Garcia as "salesman." At right Ada Marie Dritsas, a teacher in New York City, was seized with Sueirro as material witness, later released.

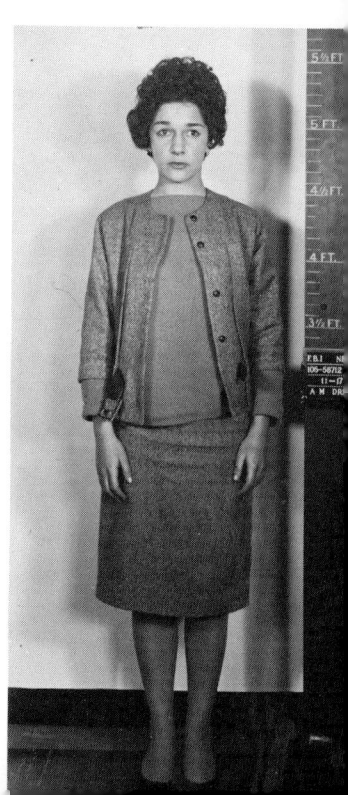

Dowd checked Prokhorov for weapons. Like Drummond, he was clean. But Agent Selleck didn't find the car that spotless. A .22-caliber Zephyr revolver with four bullets in the chamber was tucked in the glove compartment. Except for the spare tire and jack, the trunk had only one other tangible item—a miniature camera, the type used by Soviet espionage agents in their work.

The real evidence that was to provide the Government at a later date with the means to get a conviction against Drummond was on the front seat between where Drummond and Prokhorov had been sitting—six classified Navy documents.

As handcuffs were clamped on Drummond and Prokhorov, Agents Weiss and Puckett were extending this same service to Vyrodov whom they had found at the counter in the diner sipping a cup of coffee. His surprise was no less than Drummond's or Prokhorov's when the agents asked him to come along. The suspects were hustled into the FBI cars and driven to the bureau's offices in Manhattan. Their own cars were brought back to the city by other agents.

Drummond was reluctant at first to cooperate in his questioning, maintaining an attitude of injured innocence.

"I didn't do a thing," he insisted. "I am innocent of any wrongdoing."

But under further interrogation by Agents Palguta and Weiss, Drummond soon broke down and admitted that he was passing Navy secrets to the Soviets. He attested to the various meetings at which he had been seen with the Russians, and also conceded that he had been passing documents in person and at drops.

Drummond told an unbelievable story as he detailed his dealings with the four Soviet emissaries in New York whom he named and others whose identities he was uncertain of.

"There were so many of them that I got all mixed up doing business with them. I had to use code names to tell one apart from the other. Those Russian names—I could never remember them." But Drummond was able to identify four of his Soviet diplomatic contacts and to tie them up with a simple code he had devised to tell one from the other.

The first of these contacts was Mikail Stepanovich Savelev, who had called himself only "Mike" when he met the sailor in New York in 1958. Drummond referred to him as "Mike Number One." "That was so I could tell him apart from the others who eventually took over," Drummond said easily. Savelev had returned to Moscow in mid-1961.

Vadim Sorokin, who began to deal with Drummond sometime in the summer of 1961, was known to the sailor as "Mike Number Two." Before Sorokin left the country in May, 1962, Drummond was put in touch with Prokhorov, who became "Mike Number Three."

Drummond said he had little dealing with Vyrodov, and therefore did not find it necessary to give him a numerical "Mike" designation, although appropriately he could have been Number Four.

In his statement, the FBI said, Drummond told Palguta that he was penitent of his role as a traitor. He startled his questioners by volunteering himself for the role of a double agent for the United States.

"I am ashamed for the disgrace to my family. I regret everything and I want to die honorably in dishonor rather than dishonorably in dishonor. Please let me spy for you . . ."

The FBI never took the offer seriously.

Asked how much he had been paid for his services to the Soviets, Drummond coolly estimated that he had received between $20,000 and $24,000 over the period of years that he had worked with Soviet spies. "I guess you could say it was around twenty-two thousand," he said candidly. He explained that payments ran between $250 and $500 as a rule, but he recalled three "unusually large payments" that amounted to $1,000, $4,000 and $6,000. With the $6,000, he said, he bought the Havana Bar and Grill.

Drummond was then questioned about the "system" he had employed over the years to remove the naval documents from the files without being observed.

"I would take them out on a Friday night," he said as calmly as if he were talking about some routine of his job. "Then I would get them back on Saturday morning and return them to the file."

Q: What did your contacts do with the documents while they were in in their hands?

A: I guess they photographed them. They gave me that camera you found in my trunk and sometimes I took pictures of the papers in the office, the ones that couldn't be removed.

Q: What methods did you use to pass the documents?

A: Several . . .

Drummond then talked about the drops under the abandoned steps in East Providence and the hollow rusty pipe in the Fall River park. He also related that the Soviet agents gave him a pencil, whose writing was invisible, to copy material that he could not remove from the office without being detected.

Q: Did you always get paid for delivering the material?

A: Sometimes they didn't pay right away. When I needed dough I'd come to New York and go to the Soviet Mission. I'd tell them I needed cash. They used to get disturbed at my visits. They would say that I was embarrassing them by coming to the Mission. But I just kept coming whenever I felt like it. They finally told me to stay away and promised to pay more money for what I was doing if I listened to them.

Q: Did you ever think of quitting this business?

A: Yes, I once did try to get out, but they wouldn't let me. That was in London. I wanted to marry a French girl, but they told me I couldn't. They said it would interfere with the work I was doing for them. They said I would be more useful as a single man. And the ironic part of it all was that I really started to take their money because I wanted to marry that girl.

Q: You didn't marry the girl?

A: No. And that hurt so much that I figured I would be better off to get out of the Navy to get the Russians off my back. I figured that if I left the service I would be useless to them in espionage.

During the questioning, Drummond insisted he did not pass legitimate secrets to the Soviets. He said he "doctored" any information he turned over so it was of no real value to the Russians. He insisted they never suspected he was "taking them . . . making suckers out of them."

Drummond said that one of his duties at Newport was to burn obsolete classified documents. It was some of these papers that he turned over to the Soviet agents. He was further quoted: "When I'd remove papers from the office files, I'd do so in grab-bag fashion."

While the agents questioned Drummond, other FBI men tried to interrogate Prokhorov and Vyrodov who were held in another office. The Russians refused to answer any questions and insisted they had diplomatic immunity.

Harvey G. Foster, the agent in charge of the New York FBI office, decided before releasing the Russians he would pull a little coup of sorts. Foster was aware that no Soviet diplomat ever trapped so neatly as these two, had ever been subjected to the humiliation of being positively identified by a fellow diplomat of his mission. He had an agent phone the Soviet Mission at 3:30 a.m. and say that the FBI was holding two strangers who "claim to be Soviet diplomats. Can you please help us clear up this situation?" The nature of the case was carefully withheld so as not to tip off the Soviets.

Within a half hour, three Russians—Roland M. Timbebaev, the Mission's counselor; Igor S. Tumanov, an attaché; and I. I. Techeprov, an aide—appeared at the FBI. They were led into the office where Prokhorov and Vyrodov were seated.

Timbebaev, the lawyer, looked at the two diplomats and blurted, "These gentlemen are members of the Soviet Mission."

"Thank you very much, sir," Foster smiled. Then turning to the diplomats caught as spies, "You may go now."

It was the first time the Soviets had fallen for this bait and, in the presence of the law, allowed one of their own people to identify a fellow delegate suspected of spying.

At 4 a.m. Drummond was taken to the U.S. Courthouse in Foley Square where U.S. Commissioner Earle N. Bishop was waiting after being roused from bed to preside at the arraignment. It was a brief session, held just long enough to determine the charges against Drummond—they were espionage and conspiracy—and to set bail, which was fixed at $100,000. The sailor was then remanded to the Federal House of Detention to await a hearing, and what ultimately would be the action of the Federal grand jury.

Drummond's arrest created a nationwide, even an international, stir. Not only was he the first American-born citizen since Judith Coplon to be charged with treason involving UN-based Soviet agents, but he was the first Negro in the nation's history to stand accused of espionage.

The shock of Nelson Drummond's arrest devastated his parents living in West Baltimore, Maryland.

"It's enough to make you wish you were dead," murmured the father, Archie Drummond, who, though more poor than middle class, was nevertheless a respectable, hard-working citizen of the community. With his wife, he had raised four other children on a minimum income provided by his job as a maintenance man with the city's Bureau of Recreation. The look in his eyes, the heartbreak that showed on his face betrayed his wishfulness when he said, "I hope there's nothing to it." Then he thought about that a while. He shook his head. "But they usually don't arrest you unless they have something."

The sailor's mother spoke with tears trickling down her cheeks, lips trembling. Her grief was easy to see as she sat next to her husband who was trying to comfort her.

"We tried to give him all the advantages we never had," Mrs. Drummond said. "It just doesn't seem real."

The father had only one complaint. He was disturbed and "hurt" because the FBI did not notify him of his son's arrest. The parents got the news from a newspaper reporter.

"If it hadn't been for that, my wife and I couldn't have taken the news when we heard it later over the radio," Drummond murmured. "The FBI should have notified us about the arrest."

The day after the arrest and on State Department orders, the United States Mission to the UN delivered a strongly worded note to the Soviet Mission.

"As host to the United Nations, the Government of the United States strongly protests these espionage activities directed against the internal security of the United States," read the note which mentioned Prokhorov and Vyrodov by name and accused them of paying substantial sums for classified documents they received.

"Not only are such activities clearly outside the scope of the official responsibilities of these members but they are an outrageous violation of their privilege of residence . . . The United States Mission requests the permanent Mission of the Union of Soviet Socialist Republics to take the necessary steps to effect the immediate withdrawal of Mr. Prokhorov and Mr. Vyrodov from the United States."

The Soviet Mission wasted no time shooting back its reply. It charged the Soviet diplomats had been seized "illegally and without any reason." It contended that Prokhorov and Vyrodov had told the agents they had diplomatic immunity but that they were "illegally arrested" despite this.

"Physical measures were used to take the men," the note went on. "This included handcuffing of Mr. Vyrodov. According to a doctor's certificate, both his arms were injured."

The Russians said the FBI searched the diplomats, confiscated Prokhorov's money, tried to question them both, and "cruelly denied their demand that they be permitted to get in touch with the Soviet Mission."

On October 1, 1962, just three days after the case broke, the Soviet Mission to the UN was minus two diplomats. Prokhorov and Vyrodov were on their way home.

"Happy to leave this country where there is no law," fumed Prokhorov as he boarded a Sabena Belgian Airlines jet at Idlewild Airport on the first leg of his trip to Moscow. With him were his wife and two children, and Vyrodov, who had no family to take back home. Some twenty members of the Soviet Mission were at the airport to wave good-bye.

Now the spotlight turned to Nelson "Bulldog" Drummond, the accused sailor, who was literally left holding the bag.

On October 5 a Federal grand jury returned a two-count indictment against the sailor. The first charge: espionage. The maximum penalty upon conviction: death in the electric chair.

The indictment also named the four former secretaries—Prokhorov, Vydorov, Savelev, and Sorokin—as co-conspirators but not defendants; while Drummond was accused of conspiring to turn over to the Soviet Union or its agents "documents, writings, code books, signal books, sketches, photographs, photographic negatives, blueprints, plans, models, notes, instruments, appliances, and information relating to the national defense of the United States with intent and reason to believe that they were to be used to the injury of the United States and to the advantage of the Union of Soviet Socialist Republics."

The second count alleged that Drummond attempted to obtain information relating to naval weapons systems, maintenance data relating to submarines, and electronics data.

The indictment further stated that Drummond had received $6,000 from Sorokin alone and, altogether, some $22,000.

Judge David N. Edelstein, who accepted the indictment, ordered a hearing for the following Tuesday at which time Drummond appeared and pleaded innocent. Judge Edelstein then set down the trial date for October 10. But the usual legal wrangles and arguments and crowded court calendars held off the start of the trial until spring.

The proceedings finally got under way May 13 before Federal Judge Edward Weinfeld and an all-male jury. The prosecution was headed by U.S. Attorney Henry Morgenthau, Jr.; the defense, by Attorney William Chance, Jr. The trial lasted until May 22. The case went to the jury at 2:40 p.m. Deliberations were interrupted for dinner, then resumed until 1:40 the next morning when the jury quit for the night.

It reconvened at 10 a.m., but at the end of the eighteenth hour the jury notified Judge Weinfeld that it was hopelessly deadlocked. There was one holdout against conviction and there was no possibility that this dissenter could be persuaded to change his mind.

Regretfully Judge Weinfeld dismissed the jury.

"It seems," he said, "we'll have to start all over again. It is my custom not to thank a jury for a verdict, and I will not do so now."

Then he ordered a new trial to begin on June 3. Drummond's counsel tried to get a reduction of the $100,000 bail.

"The bail already fixed is eminently fair," Judge Weinfeld said. Drummond went back to the Federal House of Detention to await the second trial.

After the disagreement was announced and the jury dismissed, it was learned that the jury had taken a vote twenty minutes after it had retired to weigh the evidence, and the vote was eleven for conviction and one holdout. More than twenty-four hours later, after four ballots had been taken, the vote remained unchanged.

Jury Foreman Harry Schmitt, a statistician, of the Bronx, and six other members of the panel identified the holdout juror as Edward L. Watkins, a clerk, of Harlem. He was the only Negro member of the jury. There was only one issue that could not be resolved, according to some of the jurors polled—Drummond's race. Armand J. Menrad, a cook, of Manhattan, and Gordon Henee Price, an advertising art director, of Ossining, were among the jurors who shared that view.

However, Watkins denied that his decision was influenced by the color of the defendant's skin. "I would have voted the way I did no matter what color he was. I felt he was guilty. I had a choice between giving this man the electric chair or life. Well, I could see life imprisonment, but not electrocution."

Watkins said he would have voted guilty on the conspiracy count if the others had favored acquittal on the espionage charge. Conviction for conspiracy does not carry a mandatory death sentence; for espionage it does. Since the others did not accept Watkins' plea for acquittal on the charge that meant capital punishment, he would not yield on the other. Actually, if Watkins had voted for acquittal on the espionage charge and cast a vote for conviction on conspiracy, Drummond conceivably could have been brought up for trial on espionage at a later date.

"You must remember," Watkins said. "I've never been a juror before. All of a sudden they sat me down in a trial in which a man's life is at stake. That's quite a jump."

One juror insisted that Watkins had said, "My people are fighting for their lives in the South. This is a frameup of a colored man by the FBI." The juror said Watkins didn't believe the testimony of one of the FBI agents who was from Mississippi. Watkins denied it all. Another juror said that if Drummond were white, he would have been convicted in five minutes.

At any rate, the Government was committed now to go through the whole costly and time-consuming process again.

The second trial was postponed from its originally scheduled date and did not get under way until July 8 in Room 110 of the Federal Courthouse in Foley Square. The presiding judge this time was the enormous, mustached, one-time police commissioner of New York City, Thomas M. Murphy. Chance again was on hand as defense counsel and Morgenthau sent his chief assistant, Vincent L. Broderick, to conduct the prosecution.

A jury of ten men and two women was selected this time. Again as before one juror was a Negro—Mrs. Pauline Blanchard, an employee of the State Unemployment Insurance Office, of Washington Avenue, the Bronx.

The proceedings got going in an atmosphere far different than one might expect in an Ian Fleming-James Bond thriller. There was little of the glamor and swagger built into the everyday adventures of the fictional British intelligence officer.

As Chief Assistant U.S. Attorney Broderick presented the prosecution case, it resembled more an architect's blueprint than something torn from the pages of a spine-tingling spy adventure. Just to detail the floor plan of the Newport Naval office in which Drummond worked at the time of his arrest was an all-day job. The buildup was helped by FBI Agents Selleck, Dowd, and Behrends, who had had their eyes on the defendant both from behind the peephole in the bookcase and on the TV monitor in another nearby office.

Drummond's commanding officer, Lieutenant Carter, also testified and told what the defendant's duties actually were: rerouting mail, expediting various clerical tasks, picking up registered mail. It didn't sound so important. It didn't impress courtroom observers who had heard the Government claim that Drummond had virtually unrestricted access to vital and classified secrets pertaining to the national defense. But it is the jury's job to judge, not the courtroom observer's.

At last Drummond's turn came to take the stand in his own defense. He was carefully taken by his attorney over the course of his espionage activities. Drummond testified to the London meeting with the stranger who paid him seven hundred dollars for the Navy commissary pass.

Q: What happened then?
A: I wasn't able to get the pass. The man got angry. He said he wanted me to produce it. Then he introduced himself as a colonel in the Russian Army. We stopped talking about the commissary pass then. He made me know that I was expected to produce information from the files of the Navy activity to which I was assigned. I told him he was nuts, he was crazy, but he answered that "we think you will do it."

Drummond said he was held virtually a prisoner in "an old-style English mansion" and threatened. "They kept me there several hours. There was a burly bodyguard who went along with the Russian officer."

The defendant said that among the documents he passed to the Soviets in London was a "list of U.S. air bases in England which I faked and stamped NATO secrets." Drummond insisted he had not given the Russians the real list but a phony one.

"I was just trying to get them off my back," he said. "But I couldn't."

Drummond then told how he contemplated leaving the Navy after sixteen years because he thought it would make him useless to the Russians in espionage. He also told of the Russian efforts to prevent him from marrying the French girl for fear it would interfere with his spying activities.

Drummond then swore that he doctored the documents he passed to the Russians so that they weren't ever of any real value.

"Sometimes I'd give them obsolete documents that were about to be destroyed, and they never knew the difference."

Trying desperately to explain away some of the many damaging admissions he had made to the FBI after his arrest, Drummond testified that he ultimately struck on an idea he thought would work to get rid of the Russians.

"I asked them for six thousand dollars. I figured they would tell me to go away, tell me I was crazy. I was surprised they even listened." He was more surprised when they gave him the money. And with it, he said, he bought the bar and grill in Newport.

There was one even more startling bit of testimony that Drummond provided in his behalf during his two days on the stand.

"I bought a gun—a twenty-two-caliber revolver—before that last meeting I had with the Russians in the Larchmont diner. I had made up my mind to kill the contact man, Mike Number Three [Prokhorov]."

But this was a contradiction of his previous day's testimony when Drummond had said he had carried the gun every time he met one of his contacts over the years. During his first day on the stand, Drummond said he wanted to kill Mike Number 3 because he was being hounded by him. In later testimony the defendant said he was afraid the agents had found out the documents he was passing along were worthless, and "I was afraid they'd try to kill me." Still later he said he was going to shoot the Russians because his family had been threatened by them.

Q: Why didn't you go through with your plans for the killing?
A: I couldn't find a suitable occasion.

Drummond also told of his offers to become a counterspy.

"I said to the FBI men the night I was arrested and later I wrote it in a letter from the jail to Attorney General Robert Kennedy, asking that my hundred thousand dollars bail be reduced to twenty thousand, and if the FBI supplied the money to my wife so I could be set free, I would jump bail, defect to Russia, and from there act as an agent for the FBI. I wrote that I am a good American fighting man and I would like a chance to make up for my faults."

Then in a statement read to the jury by the prosecution, Drummond was quoted as saying: "I hold profound hatred against these bastards. I am prepared to offer my life for my country."

In the statement, Drummond said he had spoken to his wife when she visited him in the Federal House of Detention about his proposal to become a counterspy, and that he asked her if she wanted to go with him to Russia for that purpose.

"She said, 'Just tell me when, where, how.' "

As this portion of the statement was read, Lucille Drummond, who was sitting in the first row in the spectators' section, buried her face in her hands.

Of all the witnesses against Drummond, none was more forceful, nor more damaging, then FBI Agent Palguta. The balding, frowning G-man spent three days on the stand. He demonstrated a remarkable facility for remembering what Drummond had said to him during the questioning following the arrest and recalling the details of the trackdown.

Defense Attorney Chance appeared at times to become exasperated with the witness's extraordinary recollections. Chance also was disturbed over the statements Palguta had obtained from Drummond. The attorney interrupted the agent at one point to ask how much time it took "to teach" Drummond to draw up the admissions. Judge Murphy was surprised that Chance would use such a phrase. The lawyer apologized.

When Chance had placed Drummond on the stand, he exposed him to cross-examination by the prosecution. Attorney Broderick questioned the defendant relentlessly. One of the highpoints of the prosecution's cross was this brief but damaging exchange:

Q: How many times altogether would you tell us that you met or dealt with persons you believed to be representatives or agents of the Soviet Union?

A: Approximately sixteen times . . .

Altogether, the same twenty-three witnesses called at the first trial appeared at the second.

The case went to the jury at the end of nine days, July 19. Judge Murphy, who in his days as an assistant U.S. Attorney successfully prosecuted Alger Hiss for treason, showed the true impartiality that is needed on the bench. He emphasized to the jury in his charge that "there is conflict on substantial matters, and the different versions cannot both be true." It was up to the jury to resolve them. He said further that the jury must try the case "without sympathy or bias or prejudice . . . in a courtroom persons of every race, color, or creed stand equal."

The jury began deliberations at 11:05 a.m. Three times during the day, Jury Foreman Robert Leopold, an office manager, of East 83rd Street, Manhattan, sent requests for exhibits or reviews of testimony. About twenty minutes after the jury retired to its room, Leopold sent a note to the court asking for two photographs taken by the FBI men from the closed-circuit television monitor up in Newport. These photos showed Drummond removing documents from the Navy file cabinet. The jury later asked for copies of statements Drummond made to the FBI and for the six Navy documents the agents said were found in Drummond's car in Larchmont the night of his arrest.

Among those in the courtroom as the jury went out to weigh the evidence was the infamous Jack Soble, who was convicted in 1947 as a spy for the Soviet Union. He had recently been released from prison after doing five years. His presence had been noted on two prior occasions during the trial, and on this one he was exchanging friendly observations and banter with some of the prosecution staff, the same prosecution staff which had also presented the case against him.

The jury took time out for lunch and dinner. After dinner, the jury returned to the courtroom to notify Judge Murphy that it had reached agreement on the first count without specifying whether it was guilt or acquittal, but it was deadlocked on the second.

The judge read the jurors excerpts from a century-old Supreme Court decision that defined responsibilities of veniremen. Then he sent them back to try again to reach agreement, pleading for an open mind to the arguments of the members of the jury and warning against clinging to one's own stubborn, unreasoning opinion.

At 9:26 p.m. the jury returned to the courtroom one more time. It wanted to hear the judge's charge on the second count. Murphy re-read it and then told the panel that if it decided Drummond had been prepared to deliver the documents that night of September 28 in Larchmont, even if actual delivery had not taken place, it could vote for conviction.

Eleven hours and forty minutes after it received the case, at exactly 10:45 p.m., the jury came back to the court with the same story—it had reached a decision on the first count but not on the second. Murphy said he would accept the finding.

Then Foreman Leopold read the verdict: guilty on the first count. And on the second it was a hung jury.

Judge Murphy declared a mistrial on the second count, then set August 15 for sentencing on the first. The verdict meant Drummond could receive the death penalty, but he could also escape it. He was remanded to the House of Detention to await sentence. This time he was denied any bail.

Drummond, who was dressed in a gray seersucker suit and brightly colored flowered shirt, took the verdict without emotion. Lucille also failed to evoke any outward disturbance at the jury's decision. The prisoner smiled wanly at his wife as he was led out of the courtroom in handcuffs.

As they had done after the first trial, newsmen went after the jurors to learn who the holdout was. Again as before, the poll showed it was the lone Negro member of the panel who blocked conviction on the second charge, of passing Navy documents to Soviet agents.

Mrs. Blanchard had nothing to say to the press, radio, or television reporters who tried to query her. But one juror, interviewed by New York *Journal-American* Reporter Frank Borsky, commented:

"Mrs. Blanchard told us she didn't believe any of the FBI men. She said she preferred to believe Drummond's word against theirs and that her mind simply was made up. It was hard to convince her. She didn't talk much or give any of her reasons. That was the frustrating part. We did our best to explain the case . . . but it all seemed lost on her. She either didn't listen or didn't want to listen. Right from the start, eleven jurors felt completely convinced of Drummond's guilt.

After several hours, Mrs. Blanchard changed her mind on the first count."

That was almost the same account that had been given of the deliberations made by the first jury. The foreman of that jury, Harry Schmitt, was asked his opinion about the second jury's verdict.

"Drummond should have been found guilty in the first trial," said Schmitt. "He was guilty then and he's guilty now. There was never any doubt in the minds of eleven jurors on that first jury. We were convinced that the Russians were not paying him large sums of money for that long a period for nothing . . ."

On August 15, 1963, Judge Murphy convened his court and summoned Drummond before him. The stocky defendant, attired in a neat blue suit, white shirt, and blue tie, stood listlessly before the bench. His wife sat in the front row of the spectator seats, nervously clasping and unclasping her hands as the proceedings began.

His face solemn, his stare fixed straight at Drummond, Judge Murphy slowly intoned the words that castigated the defendant for his crime.

"Yours was a most awful crime. One so heinous that the Congress has empowered the court to impose the death sentence for it . . ."

Drummond blinked and lowered his head. He seemed to be expecting the worst. Lucille clenched her fists.

"The evidence against you is overwhelming," continued Murphy in the utter silence of the crowded courtroom. "You have sold the security and safety of your country for twenty-four thousand dollars while you were a uniformed member of the United States Navy. Because of compassion for your innocent wife and the true devotion of your family, I will not impose the death penalty, but I will, and do sentence you to prison for the rest of your natural life."

Drummond, now seven years older than the day he met his first Russian in London, had reached the end of his treasonous trail, and justice had taken its course. He took the verdict with a quiver of his body and a slow, deliberate shaking of his head. Even escape from the chair was no occasion for rejoicing for the 34-year-old convicted traitor. There were to be those cruel, terrible years of confinement for the rest of his life in a prison where he would be among the lowliest creatures of society, living with killers, rapists, degenerates, and other criminals. And somehow Drummond seemed to know that his crime was the worst. He would be the one among thousands behind those grim prison walls who would hold the distinction of having been committed there for a crime that the judge himself called "most awful" and "heinous."

Lucille reacted to the verdict with an audible gasp. Then she covered her face with both hands, her shoulders shaking violently.

It was all over.

The Government announced later that it would hold open the espionage count on which the holdout jurors twice blocked a verdict. Also still facing Drummond was a Navy charge of stealing government property—the documents.

But it is doubtful that he will ever be brought to trial on either of these two charges. Nelson Cornelius "Bulldog" Drummond can only serve one lifetime, one nightmarish eternity, for betraying his country and his countrymen.

15 : "... And They Seemed Like Such Nice, Quiet People"

SOMETIMES spy catching is a frustrating and exasperating process for the FBI. This was very much the case in the early days of May, 1963, when the Bureau received word that Petr Egorovich Maslennikov was packing to leave for Russia. The square-faced, soft-spoken First Secretary of the Soviet Mission to the UN, a blond, stiffly erect individual with a military bearing, had been under surveillance for more than a year.

Few Soviet delegates who are sent to the UN attract suspicion until they get involved in some facet of espionage. Contrary to Soviet claims, the FBI does not shadow *every* Soviet emissary and employee at the UN or at the Embassy in Washington. Congress would have to greatly increase the FBI's appropriation to give it the wherewithal for such intensive probing.

But there are times when the FBI will train its eye on certain Soviet individuals as soon as they step off the boat or plane here. Petr Egorovich Maslennikov was one of those. He was well-known to the Central Intelligence Agency long before he came to the U.S.

Maslennikov was a Soviet Military Intelligence officer. Traditionally his background would have called for an assignment to the Military Staff group at the Soviet UN Mission. But Moscow detailed him to serve as an assistant to the Soviet Ambassador in New York.

The wisdom of this move isn't fathomable. There is a suspicion the Soviets could have just thought that the 43-year-old Maslennikov might attract less attention in a non-military assignment. But it didn't. The FBI shadow fell over Maslennikov the moment his plane brought him to New York City's Idlewild Airport in early January, 1962.

Before many days passed, Maslennikov was spotted traipsing about town with an old comrade from their days together in Soviet Military Intelligence, a squat, square-jawed chap named Aleksei Ivanovich Galkin. Like Maslennikov, Galkin had also commanded the FBI's interest because of his background and training. G-men had kept tabs on Galkin for several years, but had never uncovered any dark role that he might have been playing. He minded his manners well and seemed to devote himself wholeheartedly to his post at the UN as First Secretary of the Byelorussian Mission.

But once Maslennikov arrived, the pattern changed. So much so that the FBI intensified its surveillance immediately. And soon it saw a picture shaping with certain faint shadows that had the ominous configuration of a conspiracy.

It was their subway trips on the IRT line to Flushing, starting the second week after Maslennikov's arrival, which settled the mantle of suspicion on them. Ostensibly their journeys could readily have been dismissed as social sojourns, for their destination invariably was the apartment of still another Russian national, Ivan Dmitrievich Egerov. He was the $10,000-a-year personnel director of several UN administrative branches and councils. Egerov lived with his wife Aleksandra in a third-floor $135-a-month two-room apartment.

The job itself that the slim, black-haired Egerov held appeared to be mundane and largely uninteresting, and, except for whatever peripheral security information he may have picked up, in general was separate and apart from the inner workings of UN diplomacy. As a result, nothing on the job seemed to place Egerov in a sensitive position. Yet some things were noticed. It was Egerov's habit, for example, to socialize only with Soviet bloc diplomats and occasionally members of the Afro-Asian nations. In a way, that was a bit odd, since even agents coming directly from Moscow for espionage purposes alone made it a point to expand their social contacts and become as friendly as possible with Western diplomats.

It was probably Egerov's own shy personality along with his limited facility with the English language that kept him to himself. At official functions, according to reports the FBI received, Egerov was very correct and unobtrusive and, the FBI concluded, probably something of a bore. He resolutely avoided all UN reporters and correspondents, and the result was that few of the journalistic fraternity at the world headquarters of the United Nations could identify him by nationality and name.

Between 1960 and early 1962, therefore, Egerov had committed no overt act that commanded more than peripheral attention from the FBI. But the moment Maslennikov and Galkin began their curious subway rides out to Flushing to visit him, the alert signal went up and earlier tactics were abandoned for the new intensified plan of operation. The FBI began inquiring offhandedly, casually, unobtrusively, among his neighbors and co-tenants into Egerov's habits, attitudes, personality.

They learned, too, more about Egerov's short and rather plain-looking wife, Aleksandra. Like her husband, Aleksandra was apparently introverted, insecure with her knowledge of English, and quite content to spend her days alone at home or visiting with other wives of intermediate level Soviet bloc diplomats. Plump, Slavic in her facial contours, with slightly slanted eyes and high, rounded cheekbones, Aleksandra Egerov seemed to match her husband's quiet personality.

And, until early 1962, the FBI had never even seen her.

Neighbors in the suburban-like Flushing neighborhood said they were hardly aware of the Egerovs, and if they gave them any thought at all it was simply to notice them as a pleasant couple more interested in keeping to themselves than in becoming a part of the local social fabric.

None of the other tenants in the building recalled the Egerovs having visitors or throwing parties, and the superintendent remembered that the Egerovs asked for his assistance only once, when they were having trouble with a light switch.

None of the neighbors recalled seeing any children with the Egerovs. Yet a check with the State Department revealed that the couple did in fact bring a son with them to the United States from Russia, but that the boy was sent back in July, 1961, at the age of twelve, for schooling in the Soviet Union.

Although Egerov and his wife, through their new and sudden association with Maslennikov and Galkin, came under the watchful eye of the FBI on a steady basis, the agents concentrated on a vigilant observation of the activities of the two top Russian professionals and shadowed them virtually around the clock.

The wearisome trailing began paying quick dividends. A pattern of operation soon became discernible to the FBI, involving not just the visits to the Egerovs, but to assorted rendezvous points to the city which the FBI immediately suspected were actually drops for espionage material. At the same time, another element to the operations began to emerge, and as the FBI concentrated its surveillance and investigation on this angle, it became evident that the whole plot was triangulated between the UN, the Egerov apartment in Flushing, and Washington.

The first intimation that Maslennikov and Galkin were up to something came on September 23, 1962, when a pair of FBI agents picked up Maslennikov and Galkin in the late afternoon as they left the UN Building and walked to Grand Central Terminal three blocks away and boarded a New York Central commuter train. It was a sudden move, an unexpected one, and the FBI agents had no idea where the trail was leading. However, they were prepared for an assignment that might take them several days and had in fact barely deposited themselves in separate seats at either end of the coach in which Maslennikov and Galkin were also traveling, when the two Soviet diplomats rose and joined the commuter swarm disgorging itself at the Graystone station in Yonkers, just north of the New York City limits.

The FBI men picked out Maslennikov and Galkin from the throngs of brief-case-carrying, seersucker-suited young commuter executives and their uniformly cool, freshly coiffured wives waiting for them in the family Ramblers, Porsches, Volkswagens, Cadillacs, and other wagons that are the mark of suburban life. The G-men trailed their quarry out beyond the parking lot and up a tree-shaded street to a drugstore.

As the agents watched from a distance, they could see through the open door a man emerge from a pay telephone booth just as the Russians entered and then casually walk away. Galkin then entered the phone booth, appeared to make a call that lasted about a minute and a half, and then stepped out of the phone booth and, with Maslennikov, left the drugstore and returned to the Graystone station where they boarded the next New York-bound train.

To the uninitiated, the phone booth incident would seem completely innocent, but to the highly trained FBI agents it was far from innocent. From the fleeting look that passed between Galkin and the man who preceded him into the telephone booth, and from Galkin's quick, fluid motion as he slipped something into his pocket while in the phone booth, the FBI men were fairly certain that they had just seen a drop.

Maslennikov and Galkin were followed back to the city, but not by both agents. One G-man took off to fall in about fifty yards behind the mysterious stranger. The stranger walked for about a half hour, apparently aimlessly, in what the FBI perceived was a standard maneuver to throw off any pursuers. Then, quickly, at an intersection he hailed a taxicab fortuitously stopped there for a light, hopped into it, and sped away, leaving the FBI man stranded. The stranger evidently had been waiting for just such an opportunity, and in such circumstances there is nothing any sleuth can do but shrug it off as a bad break. Thereafter, the Graystone drugstore was kept under intensive surveillance, but never again was it used as a drop.

Over the next several days, the two Soviet diplomats made two more pilgrimages to Egerov's apartment. It now began to seem to the FBI that Egerov might be receiving instructions, possibly information, and transmitting this to someone. But to whom? And what was the nature of the information? The answers to both questions continued to elude the FBI.

Egerov himself had not yet made any overt move to link him to espionage activity. Then, on February 6, 1963, his time appeared to have come. At 7 p.m. he and his wife left their apartment, got into their 1960 black Pontiac sedan and drove off. They cruised around Queens for approximately an hour, always in a westward directional drift until they were in the Astoria section of the borough, practically just across the East River from the UN. Egerov tooled slowly through the streets of Astoria until 8:15 p.m. when, in the gathering darkness, he slowed down at an inconspicuous locale, on 19th Street which ran parallel to Astoria Park and beneath and between the shadows of the Triborough and Hell Gate Bridges. There he stopped.

He talked briefly to his wife sitting beside him in the car, and then got out and walked down the steps in the park leading to the municipal swimming pool. But instead of heading for the entrance, Egerov strolled around the side of the red brick wall and re-emerged ten seconds later with something clutched in his hand.

Back behind the wheel of his car, he handed the object to his wife who put it in her purse, and the two drove off.

Egerov had apparently accomplished his first observable act of spying, and his assignment, the FBI believed, was to pick up material left at the swimming pool drop.

One of the FBI agents had remained at the park to see if he could spot anyone. But the park was deserted. It was winter and the pool, of course, was closed. The agent saw no one, and, therefore, it seemed unlikely that another Soviet operative had actually met Egerov in that brief moment around the wall's corner. More probably some accomplice had simply left the material at a previously designated spot, perhaps in a trash basket the FBI man observed there, and had gone away before Egerov arrived.

Egerov and his wife returned home, saw Maslennikov and Galkin once again two evenings later, but they did nothing suspicious until five additional days had passed. Then the slim Russian and his plump wife took another outwardly looking aimless drive through Queens. This time they journeyed to a quiet, residential neighborhood of Woodside, midway between Flushing and Astoria. Egerov parked his car near an intersection about two blocks from the Long Island Railroad's Woodside station. He opened the door on his side and with his left hand threw a small brown envelope beneath his car, as though he were discarding some trash. Then he drove away.

This time the FBI did not follow. This time it was quite clear Egerov was making the drop. And now the FBI agents in their own car across the street and a hundred feet behind sat watching. They did not wait long.

Less than a minute later, a 1958 blue two-door Ford sedan pulled up to the same corner and parked a car's length behind the spot where Egerov had stopped. The driver got out, picked up the envelope, and turned back to his car. In so doing, he unknowingly faced into the binoculars in the hands of the one agent and the telescopic-lensed camera of the other.

He drove away with the agents behind. The stranger headed into Queens Boulevard, one of the borough's main thoroughfares, and followed it out to the entrance onto the Grand Central Parkway. Ten minutes later he was at La Guardia Airport, where he left the car in the parking lot and boarded the next shuttle flight to Washington.

The agents did not have to follow him to the capital. A simple phone call to the New York Bureau office giving the stranger's full description and his destination touched off an immediate teletype advisory to Washington. Other agents were waiting to pick up the suspect's trail when he debarked at the nation's capital. At the airport in New York, the first pair of agents kept themselves staked out at the parking lot to see who picked up the car. Twenty minutes after the plane took off, Maslennikov and Galkin drove to the lot. Galkin got out and drove the car away.

In Washington, an FBI team watched the shuttle flight arrive and the passengers debark. From the moment the suspect was spotted, an inseparable shadow in the persons of four crack G-men fell across him. The mysterious traveler took a taxi from the airport to 2839 27th Street, just off Connecticut Avenue. The building housed sixteen apartments. The stranger disappeared behind the entrance door. As soon as it was safe enough, the FBI men also went into the building. They heard footsteps climbing to the fourth floor. Keys jangled, a latch clicked open, and a door slammed. The FBI men were easily able to tell by the direction of the sounds they heard which apartment had been entered.

And then it was a simple routine of looking at the name on the bells and mailboxes downstairs to determine the identity of the tenant. There were two—Robert K. Balch and Joy Ann Balch. The names meant nothing to the FBI. They surmised they belonged to a husband and wife or brother and sister.

An intensive rundown through official records—military, civil service, FBI, and capital police yellow sheets—was begun at once. By the following day the FBI knew the backgrounds of both. They were husband and wife. Balch was a part-time student and teacher in a private school across the Potomac in Alexandria, Virginia, licensed to teach by the Virginia Department of Education. Inquiries at the apartment revealed that Joy Ann Balch had lived there previous to her marriage under her maiden name of Joy Ann Garber. An FBI man, tailing her as she left the building at 8:25 a.m., found she worked as a manicurist in a downtown Washington beauty salon.

On the surface, the information seemed legitimate enough. But as the investigation probed deeper, a strange picture began to emerge. In checking out the information that Balch had submitted in applying for his teaching certificate, the FBI agents were astonished to learn that there appeared to be two Robert K. Balches with seemingly identical backgrounds.

Beginning with his birth certificate registered in an upstate county in New York, the FBI traced his life's progress and found that the Robert K. Balch living in Washington had somehow also become a Roman Catholic priest living in Amsterdam, New York. Their backgrounds were abolutely identical. The parents' names were the same, the dates of birth were the same, the schools they attended were the same, the graduation dates were the same. The total picture, in fact, pointed to two possible alternatives. Either Robert K. Balch was living a double existence and somehow was diabolically combining twin careers as a Catholic priest and a teacher, as well as that of a Soviet spy; or, more probably, the Soviet spy was arrogantly appropriating a living Catholic priest's identity to cover up his own.

It took no more than hours to clarify the fact that there was a Reverend Robert Keistutis Balch serving a parish in Amsterdam, New York. It was now clear that the probable was true. Someone had appropriated the priest's identity.

Now the FBI reasoned that if the ersatz Balch was living under an assumed name, so was his wife. And a similar inquiry into her identity was launched. Implausibly enough, the probers found that Joy Ann Balch, previously Joy Ann Garber, had adopted the same maneuver as her husband and had literally stolen the identity of a woman who was now Mrs. Robert Seskin, a housewife in Norwalk, Connecticut. Neither Mrs. Seskin nor Father Balch had any inkling that they were the dupes in so bizarre a masquerade.

By late April, 1963, nearly all the pieces had fallen into place. The Washington Balches were phonies, but who were they? The FBI could not determine that, short of taking them in custody and questioning them. The time for that would soon come.

Meanwhile, the loose ends on the case had to be tied up. FBI agents in Washington and New York began collating all the available information.

The evidence showed that the two suspected masterminds, Maslennikov and Galkin, were collecting highly classified information. How the FBI knew this has not been revealed to the authors; the FBI and the Justice Department withheld these details because the case —as the surprising climax will show—is not yet closed. Nevertheless, the FBI has said that the information was technical in nature and related to the national defense, and particularly to military installations, naval facilities, shipyards, military waterfront operations, and troop movements. The data, according to the FBI, was transmitted onto magnetic tapes in some instances, then placed in protective capsules for delivery to the Soviet spy network.

This much was revealed about the operation: Maslennikov and Galkin used the Balches and the Egerovs as intercity couriers. When the transmission of secret information from New York to Washington became necessary in the opinion of Maslennikov, either he or Galkin would travel out to Flushing for a "social visit," carrying the magnetic tape to Egerov. Egerov would then arrange a drop delivery locale with Balch, and Balch would catch a shuttle flight to New York, pick up the material from the drop, and immediately fly back to the capital.

Similarly, if Maslennikov decided he wanted a first-hand look at espionage material channeled into the Soviet Embassy in Washington, Balch would be utilized as the courier carrying the information north. This time, Balch would deliver to the drop and Egerov would retrieve the material and hand it over to Maslennikov and Galkin on their next visit to his apartment in Flushing.

Very rarely Egerov would be unable for some reason or other to perform the assignment. In that case, Maslennikov and Galkin would have to carry out that duty themselves. The Graystone drugstore drop was one such incident.

With the full sinister picture of the triangular operation in clear focus and each perpetrator's role fully understood, it now became simply a matter of waiting for the right moment to close in, a time when the physical evidence of the magnetic tape was present to implicate the conspirators.

The long cold winter had now gone its weary way and the warmth and green of spring were rejuvenating the land when the FBI was given an unexpected and terribly disappointing jolt. In early May Maslennikov and Galkin abruptly halted all official activity at the UN and virtually overnight departed New York for Moscow. Characteristically the Russians gave no reason for the departure, nor could the FBI determine any way in which the two professional spies might have been tipped off.

Possibly the Soviet espionage network had somehow picked up on its antenna some slight but discomforting disturbance and decided to play it safe. Conceivably the FBI inquiries among tenants and others who knew the fraudulent Balches and the Egerovs had somehow become known to the Soviets at the UN. Whatever the reason, Maslennikov and Galkin were now frustratingly beyond the clutch of American justice—whatever that means in dealing with Soviet agents who have the protective cloak of diplomatic immunity. At worst, if Maslennikov and Galkin had stuck around, they would have been taken in custody for a few hours, then freed, and booted out after the now-routine procedure of a State Department demand to the Soviet Mission for their expulsion. Can anyone venture to say that the end would have been any different if Maslennikov and Galkin had not left the country when they did?

So Maslennikov and Galkin, the big game, were gone. However, the FBI was determined not to let the same thing happen to the Washington Balches and the New York Egerovs. After synchronizing their plans, separate teams of FBI men in the nation's capital and in New York drew in their nets simultaneously.

Just as the fiery-red sun of an intensely hot July 3 began to dip in the western horizon, four FBI men drove along Connecticut Avenue to the Balches' apartment at 2839 27th Street and came to a halt directly in front of the building. It was 6:30 p.m.

Another agent, on stakeout, nodded the signal that meant the Balches were home. All five agents moved quietly up the stairs to the fourth floor and a moment later confronted Robert and Joy Ann Balch.

"We're the FBI," the lead agent stated bluntly. "You're under arrest."

The five agents swept into the apartment and two of them quickly clamped handcuffs on the astonished couple. The FBI men looked around the flat. They had plainly made their move just in time. Two steamer trunks, nearly full, were up against the wall, open. Clothes and possessions had been jammed every which way into them. The closets were empty. Two plane tickets on Sabena Airlines to Copenhagen were on the dresser. The couple's passports were beside the tickets. The FBI had gotten there with only a few brief hours to spare.

The Balches were taken to the District of Columbia jail in the early morning hours of the next day, after they had undergone intensive questioning at the FBI offices. It was a hopeless effort questioning the Balches. They refused absolutely to say anything.

"You still have to prove these charges," Joy Ann Balch screamed at the FBI men as they led her for the formal booking before a U.S. commissioner.

Balch was somewhat calmer. "The only declaration I wish to make is that I deny all charges," he muttered, practically under his breath.

Unknown to the Balches, the same swift justice was closing in on their co-conspirators two hundred and fifty miles away in Flushing, Queens.

Precisely at 6:30 p.m., the FBI surprised the Egerovs, and with a curt declaration that they were under arrest, flashed their two sets of handcuffs. Numbed into inaction by the unexpected raid, Egerov meekly held out his hands as the manacles snapped around his wrist. But the plump and deceptively docile-looking Aleksandra suddenly unleashed the fury of a wounded tiger and lunged at her captors. Growling, snarling, and cursing at them in Russian, her arms flailed at the FBI men and her feet whipped out in viciously aimed kicks. But the agents managed to take her in tow and brought her down to the waiting car with her husband.

Neighbors were astonished at the arrest of the Egerovs. A housewife living on the same floor looked out the door as they were taken away and shook her head.

"I knew they were from the Soviet Mission," she said. "But they were so very ordinary someone might have thought they were just another immigrant couple living here as American citizens. And they seemed like such nice, quiet people. I can't believe they were spies."

Like the Balches in Washington, the Egerovs were arraigned before a U.S. commissioner in the Federal Courthouse in Brooklyn which has jurisdiction over Queens and the Long Island area. Like the Balches, they were held without bail and remanded to the Federal House of Detention.

They were allowed to call the Soviet Mission and a representative from the Mission soon appeared and demanded the Egerovs' release on the grounds that they were protected by diplomatic immunity. At the same time, the Soviet Embassy in Washington called on the State Department, and another Soviet diplomat at the United Nations appealed to the Secretary General's office for the Egerovs' release. But in all cases, the Soviets were turned down flatly. They were told that the much-abused shield of immunity did not extend to Egerov nor his wife. He was simply an employee of the United Nations, not a diplomat acting as a representative of his government, nor employed in the Soviet Mission.

The Egerovs and the Balches both languished in jail as the machinery of the American legal process went to work to bring them to trial after indictments by Federal grand juries were returned in Washington and New York against them.

But then an almost inevitable development occurred, a development that had now become monotonously routine in the handling of Soviet spy suspects. Washington and Moscow worked a deal. We would give them Ivan Dmitrievich Egerov and his wife Aleksandra in return for two Americans then being held in Russia on similar charges.

On October 12, 1963, the discredited Egerovs sullenly boarded a plane at Idlewild Airport that took them back to Moscow. And somewhere, as the plane crossed the Atlantic, another airliner was bringing home the Reverend Walter M. Cizek of Shenandoah Valley, Pennsylvania, a 58-year-old Jesuit Missionary, and Marvin W. Makinen, 24, of Ashburnham, Massachusetts. Makinen, a visitor to the Soviet Union, had been arrested on espionage charges in 1961 and had served two years of an eight-year prison term. Father Cizek, gaunt, weakened, but not broken, was coming back after twenty-three cruel, almost unbelievable, years in a Siberian labor camp where he had been confined by Stalin for alleged activities against the State.

From the United States' point of view, it was more than a worthwhile exchange. The Egerovs would never again take part in espionage against the U.S., while on the moral level, releasing Father Cizek—and Makinen, too—was infinitely more humanitarian than incarcerating the Egerovs.

As for the Balches, no such deal was arranged. These transactions are always kept secret until the final details are completed and the accused spies are actually released. But in the Balches' case, why should there be a deal? Who said they were Russian? The truth of it was that no one really knew who they were. The couple steadfastly refused to answer the questions of the FBI and the assistant attorney generals who tried to pry from them their real identities and their places of origin. They could have dropped down on the United States from Mars so far as anyone knew. The Russians pretended not even to be aware of their existence.

The case was put on the Federal Court calendar in the District of Columbia for trial January 6, 1964. But it was postponed again and again. Observers familiar with espionage matters had a feeling that the Balches would ultimately be released and deported, since convictions are rarely obtained when the defendants' very co-conspirators have been given their freedom. The case of Willie Hirsch was a classic example. When Igor Yakovlevich Melekh was deported, the Federal prosecutor no longer had a case against the German-born illustrator and it was dropped. Hirsch was then deported.

In the latest espionage case, however, the Government suddenly announced it was finally ready to go to trial, and on September 29th the proceedings got under way in Brooklyn's Federal Court. By now the Government had developed additional information against the Balches, but it apparently contributed little material value to the case. The most important of this evidence was that Balch was at last identified as one Aleksandre Sokolov, from Tiflis, Russia. But the Soviet Union still evinced no interest.

The indictment under which the Sokolovs were to be tried named Egerov and his wife, as well as Maslennikov and Galkin, "plus various other officials of the Soviet Military Intelligence."

Defense Attorney Edward Brodsky, representing the Sokolovs, demanded to know who these "various other" people might be. The Government furnished a list: Dmitri Fedorovich Polyakov, Anatoli Borisovich Senkin, and Lev V. Sosnovski. But, alas—the Government attorneys shook their heads—they too have returned home. It was explained that these Russians held posts at the UN, and served as couriers in transmitting stolen data to Moscow.

Only one witness of any substance appeared to be waiting in the wings to put the finger on the Sokolovs, or Balches. This was Kaarlo Rudolph Tuomi, a 45-year-old Finn who had been a trusted officer in the Soviet Union's Military Intelligence Bureau. What role he played in the case was not clear, but this much about his past was revealed: Tuomi was recruited into the GRU, the Chief Intelligence Directorate, after the Russians conquered his homeland during the bitter winter campaign of 1939–40; then several years ago he gained a measure of revenge by enlisting in the CIA as a counterspy after being sent here by the Russians to work with a Soviet espionage ring operating in the U.S.

But Brodsky, a brilliant 34-year-old attorney who had been chief of the Government's special prosecution division of the Southern District of New York during 1961–62, threw a well-aimed monkey wrench into the prosecution's case right at the start. Brodsky informed Judge John F. Dooling, Jr., that the prosecution must produce all the addresses of some 80 Government witnesses it planned to summon to the trial—including the addresses of 75 FBI agents and others who took part in the trackdown of the Soviet spy ring.

Otherwise, the defense declared, all witnesses "whose abode was not given" must be excluded. That meant Tuomi, the star witness, too.

Judge Dooling ruled for the defense, saying that the home addresses of all witnesses—including the 75 FBI men and Tuomi—be given to Brodsky, and the Sokolovs, if they wanted them.

"Opponents of the FBI would give quite a bit to have all those home addresses," observed Paul C. Vincent of the Justice Department, who came up from Washington to assist U.S. Attorney Joseph P. Hoey, of the Brooklyn District, in the prosecution.

Judge Dooling then addressed himself to Vincent.

"If you tell me that disclosure would imperil the life of a man or the security of the United States, I will not disclose the addresses."

Vincent replied, "I can make no such statement, as it would be speculation."

"The defendants," the court declared, "have a statutory right to see such a list, under a law of 1795 wherein access to witnesses specified their abode."

The defense then leaped in with a motion to dismiss the 15-month-old indictment, but it was denied by the court. The trial was to go on, one way or another. In an anteroom 300 prospective jurors who had been waiting heard the call, and three days later the panel, including alternates, was picked. The morning of October 2 was to see the jurors sworn in and the trial get under way with opening statements by prosecution and defense.

The jury was sworn in but no opening statements were made. Instead a recess was called amid an air of great bewilderment. When court was convened at 3:10 p.m., U.S. Attorney Hoey rose and addressed himself to the bench in a very dispirited voice.

"Your Honor, I have been instructed by the Attorney General [Acting Attorney General Nicholas de B. Katzenbach, in the absence of Robert F. Kennedy who had resigned to run successfully for the U.S. Senate in New York] that in the interest of national security, he would not offer any evidence relating to Overt Acts 6 and 7 of the indictment. The Government could not make an opening statement that could withstand a motion for dismissal."

The slender, timid-looking 40-year-old Sokolov reached out almost in triumph and squeezed his wife's hand. Dark-haired, dark-eyed, 34-year-old Joy Ann wept softly.

"These are the only acts within the conspiracy which connect the two defendants with this conspiracy," Hoey continued. "The Government moves to dismiss this indictment against both these defendants."

The move was sudden and dramatic and left courtroom spectators and jury alike thoroughly stunned.

Judge Dooling's sentiments were reflected strongly in his statement to the jurors before dismissing them.

"Your first sense of this must be a mixture of mystification and the futility of our week's work together," he said solemnly with no trace of the smile so often lighting his face the first few days of the proceedings. "Neither you nor I can know with what complexities our Government has had to deal and deal responsibly."

Judge Dooling explained that the case could not be tried because the defendants were entitled to a public hearing—open in every respect.

"The interests of our national security, it has been concluded, precludes that. No trial at all is better than a secret trial on shapeless charges, without witnesses. We can take pride in the majesty of spirit that disdains to deviate one iota from principle in order to attain a particular objective. We can count ourselves honored to witness this dignified act of constitutional government. This is government as free men would have it."

With that the jury was dismissed.

The defendants were met at the door by agents of the Immigration and Naturalization Service and presented with an aliens' arrest warrant. They were not surprised and evinced no outward emotion as they were taken in custody after their brief moment of freedom which had brought them from the front of the courtroom to the back. The arresting officers whisked the couple to 20 West Broadway in Manhattan, where a hearing was held before the district's immigration director, Peter Esperdy.

Esperdy remanded Sokolov to the Federal House of Detention and his wife to Civil Prison to await deportation proceedings.

When the hearing was held, both Sokolov and his wife expressed a desire to be deported to Czechoslovakia. The Czech government, acting through its emissary in Washington, granted the couple's request —and on the night of October 15, 1963, Aleksandre Sokolov, alias Robert Keistutis Balch, and his wife Joy Ann Sokolov, alias Joy Ann Garber and Joy Ann Balch, left New York aboard an Air India flight for their new homeland.

The FBI had little doubt the Sokolovs were heading back to Russia where they would be welcomed with open arms.

Spies such as the Sokolovs were suspected of being are a rare type. They are dedicated to their profession, true to their masters.

No doubt the Soviet Union can find employment for them elsewhere.

16 : The Electronics Engineer and the Russian Chauffeur

THE FBI agents felt the cold late October drizzle trickling down their necks and into their already badly soaked shirt collars, and in the gloomy darkness they must have silently cursed all the spies who had lived. Only a nut would be out on a night like this. The agents, shivering against the cold and misery of the night, hugged the rain-shiny tree trunks that served as their covers.

Standing back in the shadowy stand of maples edging the parking lot at the old stone Erie & Lackawanna Railroad station in Englewood, New Jersey, only one thing made their ordeal any lighter. They knew the Russian spy beneath the tree just fifty feet away from the nearest FBI man was getting just as wet. If only the trap worked—a trap that had been eighteen months in the making—the FBI men might just get home before pulmonary pneumonia brought their lovely wives to premature widowhood.

The agents were all in their places. They were ready. Now it all depended on the greed of John William Butenko.

The trail that, an hour from now, might end in the smashing of one of the most dangerous Soviet spy operations to threaten American security in recent years, had begun a year and a half ago—eighteen months cluttered with an endless series of pursuits, stakeouts, travels, dead ends, messages, and rain-soaked nights of sometimes fruitless surveillance. But all together, they had brought the FBI to the threshold of success.

Now, in the immediate vicinity of the old railroad depot, thirteen FBI agents were carefully positioned according to the pre-planned strategy that had been so laboriously laid out. Some were hidden in some of the hundred dark pockets of shadow around the depot. Others were in cars. Several hid behind trees and absorbed the full brunt of the drenching downpour. Two had movie cameras equipped with infra-red film, ready to shoot through the misty black of night at the 1956 green Ford sedan with the two suspected Russian spies inside. Off near the parking lot entrance beneath another waterlogged maple stood a third spy, hunched deep into his double-breasted black raincoat, serving as a lookout, unaware that all around him were the FBI agents poised for the kill.

All that remained now to complete the gloomy tableau was the arrival of John Butenko.

Let us introduce some of those in the cast of G-men, those who played predominant roles and who later on will show up with star billing in the halls of justice where the case ultimately winds up:

Special Agents Edmund Birch, William V. Schmaltz, Thomas B. James, Robert Haines, Allan A. Anderson, Arthur K. Dowd, Jr., Carmelo Graffagnini, Edward Moody, George Allf, George MacDougal, Robert Conway, Joseph L. Conway, and Bernard J. Dabinett.

Thirteen agents are named here and eleven of these were posted around the station now. Despite the rain, there was little doubt in the minds of these thirteen G-men that Butenko would show up. The agents knew Butenko as they knew few other suspected traitors. They had virtually eaten and slept with him ever since he had first drawn attention to himself as a suspected collaborator with the Soviet espionage tangle at the United Nations.

The FBI's first encounter with John William Butenko came early in 1962 when he crossed the sights they had trained on a dapper, 39-year-old attaché in the Soviet Mission to the UN named Gleb A. Pavlov. They had been watching Pavlov on and off since he had landed in America in 1960, but to all appearances the handsome Moscow-trained diplomat was hewing to the line and staying clear of espionage work. At their first sight of Butenko, the FBI had no idea who he was. But when he and Pavlov met, they decided they had better do a little checking.

It was an easy matter to put a shadow on the unsuspecting Butenko, and very soon they had a fairly comprehensive file on him. Several things in his background raised the flag on the man and made it more than prudent that they keep a closer watch on him.

In their characteristically thorough way, the FBI was able to catalogue virtually all of the important landmarks in Butenko's life. They discovered he was born on July 6, 1925, in New Brunswick, New Jersey, the son of parents who migrated from Kiev, Russia, during the reign of the czar. His father had been naturalized and made his home in New Jersey almost from the time of his arrival in this country. Butenko attended New Brunswick High School and was graduated in 1942. He joined the Navy and served with the Seabees from December 24, 1943, to December 1, 1944. Then he was returned to civilian life because of an emotional instability. He received a medical discharge under honorable conditions.

His naval medical history was and is a confidential record, but there is later evidence to indicate that among his emotional defects was a predilection for violence. Nothing on the public record pointed to the young Butenko as a social animal. On the contrary, the facts and marginal notations on his life portrayed him as an introvert, an isolate, a loner.

Soon after his discharge from the Navy, he entered Rutgers University in New Brunswick and spent four years there, studying electrical engineering. He finished well up in his class, but his behavioral patterns remained the same. He continued to be withdrawn, aloof. He was graduated with honors from Rutgers in 1949 and then embarked on an electrical engineering career which took him bouncing around from job to job, although usually within the New York-New Jersey metropolitan area. He held several engineering jobs with the Radio Corporation of America in Harrison; with the Armed Services Electro-Standard Agency at Fort Monmouth—both in New Jersey; and with the Civil Aeronautics Administration in Jamaica, Queens.

In 1960, the now 35-year-old, bushy-haired engineer applied for a position with the International Electric Corporation in Paramus, New Jersey, a subsidiary of International Telephone and Telegraph Corporation. He was conditionally hired while he underwent a six-month-long Air Force clearance investigation, and then he landed a $15,400-a-year job as a control administrator. With his top-secret credentials, he had unrestricted access to documents and information about International Electric's most important and secret job—managing the production of a world-wide electronics control system for the Strategic Air Command, the nervous system vital to the manned bomber weapons-delivery system that gives the United States so powerful a nuclear deterrent force. Specifically, it was Butenko's primary duty to maintain a master schedule of every aspect of International Electric's contract with the Air Force. The project had the designation 465L.

Thus the FBI had shaped a skeletal profile of Butenko from his public records. For the bones and flesh, they looked beyond the written file and studied the man himself.

They saw an enigma. For example, Butenko seemed to be a devoted son who tenderly cared for his ailing father. The father, in his eighties and widowed now, was confined to a wheelchair. Butenko spent a good deal of time offering companionship to the old man who lived with him in a $140-a-month three-room apartment in a Tudor-styled, seven-unit apartment building on a patch of beautifully landscaped grounds at 366 Park Avenue in Orange, New Jersey. By every account he was a dutiful son. When he had to leave town, he would ask the landlord to look in on his father whose confinement was a result of a broken hip suffered in a fall.

Other reports showed him to be kind and thoughtful in other ways. He would frequently ask neighbors' children to join him for milk and sandwiches at home and let them stay a while and watch color TV. Though a bachelor, he never seemed to have any dates with women and rarely entertained. In general, he avoided socializing with others in the community, but during the summer of 1962 he did join other residents in the apartment house for probably the first time in a swimming and picnic outing at New Jersey's Lake Hopatcong.

But there was another side to John Butenko's personality, a side that seemed strangely discordant to the dutiful son, the avuncular pal to the neighborhood small fry. The FBI learned, for example, that while Butenko was living in Franklin Township with his mother and father, he had become involved in an angry argument with his mother and, in an outburst of rage, struck her and broke her collarbone.

And still other reports the FBI pieced together through scrupulous inquiry depicted Butenko as a rather heavy drinker who liked the horses, who plunged heavily in high-stake card games, and who frequently ran into debt. And one other report, never fully developed for lack of adequate information, stated that Butenko "defended homosexuals."

By the time the FBI began investigating him because of his alliance with the Soviet attaché, Gleb Pavlov, Butenko had developed a reputation for being excessively interested in money, particularly the stock market and insurance and investment trusts. One associate, Alfred A. Arky of West Orange, Butenko's attorney, said he was with Butenko at a party when the engineer discussed the gold standard and international exchange with considerable insight.

With this accumulation of background information on him, the FBI concentrated now more on Butenko's relationship with Pavlov and with others who, by the nature of their work, had come under the FBI's watchful eye. One was Vladimir I. Olenev, a Soviet UN Mission aide, the other, Igor A. Ivanov, a chauffeur for the Amtorg Trading Corporation, the Soviet corporate invention established in this country to promote Russian trade. This, as the FBI has indicated publicly, is an outfit that quite often serves as a cover for Soviet spies.

With increasing frequency, Butenko would meet with one or more of the Soviet trio until it became clear they were absorbing most of his non-working time. For the FBI agents assigned to the case, Butenko's association with Pavlov, Olenev, and Ivanov had all the earmarks of an old familiar refrain—conspiracy. The question was did Butenko enter the conspiracy, if that was what it was, voluntarily or involuntarily. The FBI knew from long experience that Butenko was a classical example of the potential espionage recruit. His heritage was Russian. He could speak the Russian language. He had a good technical education. He was in a sensitive and, therefore, valuable job. And beyond all that, he had uncles, aunts, and other relatives in Russia and was thus vulnerable to blackmail.

On the other hand, Butenko displayed enough characteristics to lead the FBI to believe that he'd be willing to sell his services to the Soviets, or perhaps to anyone, for the right price. Whatever the genesis of his relationship to the Russian triad of Pavlov, Olenev, and Ivanov, the FBI decided that too much was at stake to waste any time on idle speculation.

By mid-summer of 1962, John Butenko never strayed from the sight of an FBI agent. He was watched constantly. And soon it became apparent from the timetable of his meetings with the Russians and from the elaborate, although unsuccessful, steps he took to shake any possible followers, that Butenko was indeed involved in something inimical to the nation's security.

One thing seemed obvious. Butenko must be giving the Russians information dealing with the electronic control system of the Strategic Air Command to which Butenko, of course, had unlimited access. It therefore became imperative to cut off the flow of information, and yet at the same time preserve Butenko's value to the Russians.

The FBI hoped in doing that to accomplish two purposes. One would be to feed the Soviet espionage monster false and misleading information, and the other was to prolong Butenko's role as a suspected spy until the FBI could determine the full nature and scope of the operation and learn the identity of everyone involved.

The result was a highly secret agreement between the FBI and two or three of International Electric's top officials. Together they arranged not only to continue to give Butenko access to documents about the SAC communications project, but to carefully doctor them in such a way that the Russians were getting false information without arousing Butenko's suspicions.

As the months wore on, Butenko's meetings with the Russians, Pavlov in particular, became more frequent. Yet the G-men never actually witnessed an overt act of espionage. The FBI was quite certain by now that Butenko was transmitting information to the Russians, and still there seemed to be no way to catch him at it. And without documentary evidence there could be no way to make their case stand up.

It wasn't until April 21, 1963, that the FBI got a first glimpse of Butenko passing something to the Russians. On that day, Gleb Pavlov drove into New Jersey with Olenev and Ivanov and headed for a restaurant in the community of Northvale. There Pavlov temporarily abandoned Olenev and Ivanov and waited, with his car's engine running, against the curb on the highway until a white 1959 Chrysler New Yorker slowed down, edged toward Pavlov's car, and then swung out again, accelerating.

Pavlov's 1956 green Ford stationwagon with New York license plate No. 2N-3078 shot out into the highway, and soon the two cars were rolling in tandem toward Closter, New Jersey, where both came to a stop at an A&P Supermarket parking lot. There Butenko—for he was the Chrysler's driver—handed Pavlov a brown leather briefcase. Then Pavlov drove back and picked up his confederates at the restaurant in Northvale.

On other occasions the FBI witnessed similar meetings in New Jersey, always at a restaurant but always at a different one. And always the same roundabout tactics were used in the rendezvous. In one of these, a fourth Russian went along. He was Yuri A. Romashin, another Soviet Mission aide. But it was always Pavlov who appeared to be masterminding the meetings, who did the talking, who stayed with Butenko, while the others spent the time poring over the contents of the briefcase. The FBI drew the conclusion that Pavlov was the arranger, the "fixer," and that the others, particularly the new man, Romashin, were the technical experts capable of comprehending and assessing the significance of the data delivered by Butenko.

Another rendezvous came on May 26. This time Pavlov, Olenev, and Ivanov drove to the vicinity of Closter where Olenev and Ivanov got out of the car and went into a roadside restaurant. Pavlov, behind the wheel, remained in the car. Minutes later, with a tan leather case in his possession, Butenko also drove to the vicinity of Closter. This time Pavlov and Butenko did not make immediate contact but waited until nine o'clock at night when they met at a pre-arranged destination. Butenko got out of the car with the attaché case in his right hand, walked to Pavlov's Ford, climbed into the front seat beside the Russian official, spoke to him for about three minutes, then emerged and went back to his own car—empty-handed.

The next day Butenko drove from Paramus toward Fort Lee. At the same time, Pavlov, carrying a reddish-brown briefcase, headed for Fort Lee and later rendezvoused with Butenko outside a restaurant. When Butenko drove off, the reddish-brown case was in his car. Later that evening, Butenko and Pavlov met again in Paramus and talked together in the front seat of Butenko's car. Meanwhile Romashin, apparently just killing time, was driving back and forth between Paramus and Teaneck. A short while later Romashin met Pavlov in front of a Paramus restaurant, picked him up, and drove back to New York City.

All the while, of course, the FBI was watching every move.

Now that they knew the modus operandi, the FBI decided to move in on the conspirators. All that had to be done was to catch the Russians with a briefcase in their hands. The FBI wasn't at all skeptical about the contents it would find in the briefcase. It had a pretty good idea what they would be.

On the night of Tuesday, October 29, 1963, that cold, rainy night laden with the first shivering suggestion of the coming winter, the FBI agents on the case finally got their chance. They were ready.

From previous observation, they knew the Russians reached the rendezvous point first and were then joined by Butenko. And thus it was that, as Pavlov's 1956 green Ford sat idling in the darkness of the Erie & Lackawanna Railroad station parking lot in Englewood, the eleven FBI agents, including the five with the thoroughly soaked shirt collars beneath rain-soaked maples, were there and waiting to spring the carefully laid trap.

Actually the agents waiting for Butenko's arrival had a firm idea he'd be coming, for they had received a radio message from Agent Arthur Dowd that the engineer had just left his house. Another agent, Allan A. Anderson, had watched Butenko come out of his apartment at 366 Park Avenue in Orange and walk to the lot behind the house. He saw him open the door and lift a reddish-brown leather attaché case into the passenger seat. Butenko couldn't see Anderson because the agent was in another apartment in the housing development, looking down from a window.

And as Butenko drove off, Dowd followed a short distance behind in his own car, radioing ahead an alert to Englewood.

It was not quite eight o'clock when Butenko's car approached the parking lot in the railroad depot, picked up the waiting green Ford in its headlights, drove by once, then twice, and then finally cut into the parking lot itself and drew up behind Pavlov's machine.

On both his preliminary passes, the FBI men in the three separate cars, parked haphazardly and discreetly distant enough from the parking lot, ducked down and were not seen by Butenko. As the FBI men looked on, Butenko got out of his car, carrying a leather attaché case, and climbed in beside Pavlov in the Ford.

The lookout man in the double-breasted black raincoat, standing soaked under the tree—the FBI would soon learn it was Romashin—waited. The FBI waited.

To make the arrests valid, the G-men would have to find the incriminating documents in Pavlov's car. After a moment, Butenko hopped out of the Ford and dashed back to his own car. Romashin ran through the rain to join Pavlov. Ivanov was also in the car. Then both cars headed for the roadway. Neither made it.

Engines roaring, the three FBI cars burst forward and converged on the parking lot, blocking the conspirators' exit. Then the FBI agents bolted from their cars and other vantage posts and descended on the suspects who sat frozen like so many marble statues in their cars.

Inside Pavlov's car, the G-men found Butenko's briefcase jammed thick with highly secret papers from International Electric Corporation. A further search uncovered a small automatic .35-mm. document-copying camera ingeniously camouflaged as the cigarette lighter on the dashboard, and other evidence that would be revealed later at the trial.

All of the suspects were taken under armed guard to the FBI offices in Newark. Within two hours Pavlov and Romashin were freed under the provisions of the UN Charter granting diplomatic immunity, a familiar story by now. But Ivanov, who had no such protection since he was an employee of Amtorg, a commercial enterprise, and Butenko, who, of course, was an American citizen, were held on espionage charges. Only Olenev eluded arrest. He wasn't with the boys this night.

Butenko and Ivanov were arraigned at 2 a.m. before U.S. Commissioner Theodore C. Kiscaras in Rutherford, New Jersey, and held in $100,000 bail each. They were then lodged in the Hudson County Jail in Jersey City. Later on that morning of October 30, the State Department delivered a note of protest to the head of the Soviet Mission to the UN and demanded the expulsion of Gleb Pavlov, Yuri Romashin, and Vladimir Olenev for their espionage activities against the

United States. Within forty-eight hours all three were on their way back to Moscow.

On November 7, a Federal grand jury, sitting in Newark, returned true bills against the Russian diplomats in absentia, charging them as co-conspirators but not defendants. The panel reserved its big punch for Ivanov and Butenko, charging them with the capital crime of espionage.

They were arraigned on the indictments before Federal Judge Thomas F. Meaney in Newark and remanded back to the Hudson County Jail without bail on the plea of U.S. Attorney David M. Satz, Jr., who argued that bail should be denied since the offense carried the death penalty upon conviction. The wording of the charge, he emphasized, was "delivering to a foreign government information relating to the national defense of the United States."

Judge Meaney set a hearing for November 15, when the two suspects would be allowed to plead.

Attorneys for Butenko and Ivanov promptly sought relief in the Circuit Court of Appeals for the Third District, sitting in Philadelphia, from the ruling that prohibited them from posting bail. The court denied the motion. On November 15, Ivanov and Butenko appeared in Newark's Federal Court and both pleaded not guilty to the indictment.

In order that no question could be raised about Ivanov's misunderstanding the proceedings, Judge Meaney insisted that the indictment be read in Russian, and the translation was done by Aleksei Kozikov of the Soviet Embassy in Washington. Assistant U.S. Attorney Sanford Jaffe indicated that the trial would begin the following January.

In a surprise move on December 19, though, the Russian Embassy in Washington deposited with the clerk of the U.S. District Court in Newark a certified check for $100,000 to obtain Ivanov's release. The action had been rumored for days and it appeared to be in line with the continuing trend toward more cordial relations between the United States and the Soviet Union. The U.S. Government evidently felt that releasing Ivanov on bail would be an appropriate gesture of good will. In return, Moscow went so far as to guarantee Ivanov's appearance at his trial. Ivanov was released with the proviso that he was not to leave the New York-New Jersey area.

Meanwhile, Butenko languished in his jail cell. No privilege of bail was granted to him. Then, in still another unexpected move, U.S. District Court Judge Anthony T. Augelli ordered Butenko committed to "a suitable federal institution" to determine whether he was mentally competent to stand trial.

Surprisingly enough, the motion to commit Butenko was made by his own co-counselor, Stephen Maskaleris, who based his request on the finding of two doctors whom he had asked to examine his client in the county jail. Butenko reacted furiously to the attorney's suggestion and promptly fired Maskaleris. Butenko didn't want to be examined.

The usual delays involved in accumulating evidence and preparing a case of this magnitude kept advancing the trial date until it was finally set for the fall of 1964.

Prosecutor Jaffe saw a long, bitterly fought court battle that would last at least four weeks. He had correctly assessed the bitterness, but was only half right about its duration. It lasted eight weeks.

The trial opened October 5, 1964, in Newark's Federal Court, with Judge Augelli presiding and a panel of 500 prospective jurors reporting. But with the decision not to prosecute Aleksandre Sokolov and his wife in Brooklyn just recently very much in everyone's mind, the question of whether the Government would go through with its case against Butenko and Ivanov became a guessing game of increasing engrossment. Would the Government divulge the home addresses of undercover agents it planned to call as witnesses against Butenko and Ivanov?

Attorney Raymond A. Brown, of Jersey City, who took over as Butenko's new counsel, and Attorney Samuel A. Larner, of Newark, who was defending Ivanov, both promised they would demand full disclosure of the home addresses. Moreover, both lawyers made it known they would seek a postponement because they didn't believe their clients could get a fair trial at the time because of the high public resentment over the scuttling of the Brooklyn case.

Judge Augelli, who was quite aware of the Government's reluctance to turn over the data on the witnesses in the Brooklyn trial, and who was also quite aware of the 169-year-old Federal law that says it must, made it clear from the start that the prosecution had no choice but to turn over the list.

Assistant U.S. Attorney Jaffe, who headed the prosecution staff, then surprised everyone by presenting a roster of 89 names of potential Government witnesses—with addresses for each which spanned the length and breadth of the land and even touched such far-off places as Greenland, Denmark, and Norway. The list included 36 FBI agents and five military people.

In turning over the list, Jaffe pleaded that the defense treat the data confidentially "for the sake of national security." The defense attorneys said they had no intention of hurting the United States—but they quickly leaped on the prosecution for omitting the three ousted Soviet diplomats in the list and cited this as grounds for dismissal of the charges.

"We should have been able to talk to these people," Butenko's lawyer, Brown, said.

Ivanov's attorney, Larner, claimed the Government's choice in deporting the three Reds deprived the defendants of one of their basic rights under the Sixth Amendment—compulsory summoning of witnesses. Thus the Government had no right to try Ivanov and Butenko now.

This, of course, was the ground on which the case against Willie Hirsch went down the drain, after Igor Yakovlevich Melekh was booted back to Moscow.

But Judge Augelli, who speaks with a nasal Jersey City accent and is in the habit of wigwagging a yellow pencil at the person he is addressing, promised the lawyers a ruling. Augelli reached his decision October 24, by which time a jury of eight women, four men, and four alternates had been seated.

"The State Department," Augelli declared, "has been reasonable in accordance with the principles of diplomatic law. . . . I find there is no evidence that the three ousted diplomats would have voluntarily testified." Thus he refused to dismiss the charges.

The prosecution opened by telling the jury just how important the Strategic Air Command's Project 465L was to the security of the United States in peace and war.

"The basic functions of the project," Jaffe asserted, "are to enable the SAC commander to alert and execute his forces, to keep abreast of the present status of all the weapons in his command, and to make tactical decisions based on the information already in the system and to conduct exercises."

Jaffe told the jury that Butenko had access to all documents relating to the project—and that together with the three departed Russian United Nations diplomats, Butenko and Ivanov had conspired to "communicate, deliver, and transmit" information relating to the command and control system of SAC to Russia.

As the prosecution launched into its case, a parade of FBI agents who had worked on the long trackdown and arrests took the witness stand and testified.

Agent Schmaltz told the court how he saw Pavlov and Butenko meet in the A&P supermarket parking lot in Closter on April 21, 1963, and revealed how he observed them through field glasses and also how he spotted the number of the stationwagon, New York plate 2N-3078. . . . G-man Thomas James related how he followed Butenko from his home in Orange on May 26, 1963, and watched him drive his car into that same lot to meet Pavlov, while two other men stood nearby. . . . FBI man Robert Haines talked about the next day when he saw Pavlov leave the Soviet Mission on East 67th Street in Manhattan with a reddish-brown briefcase under his arm, and five minutes later observed Ivanov come out of the same door. . . . Agent Anderson spoke about the time he secreted himself in the apartment over the garage next to the parking lot behind Butenko's home and watched the engineer go into his car with that same reddish-brown leather attaché case that G-man Haines spotted the day before in Pavlov's possession. The defense wondered how Anderson could see in the darkness of 6:55 p.m. and the agent said there was a light shining from an apartment house and that the dome light of Butenko's car, which went on when he opened the door, gave him all the illumination he needed to see. . . . Agent Dowd told of how he followed Butenko to the rendezvous with the other Russians in Englewood's railroad station. . . . Agent Graffagnini carried the ball then by relating how he picked up and spotted the three Russians waiting in the station lot for Butenko, identifying the trio as Ivanov, Pavlov, and Romashin. . . . Agent Moody added more details to this testimony. . . . G-man Allf told how he moved in on Ivanov and Pavlov for the arrest. . . . Agent MacDougal told about two shopping bags in the back of the Russian car which contained photo copying machinery, two converters that enabled the auto's current to power the photo copyers, short-wave radio transmitter and receiver, and, most damaging, a set of the specifications of the Strategic Air Command which the defense claimed was transmitted by Butenko to the Russians.

Agents Conway and Dabinett also testified about the actual arrest of Butenko and the others.

Other witnesses also were called. Mrs. Marilyn Brillo, employed as secretary to the security officer of International Electric, took the stand and identified security guides and manuals that had been furnished to Butenko. Then Robert McCarten, the senior technical writer and custodian of documents for the data information center at the firm, testified that the list of numbers on the company's secret papers was the same as those found on a small map of an area of Bergen County, New Jersey, in Butenko's possession the night he was seized.

Meanwhile, as the trial progressed, it became evident that the case was rapidly establishing itself as one of the classics in American jurisprudence. More and more, attorneys and other students of the law were observed in the always-crowded courtroom, watching the proceedings with absorbing interest.

The defendants themselves, although in close physical proximity, seemed to be miles apart in their reactions. The bespectacled, thin-lipped Butenko showed a deep and intense interest, often reacting to testimony with anger, agitation, incredulity, and sometimes sardonic amusement. Ivanov, on the other hand, seemed almost phlegmatic. The blond, heavy-jawed Russian almost always appeared to be relaxed. His right ear was always connected to a hearing device. The device was provided through the courtesy of the State Department, which supplied a staff of two Russian-English translators who gave a running account in Russian to Ivanov as he sat at the defense table.

Now and then, too, observers caught sight of Soviet Government officials including one of the "heavies," Aleksei Kozikov, who was better identified now as chief of the consulate division of the Soviet Embassy in Washington.

Kozikov and other Russians seemed to have a great deal of interest in the testimony that finally came from the military.

Major Henry E. Davis, field test officer of SAC, was the first on the stand and he described SAC's system of processing data at the International Telegraph & Telephone Company's plant at Paramus. The defense got to Major Davis on some points by compelling him to admit a number of the documents in Butenko's possession the night he was seized were not classified. But he would not go so far as to say the documents were available to the public, as the defense tried to do.

Lieutenant Colonel Thomas I. Allison, another SAC officer, came under pounding cross-examination when he insisted the Air Force had not authorized public disclosure of the information in the documents. Allison, an operations planning officer, held the stand for two days. The defense finally got Judge Augelli to strike out the colonel's testimony because he had failed, in the court's opinion, to qualify as an expert in certain areas of the National Defense system.

But Lieutenant Colonel Jack B. Robbins chief of the computer division for the 465L project, was accepted as an expert by defense attorneys—and his answers were very similar to Allison's.

When the Government finally rested its case on November 18, the defense motioned the court for a directed verdict of acquittal on the ground that "the Government has failed to prove that a conspiracy existed" and that the Government "has tied its case together with chewing gum."

Judge Augelli, patient man that he is, listened to the arguments in the same persevering mood that he displayed from the start of the trial, then ruled against the motions that sought to set aside the charges.

The defense opened with its own round of witnesses. Mrs. Gaetano Cunsolo, secretary to A. P. Schneidau, Butenko's superior on the secret military project, told the court that Butenko once raised the question to her about what would happen if she and Schneidau were both sick at the same time and there was no one around to open the safe containing the important documents. The attractive brunette witness then told of how Butenko once asked her for the combination to the safe, but that she saw it as just a casual request and thought nothing of it. Of course, she did not give him the combination.

Schneidau also testified, saying he saw Butenko take some documents home to work on—and that this was at a time when the FBI had already alerted him to their investigation and requested him to keep an eye on the engineer.

The defense then called Butenko's 73-year-old landlord, Irving

Barenberg, who told of how FBI agents made a number of visits to his tenant's apartment during a six-month period in 1963. He said they did not show him a search warrant. Attorney Brown leaped on this statement and said if the information accumulated by the FBI had indeed been obtained without a warrant, then Butenko's rights had been violated—and the court must rule that any such evidence obtained without a warrant was inadmissible.

Prosecutor Jaffe argued that Brown's motion came too late.

Augelli took the motion under advisement, then ruled that he was satisfied it was all very legal.

On November 25 Butenko strode up to the witness' chair for what amounted to a very routine appearance.

"I never made any agreement with anybody to pass any information," Butenko testified. "The agents took my dispatch case from me while I was in my car." The Government charged Butenko's case had been taken from the Russians' car.

Testifying in bursts of loquacity, punctuated by pauses and frequent sidelong glances at the ceiling, Butenko was questioned extensively by Brown about his real reasons in meeting with the Soviet officials. The explanation was that he was trying to get information on some relatives in Russia from whom he had not heard in some time.

Butenko also charged that he was framed by the FBI. He categorically denied passing documents to the Russians and insisted he never met his co-defendant, Ivanov, until they were brought together at their arraignment following their arrest.

The defense rested on November 30. In closing, Brown asked again for a declaration of mistrial on grounds that the prosecution had put questions to Butenko under cross-examination that conveyed innuendoes which could well lead to his conviction.

In his summation, Government attorney Jaffe insisted the prosecution had proved its case and that no doubt remained of Butenko's plot to betray defense secrets as he worked on SAC projects.

"This is no Alger Hiss story," Jaffe exclaimed.

Brown leaped to his feet and again demanded a mistrial, this time on the ground that the jury would be prejudiced by the reference to the former State Department official who was convicted of perjury in 1950 for denying that he had passed State Department documents to a confessed Soviet spy courier.

Jaffe quickly apologized.

"I'm sorry. That's a slip of the tongue. I had meant to say Horatio Alger."

Judge Augelli, waving his yellow pencil at Brown, smiled:

"I believe it was a slip of the tongue."

In summing up, Brown painted the FBI, the Air Force, and the Justice Department as "an overpowering machine that has to be stopped." He said the Government had failed to prove the charge that Butenko, Ivanov, and the three expelled Soviet diplomats had plotted to pass Air Force secrets to Moscow.

"This man is innocent, whether you like the Soviet Union or not," Brown said of Butenko. "I resent the flag being waved in my face; the flag should be above us."

He took a parting shot at the FBI, which he pointed out had forty agents working for more than six months to track the spy ring—which some courtroom observers interpreted to mean it was just too much manpower to nail a handful of Red espionage agents.

"The press and everybody else grovels before the FBI," the defense attorney shouted. "Since when are they not above being believed?"

The Russian chauffeur's attorney, Larner, was briefer in his summation. He cited Ivanov as "a little man" who was not trained to be a spy.

"He's a Russian and that's a dirty word in this case," Larner said, asking the jury to acquit Ivanov.

The jury took eight and one-half hours—with an hour out for dinner—to reach a verdict. It was announced by Miss Michelina M. DeLuca, the foreman, and the finding was—Guilty.

As the verdict was read, Butenko was visibly agitated and fought for self-control. His face turned ashen and his jaw muscles churned furiously as he gnashed and ground his teeth. Ivanov took it with an air of detachment and his only motion was to swirl back and forth slowly in his swivel chair.

The defendants had been found guilty on two counts of the indictment for conspiracy to commit espionage; in addition Butenko was convicted of failing to register as an agent of a foreign power.

Both Butenko and Ivanov were aware of the consequences as Judge Augelli revoked Ivanov's $100,000 bail and ordered both defendants committed to the Hudson County Jail in Jersey City pending sentence, which he put on the court calendar for December 18. Both Butenko and Ivanov knew, as they were led out of the courtroom, that they could be sentenced to the electric chair.

But Judge Augelli proved himself a far more humane person than the extremes of the law dictated when he convened court on the 18th. He gave Butenko thirty years on the charge of conspiring to spy for Russia, and two five-year terms for acting as a Soviet agent, the latter terms to run concurrently with the first. Ivanov was slapped with a twenty-year sentence on the espionage conspiracy conviction, and he also received five years on the second count—being a Soviet agent. That term, too, was to run concurrently with the first.

Neither Butenko nor Ivanov had a word to say after sentence was passed, but earlier both had been given opportunities to address the court and both took advantage of them.

Butenko thanked the court and his counsel, then said:

"I realize I have been found guilty according to our form of justice by a jury. However, I know I am innocent. I have done nothing to harm the security of the country. I just want to ask the court for mercy and clemency . . . I hope that someday time will vindicate me."

Ivanov, who had claimed he speaks no English, made a statement through an interpreter, a sentence at a time:

"I came to this country to work as a chauffeur, and I worked here only as a chauffeur. During my stay in the United States, including up to today. I did not come to break any laws. I consider my arrest an unfortunate misunderstanding. I fully and completely reject the indictment in this case. I am not guilty."

When he addressed Butenko, Judge Augelli abandoned all the light-handedness and judicial good humor that became his trademark during the trial. Somber and almost with an angered look, Augelli declared:

"I regret to say I have found no extenuating or mitigating circumstances in your case. Our national security is of vital importance to all of us. It is distressing to note a native-born American who has enjoyed the benefits of education could commit so heinous a crime."

The eight-week trial was over. But no sooner had it ended than a now-familiar pattern in Soviet espionage cases again emerged. On December 23, just five days after the trial ended, Igor Ivanov was freed in $100,000 bail pending appeal of his conviction. A three-judge panel in the Circuit Court of Appeals for the Third District in Philadelphia granted the petition by Ivanov's attorney.

No such pre-Christmas freedom was granted Butenko, who was confined without bail.

Ivanov's lawyer told the Circuit Court that the Soviet Ambassador had asked the State Department to intercede with the Justice Department to have bail granted for his client. The court granted it after Jaffe said he had no objection.

The authors hold it is bad form to prognosticate how the courts will eventually rule on the appeals of Butenko and Ivanov.

But if the cases of Valentin Gubitchev, Igor Yakovlevich Melekh, and Alexandre Sokolov and his wife Joy Ann Balch Sokolov are to serve as a criterion—what else but freedom lies ahead for Igor Ivanov?

17 : Espionage: Here to Stay

SPIES and espionage rings have a lurid history that reaches back into the eras of King David and the Pharaohs, painting a melodramatic record of cloak-and-dagger thrillers across the centuries.

It is now in the sixth decade of the twentieth century and today, as in antiquity, the motivations are the same: to seize power, to expand power, to prevent the diminution of power. It is paradoxical and, in a way, sad that despite all the enlightenment the centuries have brought us—great, unimagined advances in technology, medicine, education, the welfare of man—despite it all, the primordial drives of power and fear still rule and dominate civilization.

The governments on this earth exist to a large extent in fear of each other and measure power and prestige by the "instant kill" capabilities of their nuclear weapons and industrial and military arsenals. Each of the rival power groups needs to know what the other has in instant striking potential and, more important, how it intends to use that potential.

Thus the business of espionage goes on daily in an endless battle of wits and courage to gain small fragmentary advantages. The United States and its allies, of course, are forced into espionage activities as a matter of survival, but the episodes described in this book might never have occurred if the Soviet Union had joined the wartime allies in building a genuinely peaceful world devoid of any territorial or ideological ambitions by any single nation or power bloc.

But the contrary happened under the terroristic postwar rule in Moscow of Joseph Stalin, whose obsession was nothing less than world domination.

Such a sinister dream called for extensive information on the strength and weaknesses of the governments and nations earmarked as the next victims. Within a brief year of the end of World War II's alliance, he had built up a most formidable espionage and sabotage network, one that virtually girdled the world. From then on, his agents and spies, plotting—even murdering—with appalling indifference, made it their business to organize and use as operating bases the local Communist Party in each country.

Moreover, Soviet embassies, consulates, and trade missions were systematically converted into spy and espionage centers, and also into sanctuaries for the instigation of revolutions and bloody riots.

Despite his pose in recent intervals as the peace champion, Nikita Khrushchev was as much the mastermind of present-day Communist espionage as Stalin was in his day. The aim is still—ultimate supremacy over the world. Just how assiduously Khrushchev employed espionage in the pursuit of the Kremlin's design to dominate other nations—and what we may expect from the *new order* now headed by Premier Alexei N. Kosygin and First Secretary Leonid I. Brezhnev —is clarioned in clear and unmistakable language by FBI Director Hoover, who has told us:

"The espionage potential of the Soviet bloc is tremendous. The extreme security hazard inherent in their operation is indicated somewhat by the fact that our State Department estimates that Russia and the Chinese Communist bloc countries have some three hundred thousand trained spies serving throughout the world.

"Through subterfuge, deceit, and deliberate circumvention of regulations, the Soviet bloc officials stationed in the United States have systematically developed one of the best industrial spying systems in the world. One defector has stated that the ease with which data is obtained in the United States has eliminated much of the hazardous and time-consuming clandestine operations which otherwise would be necessary. Another has estimated that the Soviet military attaché's office in the United States is able to obtain legally ninety-five percent of the material useful for its intelligence objectives and that the Polish military intelligence secures more technical data in the United States than in all the other countries of the world."

Still another Soviet defector told Government sources in Washington that the annual budget for espionage and subversion set by Khrushchev for 1964 was $1,500,000,000, most of it to finance the network operating in America.

There is no reason to believe the Kremlin's budget for this purpose in fiscal 1965, 1966, or 1970, will be any less despite the thaw in the Cold War. There is no reason to believe that the Soviet Union will not attempt to subvert another Henry Farmer or Frederick Timsford during this year, or the next, or five years from now. There is no reason to believe an American soldier, another Colonel Frank S. Pilgrim, will not be approached in Berlin, or another sailor such as Cornelius "Bulldog" Drummond will not be stopped on a London street and asked to perform some clandestine assignment for the Moscow espionage network.

Nor, of course, is there any reason to believe that the United States and its allies will lessen their efforts to learn about Russia and her satellite bloc countries through the tried-and-true course of espionage.

The authors have concentrated in this work on exposing only the Soviet espionage conspiracy anchored in the United Nations, chiefly because none except the Soviet bloc operates from behind this privileged sanctuary. Here both deception and criminal activity, as we have shown, are carried out in defiance of all the international treaties and laws of the host country, the United States of America.

It is precisely to alert the American people to the perils of that deception that this book has been written. Yet, despite the incidence of Soviet espionage emanating from the United Nations, we must not be spurred into rash and intemperate decisions and actions. We must not move beyond the confines of our democratic traditions even though we have seen the extent and scope of Soviet espionage and the methods employed to exploit the freedom inherent in our society.

Everyone can help to minimize the threat of the Red enemy by being as alert and intelligent as Frederick Timsford, Richard Simmons, Richard A. Flink, and the other real-life heroes of this book. There should never be hesitation in advising the FBI of a suspicion raised by Soviet activity that may seem even remotely to breach the bounds of legitimate and ethical dealings.

Anyone—an engineer, a draftsman, a salesman, an officer of a company, an exhibitor at a technical exposition, a politician, a government employee—is a potential target of Soviet espionage. Therefore, everyone must be deeply aware at all times about the danger and be prepared to meet it with imagination, intelligence, and aggressive thinking.

If all responsible Americans remain alert and sensitive to the threat of the Communist enemy, Russian and satellite spies will find it difficult, if not impossible, to do business with them. And those agents who try will not succeed. Fighting the Communist conspiracy is everybody's business.

Index

HEARTBREAK HOTEL

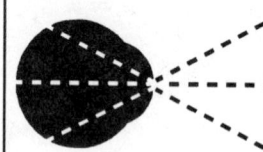

This Large Print Book carries the
Seal of Approval of N.A.V.H.

HEARTBREAK HOTEL

JILL MARIE LANDIS

THORNDIKE PRESS
A part of Gale, a Cengage Company

Farmington Hills, Mich • San Francisco • New York • Waterville, Maine
Meriden, Conn • Mason, Ohio • Chicago

Thorndike Press® Large Print Clean Reads.
The text of this Large Print edition is unabridged.
Other aspects of the book may vary from the original edition.
Set in 16 pt. Plantin.

LIBRARY OF CONGRESS CIP DATA ON FILE.
CATALOGUING IN PUBLICATION FOR THIS BOOK
IS AVAILABLE FROM THE LIBRARY OF CONGRESS

ISBN-13: 978-1-4328-6437-8 (hardcover alk. paper)

Published in 2019 by arrangement with BelleBooks, Inc.

Printed in the United States of America
1 2 3 4 5 6 7 23 22 21 20 19

Maggi Davis a.k.a. Mom.

B., K., and T.
Here's to hot Anini nights.

The Tiki Goddesses of O'Kauai
You all know who you are.

Lis and Bran
Beth
Robin

Ellen Marie
Abby
Jack

"It's never too early to start sucking up
to Auntie."

CHAPTER ONE

Wade MacAllister had spent most of his life wishing he had more of everything — more luck, more talent, more money.

He had money now. More money than he'd ever imagined. If he'd been blessed with real talent, maybe his luck wouldn't have run out.

Steering his Harley into a scenic turnout with a view of the Pacific, he killed the engine and set the kickstand. The heavy black and chrome bike listed to one side, poised above the pavement, heat radiating off the pipes. Though silent now, the growl of the engine still hummed in his ears.

Beyond the lookout, the ocean rose and fell, its rough surface surging in every direction, pulled by the tide, the wind, and the swells. Gathering twilight made it harder to see. Wind gusts off the water matched the rhythm of the waves. The chill in the air cut through his leather jacket, reminding him that he could still feel. That he was still alive.

The night was moonless and melancholy. Restless like him.

"Make up your goddamned mind." The mumbled words were quickly swept away, carried off on the wind, drowned by the roar of the waves. "If you're going to do it, get it over with."

He glanced up and down the highway. There were no cars in sight. He was ever conscious of the gun in his saddlebag, a classic Colt .45, Gold Cup Trophy model he had picked up from a dealer in Phoenix. He'd practiced at a firing range to make sure he knew how to use it, though for his purposes, a good aim wasn't important.

Tonight, like every other night, his fertile mind conjured memories of things best forgotten. He tried, God knew he'd tried, but there was no way he could ever forget the twelve women murdered in unspeakable ways. Lovely young women who had died violent, heinous deaths. Acts spawned by a sick and twisted mind.

His sick and twisted mind.

Do it right now. Right here. Get it over with.

But there was more than a whisper of daylight left. His mind spun out the what-ifs. What if an unsuspecting driver pulled over? What if a car full of people drove by, saw his body lying there? What if there were kids in the car? What then?

He needed to go somewhere off the beaten track, somewhere lonely and solitary. A secluded place more in keeping with the way he'd always lived his life.

He'd know it when he saw it and when he did, maybe then he'd find the courage to put an end to everything.

The twelve women.

The constant moving. The disguises.

He'd find the right place and then maybe he'd find the courage to bring the story of his life to a close.

Chapter Two

After dark, the lobby of the Heartbreak Hotel seemed to expand, like the walls of a carnival fun house. At night, the persistent pounding of the waves against the shoreline filled the rooms like the amplified beat of a solitary heart. Except for an occasional passing car, there was no competition for the echo of the waves.

Loneliness filled the rooms in the evenings, too. Tracy Potter didn't notice it as much during the day when she was running in all directions. But at night, after the workmen left, the sun had set, and her nine-year-old son, Matthew, was tucked in bed, she would struggle with an ache so deep, so raw, that it took everything she had to convince herself that circumstances change — that life was bound to take a turn for the better.

She still found it hard to believe that in a couple more weeks, her husband, Glenn, would have been gone six months.

Gone.

The word made it sound as if he stepped out to meet a client and w back any minute.

Her footsteps echoed against the scuffed hardwood floors of the wide-open lobby, falling silent whenever she paused to pick up a sticky wad of used masking tape or to carefully sidestep a pile of drop cloths the workmen had left on the floor.

Six months ago, if anyone would have told her that she'd be a widow at thirty-three, or that she'd be renovating the Heartbreak Hotel, let alone living in it, she would have laughed and called them crazy.

A few days after Glenn's death, when his accountant, David Sylvester, informed her that Glenn had been deep in debt, she thought he'd been joking. But David had been dead serious and the joke was on her.

It was a morning she'd never forget, sitting there in David's office, listening as the accountant outlined the bleak details.

"There's no easy way to put it, Tracy. You're broke. As far as I can tell, there's enough left in your joint checking account to pay expenses for the next six months, if you're careful and if you're lucky."

She knew things had been tough. She'd confronted Glenn about the mounting bills.

11

d wanted to go back to work, gladly offering to renew her real estate license. She would have done anything to help keep them from going under, but he'd been adamant. He wanted Matt to have a full-time mom. There were listings about to close. Things were just tight right now. Things were going to change soon.

Still she'd worried, and with good reason. What the accountant told her after Glenn's death made that quite clear.

"Glenn refinanced the Canyon Club house to the limit," David said. "There's no equity left. Your credit cards are maxed out, too. In fact, he made your last two house payments with his American Express Card. And unfortunately, he was underinsured. You'll be able to cover the funeral expenses, and if there's anything left, I'd advise you to pay off your car, and Chelsea's."

Luckily, hers was free and clear.

Chelsea's wasn't. Chelsea was Glenn's daughter by his first marriage. Nineteen now. A freshman at the University of Southern California. Tracy had sat in stunned silence, thinking of Chelsea, of the hefty tuition Glenn had been paying. *What now?*

"Sell the house," David had advised. "Get the bank off your back before they foreclose."

The luxurious house had been Glenn's dream, part of an upscale development he'd spearheaded. Cabrillo Canyon Club was a gated community of sixty high-end homes scattered around a golf course designed by Rex Burrell, one of the West's premier course designers. They were well built but overpriced, even in a good market. The homes all sold eventually, but not overnight.

"There is one bit of good news, I guess," David had quickly added, as if aware that she was quickly slipping into a self-induced coma. Anything to escape.

"And *that* would be?"

"That the IRS and the banks can't touch your inheritance from your grandparents. It's not much, but it'll help. And there's that old hotel on the coast road. Glenn put the title in Matt's name, with you as trustee."

"Matt? When? Why?" Matt was only nine. What had Glenn been thinking?

At first she couldn't even remember the place, and then it came to her. The Heartbreak Hotel. Perched on the coast off the old Route 1. Glenn had purchased the derelict, nineteenth-century hotel a handful of years ago, planning to tear it down and replace it with elegant condos. The project had quickly bogged down in California Coastal Commission hearings.

After the Twilight Cove Historical Society and the Central Coast Preservation League entered into the fray, he had tabled the project altogether, too busy to spend time and money fighting them all.

She had left David's office that morning determined to sell the white elephant. But prospective buyers couldn't walk away fast enough once they learned that the hotel was to be registered as a historic landmark — thanks to the Twilight Cove Historical Preservation Society — and that the Coastal Commission had deemed the prime ocean-front land beneath it off limits to any new development.

She'd looked into renewing her real estate license, then realized that it might be months before her first escrow closed, if and when she got a quick listing and actually sold something.

Forced to do the only thing she could under the circumstances, she'd taken a leap of faith, relied on her ability to see things the way they could be, not the way they were, and used her inheritance from Grandma and Grandpa Melton to clean up the Heartbreak.

Now darkness was quickly gathering as she walked over to a bank of wall switches behind the desk, flipped on the lights, and surveyed the progress. Though the place would never be a five-star hotel, it was finally coming along.

Six guest rooms were already completely finished. There were three left to paint and furnish. The painting was nearly finished in the lobby. The adjacent sitting room was no longer as dingy and derelict as it had been the day she took her first hard look around.

Even she, a consummate optimist, had been hard-pressed to envision possibilities for the place. If Matt hadn't been with her the first time she walked through, she'd have been tempted to break down and bawl her eyes out.

Old wallpaper had to be stripped. Thankfully, the hardwood floors were still solid, but needed refinishing. An army of termites had taken up residence in the walls. She'd handled the damage with spot repair and fumigation. Basic cosmetic renovations and a race to open for the coming tourist season would never have been her first choice, but she'd seen no quicker way out of her financial crisis.

Walking away from their home at Cabrillo Canyon Club, selling off almost everything, including the designer furnishings hand-chosen for the house, hadn't hurt anything but her pride. But then, she'd never really felt as attached to the Canyon Club house as Glenn. It had been his dream to live in an impressive showplace — one that left no doubt as to his success.

It wasn't like her to look back, so counting on the future to bring change, she glanced out the wide bay window that curved around the entire front wall. It was gloomy out tonight. Not a single star brightened a heavy sky.

She was headed for the sunroom and small kitchen area off the lobby when she heard the deep-throated rumble of a motorcycle on the coast road. When the sound abruptly stopped, she froze.

Alone in the empty room, she was suddenly all too aware of how vulnerable she and Matt were, living out on this deserted stretch of road. It was one thing to have considered running the Heartbreak all by herself, but the cold, stark reality of it chilled her blood. She held her breath, hoping to hear the motorcycle start up again.

CHAPTER THREE

He couldn't have conjured a better place to stop.

Poised in isolation on a remote stretch of road bypassed by the main highway, the huge two-story wooden hulk had been visible from a quarter mile away. Reminding him of the Bates Motel in *Psycho,* it rose stark and ominous against the night sky. The place beckoned him, compelled him to slow down as he neared.

Complete with a widow's walk, the old hotel clung to the bluff above the Pacific. It might have been abandoned, except for the neon sign out front that blazed EAR EAK HOT L in hot pink. Below that, in aqua letters, glowed the word VACANCY.

Once he saw the place at close range, there was no way he could ride on. No way he could leave.

Perfect.

He rolled the bike beneath the eave of the

building where it would be out of a slow drizzle that was making a halfhearted attempt to turn itself into rain. Quickly he unsnapped the saddlebag, pulled off his helmet, clamped it beneath his arm, and ran splayed fingers through his short hair, forcing it to spike up in front. Taking a deep breath, he headed around the corner of the building along a path nearly covered by weeds.

Hoping like hell that whoever was manning the front desk wouldn't recognize him, Wade cleared the worn treads on the front steps and stared at the oval, etched glass window in the front door. He gave in to an overpowering need to step inside.

Chapter Four

She knew all along that she would be obliged to greet late arrivals and that she'd be vulnerable every time she opened the door to a stranger. Thankfully, she'd been a firm believer in the innate goodness of people and had been all her life, but the minute she heard footsteps thudding on the porch outside and then an insistent knocking, Tracy found herself slipping her cell phone out of her pocket. Clutching it in her hand, she crossed the lobby. Through the window set in the front door, she saw the silhouette of a man.

He stood beneath the golden glow of the porch light — tall, not thin, not heavy. Solid, with wide shoulders beneath a black leather jacket that glistened with moisture. His deep-set dark eyes stared back.

While he waited for her to open the door, he wiped his face with the back of his hand and she realized it must be raining. She stepped closer to the window in the door and noted the shiny black helmet beneath his arm and motorcycle saddlebag dangling from his left hand.

"We're not open for business." She raised her voice so he could hear her through the oval pane.

He leaned closer. He was smooth-shaven and his clothes appeared to be clean.

"Your sign says vacancy." His voice was low, but she easily heard him through the window and suddenly realized that she must have accidently hit the switch for the neon sign when she turned the lights on.

"We're not open yet," she told him again, damning the sign. Fixing the thing hadn't made it to the top of her to-do list yet, nor did she have the money. So many letters were burned out that the first time Matt saw it lit up, he asked who would want to stay at a place called Ear Ache Hot-L, and she'd collapsed into gales of laughter.

"Come on, lady. Give a guy a break. It's raining." He shifted his weight and the helmet before he reached into his pocket.

Before she could react, he moved the helmet and pulled out a wad of bills and flapped them back and forth, then pressed them against the window.

"I've got cash. I just need one room for

one night."

Tracy sucked on her upper lip and frowned.

He was a good head and shoulders taller than she. Stronger, obviously.

Wet. Possibly tired.

He had the money, he needed a room, and she had an abundance of those — not to mention a bank account in need of an injection.

"It's one twenty-five a night." She quoted what she thought was an outrageous fee for a room in a place still being renovated.

He leaned closer to the oval pane. "I'll take it."

She'd always thought you could tell a lot about a person by their eyes. Though this man's appeared to be open and honest, there was something else in them she recognized. Something she'd seen looking back at her from the mirror lately — a deep, abiding sadness that no amount of positive pep talks could erase.

That underlying sadness moved her more than the fact that there were day laborers to pay tomorrow, additional paint yet to buy, not to mention extra bedding and linens on order. At the rate she was going, she'd have very little money left to fall back on if the Heartbreak didn't immediately take off.

She wasn't exactly desperate. Not yet anyway. Besides, desperate wasn't a word she ever used. It conjured hopelessness and despair. She certainly wasn't hopeless or desperate. She was still determined to start over, to make something of the Heartbreak.

And she could certainly use the extra cash.

Besides, she was going to have to act like an innkeeper sooner or later. Why not start tonight?

She pasted on a big smile, opened the door, and indicated the torn-up lobby with a flourish and a little too much exuberance.

"Welcome to the Heartbreak Hotel. You're our first official guest."

She found herself wishing he would at least smile back.

CHAPTER FIVE

He noticed a smudge on her nose and a streak of white paint in her blond hair. The minute he stepped into the lobby, her megawatt smile dimmed slightly, as if she'd suddenly thought better of letting him in.

He shot a glance around, noted the paint cans and battered aluminum ladder, the recognizable shapes of two sofas smothered by huge drop cloths near a river rock fireplace that nearly covered the entire wall of an open sitting room across the lobby.

His gaze drifted back to her face with its finely drawn features, her aquamarine eyes, her plump lower lip. She was wearing a pastel silk blouse and fitted khaki pants that showed off a trim figure softly rounded in all the right places. Her white Keds were still clean. Even with the paint smudge on her cheek, she looked as out of place here as a pile of French fries on a diet plate.

"Right this way." As she headed for the

reception desk, he followed, watching her cross the room. Her blond ponytail bounced against her shoulders, and oddly enough, his pulse seemed to beat in time with her step. His stomach knotted.

How long has it been? Incredibly, he couldn't remember the last time he'd slept with a woman.

She pulled a huge, worn, leather-bound register out from under the counter, swiped the dust off it with her palm.

"This is the original hotel register. I —" She stopped abruptly, then started over. "*We . . . we'll* be getting on-line for credit cards, naturally, but since I . . . *we're* planning on making this a traditional sort of inn, I thought it would be nice for guests to sign in."

He made no effort to respond. He didn't want to know her. He didn't *need* to know her. It was the place itself that had drawn him here, this timeworn monstrosity of a hotel wearing a new coat of paint.

At a tall oak desk, the woman watched him count out the cash. He pushed the bills toward her.

"That's one twenty-five." He noticed how rough and unused his voice sounded.

"Thank you. Now, if you'll just sign in here, Mister . . . ?" Suddenly efficient, she

24

spun the huge register 180 degrees and offered him a pen.

He hesitated, then gave her an alias for his
last name. "Johnson. Wade Johnson."

"I'm Tracy Potter." As she handed him
the pen, he couldn't help but notice her
wedding ring. The diamond almost blinded
him, even in the dim light. It was impressive enough to warrant a second glance.

So where in the hell was her husband? Her
rich husband?

What kind of guy would let her open the
door to a stranger? Some idiot upstairs
watching reality TV?

Quickly, he took the pen and signed the
name Wade Johnson. Instead of handing it
back, he carefully placed it in the spine of
the register.

"Would you please add your license plate
number too? You rode in on a motorcycle,
right?"

"Yeah." He must have looked curious
about how she knew.

"I recognized the sound. We had a neighbor who had one," she said.

"I parked close to the building, out of the
rain. Is that all right?"

"Of course."

He closed his eyes, pictured the license
plate, scribbled the number behind his

name. When he looked up again, he caught her eyeing him carefully, and for a second he was afraid she might have recognized him. But aside from her direct gaze, she didn't let on that she had a clue who he was.

He couldn't tell her age. There was barely a line on her face, though she looked a little tired.

As an awkward silence lengthened, her smile wavered uncertainly.

"Unless I miss my guess, this is the part where you give me a key and show me to my room." The old Wade would have smiled at his attempt at humor. The new one didn't remember how.

She blinked, a mere flick of long gold lashes, almost as if she were awakening from a trance, and her smile turned shaky as she reached into the open drawer and took out a room key, an old brass original. The key ring sported a plastic dolphin with the words Twilight Cove printed on its blue-gray sides — a trinket from one of the many tourist stops in the nearby hamlet he'd blown through on the Harley.

"Right this way," she offered, stepping out from behind the desk.

He followed her through the lobby and down a narrow hallway lit by a series of dim lights, their flame-shaped bulbs a reflection of the past. They passed a series of tall doors fitted with old-fashioned glass transoms above them. A chilly breeze fluttered the sheer curtain over a long narrow window at the far end of the hall. The place had an empty, eerie feel to it, yet he felt oddly comforted, as if the building itself were drawing him deeper inside. As if he were being seduced by the Heartbreak.

"I'm sorry about the paint smell," she said, breaking the spell, reminding him that he wasn't alone. "Fortunately, it's not as strong back here as it is in the lobby."

When he didn't immediately respond, she glanced back over her shoulder expectantly.

He mumbled, "No problem."

"Great." She slipped the key into the lock and opened the door.

Wade walked in, tossed his saddlebag and helmet on an upholstered chair just inside the door. He expected her to leave, but she hovered, uncertain, while he gave the room a cursory glance.

Stark white walls adorned with splashes of color from framed crate labels depicted scenes and the names of various fruit orchards of old California. The atmosphere was warm and inviting without being gaudy, fussily old-fashioned, or overblown with

27

floral prints.

"This is fine. Thanks." He held out his hand, and she finally dropped the key into his palm before flashing him another awkward smile and hurrying out.

She closed the door softly behind her.

CHAPTER SIX

Outside the room, Tracy collapsed against the wall beside the door and pressed her palm over her racing heart. The damn thing was thumping along worse than a flat tire on a rutted road.

Doubt and fear had almost turned her into a complete, bumbling idiot the minute Wade Johnson had walked through the front door, but she had to give herself credit. She didn't think she'd done all that badly, seeing as how this was the first time she'd welcomed a complete stranger.

At night, no less.

How on earth am I going to do this over and over again?

Damn you, Glenn.

She wasn't a quitter. She was a woman with goals and objectives. She always had been and she didn't intend to change just because her luck had soured. She'd moved to California straight out of college and had

29

landed her first job selling real estate on her first interview. She'd made a success of it, too, right up until two years ago when Glenn finally convinced her to stay home and take care of Matt.

She wasn't in the habit of failing. Making a go of the Heartbreak was not only a matter of survival, but a way to gather the pieces of her own life back together.

When she heard Wade Johnson moving around inside his room, she tried to conquer her nerves. Stepping away from the wall, she walked to the end of the hall and closed an open window before she headed back to the lobby. The old floorboards creaked and complained beneath her as she passed the door to his room. She hurried by, hoping he didn't think she was hanging around in the hall for some reason. Hoping he didn't step outside to ask why.

Upstairs in their second-floor apartment, she found Matt sound asleep, stretched out on the couch with the television on. She sat down beside him, brushed his shining rust-colored hair off his smooth forehead. How often had they laughed about Matt being Glenn's clone with his sandy hair and freckles, his blue eyes?

Whenever she looked at her son now, she

saw Glenn again — his smile, the way he walked, the way he shrugged. She heard Glenn's voice in Matt's laughter. It wasn't until she slipped her arms beneath him, picked him up to carry him to his room, that she realized not only how heavy he'd grown, but how infrequently Matt laughed these days.

He was nine, after all. Certainly not her baby anymore. She thought of the not-too-distant future when he'd be too heavy for her to carry. No matter what Glenn had been into, no matter how he'd wound up disappointing her, it still broke her heart knowing that Matt wouldn't have his dad around to watch him grow into a teen, to tease him about his first date, his first kiss, or to teach him to drive.

She walked down the short hallway that led to one of the apartment's three bedrooms. She'd given Matt the brightest corner room, decorated it with his favorite posters, model boats, his nautical navy-and-white-striped spread.

She'd tried to make the move a smooth transition for him, and though the Heartbreak was home to them now, it still didn't quite feel like one. She tucked Matt in, brushed her fingertips over the sheet after she drew it up around his shoulders. A falling mist teased the canvas curtains over his window. Once more, she shut out the night breeze. Before she closed the curtains, she glanced out at the moonless night. Low-lying clouds hung heavy over the water.

She went into her own room and turned down the bed, used to climbing into the vast emptiness alone. Long before Glenn died, she'd grown used to going to bed alone. He'd tried to convince her that his expanding developments like the La Hacienda project in Santa Barbara's redevelopment area forced him to stay overnight in the area. Once she'd spent the night with him in the studio he kept there, intending to make it a romantic getaway.

Equipped with a utilitarian leather sofa bed, a desk, his computer, and piles of paperwork, the crowded space had been nothing more than an office with a bed in it. Glenn had been preoccupied that weekend and spent most of the time fielding phone calls. She'd never made the trip again.

After that, she'd tried to make up for his time away by making his nights at home special, but more often than not he was exhausted and running on empty. Seeing how hard he was working, she hated doubting him, but resentment and worry slowly set in.

She had never asked for the Canyon Club house. She didn't see why he had to have a new Mercedes every year or why he was so driven. She would have given it all up, gone back to working alongside him just to have him home more.

Finally, pushed to the limit, she'd confronted him shortly before he died, asking him point-blank if he was having an affair. He'd been so angry, so hurt and insulted, that she'd ended up apologizing. Over and over he had always insisted, *"I love you, Tracy. I'll always love you. You're my rock. My oasis."*

With a sigh, she walked into her private bathroom, a quarter of the size of their walk-in dressing room at the Canyon Club house, and leaned against the sink. For a moment or two she stared at the drain. When she finally raised her eyes and looked in the mirror, she hardly recognized the woman looking back.

She'd always looked younger than her years, but she'd definitely aged over the past months. There was no denying it. Shadows were lodged beneath her eyes. There were a few new lines here and there that definitely hadn't been evident before she'd lost eight

33

pounds.

Glenn had been having money problems. He was always talking about deals about to close, for lenders to come through for clients. He had contractors to pay. He made excuses for why he wasn't paying off the credit card bills. She had offered to do all the bookkeeping and help shoulder the load. He told her he was happy with David Sylvester and bought her a diamond tennis bracelet. Two months ago, she'd turned it over to an upscale consignment shop.

They used to share everything, but slowly he became more and more distant. So distant that just before he died, they were constantly arguing. For Matt's sake, they'd settled into an unspoken agreement to live under an illusion of normalcy.

Once Santa Barbara is behind us, things will get back to normal.

That was his mantra. But coinciding with the La Hacienda project was the new tract of upscale homes inland from Avilla Beach. Later there came another golf club home development plan.

She understood his need to succeed. He'd told her stories of a childhood lived in poverty, of his vow never to be hungry or poor again. He didn't want his children to want for anything.

He gladly paid Chelsea's tuition and all of her college expenses. He was making payments on her car. The girl had been so distraught at Glenn's funeral that Tracy had decided to wait until after finals to tell her that unless they could find a scholarship, there would be no tuition for the University of Southern California next year. In what little spare time she had, Tracy had already started researching possible scholarship opportunities.

She whispered to the woman in the mirror, "What in the hell really happened? What were you into, Glenn?"

She had almost convinced herself that he was doing drugs. Afraid that he was too proud, or too deep into them to ask for help, she'd surfed the Internet, looking up everything she could find on drug addiction. Determined to confront him, she never had the chance. The autopsy proved that he'd died of an aneurysm. It also clearly stated that there were no drugs in his system.

Whatever happened, for whatever reason, it all happened. Glenn was gone and she was starting over.

How many people even get another chance?

She was lucky. She still had her life to live and a boy to raise. For what it was worth, she had the Heartbreak and enough money to dress it up and make it livable.

She opened the medicine cabinet, picked up a jar of facial cleanser; began to smear cream on her face. She removed her mascara, her lipstick, what little foundation she wore. Then she scrubbed her face with soap and water, patted it dry with a towel.

Bone tired, she brushed her teeth and turned off the light. Bathed in darkness, she walked down the hall to a small, dark stairwell that led to both the attic and the widow's walk. She loved to go outside at night, inescapably drawn by the sound of the sea.

The light rain had stopped, so she stepped onto the narrow walk that spanned the house. In the daytime it afforded a panoramic view of the ocean and the coast in both directions.

Why wasn't it called a wife's walk? she wondered. *Why was it just for widows?*

She couldn't resist escaping up here once or twice a day. Tonight, buffeted by the chilly wind, she drew her robe close and wondered if there had ever actually been another widow living here, one who used this walk to escape and think about her life. Perhaps another woman facing a new start, a woman who took time to stare out to sea and dream of better days to come.

She felt strangely comforted high above the rolling surf, beneath the wide-open sky. Alone on the widow's walk, she'd even managed to find moments of profound peace.

But not tonight. Tonight her thoughts drifted to the man downstairs.

Who is he? What is he? Where is he going? Why stop here when there are plenty of other places, less expensive, far better places to stay up and down the coast?

She couldn't help but remember the haunted loneliness in his eyes, as if he carried the weight of the world on his shoulders. That look made her feel as if they were somehow connected on a level neither of them could escape.

Had he felt it, too?

She decided it was a fanciful thought conjured by an overworked mind. She let the night wind carry it away.

When a shiver passed through her, chilling her, she wrapped her arms around herself. It didn't matter who or what he was, or where he was headed.

He was only passing through.

CHAPTER SEVEN

Downstairs, Wade pulled a new bottle of tequila out of his saddlebag, filled one of the glasses he'd found on a white Lucite tray on the dresser and downed half the drink.

Refilling it to the top, he carried it and the bottle over to the nightstand and sat down on the edge of the bed. Reaching for the gun, he laid it across his lap and knocked back another shot of tequila.

He snapped off the light and let his eyes adjust to the dark and the weight of the gun on his lap. Instead of focusing on whether or not to use it, his thoughts strayed to the woman.

The twenty questions game was ingrained in him now, as much a part of him as breathing. It was an occupational hazard — playing twenty questions.

Who is she? What drives her? What does she want?

What's she most afraid of? How did she get here?

She was definitely uncomfortable with him. He'd seen it in her eyes, heard it as her words rushed out the nearer they got to the room. There was a considerable amount of cash in his pocket and he'd bet all of it that there was no one but her on the premises.

No husband waiting for her upstairs. No one to protect her.

If she were *his* wife, he'd never let her open the door to a stranger.

She would make a perfect victim. A lovely woman all alone in this cavernous, run-down shell echoing with bone-chilling emptiness. It was the perfect night for a murder, too. Moonless and misty.

He stroked the barrel of the gun lightly, the way a man might run his fingers along a lover's spine. Though bottomless self-loathing coursed through him, he knew that he'd never have the courage to use it. Not ever.

He didn't deserve to take the easy way out. Not when fitting justice would be to live out the rest of his life facing his demons.

He poured himself more tequila — liquid courage that numbed the senses but unfortunately not the mind. His thoughts strayed to the woman again.

What was her name? Suzie? Patti? Mitzi?

Definitely something preppie. Something that ended with an *i* that she had probably dotted with a big fat heart in high school.

She looked like the type who actually meant it when she told people to "Have a nice day."

He shifted, leaned against the white lacquered headboard, closed his eyes, and tried to imagine shooting himself. What a joke. He was afraid to get a flu shot. Besides, it would be a damn shame to mess up these freshly painted walls.

He pictured Mitzi? Patsi? Trixi's? face when she chased the sound of a single gunshot and found him lying here with his brains spattered all over her white walls and pristine new bedspread.

Why kid yourself?

He couldn't do that to her or anyone else any more than he could do it to himself. He set the gun on the nightstand, listened to the sound of the ocean filling the room. His mind refused to turn itself off. There was really no rest for the weary — or the guilty.

Resigned, he sighed heavily, turned off the light, and sat there staring into the darkness.

A terrible ache, a tearing, ripping asunder. His heart feels as if it is about to explode with the pain. Unlike anything he's ever experienced before. Deeper than physical hurt, the longing tears into him, pulsing, matching the pull of the tide, the sound of the sea that surrounds him.

Dream or reality? He has no idea, and yet he sees her clear as day, standing on the bluff. A raven-haired woman in yellow silk. The gown is old-fashioned. Long. It presses against the length of her legs, caressing the juncture of her thighs, outlines her high, full breasts. The sea breeze teases wayward strands of her hair, tangles it gently in her lashes. She brushes it back, draws a wisp of it across her lips with hands that he longs to feel caressing him.

He can taste her lips — and yet he hungers for her like a starving man.

Suddenly his world turns upside down. She's no longer there. Blackness engulfs him. He is blinded by the sun's rays blazing down through fathoms of water. He stares at the refracted sphere and shafts of light shimmering all around him. His lungs are bursting. He knows better than to gasp for air until he's fought his way to the surface.

When he does, he is surrounded by emerald water capped with frothing white. He bobs on the crest of a swell, his life reduced to nothing more than the pieces of wreckage floating all around him.

I'll survive.

The promise is for her, not to soothe himself.

I'll live to touch you again.

Nothing can keep me from you.

Not even death.

Wade awoke with a start, fighting for breath. He swallowed air in huge gulps, wrapped his hands around his throat as if he were choking. Disoriented, he glanced around the dark room, struggling to remember where he was. Words came to him in a bright neon memory. *EAR EAK. Heartbreak. The Heartbreak Hotel.*

He ran his shaking hand through his hair and over his eyes. His pounding heart out-raced the rhythm of the waves that filled the room. The smell of paint lingered, not heavy enough to make him nauseous, but perhaps enough to account for the nightmare. Or was it a dream that had seemed all too real?

Shit. Even with all that had gone down in the last couple of years, he'd never suffered a full-blown panic attack, but he had a

42

hunch that's what was happening. Doubting his ability to stand, he sat and listened to the thunder of his heart ringing in his ears.

He closed his eyes and immediately had the sensation that he was being rocked by ocean swells — not the greatest feeling in the world for a guy prone to seasickness. Over the beat of his heart, he thought he heard a woman crying.

He strained, listening closely, and decided that somewhere nearby, a woman was definitely sobbing. The sound was deep and intense, dredged up from the depths of her soul. It drew him off the bed. He tested his legs, found standing far easier than he expected.

He rubbed the tightness in the back of his neck as he walked over to a narrow French door set with a series of rectangular windowpanes. It opened onto a wide porch overlooking the Pacific.

He opened the door and the chilly night air hit him like a slap. The first thing he noticed was that the rain had stopped.

And so, evidently, had the sobbing.

Had the mournful sound been a remnant of the nightmare? A figment of his overly fertile imagination? The voices of the Even Dozen tended to haunt him, too. Voices he'd only heard in his own mind.

He drank in gulps of night air. Filled his lungs with it. As his heartbeat slowly settled into a normal rhythm, he closed the door, pulled the drapes. Wandering back to the bed, he felt surprisingly calm despite what had just happened. More so than in a long, long while.

It wasn't until he turned on the light and found himself digging through the drawer in the nightstand for a pad of paper and pen that he realized he had an overwhelming urge to write again — and that scared the hell out of him, more than the dream. More than the panic attack or whatever the hell had just happened.

He slammed the drawer shut. Then he reached for the clock on the bedside table. Two hours had passed since he first checked in.

He pulled off his boots, turned off the light, and stretched out on top of the comforter. Stacking his hands behind his head, he lay in the dark staring at the ceiling. He needed more than tequila.

He needed a damn laptop.

But he had vowed that when, and if, he ever had the urge to write again, he would fight it.

Easier said than done.

He closed his eyes, let the sound of the ocean fill his head. Forced himself to inhale and exhale, keeping time with the waves, counting each breath.

The next thing he knew, someone was knocking on the door.

Knocking incessantly.

His head was pounding. The knocking didn't help. Neither did the harsh sunlight invading the room through the cracks between the white curtain panels. Wade rubbed his eyes, glanced at his watch.

Eight-thirty already? The damn thing must be fast. There's no way I slept through the night.

But the clock on the bedside table concurred. He got up and headed for the door, if for no other reason than to put an end to the infernal sound of bare knuckles rapping against hardwood. He was halfway across the room when he remembered the gun.

He hurried back to the bed, slipped the Colt into the drawer between copies of Gideon's and *The Wisdom of Buddha.* When he caught sight of the notepad beside the phone and recognized the tight scrawl filling the top sheet, he picked it up.

Every single sheet of paper in the four-by-five notepad was filled with his handwriting.

Notes that made little sense now. Notes he didn't recall writing.

Confused, appalled, he tossed the pad inside and closed the drawer.

Shit. The knocking started up again.

Before he got to the door, his instep came down hard on the heel of the boot lying beside the bed. He cursed and hopped the rest of the way, then flung the door open.

There she was, cheerfulness personified, her blond hair pulled back into a perky ponytail that bounced as she jumped back. Her eyes were far bluer than he remembered. Her plush lips formed a silent "O." High color bloomed on her cheeks, but she didn't turn tail and run. She didn't even budge. But her smile quickly bloomed the same.

"I'm sorry, Mr. Johnson . . ." She glanced down at his stockinged feet, then slowly raised her eyes to meet his again. She didn't try to speak until she'd run her tongue across her lips, a quick, unconscious move that made his gut tighten.

"Last night . . . I forgot to tell you that I'd be serving you coffee and pastries in the sunroom. They're complimentary. It's still a bit of a mess, but the back porch is really nice and it has a view, too. Or if you'd like, you can bring your breakfast back here."

She glanced at her watch, a slim, gold Rolex. "It's getting late and I'm expecting the workmen to arrive by nine . . ."

"Coffee?" Now that he thought about it, hot coffee sounded pretty damn tempting. Almost as tempting as she looked. He got a whiff of a tantalizing aroma wafting down the hall. Maybe a good cup of coffee would clear the cobwebs. Give him the courage to open the damn nightstand drawer again and read what was on the notepad.

"Fresh ground," she informed him.

"Plain or flavored?"

"Oh. Just plain. I'm sorry, I —"

"I hate flavored coffee."

Her megawatt smile quickly rebounded. "Me, too. But I'm planning to offer choices, though, when I'm *officially* open."

"Choices are good."

This morning she had said I, not *we.* He glanced at her ring finger again, at the boulder sparkling on it. At the moment she was twisting the ring round and round.

He *was* hungry.

He shoved his fingers through his hair again, figured he had camel breath, took a step back.

Her gaze flicked past him to the bed. "Did you sleep well?"

"Yeah. Fine." Slowly he ran his gaze over

47

her, studied her eyes. There was a sadness that belied the heroic effort she was making. Had she been the one he'd heard crying in the night? Had that been real or inspired by a dream?

For fear of being recognized, he'd made a habit of spending no more than a couple of nights in any one place. He usually paid cash and left well before dawn, before anyone else was stirring. But here, not only had he overslept, but for some damn reason he found himself in no hurry this time.

Hell, he even found himself considering her feelings. She was new at this, that much was obvious. Maybe that explained why he didn't want to disappoint her.

"Look," he said, hoping he wasn't going to regret it, "give me a minute, okay? I'll be right there."

She looked so pleased he almost didn't regret accepting the invitation.

"I'll see you in the sunroom," she said softly. "It's down the hall, just beyond the lobby."

CHAPTER EIGHT

Matt Potter watched his mom fuss with the pot of coffee, the basket of muffins, even the fancy white napkins she used to use at the Canyon Club house on the golf course.

He sat on the tall swivel stool beside the high registration desk and twisted the stool back and forth. It squeaked something terrible. If his dad were here, he'd say, "That thing needs some WD-40. Wanna help me fix it, Matt?"

Thinking about his dad made him sad, so Matt stopped moving the stool and rested his cheek on his arm as he spied on Mom.

She'd been acting really weird all morning. The banana-nut muffins had been cooling on the kitchen counter before he was even out of bed. That's how he knew something was up. Then Mom told him that their first guest had checked in last night.

He'd followed her into her room, watched her put on mascara and lipstick and comb her hair. She always fixed herself up right before his dad came home, too, even though she never got very messed up. She always wanted to look good for Dad.

But this morning she'd done the exact same thing for the first time in a long time, and he couldn't figure out why she cared so much about some guy they didn't even know. The idea made him feel creepy way down deep in the bottom of his stomach.

He looked around the lobby, at the dark wood walls and scratched floor, and for a couple of minutes was content to watch dust motes sift and shimmer like flecks of gold in streaks of sunlight by the windows.

He hated the Ear Ache Hotel even more than he had the Canyon Club house. He wanted to move back to Twilight Cove, where they used to live. What he *really* wanted was a house by his best friend's, Christopher Montgomery's, up on Lover's Lane. He begged Mom all the time, but she just said they had to live here for a while longer — at least until she got the hotel running and maybe they'd have some luck finding somebody to buy it.

Maybe *then* they could move to another house, a real house, close to his blood brother, Chris.

He checked the watch Dad had given him

for his birthday last year. It was a way cool G-Shock, the kind all the surfers wore. Since it was waterproof, he never took it off, not even when he took a bath.

It was almost nine. Almost time for Chris and his mom, Carly, to pick him up. She was going into San Luis Obispo to do some shopping and had invited him to go along to see the new Disney movie. He'd wanted to go until Mom told him about the guest. Now he didn't know what to do.

Just then, the guy walked in. Matt slipped off the stool and slithered along the tall registration desk like one of the Spy Kids. He looked at his watch again. 9:03. It was important to check the time when you were spying on someone.

At least that's what Chris had told him. Chris's dad, Jake, was a private investigator who used to spy on people from inside his car and other cool stuff like that, but now he mostly wrote books on how to be a detective so that he could stay home with Chris and Carly.

He eyeballed the guest, who was pretty tall. Taller than Mom anyway. He had on old black cowboy boots with pointy toes and heels. They weren't shiny and they looked pretty worn-out. He was wearing Levis and a black T-shirt tucked into his pants, but no belt. And he had muscles.

Dad never had muscles. He always talked about wanting to lift weights at the spa at the country club, but he was always working and never had time.

Maybe if he'd have worked out he'd have been healthier and he wouldn't have died. Maybe.

Afraid he might start crying, he concentrated on the guest instead.

The guy wasn't carrying a suitcase or anything as he walked over to where Mom was still messing with the coffee cups and napkins and rearranging the muffins on a pink glass plate with a paper doily on it.

How many muffins did she think the guy was going to eat, anyway?

Matt watched the man stare at Mom until she finally looked up and noticed him. She smiled up at the guy in a way that she never smiled anymore. It was a kind of nervous, grown-up smile of some kind.

Something about the way she was fussing and talking and smiling and pumping coffee for the guy made Matt's stomach hurt even worse, so he pushed off the side of the registration desk and walked over to Mom, then he leaned up close to her side, trying to make himself look taller. He stared at the guy without smiling, hoping the man would take the hint and go away.

CHAPTER NINE

"Matt, this is Mr. Johnson." Tracy automatically finger-combed Matt's hair. When he didn't respond immediately, she gently nudged him with her hip. "Honey —"

"Hi," he mumbled. "Nice to meet'cha."

She didn't press for more. He'd had so many adjustments to make that now wasn't the time to ride him about his manners.

With her hand on Matt's shoulder, she concentrated on Wade Johnson. His dark hair was still damp from the shower and if he'd tried to comb it, it didn't show. It was obviously dyed rock-star black and just long enough for the front to spike up in an artfully mussed, retro style. His jeans were faded, worn thin over knees and thighs. From the looks of it, his cowboy boots were the real deal. The leather was cracked and aged. They certainly didn't look like he wore them only to cowboy bars.

There was a swagger in his slow easy

stride, and she embarrassed herself by staring at the way the jeans perfectly fit his butt when he turned around to choose a muffin.

"Mom?"

Startled, she looked down into eyes exactly like Glenn's.

"What, hon?"

"It's almost time for Carly and Chris to pick me up."

"I know. You can wait outside, if you want, but stay on the porch."

"I'll wait right *here.*" He was staring at Wade Johnson.

"How old are you, Matt?"

The man's casual interest surprised her. Up to now he'd been silent but observing, giving little indication that he cared about conversing with either of them. She waited for Matt to respond, pleased when he spoke up this time.

"Nine."

"You recommend these muffins?"

Matt shrugged. "They're okay."

"They're banana," Tracy added. "My grandmother's recipe."

"Sounds good." He put two on one of her dainty, flowered dessert plates that was dwarfed in his hand, picked up a china coffee cup, and headed out to the porch. The fragile cup and plate looked ridiculous in

55

his hands, and she made a note to bring down some of her white ceramic mugs, too.

She watched him carry his coffee and muffins outside. In the light of day, he didn't seem the least bit intimidating.

This morning his reticence seemed far less sinister, as if he were deliberately quiet. Maybe even a bit shy. His face was rugged — certainly not pretty-boy handsome — but good-looking all the same. She was about to follow him out onto the porch to make sure he was comfortable when the front door opened and Christopher Montgomery came bounding in.

Matt stepped closer and whispered, "Maybe I should stay home, Mom."

She smoothed her palm over his cheek and wanted to cry for all the joy that had gone out of his life when Glenn died. "I thought you wanted to see the movie."

"I do, but —" he glanced toward the French doors that Wade Johnson had just passed through.

"No buts. I've got a lot to do today and, besides, Diego and the workers will be along in a few minutes."

"You're *sure* you'll be okay?"

She gave him a quick kiss and laughed when he quickly scrubbed it off.

Chris crossed the lobby. Carly waved as

she came through the door and followed Chris in. Tracy reminded Matt to run upstairs and get his sweatshirt, and the boys hurried off together.

California casual in jeans and a sleeveless shell, Carly brushed back her long blond hair, her smile infectious, her friendship never in doubt. She'd shown up the morning of Tracy's moving sale with a thermos of coffee, price stickers, and marking pens, and stayed all day fending off rude shoppers, keeping an eye on the boys, and helping raise Tracy's spirits. That night she'd even insisted that Tracy and Matt join the Montgomerys for pizza.

They'd shared the holidays, too. Their friendship was the only thing that had kept that first Christmas without Glenn from being a complete nightmare.

"How's it going?" Carly asked, looking around the lobby. "It looks a heck of a lot better in here every day."

"The painters are almost done, and as of yesterday, I've got six rooms finished." Before she could go on, Carly reached into the leather backpack over her shoulder and pulled out a stack of envelopes tied with a piece of polka-dot grosgrain ribbon.

"I was afraid I'd forget these."

Tracy recognized the invitations to the

open house celebration she had planned for mid-June. Carly had volunteered to hand-print the addresses in precise, graceful calligraphy. They were perfectly lettered works of art. She gave her friend a quick hug.

"Thanks, Carly. You'll be back before the party, won't you?"

"You sure you'll be done in time?" She glanced around, frowning.

"I have no choice. I'll make sure the lobby is finished. I've only got this tourist season to make it. Failure isn't an option. Please tell me you'll be back in time."

"We wouldn't miss it. Besides, Chris really wants to be home for the last day of school. I feel bad enough that he's missing the last few weeks, but he's finished all his important tests and his teacher is sending along some assignments."

The Montgomerys were heading for an art showing in Taos, where Carly was almost as well known for her distinctive painting style as she was here along the coast.

Tracy watched proudly as Carly scanned the lobby, noticed the muffins and coffeepot laid out with linen napkins, jam, a crystal honeypot, and little silver spoons on a pretty white tray.

"Help yourself," she offered.

"What's up? All this isn't just for me."

58

Tracy glanced toward the wide French doors opening onto the veranda and pulled Carly aside. "Our first guest checked in last night. He's outside having breakfast . . ."

Carly glanced over her shoulder. "Is that *his* Harley parked outside?"

"Yes."

"Did he check in alone?" Concern crinkled her brow as she added, "You aren't even open yet."

With a sigh, Tracy tried to pretend she hadn't had plenty of her own misgivings last night.

"Look, it was late when he got here. It was raining. Besides, he seemed perfectly harmless." She knew *that* was stretching the truth, but so far her intuition had proved right. Wade Johnson might not be very congenial, but he seemed perfectly normal.

"But you had no idea whether or not it was safe to let him in."

"How am I ever going to know who's okay and who isn't?" She sighed and absently twisted her wedding band. "God knows, I needed the extra cash." She looked around the half-finished lobby, visualizing it the way it would be when everything was finished.

Unconvinced, Carly shook her head. "I wish you'd have called us. Jake might have been able to check him out."

"I have to stand on my own two feet, you know? I can't depend on you and Jake, or anyone else. I'm going to have to go with my gut, and last night it told me this guy wants to escape."

"Are you suddenly psychic?"

"Okay, I'll admit that at first I was nervous, but it turned out all right. I can't have Jake running ID checks on every guest, can I?" She didn't want Carly to think she wasn't grateful for her friendship — even her overprotectiveness. "I appreciate how much you care, both you and Jake. I don't know how I'd have made it through these past few months without you."

"Enough of that. You'd have done the same for me."

"I know, but —" At a loss for words, Tracy fell silent.

As Carly picked up a muffin, Tracy wondered if she really would have been there for Carly had their situations been reversed. Their lives had changed with lightning speed once Glenn had become involved in the Canyon Club and other projects, but Carly had always made it a point to keep in touch, to see that the boys saw each other as much as possible over the summer.

"By the way," Carly sniffed the muffin before she broke off a morsel. "Jake said he'd have time to go over Glenn's accounts while we're in Taos, if you'd still like him to."

Months ago she had voiced her concerns to Jake, wondering how Glenn had managed to lose everything so relatively quickly. Jake said that he'd be happy to help and offered to go through the books, but there had been so many other pressing details that she hadn't thought about taking him up on it.

"I hate to have him working while he's away," Tracy admitted.

"Hey, he'll have little else to do but keep Chris amused while I'm getting the gallery show pieces together. Besides, he loves following money trails. It was one of his investigative specialties, you know. It'll keep him from getting rusty."

When Carly headed for the porch, Tracy dogged her heels. "Where are you going?"

"I want to get a look at your guest."

Just then, Wade Johnson appeared in the open doorway with his empty coffee cup in hand. When he noticed Carly, he gave her a nod, a quick once-over, and headed straight for the coffeepot.

Undeterred, Carly followed him, offered her hand, and introduced herself.

He shrugged, shifted his coffee cup, and

61

shook Carly's hand and said, "Wade Johnson."

"Are you from around here, Mr. Johnson?"

Tracy's face caught fire as Carly got right to the point.

"Just passing through."

"Why don't we wait for the boys outside?" Tracy suggested, afraid Carly would give him the third degree, but her friend didn't budge.

Wade helped himself to more coffee and Tracy was relieved when, as if on cue, the boys ran back in, all arms, legs, and impatience bundled into two very hyper packages.

"Let's go, Mom!" Chris was halfway to the door with Matt trailing slowly behind. "We gotta have lunch before the movie."

Carly turned to Tracy and sighed. "He just had breakfast."

"I know what you mean. Bottomless pits."

Tracy walked Carly out to the front porch. The midmorning sky was so bright with sunshine that it was almost impossible to believe that it had been gloomy the night before.

"I can see why you let Mr. Johnson in," Carly said as she dug the car keys out of the pocket of her jeans. Out at the curb, the boys were already climbing into her Volvo wagon.

"What do you mean?"

"He's hot. Even has a bad boy look about him. But not real bad, though. Strong, silent type, maybe? But what's with the hair?"

"Have you watched MTV lately? Dyed hair is in. The more obvious, the better." Tracy laughed, unwilling to admit that on Wade Johnson, it looked better than interesting.

"He's not exactly a kid."

"I kind of like it."

"How much?" Carly cocked an eyebrow.

Tracy immediately blushed and stared down at her hand, where the diamond on her ring finger glimmered back.

"Oh, damn. I'm sorry, Tracy."

"Hey, that's okay." Tracy shrugged. "I noticed his looks, is all."

"You'd have to be blind not to — look, Tracy, there's no need to feel guilty. Glenn's gone. You've got the rest of your life to live." Carly took her hands, forced her to look up.

"It's too soon."

"Hel-lo, it's *me* you're talking to. Carly. You've admitted things weren't that great between you and Glenn the last couple of years. Your marriage wasn't any bed of roses."

Her hope of a fantasy fairy tale marriage had been just that — a fantasy built on deception, overextended credit, and if not outright lies, then evasion. A world of glamour without substance. Near the end, her marriage had been as bankrupt as their money market accounts.

"I get nervous when I think about . . . dating anyone."

"Who's talking about *dating*?" Carly laughed and hugged her close. "Hey, do what you feel like doing, Tracy. You'll know when you're ready."

"Maybe I should stop wearing my wedding ring." She stared down at the diamond that she was wearing not out of loyalty, but habit. It reminded her of their wedding day, when their vows were fresh and new and real. When life seemed filled with endless possibilities.

"Wear it as long as you need to," Carly advised. "Besides, if you're going to continue to check in late-night guests alone, you might as well let them think there's a Mr. Potter waiting for you upstairs."

Tracy glanced out at the car. The boys were already buckled into the backseat, heads together.

"You'd better go. No doubt they're plotting something." Tracy waved back when she saw Matt waving to her. At least he was smiling now, which made her feel better about insisting that he go along.

"I'll have my cell on. If you need anything from town, call me and I'll pick it up," Carly offered. "And plan on coming over for dinner tonight. You can bring the account books."

"I will. Be careful." The panic that set in whenever she was about to be separated from Matt these days came swift and sure, surprising her as it always did. Just as he was reluctant to leave her, she had to fight her own reservations about letting him out of her sight.

Life seemed so very fragile now. Still, she refused to let unfounded fear smother Matt.

Just as Carly was backing out of the driveway, Diego Rios pulled in with a minivan full of day workers from nearby San Luis Obispo. When six men piled out of the car instead of the four she'd agreed to pay, Tracy sighed and hurried down the steps to head them off before they all went inside.

CHAPTER TEN

Alone inside, Wade wandered across the lobby to the front window. He found the view down the coast road spectacular, but just as compelling were the snatches of conversation between the women that he'd heard drifting through the open door.

His hostess was alone — except for the boy. Alone and living unprotected. Ms. Potter's friend had questioned her about letting him in last night, having more sense, it seemed, than Tracy Potter.

Tracy sounded matter-of-fact rather than desperate when she claimed that she had to have the hotel up and running because she had to make a success of it this season. The fact that she was strapped for money surprised him, especially with that ring on her finger. It was worth plenty, and proof that women could be far more sentimental than practical.

What had happened to the husband? he

wondered. *Separated? Divorced? Widowed?*

He couldn't help but think of his mother, of the way she'd always scrimped and saved to make it on his dad's military benefits. It had been just the two of them for as long as he could remember, just him and his mom living in a crowded one-bedroom walk-up above a Korean-owned minimarket and deli in New York.

The Heartbreak was a far cry from the dingy place he remembered growing up in. Tracy Potter's circumstances were obviously quite different; still, it was just her and the boy. At least right now that was the case.

His attention was drawn to the small parking area off to one side of a rose garden gone wild. Hands on hips, her ponytail swayed back and forth like a pendulum as she spoke to what appeared to be the foreman of the crew loitering nearby.

The silver-haired Hispanic man kept gesturing toward the side of the building, where six men in faded jeans, T-shirts, and baseball caps were slouching in silence. Their postures pretended disinterest but their eyes spoke volumes. They needed work and desperately needed the discussion to go their way.

Wade stepped out onto the porch, leaned back against the wall, and listened to the exchange.

"You see, Missus, you like to be finished on time, you need them all."

"I *know* I need them. That's not the issue. I can't *afford* all of them. Four." She held up four fingers. "I can pay four today. I told you that yesterday."

"Okay. Okay. Maybe you pay five, okay?"

"Four, Diego. *Quatro.*"

Wade pictured his mother bartering with the grocer downstairs, something he hadn't thought of in years. There was nothing she hadn't done to keep food on the table. She took in ironing and mending to supplement her military dependents' allotment, cleaned and ran errands for the elderly man who lived across the hall. The one job she loved most was writing confessions. She had a file folder full of clippings, stories she'd sold to *True Confessions*. Stories of love, lust, and betrayal. All fiction. She never dated. Never had affairs. She worked hard, wrote for fun.

Over in the parking area, Tracy still hadn't backed down. The foreman had walked over to where the men waited and after a spate of Spanish he came back to talk to her again.

"Okay. You pay six —"

Wade gave her credit for her tenacity. He almost went to her rescue, but she held her ground and smiled, though she emphatically shook her head no.

"I can pay *four.*"

Diego nodded vigorously. "*Si!* But you *get* six. You pay for four."

She shook her head. "That's not fair, Diego. I can't ask two of them to work for nothing."

"Ah, but you don't ask. I ask. They say okay." He shrugged, "That way, everyone makes some money today. Okay, Missus? A little is better than nothing."

Wade watched Tracy stare over the hopeful workers who were more than ready to put in a full day's work and settle for whatever cash they could make.

"I'll give them all lunch," she offered.

Diego's smile quickly reappeared.

"*Lunche,*" he called out to the men in Spanglish, a combination of Spanish and English spoken all over California. Satisfied, the men headed inside, obviously already familiar with the place as they made their way up the front steps.

Each nodded politely to Wade as they went inside. He had no desire to follow them. Instead, he waited for Tracy. When she finished talking to Diego, she finally noticed him in the doorway.

"Nice going," he complimented as she came up the steps. He meant it, too.

69

She seemed as surprised by his sudden willingness to talk as he was. It was the first time in a long while that he'd dared to exchange more than a few obligatory words with anyone, but watching Tracy Potter's little drama unfold had reminded him of a life he hadn't lived since childhood, and made them seem connected somehow.

"I feel guilty." Her gaze flicked to the sunroom, where the men were already setting up for the day. A team of two carried paint rollers and pans down the hall where the guest rooms were located. "I wish I could pay them what they deserve."

"A little is better than nothing," he quoted.

"Still . . ."

"Their foreman knew exactly what he was doing when he brought too many men."

Finally, she turned her gaze on him. It was liquid blue. Her stunning eyes were wide and full of such promise that for a moment he almost missed the shadow of sadness he'd seen there last night. Looking deeply, he saw it hadn't entirely left her.

He was mesmerized and at the same time bereft, knowing that, unlike Mrs. Potter, he no longer had a dream to fight for. He no longer possessed a single drop of hope for a better day.

Time stopped as he stared down into her eyes and momentarily, he lost himself. Her nearness warmed him, awakening something inside him that he'd thought long dead, something he'd convinced himself he didn't deserve to feel anymore.

Mentally he shook himself and finally looked away. He held up his empty cup.

"The coffee was great," he said.

"Would you like some more?"

"I've had plenty, thanks."

"How about another muffin?"

"They were great, too, but no thanks."

When she dropped her gaze, when her eyes left his, he felt the kind of chill that comes whenever a cloud passes in front of the sun. Amazed, he was a little resentful to think that she'd awakened such feelings in him at all.

He didn't deserve to feel anything anymore. Certainly not anything this good.

"Checkout isn't until noon." Though she said it casually enough, she was studying him intently, assuming he had somewhere to go, some destination in mind.

He had nowhere to go. No one was waiting for him. Because of this place, maybe because of her, he was still alive.

He thought of the notepad in the nightstand, square slips of paper covered with cramped scratches, the start of something. Notes? Sentences? He didn't even know what he'd written yet. Words inspired by dreams. Probably middle-of-the-night non-sensical rambling.

"I'd better see if the men need anything." Tracy shoved her hands in the back pockets of her jeans.

The move was totally innocent on her part, but it emphasized her breasts. She was too preoccupied with the workers, with her need to get the hotel ready for her grand opening, to be trying to seduce him. She had no idea the effect she was having on him, which made her even more enticing. He stared at her flawless profile, her trim waist and hips outlined in casual jeans, her spanking-white canvas shoes.

He'd be a fool to think about the luxury of hanging around, crazy to risk being recognized, no matter how greatly he was tempted.

"Thanks for opening up for me last night. I appreciate it."

The fingers of her right hand twisted the wedding ring on her left in an absentminded gesture. "Are you on your way home?"

Home? He didn't have one anymore. "No, just traveling the coast."

"What do you do?" Though she had plenty

to do, she didn't appear to be in a hurry to leave.

His mind quickly touched on possible answers the way a steel ball clangs around in a pinball machine. It finally landed.

"I'm in advertising." He had no idea where that came from, but he went with it.

"Where?"

"In L.A." *General enough.*

"Do you come up with jingles? Like Barry Manilow?"

"Not really."

"Do you write commercials?"

He shook his head, tried to think of a way to smoothly segue out of the conversation. "Just copywriting. That's all. Pretty tame stuff."

"Well, good luck then. If I don't see you before you go, just leave the key in the room."

"I will."

"Be safe."

He pictured himself going back to his room, showering, changing into a clean shirt, wrapping the Colt in his dirty one, and shoving it into the bottom of the saddlebag. Last night he'd put to rest the notion of suicide. He was too big a coward to take the coward's way out. He thought of the string of months he'd spent aimlessly wandering the countryside on the Harley. Of all the sleepless nights and restless days he'd spent roaming around alone.

He thought of the way she'd taken a chance last night, opening the door to him, trusting that he was one of the good guys when she had no reason to. He thought of the Even Dozen murdered women and the guilt that never left him.

Most of all, he thought of how fate had led him to the Heartbreak Hotel last night, and now he was in no hurry to leave. Not yet, anyway.

She was concentrating on one of the painters, who was carefully masking off the molding around the floor.

"Tracy?"

"Yes?" She turned, hesitated.

"I'd like to stay a few more days."

She brushed aside a wisp of hair that had slipped artfully over her left eye. "You're staying?"

He nodded. "If it's no problem." He started toward her, digging in his pocket for cash. He counted out nine hundreds — enough for a week's lodging.

"Of course not." Her gaze flicked down to his hand.

He rolled up the bills. Their eyes met as he handed them over.

"You plan to stay a whole week?"

He said the first thing that came to his mind, probably the closest thing to the truth that he'd told her since he'd arrived.

"I really have no idea."

CHAPTER ELEVEN

He's staying.

She didn't know why she felt so relieved. Perhaps just knowing he was downstairs last night had taken the edge off her loneliness.

"I'll be in to make up the room in a few minutes," she promised.

"No hurry. I'm going out for some supplies."

"There's a grocery store near the Plaza in Twilight Cove. Take the coast road a couple of miles south to where it hits the main highway. That'll take you right through the center of town."

"Thanks." He gave her a fleeting smile.

The "William Tell Overture" pealed out of her pocket as her cell phone went off. Wade nodded good-bye and headed for the door. She flipped the phone on and watched him walk away.

"Hello?"

"Tracy? It's me. Chelsea."

Hearing the tone of anguish in Glenn's daughter's voice, she jogged up the stairs to the apartment. She walked into the kitchen, heard the Harley start. Beyond the front window, Wade pulled out of the drive, headed toward Twilight. "How did finals go?"

"I think I did all right." Chelsea was less than enthusiastic.

"You sound down today."

Chelsea sighed heavily. "I really miss Dad."

"I know. It's tough."

Tracy had no idea whether or not Chelsea had been aware of the strain between them before Glenn died. If she had, the girl had never let on. Though she and Chelsea had never shared the close relationship Tracy once hoped for, her heart naturally went out to her. She had never expected to take Glenn's ex, Monica's, place in Chelsea's life, but before she married Glenn, she had hoped that she and the girl would at least become friends.

It took a few years before Chelsea accepted the fact that her father was never going back to Monica. If there were times when Chelsea acted self-centered and spoiled, it was because Glenn and Monica had continually competed for her loyalty.

"Mom married the dweeb and went to Austria for the summer." Chelsea laughed, but the sound didn't cover her bitterness or her heartache.

Tracy wasn't surprised. Five years ago, Monica had moved in with a stockbroker ten years her senior. The only thing that had kept Monica from marrying him sooner was Glenn's hefty alimony payments. Tracy propped her elbow on the desk and rubbed her temple.

"When did they get married?"

"Over the weekend. They went to Vegas. Mom didn't even call and tell me until today. She knows I can't stand Chuckie."

Tracy had never met Charles Strauss until Glenn's funeral, where Monica paraded him around like a trophy, introducing him to all of Glenn's old friends.

"I know you don't much care for him, but he's married to your mom now."

"He's too stupid to see that she married him only because Dad's gone and so is the alimony."

This wasn't the time to tell Chelsea that she'd been looking for a way to help pay her tuition next year. Before Tracy could say anything, Chelsea asked, "Can I come and stay with you and Mattie this summer?"

The request caught her off guard. Chelsea

had never asked to stay past her three weeks' visitation every summer. Now that she was over eighteen and Glenn was gone, Tracy hadn't held much hope of Chelsea spending much time with her and Matt, but she'd prepared an extra bedroom for her anyway.

"Of *course* you can stay with us. We'd love it. But what about your mom? What will she say?"

"As if she'd care. They'll be gone all summer, and I feel weird staying at Chuck's alone."

"As long as you're not doing this to upset your mom, Chelsea, you know you're always welcome here. Matt will be thrilled."

"Mom hinted that I should live in the sorority house this summer, but everyone's gone until fall and I didn't want to ask you for extra money."

Truth couldn't wait any longer. There was no extra money on this end.

"Listen, there's something I need to talk to you about." Tracy knew there was no easy way to say it, so she jumped right in. "After your dad died, I found out that almost all of our money was gone."

"What do you mean *gone*?"

"That's exactly what I asked the accountant. The house was mortgaged to the hilt, the credit cards were maxed out. Your dad owed money on all his projects."

"But you guys had that big house. And Dad's new Mercedes . . ."

"All I have left is this place, and a little money that my grandparents left me. When the hotel is up and running, I'm going to list it for sale and try to get back into real estate. For now, it's providing us a place to live, and hopefully some income." The view outside the window drew her gaze again. She'd always wanted to live on the water, but never imagined this.

"I thought you were just resurrecting that dump because you missed Dad so much you needed a project. I thought you moved out of Canyon Club and sold everything because it reminded you of him. I can't believe this has happened to you."

"It happened to you, too, honey . . ."

"But Dad left me a trust fund."

"He did, but it doesn't allow for any withdrawals of funds until you're twenty-five, not even for tuition. I guess he figured there would always be plenty of other money. I've talked to a trust attorney about it and we're trying to get things worked out, but it'll take time."

"How much time?"

"She said it could be months. In the

meantime, there isn't any money for your tuition next year."

"But . . . I have to come back to SC in the fall!"

"Let's not panic yet. We've got the whole summer to figure something out. I've been looking up scholarships on the Net, but I don't have a whole lot of extra time yet. I figured you could help once finals were over. Maybe your mom and Charles will help."

"Oh, *sure*. Mom didn't want me to go off to school in the first place."

"We'll find a scholarship."

After a brief silence she added, "I don't have a clue how I did on my finals. I probably screwed up big-time. It's so hard to concentrate right now."

"I know." Tracy took a deep breath and leaned against the kitchen counter. "Listen, pack up and come up here, okay? Things will work out. You'll see." *Somehow. Some way.*

Another sigh, and then Chelsea said, "Okay, I'll see you in a few days, if you're sure it's okay."

"Of course, it's okay. This is your home, too."

She wasn't absolutely sure about anything else anymore, but welcoming her stepdaughter with open arms was what she'd always done. Chelsea was Matt's half-sister. She would never turn her away.

As Tracy negotiated the coast road on the way home from the Montgomerys later that evening, she looked forward to seeing Wade Johnson again with mixed emotions. During dinner, Jake Montgomery had successfully raised enough questions to instill doubt about the wisdom of having let Wade Johnson stay at the hotel as her only guest.

She pulled her black BMW into the dilapidated garage, once a carriage house beside the hotel, and nudged Matt awake. As the two of them walked up the path to the side door, she noticed the Harley parked beneath the porch overhang. So did Matt.

"Hey, way cool! Where did this come from, Mom?"

"It belongs to our guest, Mr. Johnson."

Matt stepped away from the bike. "The guy with the cowboy boots?"

"Yep."

He admired the bike with his hands on his hips, strutting around it just the way Glenn would have. Tracy pulled out her cell phone and hit the automatic dial. When Jake answered, she lowered her voice.

"Jake? It's Tracy. Here's the license number you wanted."

The ex-P.I. wouldn't take no for an answer earlier. He'd insisted she let him run a check on Wade's plate, just to be safe. She read him the number while Matt circled the bike, engrossed in the chrome and the flame design on the gas tank.

"Thanks," Jake said before he added, "I didn't want to head to New Mexico and leave you there alone without checking this guy out. I'll call back as soon as I follow this up."

She thanked him and said good night.

Matt was right beside her. "Can I sit on the Harley?"

"Of course not. Come on, honey. It's late." She put her hand on his shoulder as they continued along the path to the side porch. The garden on either side of the brick walkway was overgrown with ancient rosebushes, misshapen and wiry, pushing up through a tangle of weeds. She forced herself to ignore them every time she walked by. There was just too much to do inside to worry about the outside yet.

"Do you like him?" Matt asked as they stepped inside the entry. The solid door closed behind them with a resolute click. Since Wade was obviously in, Tracy turned the lock.

"Who?"

"Mr. Cowboy Boots. Do you like him?"

She'd left the lights on in the lobby. They were old fixtures, like the ones in the hall. At some point they'd been converted from gas lamps and, because of the small size of the bulbs, they gave off little more than weak, muted light.

Looking down into Matt's eyes, she realized what he was really asking and quickly knelt down on one knee and framed his face between her hands.

"Oh, honey. I don't even know him. He's just a guest. That's all. We're going to have lots and lots of guests checking in this summer."

"You were being real nice to him this morning."

"I plan on being nice to all the guests. They'll be paying to stay with us, and that's where we're going to get money for all the things we need from now on. I need you to help me welcome them to the Heartbreak, too. This is our home now, and I want them to feel as if they've come to visit. I want them to feel at home, have a wonderful time here, and tell their friends about this place."

He was quiet for a minute, digesting what she'd said. "Just because I'm nice to Mr. Johnson, that doesn't mean we'll ever forget about your daddy. You know that, don't you?"

He mumbled something she couldn't hear.

"What, honey?"

He looked up, his eyes bright with tears that sparkled even in the dim light. "Yeah."

She took his hand as they walked through the open lobby. He may have grown, but his hand was still small in hers. Small, warm, and very, very trusting.

"You can really help me, you know," she said. "When it gets crowded, it's going to be hard for me to make everyone feel at home, so I'd really appreciate it if you'd be friendly to the guests, too."

"Be nice to *strangers*?"

The question gave her pause. "Once they've checked in, technically they won't be *strangers,* but you are *never* to go into a guest's room, okay?"

He nodded. "What should I do?"

"Be polite. Talk to them. Answer questions about Twilight Cove and tell them about all the things there are to see and do around here. You know about the beaches and the trails and the shops, just as much as a tour guide would know."

"If Chris is around, can he help, too?"

"As long as you are both polite and don't get silly." Tracy slipped her apartment door key out of her pocket.

"I've got a surprise for you." The minute she said it, Matt stopped walking.

"What?" He turned and stretched his arms wide as if he could block her path.

"Chelsea is coming to live with us this summer."

"She comes to stay with us every summer. That's no big deal."

"Yes, but she usually stays for only three weeks. This time she's moving in for the whole summer."

"Into the empty bedroom?"

Tracy nodded. "And guess what? I'm going to let you help me vacuum and dust and get it ready for her."

"Big wow, Mom."

"Big wow that she's coming?"

"No. Big wow that I get to clean."

He focused on something over her shoulder. "Mom?" His voice was low and troubled.

"What?"

"It's that guy," he whispered.

CHAPTER TWELVE

Tracy turned and found herself staring into Wade's unreadable dark brown eyes. He'd walked in again without making a sound, and seeing him there, filling up the entrance to the hallway, everything Jake had cautioned her about earlier came back to haunt her.

"I didn't mean to startle you," Wade said softly. "I heard you come in."

"Mom?" Matt stepped close to her elbow, hovered there. She gently laid her hand on his shoulder before she handed him her keys.

"Why don't you go on upstairs and get ready for bed?"

"But, Mom . . ."

"Go on, hon."

He looked as if he wanted to argue, then glanced over at Wade before finally heading for the stairs. Her cheeks caught fire, even before she turned around and caught Wade staring at the neckline of her blouse. Her hand strayed to her throat. It had been forever since a man had looked at her with desire.

Perhaps the look should have frightened her, but when she realized that it was having the opposite effect on her, she was doubly shocked.

"Is everything all right?" she asked.

He paused, then slowly nodded.

"I was just wondering if you have any paper I can use. I'll replace it tomorrow."

"I have some copy paper right here in a drawer somewhere." She walked over to the registration desk, opened one of the lower drawers, and pulled out a stack of paper. "Is that enough?"

"Plenty, thanks." He curved it into a crescent in his hand. "Like I said, I'll replace it tomorrow."

"Don't worry about it." She assumed he would walk away and found herself wishing that he wouldn't. Not yet.

Carly and Jake had done a successful job of planting doubt about him, and yet she still found herself attracted to this man, even though the safest thing, the right thing to do, would be to quickly tell Wade good night, retreat to her own quarters, and lock herself in with Matt.

Until now, she always did the right thing. That had been her way since childhood. She grew up trying hard to please her grandparents. After both her parents were killed in a pileup on an icy interstate, she'd made a bargain with God. In exchange for her being good enough, and smart enough, she asked Him not to take her grandparents the way He'd taken her mom and dad. She'd kept her end of the bargain, and her grandparents had lived long and happy lives.

Doing the right thing had always been easy — until tonight.

Tonight she was tempted by something else altogether, even though she had no idea if Wade Johnson was who or what he said he was, but he'd given her no reason to doubt him.

His rugged features were softened by the gilding of lamplight. He was a good-looking man, she noticed, younger than she first thought, though the shadows of lingering sadness in his eyes made him seem older. She wondered: *What was behind the melancholy that never left him? Where was he headed? Was he married? Where was he from?* All of the unanswered questions were as intriguing as he was.

"Are you planning to burn the midnight oil working?" she asked.

"Sort of."

She found herself smiling. "Sort of? How do you 'sort of' write?"

The corner of his mouth lifted with an almost smile. "That's the easy part. Actually *working* on something is another story altogether."

Alone with him in the semidarkness, caressed by the deep, warm sound of his voice, she realized how much she had missed sharing intimacy with a man — and here was this attractive, intriguing man who left her mind filled with more questions than answers.

She brushed her hair back over her shoulder. "How long have you been a writer?"

"A long time." An answer that revealed nothing, really. "How long have you owned this place?"

"My husband bought it a few years ago. He . . . died quite suddenly, and I didn't have any recourse but to move in and fix it up."

His eyes latched on to hers, held her gaze. "You're a widow."

"Six months now," she repeated.

"I could tell you were new at this."

"I'm sure I'll get better at it. I've never run a hotel before."

"I meant that you're new at being alone

with a man."

Now her cheeks were frying. She dropped her gaze to her hands, saw that she was nervously twisting her wedding ring, and stopped. When she looked up again, she noticed that he had taken a step closer. His penetrating, deep brown eyes never wavered. He was so close she noticed he wore contacts.

"Do you know anything about the history of the Heartbreak?" He leaned against the registration desk, his stance casual, his stare intent. "Like when the place was built, or who owned it?"

Was he just making small talk? Trying, like her, to keep the conversation going?

She shook her head. "I haven't had time to do much of anything but get moved in and start the renovations. The local historical preservation society has made it their cause to put the place on the National Historic Register. When that happens, it won't look very promising to potential buyers unless I can make a success of the place exactly the way it is." Her forehead creased into a slight frown. "I think Glenn mentioned that the hotel was built around 1900."

"Glenn?"

"My husband."

"How long were you married?" He shifted, settled in.

"Ten years." A decade. Long enough to know someone intimately, to have a son with him. A decade, and yet near the end she had begun to realize that she no longer knew Glenn at all.

"Were you happy?" He didn't seem in the least embarrassed by the personal nature of his questions.

The fact that she barely knew him and that he would be walking out of her life at the end of the week made it easy to be honest.

"The last couple of years were rocky. If it hadn't been for Matt, I'd have probably filed for divorce."

He made no comment. She read no judgment in his eyes.

"How about you? Were you ever married?" She thought about it and then quickly added, "Are you married now?"

He laughed, as if the notion were somehow ridiculous. "No. I'm not married. Never have been."

Her gaze touched his dark hair. It looked as if he'd been raking his hands through it. "Why not?"

"I was married to my work."

"But now you're taking time off."

He nodded. "That's right."

"So what's the paper for?"

She watched him shrug. Again, half a smile, no more. "I'm just dabbling."

"What is it you're 'sort of' writing?"

"I'm not sure yet."

Just then the stairs creaked behind her. Wade's gaze flicked over her shoulder.

"Mom?" Matt sounded more uncertain than impatient.

She turned, saw him standing on the stairs in his pajamas, waiting.

"Are you coming to tuck me in?"

When she turned to Wade again, she noticed that he'd put space between them.

"Thanks for the paper."

"No problem."

Neither of them moved.

"Mom?"

"I'm coming," she promised. Then to Wade she added, "Coffee will be ready at 7:30. Since it's Sunday, the workmen won't be around, so it'll be a lot quieter."

"Why don't you sleep in?" he suggested. "There's no hurry."

His simple act of thoughtfulness moved her. "How about 8:30 then?"

"That would be fine."

"Great. Good night, Wade." She found herself completely at ease, even smiling for no good reason at all.

"Yeah. You, too."

It was the first time he'd heard her say his name aloud, and he was shocked at how such a short, simple word coming from her lips could send such a wave of desire through him. Headed down the hall alone, he warned himself to not go there.

Don't even think about it.

But it was already too late. Ms. Potter had taken up residence in his mind.

He hadn't wanted to admit that he was worried about her and the boy earlier. When he hadn't seen them around the hotel that evening, he found himself wondering where they were, what they were doing out so late.

She had left the front door unlocked and the lobby lights on for him, but there was something desperately lonely about the place with her and the boy gone. Every creak and groan of the old wood walls and floors seemed amplified. The surf was as loud as a freight train when it crashed against the jagged rocks below the bluff.

He'd been to town that afternoon, bought packaged fast food, a Styrofoam cooler stocked with sodas, and a new bottle of tequila. He'd purchased the only notebook left at the small Twilight Cove market — an old black-and-white composition notebook complete with faded blue lines and a few years of dust on the cover.

He'd filled it in no time at all, jotting down sensory impressions about the hotel. The sounds, the tang of salt air, the slight taint of mildew that the night's dampness inspired. The cries of the gulls in flight. The hurried *whoosh* of passing cars on the road. The stillness, the aching loneliness that seemed to permeate the very walls.

When he had heard Tracy come in, he'd left his room with the excuse that he needed more paper, but who was he kidding? His urge to see her again was so undeniably strong that it shocked him. Almost as much as the fact that her hesitance to walk away earlier seemed to be driven by something other than a mere need to be polite.

He walked into his room, deposited the copy paper on the desk littered with note-pad scraps, the composition notebook, plastic wrapping from a deli sandwich, and an open pack of ballpoint pens. Staring at the cluttered desktop, he thought about his compulsion to stand in the lobby and stare at Tracy. *What would she do if she knew who I really am?*

It wasn't as if he were desperate for a woman. There had been plenty of them in his life. None that he'd ever fallen for, though. None that inspired loyalty or commitment. They'd been flirtatious attractions that had led to physical encounters, short-term relationships that never lasted more than a few days, a month now and again.

After the murders, the string of lawsuits, the trials and publicity, women had still been attracted to him, but they'd been drawn by his notoriety, seduced by his wealth. He never knew if a woman really cared or if she was simply twisted enough to be dazzled by the three-ring circus his life had become overnight.

Eight months earlier he'd changed his looks and walked out on his old life. Since then he'd had one or two infrequent encounters while on the road. Safe-sex one-night stands that hadn't given him pause. He'd never looked back, never thought about the women again.

He'd found it easier to drop off the radar, to avoid contact with anyone rather than live his old life, and by some miracle he'd managed to keep his identity secret.

Just because he was attracted to Tracy Potter didn't mean he could get cocky and press his luck. If he were smart, he'd pack up and leave tonight.

Was he willing to take a chance, to risk

exposure, to risk it all — just to get to know Tracy Potter a little better? To be near her a while longer? Was it worth it?

Something told him that it was.

The same something that had brought him to her door.

Upstairs, Tracy made sure that Matt brushed his teeth, and then she tucked him in before she closed his door, took her cell phone into the kitchen, and hit redial. Jake answered immediately.

"The Harley plates are registered to a literary agent in Los Angeles," he said without preamble.

"That was fast."

"It helps to know people in the right places."

"He *said* he was a writer."

"Not an agent."

"Maybe he borrowed the bike." Relief sluiced through her as she leaned against the kitchen counter. She shook her hair out, rubbed her temple. It had been a long day and a very productive one. She should be dead tired, but her exchange with Wade had rejuvenated her as much as knowing that he was indeed connected to the writing world.

Jake hadn't said anything else, but she could almost hear him thinking.

97

"He's a writer on hiatus," she nudged.

"Right."

"So will you stop worrying now?"

"I'll call the agency in the morning and find out if they represent Wade Johnson." Jake sounded determined to go ahead.

"Please don't, Jake."

There was a moment's hesitation on the other end of the line before he said, "Look, Tracy —"

"The man deserves his privacy. Hopefully he'll recommend the hotel to friends when he goes back to L.A. This is the perfect spot for a writers' retreat, don't you think?"

"You're sure you don't want me to make a few calls?"

"I'm sure. I promise, I'll call you if I change my mind. Okay?"

"Did Carly give you our number in Taos?"

"I've got it. Will you call when you finish going over the books?"

"Of course."

"Thanks again, Jake."

"See you soon."

She hung up, feeling better for asking Jake not to delve into Wade's background.

She very much *wanted* Wade Johnson to be exactly who and what he said he was.

CHAPTER THIRTEEN

The room was dark as pitch, yet Wade had the distinct feeling that someone was there. Someone was watching him. Someone silent, and still.

He lay in the middle of the bed, trying to decide whether he was awake or asleep. He remembered spending a couple of hours making notes. Feeling brain-dead, he'd finally turned off the light.

Now groggy, he pushed himself up to a sitting position, disentangled himself from the spread. As usual, he'd fallen asleep fully dressed, but his feet were bare.

Drinking in air, he snapped on the light. He was alone. The door was still locked. The French doors to the porch were closed.

There was no intruder. He had no idea what time it was, except that it was still night, still dark out. The clock on the bedside table read 1:45.

He got up and went into the bathroom,

turned on the light. It blinded him. He blinked, ran water in the sink, and splashed it over his face by the handfuls, soaking the front of his black T-shirt down to his navel.

"You look like shit." He shook his head at the man in the mirror. After all these months, he was still unaccustomed to the harsh black tint on his hair, the ragged "in" style he had fashioned himself with gel, his smooth, beardless face.

At eighteen he'd grown a beard and worn one ever since, right up until the day he dropped out of sight.

There were few if any photos of him without one. He'd purposely kept the beard all through the trials, for he'd begun to plan his rebirth as Wade MacAllister again. For the first time in his life, he'd been thankful that he and his mom had moved around so much. He'd missed more picture days at various elementary schools than he'd actually made, and by the time he was a sophomore in high school he'd dropped out, studied at home, and passed the GED at sixteen. His mother was gone now. There would be no unearthing of old yearbook photos, no classmates, friends, or relations cashing in on his nightmare.

He left the light on, stumbled back into the room. The intense chill had left the air.

Light from the open bathroom door spilled out across the bed, accented the amber liquid in the tequila bottle on the bedside table.

He walked over and picked it up, screwed off the cap, lifted the bottle to his lips.

"Jose Cuervo, you are a friend of mine . . ."

The tune filtered through his mind, collided with volumes of minutiae trapped there.

The walls of the room were closing in on him, and suddenly claustrophobic, he stepped out onto the porch, closing the French doors behind him without making a sound.

His bare feet hit the wooden floorboards of the wide covered porch that was cool and slick with moisture. The paint was peeling, the surface rough and uneven.

Yet another task for the lovely Mrs. Potter's work crew.

The sound of the waves beckoned him. The sharp sting of the salt-laden breeze cleared his head. He was drawn through the garden filled with overgrown hydrangeas and marguerites — or maybe they were daisies. He never could tell the difference.

He stubbed his toe on an uneven brick, mumbled a curse under his breath, walked on until he was standing high on the edge of the sandstone bluff above the water. A fine sheen of mist shone on the surface of the dark rocks below, glistening like a woman's tears.

It was a long, long way down to the rocks. He rubbed his hand over his eyes and took a quick step back away from the edge.

Breathing deeply, he closed his eyes and let the sharp, cold mist off the water, the even tempo of the waves, soothe him. A vision filled his head, one of tall-masted ships and billowing sails, of rolling hills of green and gold and yellow, and under it all the sound and scent of the sea.

When he opened his eyes and turned around, a flash of white up near the roof of the hotel caught his eye. Hurrying toward the ramshackle garage off to the side of the yard, he slipped into the shadows where he could see but wasn't likely to be seen.

Staring at the roofline, he thought for a moment that he was hallucinating, that he was seeing the woman in his dreams, the raven-haired beauty whose loss he felt as deeply as if her life had been his own.

But the woman walking along the widow's walk in the long, flowing nightgown was Tracy Potter. With her blond hair shimmering around her shoulders, she walked to the railing, clasped her hands around it to brace herself, and leaned into the night, facing out to sea. Perhaps trying, like him, to clear her mind, hoping the elements would succeed where she could not.

She was no more than a silhouette against the night sky, a vision out of one of the gothic novels that had been his mother's favorite genre. The wide, ruffled hem of Tracy's gauzy gown billowed in the wind, outlining her trim figure, the curves of her thighs, the tilt of her breasts.

He stared, mesmerized, unable to tear his gaze away, remembered the sound of her voice, the herbal scent of her shampoo. He hadn't missed the reassuring way she'd gently touched her son's shoulder.

She was a widow, prowling the widow's walk in the dead of night.

"The last couple of years were rocky."

It had been impossible to miss the regret in her voice. Was she mourning the man who'd made those last two years hard for her?

His father had been lost to the Vietnam War. Though never outwardly, his mother had mourned him for the rest of her life and had never remarried. Working to make ends meet, constantly having to move when the rent was overdue, his mother had never had a chance to date, to meet anyone and find love again.

But Tracy's world was different. Men would be checking in and out of her life as easily as they checked in and out of the Heartbreak. She was lovely. Educated. She could, no doubt, have just about any man she wanted.

The reality of her situation irritated him. It didn't sit well with him.

His feet were cold, his damp shirtfront stuck to his skin. Almost as if she suddenly felt the same chill, he saw Tracy rub her arms. She had to be just as cold, and he was relieved when a few seconds later, she crossed the widow's walk and disappeared inside.

He counted to ten before he stepped out of the shadows and walked down the path through the untamed garden and back into his room.

CHAPTER FOURTEEN

There was something weird about Mr. Cowboy Boots. Matt was sure of it. Even though Mom said the guy hadn't checked out, they never saw him except for when he had his coffee and when he came in carrying bags of junk food — cool stuff like chips and Snickers bars and Twinkies. Stuff Mom never let *him* have.

She acted like she wasn't worried about the guy never coming out of his room, but Matt could tell she was just faking it.

Before Mom took him to school on Monday, Mr. Johnson hadn't even showed up for coffee. Every time Mom walked past his door, she would slow down and look at it funny, like she wanted to knock or something, but she didn't.

For a while she seemed like she was waiting around for the guy to show until it got late and they had to go. He tried to fake being sick so he could stay home. After all,

Christopher was skipping almost three weeks of school — but she didn't go for it.

He hoped that when he got home, the Harley would be gone and so would Mr. Johnson. But it was still parked close to the building, under the overhang.

This morning there was still no sign of their guest even though there were some huge cinnamon buns waiting for him in the sunroom. If Mom wasn't going to do anything, then it was up to him to find out why Mr. Johnson wasn't coming out.

Maybe the guy had slipped in the shower and hit his head. Maybe he had the flu and was dead in there and nobody knew it.

Maybe his brain had exploded like Dad's.

Mom hadn't ever told him what really happened to his dad. She just said that something in Dad's brain had leaked and that's why he died, but Chris told him that it was way worse than that. He said it was just like Dad had a balloon full of blood in his head and it blew up.

Maybe Mr. Johnson had a blowout, too.

Somebody had to find out, and he was the man of the house now. It was up to him. But he had to act fast, before he left for school.

Right now, Mom was busy talking to a man and a woman who had checked in last night, so he told her that he forgot his spelling and had to go get it. She was pouring coffee when he ran out of the sunroom and slipped down the hall toward Mr. Johnson's room.

Outside the room he looked at his watch, then over each shoulder before he pressed his ear to the door. He *thought* he heard something inside, but he wasn't sure.

He snuck outside and took the side steps down to the yard, then crept along under the porch railing until he came to Mr. Johnson's room. The curtains were drawn, but there was a crack between them, so without making a sound, he brought his eyeball close to the window.

The lamp was on inside the room. From what little he could see, the place was a mess. Trash covered the floor, empty potato chip bags, plastic sandwich holders, and Twinkies wrappers. And Coke cans. Lots of them. He saw a couple of empty glass bottles, too.

Finally he spotted Mr. Johnson sitting on the floor, leaning against the side of the bed. He was hunched over a notebook on his lap, writing as fast as Matt had ever seen anyone write before.

Then, almost as if he knew he was being watched, Mr. Johnson's hand suddenly stopped moving. The pen dropped onto the notebook and the man stared *right at the window.*

Matt's heart slammed against his chest. He couldn't tell if Mr. Johnson could see him or not. The crack between the curtains wasn't *that* big; still, he backed away quickly, without making a sound. He almost rolled backward down the steps.

He jumped off the porch and ran back around the way he'd come, climbed through the window, and raced back down the hall, through the lobby, and into the sunroom yelling, "Hey, Mom! It's late! You better get me to school."

By ten, Wade needed coffee in the worst way.

He'd left the room earlier, looking forward to a good jolt of caffeine. He almost walked into the sunroom, but then he heard voices — male *and* female — and immediately turned and walked back to his room.

So much for the cinnamon buns he'd smelled all the way down the hall. As hungry as he was, he was sure he could wipe out half a dozen of them.

He'd run out of supplies late yesterday afternoon, so technically, he'd had nothing substantial for dinner. Not even he could call chips, nuts, and Cheetos a meal.

As soon as he was back in his room, he pulled up the blanket and bedspread. Then he grabbed the white plastic wastebasket in the bathroom and carried it around with him, hastily picking up trash.

Two empty tequila bottles were sticking out of the top, but the floor looked a little better by the time he was finished.

He set the can down and looked around to make certain the place was presentable enough. Then he opened the curtains and stared out across the garden, out toward the horizon.

There were no passing ships. Even so, he had no problem imagining what one might have looked like a hundred years ago with its sails billowing in the wind, cutting through the foaming green water. His eyes stung. The taste of saltwater filled his mouth. Rubbing his temples, he turned away from the view and walked over to the bed where his papers and the composition notebook lay.

The notebook's pages were swollen with ink and sweat. He'd accidentally spilled Coke and tequila on some of them. There were telephone notepapers and paper napkins covered with writing stuffed inside the notebook, too. Some pages had been ripped out entirely, balled up, rescued, hand pressed, and shoved back into place.

Never one to waste words or paragraphs that could be recycled, he always saved every draft.

It wasn't that every line was that terrific — or that precious.

What's more, he hadn't even reread what he'd written yet. Not one word. It was bad enough that he was even writing again, let alone revising. With any luck, he'd toss the damn pages over the cliff, move out, and be done with this.

Two years ago he swore to himself that he would never, ever write again. He couldn't, even when he tried.

And he'd kept that promise to himself until the night he walked into this place and woke up and started scribbling on the phone notepad, completely unaware of what he was doing.

He'd hoped that he could have stopped this idiocy by now. He had no idea if what he'd written even had any merit. The urge to write had come to him so powerfully, poured out so insistently — and yet he had barely any recollection of what he had written.

Not that it mattered. Nothing would ever come of the work he'd done here. He'd make certain of it.

When he heard a quick knock at the door, he was thankful that he'd taken time to clean up the floor. He opened the door and saw Tracy nearly hidden behind a stack of fresh white towels so high that she had to peer around it to see him.

"Is this a good time? May I come in?"

"Of course." He stepped aside to let her pass and instead of closing the door, left it open while she was alone with him. He realized with blinding clarity that *she* wasn't the one that he didn't trust.

Her movements were swift and efficient as she gathered up the dirty towels and hung fresh ones. It made him uncomfortable, sharing such a small, intimate space with her. His thoughts would have probably sent her running from the room.

She had on fitted black capri pants and a sleeveless black top. The outfit wasn't meant to be provocative, but her shapely figure brought it to life, filled it with gentle curves that tempted and fired his imagination.

He still had no idea how old she was. Thirty-two at the most, he guessed. He really didn't care as he watched her move across the room, attending to the little details of life.

His gaze was drawn to the wisps of blond hair that had escaped her ponytail and

111

trailed across the pale, delicate skin at the nape of her neck. Lost in her, he forgot about the damn notebooks until she picked them up so that she could make the bed.

He held out his hand.

"I'm sorry."

"Don't be." He smiled, trying to put her at ease.

"That's nice." Her tone was light, her eyes shining.

"What?"

"Your smile. You don't smile enough, you know."

"I know." Shy as a kid, he'd never exactly become the life of the party. Over the last couple of years there had been little to smile about.

"Looks like you're still 'sort of' writing." She nodded toward the notebooks on the nightstand.

He laughed. "Sort of."

The hell of it was that he *was* writing again. The weird part was that he had no idea why or how. He felt like a dog having lied to her about being in advertising.

Then again, he hadn't *exactly* lied to her.

He *was* a writer.

He was a novelist. Or at least he *had* been, until twelve innocent women were murdered.

"It takes me an hour to write a thank-you note. I worry over every word, but Matt's a good writer." Tracy gathered up the bed-sheets and blanket, completely unaware that she was giving him an outstanding view of her trim behind.

She had the figure of a much younger woman. He'd bet a hundred bucks that she was as firm and supple under her clothes as she looked inside them.

He walked across the room, ashamed of himself for taking advantage of the view when she had no idea that's what he was doing, and all the while she was innocently talking about her kid.

"Of course, all moms think their children have talent."

His mom certainly had, too. She'd believed in him and in what she called his instinctive talent for writing. So much so that she'd encouraged him to submit a piece when he was only twelve. By the time he was sixteen he not only had a file folder of rejections, but another of check stubs, none of which amounted to much, but enough so that he tasted the hope of actually becoming a working writer able to support himself one day.

Hopefully, all mothers believed in their children.

"What's Matt written?"

"Oh, lots of poems and stories. Mind you, the spelling is a bit creative — he's still sounding out a lot of words — but he's got a great imagination. He used to write a lot before . . ." she stumbled on the words and fell silent.

He turned around, noticed her hands had paused in the act of smoothing the sheet. Their eyes met.

". . . before Glenn died," she finally finished.

"How'd it happen? If you don't mind my asking."

"Aneurysm. It was very sudden. He collapsed and was gone without regaining consciousness."

It sounded like a good way to go to him. He could think of worse. Much, *much* worse.

Outside, the morning sky was still overcast. On the far horizon, it was hard to tell where the gray sky ended and the ocean began. His stomach rumbled, reminding him that he hadn't eaten a thing since a dried-out Twinkie last night.

"I thought I heard someone talking in the sunroom earlier. Did someone else check in?" He tried to sound casual, as if it didn't matter. Until now he had felt at ease, almost

114

complacent here. That wasn't a good sign.

When he turned around, she was tucking in folded corners of the sheet, making perfect angles of it.

"Just for one night. I hope they didn't disturb you."

"Not at all. More people will be finding the place soon." He was thinking aloud more than making a comment, but she nodded in agreement.

"I hope so. I just barely made the deadline for advertising in the Chamber of Commerce lodging listing."

"Do you have a website?" he asked.

When she laughed, he couldn't help but smile, too. "Are you kidding? The business cards were just printed."

The bed was finished. She straightened, still smiling. "Anyone ever mention anything . . . odd . . . about the place?" he asked before he could change his mind. Asked on the off chance that she would say yes and then he'd know he wasn't losing it.

She shook the pillow out of the case and then lined it up to shake it down into a new one.

"Odd? Termite infestation in some walls and not others. Then there's the fact that no one painted any of the rooms for about thirty years. That kind of odd?"

"Not really." He shrugged. "Sometimes old places like this have some folklore attached."

She finished bagging the second pillow, laid it in place against the headboard, stood back, and straightened it again. "Like what kind of folklore?"

"Like ghost stories."

"Are you looking for a ghost story?"

"Not really."

At least he hadn't been, not until he couldn't explain what was happening to him.

But then again, he had been paid for making things up for most of his adult life. His imagination was trained to work overtime.

She was watching him closely. "You don't believe in that sort of thing, do you?"

"What sort of thing?"

"Ghosts."

"Not really." At least, he never had before.

"Good." She glanced around the room, assessing, and must have decided it passed muster. "Well, I'm all finished."

She crossed the room, pausing just inside the door. "Are you ready for that coffee now?"

Was she inviting him to extend their conversation or merely being polite? He found himself weighing the consequences of

116

getting any further involved.

She was a widow of only six months.

He was a shadow, hiding behind a disguise, hiding from the world at large.

But he was a shadow who wanted to be with her more than he needed that cup of coffee or one of her damn cinnamon buns.

"Sure, I'll have some coffee, if it's not too late."

"Of course not. I made a fresh pot a few minutes ago.

He volunteered to carry out the dirty sheets and towels for her.

She waited for him in the hall.

He decided maybe she was as hungry for his company as he was for hers.

CHAPTER FIFTEEN

The anticipation Tracy felt whenever she thought about seeing Wade again was ridiculous. At least that's what she tried to convince herself, but it didn't help calm the spike in her heart rate or cool the flush on her cheeks when he opened the door and ushered her into his room a few minutes ago.

When he looked directly into her eyes, she'd almost forgotten what she was doing there.

Until she'd come in to straighten up his room, she hadn't really spoken to him except in passing since Saturday night. By sequestering himself behind a Do Not Disturb sign, he'd managed to fuel her fantasies. Even though she hadn't seen much of him, it was oddly comforting just knowing he was downstairs when she turned off the lights at night. Both comforting and arousing.

This morning he looked worn out — surprising for a man who ostensibly hadn't done anything but laze around his hotel room. There were violet shadows beneath his eyes and a droop to his shoulders, though it made her blush when she couldn't help but notice what fine, solid, well-defined shoulders they were.

"Something smells great." Wade walked behind her, as closely as the narrow hall would permit.

She glanced back over her shoulder and wondered if she was imagining the intensity in his stare or not. Unable to look away, she almost tripped over her own feet as the two of them entered the lobby.

Workmen were everywhere; on ladders, kneeling on drop cloths, touching up yards of white wooden molding, scraping paint speckles off windowpanes, buffing the floor where the painting was finished.

She was proud of the sitting room, nearly finished except for a few decorator touches. Overstuffed sofas with white slipcovers and bright red and blue throw pillows faced each other, inviting guests to sit and chat. The fireplace mantel held two tall blue-and-white vases that flanked a huge mirror with a rustic crackled frame.

Soft oldies music drifted on the air as did

the heady scent of the cinnamon buns she'd made at dawn. All in all, the hotel was beginning to look just the way she'd imagined it.

"Where should I put these?" he asked, slightly lifting the sheets and towels.

"The laundry is just off the sunroom, to the right. I'll get you some coffee."

"That's okay." He paused just outside the door to the sunroom. "I can get my own. I'm sure you've got plenty to do."

Nothing that couldn't wait until she made certain he had what he needed.

She was headed for the sideboard when she heard the familiar sound of her step-daughter's voice calling from the lobby.

"Tracy?"

"You're here!" She left the sunroom and hurried to greet the striking redhead toting a heavy duffel bag through the lobby. The minute Chelsea saw her, she dropped the bag and it hit the floor with a heavy thud.

Tracy closed the distance between them and wrapped her arms around Chelsea, holding her tight.

"I'm so glad you're going to be staying," she said softly.

Chelsea drew back, obviously embarrassed by the show of emotion. "Thanks, Tracy. I really appreciate this."

"Don't even mention it. As I said before, this is your home, too."

Chelsea looked around slowly. "Wow. It's bigger than I thought."

Tracy laughed. "The more we paint, the bigger it seems to get. At first I didn't think it would ever get finished."

"Is it?" Chelsea looked around skeptically.

"Almost."

Chelsea dropped her voice to a husky whisper. "Who's that?"

Tracy saw Wade framed in the wide sitting room doorway holding a mug of coffee. She drew Chelsea across the room and introduced them and added, "Wade is our first official guest."

Wade and Chelsea exchanged pleased-to-meet-yous before he quickly excused himself and went back to the buffet for cinnamon rolls.

"Let's get your bag and I'll show you to your room upstairs." Tracy started for the duffel but Chelsea beat her to it.

They had reached the top of the landing when Chelsea glanced down the stairwell and asked, "So, what's a guy like that doing in a place like this?"

"Is it that bad?" Tracy's heart sank.

"I meant, how did he even find the place? He looks more like a rocker than someone

121

who'd stay in a trendy new inn."

"Trendy new inn? Really?"

"Okay, so that's a stretch. But it looks a lot different than when I saw it over Presidents' Day weekend. It's just not the kind of place I pictured a guy like that staying in."

"He showed up at the door a few nights ago needing a room, and to be honest, I couldn't turn down the money. Thanks to him, the rates are up."

"Is that it?"

Tracy paused, frowning. "What do you mean, is that it?"

"I don't know. You kinda lit up when you introduced us."

"Lit up?" She couldn't control her blush.

Chelsea eyed her suspiciously. "Yes. Like right now. You're blushing."

"He's just a guest."

"So you say."

Tracy couldn't decide whether Chelsea was merely teasing or actually uncomfortable with the idea as she showed her to the room she and Matt had prepared. Fresh flowers filled a vase on the student desk in the corner, and a new brocade comforter covered the bed.

Chelsea tossed her duffel on the end of the bed, and noting the size of it, Tracy hoped that everything inside would fit in the chest of drawers and small closet. Chelsea didn't seem a bit concerned as she brushed her long auburn hair over her shoulder. Strikingly beautiful, she was a quintessential redhead with deep-rust-colored hair and ivory skin dusted with freckles.

"It's weird to be here without Dad." The girl's voice sounded thick with tears, but her eyes were dry.

Tracy crossed the room and tried to hug her; but Chelsea stiffened and shrugged her off. "Don't, Tracy. Don't make me cry."

Chelsea sat down heavily on the edge of the bed, her hands clutching the bedspread. She stared up hopefully. "Have you had any luck researching scholarships?"

Tracy shook her head and answered honestly. "I haven't had time."

"I went to the counseling office and asked. The deadline to apply is passed."

Hopeless, the girl looked around the room, and Tracy suddenly saw it through her eyes. The four walls were covered in 1940s chintz paper that was faded except where pictures had once hung.

The carpet, matted and flat, had a footpath worn through it. It had been cleaned and vacuumed, and she had fresh curtains at the windows. Still, the room was a far cry from what Chelsea was used to at Monica's. She'd had her own room at the Canyon Club house, too. One that Glenn had decorated for a princess.

Looking around, Tracy refused to let Chelsea give up hope. Nor could she afford to get depressed herself. Not now.

"We'll find a way to manage."

"SC is one of the most expensive schools in California." Chelsea dropped her gaze to the floor and scrubbed the toe of her sandal against the carpet. Once pink, it had faded to a sickly color.

Tracy crossed the room and sat down beside her. Chelsea wiped a tear from beneath her eye.

"You can get a summer job while you're in Twilight. There have to be some scholarships that are still open —"

"It's too *late*," Chelsea moaned.

"It *can't* be. There are always funds available. You just have to know where to look. And I'm not counting out your mom. Have you talked to her?"

"You don't really know Mom, Tracy."

She knew enough about Monica to know that Glenn's ex was resourceful when it came to looking out for herself, but whenever Chelsea needed anything, Glenn had supplied it.

"I called her in Austria." Chelsea's voice faltered. She fell silent, swallowed, fighting tears.

"It's okay, honey."

"She said she can't do anything about my tuition and she won't ask Charles for the money. She said that she just married him and that she doesn't want to screw up this marriage." Chelsea swallowed again. "She didn't even talk to me for more than eight minutes. The last thing she said was 'Work it out.' "

"You might have to go to junior college for a semester or two . . ."

Chelsea jumped up and started pacing the room.

"That's easy for you to say, Tracy. Your whole life isn't over. You've got this place. And Mattie. First I lose Daddy and now, school. And two weeks ago, I met a great guy from Orange County!" She took a deep breath and looked panicked. "Where am I going to get spending money?"

Whenever Chelsea cried, her complexion turned a bright, mottled pink. She sat slumped on the bed, knees together, fingers clenched tight.

"I can give you a little money," Tracy offered, calculating in her head. "And you can find a summer job. As soon as guests start checking in, I'll need help with the rooms. I'd planned to hire a part-time maid and was thinking maybe you could —"

"A *maid*?" The word came out as a high, strained squeak.

"I'd never ask you to do anything I'm not willing to do myself," Tracy said softly. She'd worked at the Dairy Queen all through high school and managed to not only make straight A's but made the cheer squad and the swim team. Chelsea was every bit as capable. But was it asking too much too soon to have her take on so much after losing her father?

"Daddy would never, *ever* make me clean up after strangers in a dump like this! I . . . I just can't believe this is happening!" She grabbed her purse, slung the long leather strap over her shoulder, and walked out.

"Chelsea, wait." Tracy followed her out of the room. "Please don't drive while you're this upset."

Chelsea repeatedly wiped her hands over her cheeks, mopping her tears. Finally she stopped in the lobby and turned to Tracy, somewhat collected.

"I'll be okay. I promise. I just need to get out of here for a while. I don't want Mattie to see me like this."

"Where are you going?"

Chelsea shrugged. "Twilight, I guess."

"When will you be back?"

Another tear slipped down the girl's cheek. The feeble smile she gave Tracy nearly broke her heart.

"I don't know," she whispered. "But I won't be late."

"Be careful, okay?"

Chelsea managed to nod before she walked out.

Chapter Sixteen

A gull swept up the bluff, dropped the clam it was holding in its beak, and attempted to break it open until another bird — noisier, stronger — swooped down and stole it. Their cries sounded almost human. The screeches intensified until the smaller of the two gulls gave up and flew off.

Wade watched from the footpath behind the hotel as the remaining gray gull rode the air currents. It twirled above the rocks below the bluff. He wanted to get far enough away from the building so that he could use his cell phone without being seen or heard.

The wind off the water was picking up as he sat down on a boulder that gave him a great view of the coast. A gray cloud bank gathered on the horizon. He pulled his phone out of his jacket pocket and auto-dialed the number for the only person in the world he trusted — his literary agent,

Bob Schack.

Bob had taken him on ten years ago when no one else in the publishing world would give his work a second glance. They'd both been young and hungry then, both lacking in experience.

Schack, balding at twenty-seven, had been personable, honest, and willing to treat each client as if he or she was the only one he represented.

That in itself was a major juggling act, but somehow he'd not only managed to build a stable of working writers, but had gathered other agents together as well. Ten years later, Bob Schack had offices on both coasts and represented some of the top writers in the country.

When Bob's secretary answered, Wade gave the name Horatio Alger. He was put straight through.

"Where are you?" Schack always asked. Wade never told him.

He found himself smiling, the familiarity comforting after weeks of anonymity. Bob was probably the only soul left on the planet who truly gave a damn about him. "I'm looking at the ocean as we speak."

"Atlantic or Pacific?"

"That I'll keep to myself."

"Doing all right?"

"Great. I'm going to need a draw though."

He'd given Bob power of attorney over his considerable estate and depended on him to wire him cash whenever, wherever he needed it. Considering all the money he'd made for the Schack Agency in the past three years, Bob would have probably been willing to deliver anything Wade asked for, in person.

"How much?"

Wade named a figure he thought should last awhile, enough to cover him for a couple of months at least. "Wire it to Western Union in San Luis Obispo."

"Is that where you are?"

"No. Not at the moment. I'm not even close."

"How are you doing?" There was genuine concern in Bob's voice.

"Actually, I hate to go so far as to say I'm doing better, but I'm doing okay, actually."

"No one's recognized you?"

"Nope."

"Celebrity only lasts as long as a shooting star in this country, buddy, you know that. Maybe it's time you turned back into Edward Cain before it's too late to cash in on it."

"Edward is history."

"Oprah's people are still calling."

"I can hear you salivating over the phone. Eight months later and they still want to interview me. Edward Cain is never going to rear his ugly head again."

"Speaking of ugly heads, are you still using that black dye?"

"Afraid so. I've added some gel. You should see me."

"Spare me. That stuff kills brain cells."

"I wish." If he knew for certain that hair dye killed off memory, he'd start using it twice a day instead of every couple of weeks.

"Sally's been calling, too."

"Please. No." Sally Reinhart, known by both authors and associates as Psycho Sally, was undisputedly one of the biggest predators in the publishing pool. She sniffed out moneymaking projects the way a shark smells blood in the water.

"She wanted to know if you were working on anything yet."

"What part of I'm-not-ever-writing-again doesn't she understand?" *What part don't I understand?*

"She said she could sell a week-old salmon inside a puke-green cover if it had Edward Cain's name on it."

"Just goes to show you where people's tastes are."

His own ass was going numb from sitting

131

on the rock. He tried shifting, gave up. After a glance back at the hotel, he got up and walked along the deserted path again.

At nineteen, after having sold magazine articles and short stories for years, and having grown up on the streets of New York, where the publishing heart of the USA beat the loudest, he became determined to complete a novel and break into the business.

He grew a beard to make himself look older. His mom agreed it gave him literary aplomb. He took to wearing dark turtlenecks, cable-knit sweaters, and tweed jackets like the best-selling male novelists wore in their publicity photos.

Then he landed a day job in the mailroom at Ballard, a small-press publishing house, moved out of his mother's apartment, and rented a room in a run-down building in Brooklyn. He started submitting his work to both agents and publishers at the same time.

After a stack of rejections from both, he sent his proposal to one of the newest agents in the business, hoping the guy was as anxious to discover raw new talent as he was to gain representation.

That's how he and Bob had hooked up. The first thing Schack told him was that he did have some talent, but no voice. He'd penned two westerns that Bob likened to lackluster imitations of Larry McMurtry.

"Romance and mysteries are hot right now," Bob advised. "Put together a proposal and I'll shop it around."

Refusing to even think about writing a romance, he went to a used-book store and walked out with a bag of paperback mysteries, read enough of them to get the idea, and came up with his own series of connected books.

Determined to do something offbeat that hadn't been done, he eschewed the usual run-of-the-mill hard-boiled male detectives as well as the smart-mouthed new breed of sarcastic female P.I.s and decided on a lecherous dwarf detective with a lesbian partner.

Together, the unlikely pair — after the obligatory 250 pages — eventually solved crime after crime.

Wade was determined to become the biggest name in mysteries to hit the stores in a decade.

True to his word, Bob shopped the proposal around and, finally, a publisher bit. With the contract pending, Wade did something he'd been waiting all of his life to do: He legally changed his name, choosing the pseudonym Edward Cain.

He even planned what he'd wear when Oprah called.

He did make a name for himself, not a household name by any means, but his publisher continued to offer him three- and four-book contracts. He slowly accumulated some money and a bit of celebrity, but he was certainly not notorious.

Finally, six years and twelve books later, Bob thought the midget mysteries had run their course and encouraged Wade to write a breakout novel.

"Thrillers are really outperforming everything else. Suspense is the ticket, Wade." Bob was the only one who ever called him by his real name. The only one who even knew it. To the world at large, he was Edward Cain.

Because Bob had been right before, and because he certainly wanted to "break out" of the mystery genre, he went back to the lucky used-book store, bought a bag of thrillers, and inhaled them.

His writing credentials gave him entree to police squad rooms and ride-alongs with cops that exposed him to such grisly scenes that he couldn't sleep for weeks.

He interviewed prison inmates to get accurate glimpses into the workings of a criminal mind, took extension courses in forensic science. Then he sat down and pounded out the most violent, most suspenseful, the goriest serial-murder thriller he could conjure.

With only 250 completed pages, Bob was able to generate an auction. Three publishers bid on the proposal for *An Even Dozen,* and Edward Cain was offered just under six figures — a fortune as far as he was concerned.

Bob had been disappointed in the money, but assured Wade that the publisher would make up for the lack of advance with promotion.

Psycho Sally had won the auction, but held firm. Any special promotion for *An Even Dozen* was out of the question. Bob threatened to buy back the book and walk. When Sally told him fine, pay her back and they'd be square, Wade stepped in and told Bob to back off. He'd already spent part of the advance as a down payment on an apartment in a better area.

Unfortunately, after a long struggle with lupus, his mother passed away before the book hit the stores.

An Even Dozen was published with a minimum push. Initial sales were flat, but Bob was certain that if Wade started a second book, and stuck it out, an audience would find him.

Eventually, most of the *country* found him — but not until a serial murderer began to copycat — in gruesome detail — the twelve murders Wade had described in his novel.

In the novel, the murders had taken place in Wisconsin, each act completely different from the one before. Someone had copied ten of the murders, in the same state. Readers in the Minneapolis area recognized that the murders reported in the news mirrored those in the novel.

Edward Cain's website and the local police agency were alerted, and the authorities realized they had a copycat on their hands.

The FBI showed up to interview Wade, who could prove without a doubt that he hadn't even left the state of New York in the last month and a half.

Then two more women died, bringing the number to twelve.

He moved through life in a fog. The initial print run disappeared off the shelves within days of the first news reports. With every edition of the nightly news, with every episode of *America's Most Wanted, An Even Dozen* went into another printing.

Wade moved into a hotel under his former

name and refused to come out. He couldn't eat or sleep. The minute he closed his eyes, he saw those twelve innocent women, all murdered in unspeakable ways that had come from the depths of his imagination.

Things got worse when he began to receive death threats, not only from the serial murderer himself, but from an unstable member of one of the victims' families.

There were low points when Wade just wished someone really would kill him and get it over with.

The Wisconsin police eventually tracked down the killer, a male librarian who had a history of mental illness, but only after the man was stupid enough to check in to a strip motel under the name Edward Cain. He pleaded guilty to avoid the death penalty and was incarcerated for life without possibility of parole.

Life was bad enough, but then Sally called, demanding an Edward Cain sequel, a companion book, maybe even a trilogy. Why didn't he follow *An Even Dozen* with a similar title? Something like *Dead Baker's Dozen*? *Anything,* as long as the word *Dozen* was in the title.

Wade hung up on her. Victims' families sued him for damages. The murderer's brother sued him for preying on an unstable mind. The crowning blow came when one of the inmates on death row accused him of stealing his life story.

One day, while sitting in court, he came up with the idea to dye his hair, go back to using the name he'd been given when he was born — Wade MacAllister — and disappear as soon as the string of lawsuits ended. Thankfully, he was vindicated every time, but the trials were emotional and draining. Over and over he was forced to relive the murders, face the families of the victims, the press, the notoriety, and his own guilt. By the time it was all done, there was nothing left of his soul.

Even though every single jury had found in his favor, he still felt responsible for the deaths of the twelve women.

After the trials, he put his escape plan into action and, with Bob's help, "Edward" dropped off the face of the planet. He legally changed his name back to Wade Mac-Allister.

It was on the driver's license in his pocket. But when Tracy hadn't asked to see some identification, he'd told her he was Wade Johnson, not MacAllister. He wished now he hadn't lied to her, but that night he hadn't intended to stay. The night he'd checked in, he thought that one way or another, he'd be gone by morning.

"Wade?" Bob's voice was insistent.

"Yeah. I'm here."

Still alive. Still on the planet. Hell, Oprah still wants me.

He had more money than God, but he felt filthy spending it. He'd given much of it away anonymously, had set up scholarships in the name of each of the victims at their former high schools. Royalties and foreign rights kept rolling in.

"I'm worried about you, Wade. This has gone on too long. You ought to see a shrink. Maybe if you started writing again . . ."

"Listen, thanks for wiring the money. I gotta go."

"Wade, wait!"

"Bye, Bob."

Thanks to ID blocking, no one had the number to the cell. Not even Bob. They worked on an I'll-call-you, you-can't-call-me basis.

"Maybe if you started writing again . . ."

He'd come to the end of the path. There was nothing but the bluff and the ocean on his left, rolling hills covered in tall waving green grass, blooming yellow mustard, and wildflowers on his right.

The breeze stroked the tips of the summer grass, bowing them before it moved on. Gulls still cackled behind him as if they knew a secret they weren't willing to share.

Shoving his hands in his pockets, he turned around and took in a view so stunning that it almost hurt to see it. An expanse of dark green waters lay under the blue sky above, and there, standing full of silent secrets on the bluff, was the Heartbreak Hotel. For a minute he saw it as it was in the beginning, when it was fresh and new. He saw a woman standing on the widow's walk, young and trim, her long dark hair blowing in the breeze as she stared out to sea.

From the minute he had laid eyes on the place, it had intrigued him, drawn him in.

I should have left after that first night.

But he was worn out, sick of running from the past, from himself. He'd walked in here thinking about ending it all, and now the place was bringing him back to life. Forcing him to write again.

And then there was Tracy.

He admired her courage and her determination, her innate trust. The way she interacted with her son. It was Tracy more than anything, more than the dreams, more than the mysterious night-writing, who was holding him here.

She could certainly use his rent money — not to mention a helping hand. He wasn't fool enough to try and convince himself that helping her out was his reason for staying. He could write her a check to cover her expenses for the next year and hire a big enough crew to have this place finished in a few days.

He wasn't staying just to help out. The dreamer in him wanted to touch her, to taste her lips, feel his skin against hers. She wasn't the type who'd want a one-night stand. She was the kind of woman a man courts slowly, the kind of woman a man marries — and yet she was strong enough to make it on her own. A woman who faced the challenges life threw at her head-on. A woman devoted to her son.

He studied the hotel from a distance. After taking a long, deep breath, he started walking back along the path.

Like twin sirens, the old hotel, and the woman, had seduced him into staying.

CHAPTER SEVENTEEN

Preoccupied, Tracy was downstairs straightening up the buffet when Wade walked in.

She nearly collided with him as he walked in through the French doors. The serving tray listed in her hands. Somehow he managed to catch her and the tray both. His hands were so strong and gentle that she didn't mind that he held her a moment longer than he should have.

She pretended not to notice, but her body responded to his nearness, the warmth of the sun on his clothes and his skin, the masculine scent of his soap mingled with the tang of salt off the sea. His eyes were the color of hot fudge, and right now those eyes were focused on hers.

The spell wasn't broken until the tray in her hands started to droop and teacups slid toward the edge. She flushed and stepped quickly away, but felt him following close behind her as she moved across the room.

He leaned against the low sideboard she'd inherited with the place while she tried to focus on what she was doing. If she didn't concentrate, she risked chipping one of her precious china cups, a gift from her grandmother. She loved the way they looked like a mixed bouquet spread out on her white linen cloths and crocheted doilies.

"Trouble in River City?" So close now, his voice was deep and husky. The sound oozed over her like warm honey.

"Why do you ask?"

"You looked preoccupied when I came in. Anything I can do?"

"I'm afraid not." It was hard to think of anything but his nearness.

"Try me." His gaze roamed her face, connected with her eyes. His intensity moved her to open up.

"I'm worried about Chelsea's tuition for next fall. Her trust is tied up and it may not be available in time. I haven't had a lot of time to track down a scholarship, and most of the applications had to be in weeks ago."

Her gaze drifted to the sunshine pouring through the windows lining the porch. Birds were singing in the orange tree off to the left of the porch and, as always, there was the heartbeat of the ocean.

She sighed. "I'm not giving up, though."

"No. I didn't think you would."

"I try to look on the bright side. Take action. What about you?"

"It's not that easy."

She shrugged. "I've always tried to visualize things the way I want them to be. And I hate giving up," she admitted.

"How do you see this place?"

"All spruced up, full of people enjoying themselves."

"Do you see the best in people, too?"

As she looked deep into his eyes, it was her heart that stumbled this time, not her feet.

"Always," she said softly, sensing that somehow, her answer was important to him.

"I have a proposition to make," he said softly.

"A proposition?" She was almost afraid to hear it.

"I'd like to stay on until you open."

"Why?" she whispered.

His gaze touched on her lips. "The view is great."

"Don't you have to get back to L.A.?"

He looked puzzled for a minute. "I'm on extended leave."

"Oh."

"Yeah. Burnout. I asked for a few months off. So . . . any objections to me staying?"

"Objections?"

"Do you want me around?"

Are you kidding?

She couldn't believe it. The place still smelled of paint. The crew was milling around the lobby as a cheap radio blared mariachi music. *Peaceful?* No, but the sitting area in the lobby *was* inviting. The sunroom, with its gathering of small tables and brightly covered chairs, was both pretty and functional. There were no curtains at the bank of windows yet, and some of the woodwork was still in need of a touch-up.

"Of course you can stay, but I insist on giving you a break on the rate, seeing as how I'm not officially, *officially* open yet, and things are still a bit torn up."

"That's no way to run a business."

"Maybe not, but I'd sleep better," she said softly. When his lips lifted and smiled, she fumbled a teacup covered in purple violas.

"I'd like to pitch in. Don't try to tell me you don't need an extra hand. That way, *I'd* sleep better."

She fiddled with the cup handle, thought about what it would be like to have him stay on. "You really want to help out?"

"Yes. I do," he assured her.

She tried to come to grips with the idea that he'd be here a month more. Having coffee in the sunroom. Walking the bluff. She'd be running into him in the hall, in the lobby, not to mention working with him. She could just hear Jake and Carly now — but they weren't around to talk sense into her.

The teacup was dangling precariously from her hand. Wade reached for it and his fingers brushed hers, sending shock waves up her arm. Her skin tingled beneath his touch. He took the cup, carefully set it on the buffet.

"So is it a deal?" His face was very close to hers, his dark eyes questioning, ever intent.

The sound of his voice ended the debate raging in her mind. She found her own voice at last.

"How can I refuse?"

CHAPTER EIGHTEEN

The next morning, Tracy negotiated the crowded galley kitchen in the apartment, humming the Elvis oldie "Heartbreak Hotel."

With Chelsea and Matt engaged in some good-natured teasing in the breakfast nook, Tracy decided life was settling into a routine and that she had much to be grateful for. She actually enjoyed getting up early, whipping up fresh baked goods, brewing coffee. Only Wade and Diego's crew were enjoying them right now, but eventually the place would be full of appreciative guests.

"You'd better take off," she warned the kids, "or Matt's going to be late."

"I'll get my backpack!" He was used to careening around the spacious Canyon Club house, where huge rooms and luxurious yards separated them from their nearest neighbors.

"Keep your voice down, honey." The

reminder was automatic now. As Chelsea walked up to the kitchen sink with their breakfast dishes, Tracy poured hot coffee into an air pot and couldn't help but admire her stepdaughter. Chelsea had grown from a gangly, gap-toothed eight-year-old into a stunning young woman. Her long auburn hair was alive with natural curl and vibrant red highlights, her bright blue eyes outlined with lush, red-gold lashes.

She found herself wishing she could wave a magic wand and make life as easy for Chelsea as Glenn always had.

At least Chelsea had returned from Twilight yesterday with her spirit renewed after running into a friend from Canyon Club. Eric Nichols had told her about an internship opening available at a firm in nearby San Luis Obispo.

"Thanks for dropping Matt off at school."

"No problem. I wanted to get into town early to pick up that application."

Her determination to be chosen for the summer position reminded Tracy of Glenn's dogged persistence. Once he latched on to an idea or came up with a plan, there was no distracting him.

"What's the name of the firm?" Tracy leaned over the end of the counter where she kept scratch paper and an assortment of pens.

Chelsea dug a paper napkin out of her pocket. "Sylvester, Lease, and Lynch."

Tracy put the pen back down. "You're kidding. That's your dad's tax attorney's firm. He hired David Sylvester two years ago."

Chelsea stared down at the neat block print on the limp paper napkin and then looked up again. "Really? Great!"

"I'll give David a call and let him know you're applying for the internship."

"Would you?"

"Of course. Would you mind doing me a favor?"

"No. What is it?"

Tracy pulled the stack of invitations off the countertop and handed them over. "These need to go out today to local travel agents and other people in the tourist industry. I'm holding an open house in three weeks to show the place off."

"No problem." Chelsea shoved them into her bag.

Just then Matt reappeared, dashed through the living room, and called out, "Beat'cha to the car!"

Chelsea rolled her eyes at Tracy.

"Drive carefully, okay?" Tracy cautioned automatically.

Matt was already out the door when Chelsea grabbed her keys off the table. Before she walked out, Chelsea paused and looked back. "Don't worry, Tracy. We'll be okay. Like you always say, 'Everything will be all right.' "

Read it, damn it. I dare you.

Wade awoke at 3:40 from another dream in which he'd been drowning. Unable to go back to sleep, he started wandering around the room. Later, he found himself hunched over the desk at 7:00 A.M. and staggered back to bed.

Now, drained, exhausted, and dry-eyed, he was up again, staring at the composition notebook. He ran his forefinger down the black binding along the spine. If he were smart, if he were true to the promise he'd made himself to never publish again, he'd toss the damned thing out.

The craft had always been in his blood. He'd written ever since he could hold a pencil. Nurtured by his mother, it had eventually taken over his life, and back then he wouldn't have had it any other way. Once he'd sold his first, full-length mystery, his life had revolved around deadlines, proposals, daily page counts, and conferences.

Although he wouldn't have wanted to do

anything else, writing had never come easy. *An Even Dozen* had involved months of ongoing research, interviews, and an in-depth study into the minds of psychopathic killers. He'd loved every minute, his energy fed by the quest for information as much as by the actual act of developing the characters and the plot. He never went into writing blind, always following a well-thought-out synopsis.

Now this odd free fall into automatic writing, and the fact that he had only a vague memory afterward of what he'd written, left him completely unsettled.

Feeling like a schoolboy, he shifted on the uncomfortable straight-back chair; half afraid of what he was about to discover. With his elbow planted on the desk, he rested his forehead on his open palm, took a deep breath, and opened the notebook.

The handwriting inside was definitely his, the letters tight and even, perfectly spaced, clearly executed in his familiar loopy backhand. His mother had always insisted on good penmanship. His fine handwriting was a product of her determination and hours of practice at their Formica-topped kitchen table.

Now, after leafing through the notebook, wondering how he'd somehow filled page after page with barely any recollection, he made himself focus on the first line.

California 1901

As we stand high above the sea on the widow's walk, Violette begs me not to leave her. She places her warm, gentle hands on both sides of my face, forces me to look into her deep brown eyes, and in a voice that nearly breaks my heart, she whispers, "Ezra, please. Don't go."

"It's the last time, darlin'. I promise. The very last and then you can turn me into a damned innkeeper."

"But, Ezra . . ."

I take her hands in mine, hold them, rub my thumb back and forth over her soft skin. My hands, like my face and arms, are weathered and brown, stained from years at the helm, stained by the sun and the wind. They are hard and calloused. But her skin is soft and pale as cream, smooth as the finest silk ever imported.

I don't know how to live life on land. I've been captain of my own ship for near as long as she's been alive; and yet, for her, I'll willingly give it all up.

I'll be what she wants me to be.

I love her that much.

"I'm afraid, Ezra," she whispers. Her eyes search my face. Again she reaches up, strokes my bearded cheeks, makes me feel young though I'm already forty-five. Too old to have hoped to have her fall in love with me and yet, she has.

"You've nothing to fear," I assure her. "You're new to being a captain's wife is all." I turn her toward the Pacific. The air is heavy with spray carried on the wind. I can taste the tang of salt on my tongue.

The water is deep blue today, reflecting the sky.

The swells roll, driven by the motion of a storm brewing far away. One that will reach our shores in a day or more.

"Look there." I point to a spot on the horizon, one directly across from where we stand on the widow's walk atop the hotel. The place was her father's dream — his folly. It's too far from Twilight Cove. Too far from where they've cut the new road.

She's as stubborn as her father was, though, rest his soul, bound and determined to run the hotel herself if she has to. To make the place a success after all.

More the fool, I've agreed to help her, but then I suppose she knows I'd hang the moon for her if she were to ask it of me. I'd do anything — except I cannot refuse this one last voyage down the coast and back.

As I point out to sea, I say, "In two weeks' time, stand on the widow's walk and train your lovely eyes on that very spot on the horizon and I'll be there. You'll see the *Lantana* heaving to under full sail, flying home. Have Emilio hitch up the buggy and drive you down to Gull Harbor to meet me. Wear the yellow dress that turns your eyes as bronze as rich, thick honey."

I lean down and kiss her cheek. Her skin is warm where the sun touches it, damp from the mist. Her long, dark hair ripples, alive with curl. I pull her up against me, press her back against my chest. Resting my cheek upon her hair, I close my eyes. I hear her sigh as she stares across the bluff, toward the horizon. I know not what she's thinking. I feel her disappointment, her fear.

I reach around her, rest my splayed fingers against the swell of her stomach. She lays her open palm atop the back of my hand. We feel my son move inside her. Deep in my heart I know that the babe is, indeed, a boy. My pride and excitement know no bounds.

I pull her close and whisper against her lips, "I want our son to play innkeeper so that I can laze my days away in your arms."

"By the time he's grown and running the hotel, we'll be old," she whispers.

I realize she is thinking that by the time our son is grown, *I'll* be the old one.

"Darlin'," I say, turning her round in my arms until she's facing me, until I feel her leaning pliantly against my chest, "I'll never be too old for this."

Wade read on, immersed in the passages that followed. Descriptions of the California coast at the turn of the century. Each and every detail had a ring of accuracy to it. Not only that, but — there was much about sailing, cargoes, shipping lanes, and navigation — all of which he knew virtually nothing about.

He felt the intense pain of Ezra's leave-taking, the man's resolve, the woman's heartbreak. Unable to bear a last good-bye, Violette refused to accompany Ezra to Gull Harbor, where the ship was moored, preferring to watch the *Lantana* sail past the bluff, past the Heartbreak Hotel.

Lost in the story, hunched over the note-book, he suddenly felt a light touch upon his shoulder. He jerked upright and slammed the cover shut.

As if coming back from somewhere beyond these four walls, the hotel room slipped into focus as he settled back into the present, fully expecting to see Tracy standing behind him with a stack of fresh, white towels in her arms.

But there was no one else in the room.

The hair on the back of his neck stood up. A cold chill ran down his spine. He jumped to his feet so fast that the chair toppled to the carpet. He walked into the bathroom, pulled back the shower curtain. There was no one hiding there.

He knew Tracy would never walk in on him — let alone sneak up and touch him.

He glanced into the mirror over the pedestal sink. No matter how many times he'd looked at his face, he still had to remind himself that he was wearing tinted contacts. It was always a bit of a shock when brown eyes, not blue, stared back at him.

"You're really losing it, buddy," he mumbled.

He ran a hand over a day's growth of stubble, reached into the tub, and turned

on the shower, hoping that shampoo and lots of hot water would clear his head.

Still a bit groggy, Wade stepped out of the shower and toweled himself dry before he put on his Levis. Buttoning his fly, he crossed over to the window and opened the curtains.

Automatically his gaze drifted to the horizon, and he could see a clipper ship under full sail, white canvas billowing against a clear blue sky, the bow cutting through the waves as it headed for Gull Harbor a few miles up the coast.

He was New York City born and bred. He'd lived in his own ego-driven little world for most of his life, intent upon his career, on honing his craft. What he knew about sailing ships at the turn of the century wouldn't fill a thimble, and yet what he'd just read had such a ring of truth to it that he was anxious to research the subject and see if he were actually accurate. For the first time in years he found himself wishing he had his laptop with him.

He gathered up his writing materials a tossed them inside the desk drawer and th shook his head and released an exaspera sigh.

He wasn't ready to accept the fact th might be losing his mind. Not yet ar

There had to be some logical explanation for what was happening to him.

Maybe not logical, he amended, but some explanation anyway.

Trying to shake off the lingering melancholy that Ezra's story had instilled, he pulled a clean black T-shirt out of the dresser drawer and imagined Bob Schack laughing.

The bottom line was that, like it or not, he was writing again.

And, like it or not, he was writing a fricking romance novel.

CHAPTER NINETEEN

At ten that morning, Tracy found the coffee and date bread slices she'd set out downstairs still untouched. Apparently Wade wasn't up yet, or if he was, he was still in his room.

Thinking of the films she'd seen where stereotypical lonely young widows and divorcees constantly hounded available men with baked cakes and casseroles, she nearly groaned aloud, but there was no denying that she'd been tempted to hang around in the lobby, hoping to see him again.

When the bell above the front door rang, she buried her disappointment and put a smile on her face. It became genuine the minute she recognized Willa Conner.

"Willa! I'm so glad to see you!" She threw her arms around Willa and hugged her fiercely.

Willa felt as fragile as tissue paper. As breakable as spun glass. The designer had always been as fashionably thin as a runway model, but now, as she hugged Tracy back, she felt like skin and bones.

Willa pulled away first, but gave Tracy's hand a squeeze. They'd become friends at thirteen when Willa moved to Marshall. They'd gone to Indiana State and relocated in California together after graduation. But while Tracy married and had Matt, Willa had stayed single, focusing on her interior design career. They'd gradually drifted apart, their contact reduced to exchanging birthday and Christmas greetings and an occasional lunch together every year or so.

Tracy looked Willa over from head to toe, admiring her trendy haircut. It suited the texture of Willa's sleek, jet-black hair.

Somehow, and certainly without trying, Willa always managed to make her feel frumpy. This morning Willa looked chic, totally put together in a slim black sheath, low-heeled sandals, and a black sweater casually thrown over her shoulders. A one-of-a-kind beaded necklace of amber and crystal was both casual and elegant and completed the look.

"I've missed you," Tracy told her.

Willa gently tucked her smooth dark hair behind her right ear. "I think of you so often. I had an appointment up the coast today, so I decided to drop by. I hope that's all right. Are you busy?"

"Never too busy for you. Let's go upstairs," Tracy suggested, leading Willa up to the apartment.

When Willa complimented her on what she'd accomplished downstairs, Tracy felt a bit embarrassed because she hadn't once called Willa to ask for decorating advice. She not only hadn't wanted to take advantage of their friendship — but their tastes were entirely different.

Glenn had gently let Tracy know early on that he wanted their Canyon Club house to reflect his success, and not so subtly hinted that slipcovers and flea market finds were all well and good for young marrieds in starter homes, but they'd moved beyond that.

He wanted a showplace decorated with the finest furnishings and fabrics available. Tracy knew that Willa instinctively knew how to put that kind of a home together, so she'd suggested that Willa's firm decorate not only their home, but all of the Canyon Club models, and Glenn readily agreed. After the project was completed, he'd used the Santa Barbara–based firm, where Willa was a principal partner, on subsequent projects.

As they stepped into the apartment, Tracy shut the door and Willa paused to take it all in.

"Oh, Tracy. This is so homey."

"Thanks, but even homey is too polite. It needs new paint and carpeting, I know, but I've had to concentrate on the public spaces and the guest rooms. I'll eventually get to this, unless I'm able to sell the place first."

Over the past few months, Tracy had discovered that it was always like this when she saw anyone who'd known both her and Glenn. Now there were awkward, stagnant silences, gaping voids in conversations whenever friends tried to find the right words to express their sympathy. Usually they wound up saying nothing at all.

She never imagined it happening between her and Willa, though.

"Would you like a Coke, or some iced tea? Have you had breakfast?" she asked.

Willa waved a hand, brushing aside the thought. She looked as if eating were the last thing on her mind. "Water would be great. No ice."

Willa had always had a quiet reserve about her, one that Tracy knew hid a deep shyness. Though it was hard for Willa to open up, she had always been a good listener.

Though Willa had dated and eventually

lived with a stockbroker, after the breakup, she confided to Tracy that because her father had deserted her family when she was only three, she'd grown up with a strong desire never to be dependent upon a man for anything.

When Tracy walked back into the living room carrying a glass of water and a diet lemonade, she found Willa tucked into the corner of the overstuffed sofa, her long bare legs crossed at the ankles, her soft leather tote collapsed on the floor at her feet.

Tracy set the water down on an end table where Willa could reach it easily and then settled into an armchair nearby. It was her favorite place to sit and read during what few and fleeting minutes of quiet stillness she managed to steal for herself anymore. From here she had a clear view of the ocean. Glancing outside, she was surprised to see Wade standing on the edge of the bluff, apparently lost in the view of the expansive Pacific.

"Are you *really* doing all right, Tracy?"

Drawn back to the moment, she shrugged. There was no use keeping up pretenses with Willa.

"I'm taking one day at a time and focusing on my endless to-do list." Her gaze drifted to the window again. Wade was sitting on a wide, flat rock, watching the swells roll in. She found herself wondering how he would react if she were to walk outside and sit down beside him.

"You know me, Willa. Always the cockeyed optimist. I know I can make a success of this."

"You've always been the confident one." Willa sounded almost wistful.

"I was raised to believe in myself. I believed in Glenn, too."

Willa took a sip of water, stared down into the glass. Her fingers were long and delicate. The blue of her veins was stark against her pale skin. They'd spoken a couple of times by phone after Glenn died. Willa had called to say how sorry she was that an emergency had come up with her partner and she couldn't make the funeral. Tracy had called Willa to tell her that she was moving into the Heartbreak and to pass along her new phone number. Of course, the reason why and the subject of her finances had come up, but Tracy had explained it all only briefly then.

"He let himself become consumed by the business. He drove himself, spent more and more time away from us. I have to admit, I was worried. Who wouldn't be? I questioned him. I doubted his fidelity. I doubted myself

164

for doubting him. We argued, naturally, but he was so convincing, so sure that things were turning around. I knew things were bad, but not how very deeply we were in debt."

"You still miss him." It was a quiet, sure statement, not a question.

Tracy nodded. "In a sense, I was already missing him before he died." She cupped her hand around the bottom of the glass. Condensation collected in her palm.

It almost felt like old times, having Willa there, listening intently, concerned, and yet now there was a distinct difference. Marriage and widowhood were steps that Willa had never taken. There was no way she could really understand how betrayed Tracy felt, no matter how hard she tried.

"What about you?" Tracy asked. "Did your firm suffer any setbacks because of Glenn's death?" Suddenly embarrassed, Tracy concentrated on what was left of the pink lemonade and bits of ice floating in her glass. "His debts were so monumental. I hope your firm wasn't jeopardized."

She looked up, met Willa's eyes, needing to know the truth, though there was nothing she could do to help.

Willa shook her head. "There were a couple of outstanding bills for orders, but I was able to use the materials on other projects." Her huge, soulful eyes never left Tracy's. "Things worked out."

Relief coursed through Tracy as she sank back into the soft armchair.

"How about Matt? How's he doing?" Willa asked. "They were so close."

"As well as can be expected." Tracy thought of the empty journal in Matt's room. She'd given it to him at the counselor's suggestion, told him it was a place to write down his thoughts and feelings. She'd seen it that morning when she straightened Matt's room. It was still on his desk, where it had been for weeks, and she suspected, still ignored.

"He's coping. He has some separation anxiety when it comes to going off to school, but this morning he was actually anxious to go. I think having Chelsea here helps. Even though he had other faults, Glenn was a good father." There was no denying that Matt was the apple of his eye.

"Where is Chelsea?"

"In San Luis Obispo applying for a summer job." Tracy reminded herself to call David Sylvester as soon as Willa left.

Suddenly glancing at her watch, Willa reached for her bag. "I'm so sorry, but I've really got to get going. My appointment is in San Luis Obispo."

They both stood at once. At the door, Tracy rested her hand on Willa's shoulder, shocked at the feel of skin stretched over bone. "Are you sure you're all right? You've lost so much weight."

"I'm fine, really." Willa tossed her head and smiled. "I came to see how *you* were doing, not to worry you."

"I've got so much to do I don't have much time to think about anything else. In fact, I'm holding an open house in June. Why don't you come up for it? You're welcome to stay over so you won't have to drive back to Santa Barbara afterward. It would be so wonderful to have you here and visit the way we used to."

"I'm so sorry. I've been planning to take a little time off in June. Maybe go away for a couple of weeks, but I'll let you know if it does work out."

Willa told her about the client she was going to meet as they left the apartment. In the lobby, where one of Diego's men was wheeling in a floor polisher, Willa waited until the man walked by before she turned to Tracy.

"This place is going to be a great success, Tracy. You'll see. You'll be fine."

"You think so?"

"Of course. You'll make it happen, the way you always do."

"Thanks, Willa."

Willa's gaze shifted to a point over Tracy's shoulder. Her friend's voice lowered. "Looks like someone's waiting for you," Willa said softly.

Tracy made a half turn and her heart collided with her good sense when she saw Wade standing a few feet away with a cup of coffee in his hand. She waved him over and he joined them, though when Tracy introduced Willa, he nodded but didn't smile. There was an undeniable reticence about him as he studied Willa.

"Willa, this is Wade Johnson. He's our first guest." Tracy had to fight to peel her gaze away from Wade as she added, "I guess you could say he's the Heartbreak Hotel's writer in residence."

Willa told Wade it was nice to meet him and then turned to Tracy. "Walk me out?"

"Sure." Tracy expected Wade to excuse himself and return to his room. When he didn't, she said, "I'll be right back."

Again, he merely nodded. "No hurry. I'll wait."

Willa didn't say anything until they reached her car. Tracy noticed it was a new Volvo.

"What's up with this? You said you'd always be the princess of Porsches."

"I guess I wanted a little more metal around me, and this way I can carry interior samples and smaller pieces of furniture."

Willa's gaze touched upon the garden gone wild, then swept up the front of the hotel, over the dormer windows, the Queen Anne features integrated with the California Western exterior, the widow's walk.

Then she said, "He's handsome. He looks familiar somehow. Was he a friend of Glenn's?"

"He's from L.A. He works for an ad agency."

Willa paused before she asked, "Is he living here?"

"He's on R and R. Getting back his muse or something."

"You're attracted to him." It was a statement uttered with calm certainty.

"That's impossible. I hardly know him."

"Physical attraction is a powerful thing. Maybe you should get to know him."

If I'm that transparent, can Wade see it for himself?

Willa pulled her car keys out of her purse and hit the alarm button, unlocking the black Volvo. Her expression suddenly grew pensive before she said, "I know Glenn

169

would want you to be happy."

"You think so? If he had wanted me to be happy, he would have told me the truth from the beginning. He would have let me help him straighten things out." Willa's gaze drifted to the hotel, traveled up to the top of the building, then out to sea. When she finally looked at Tracy again, she reached for her hands and gave them a tight squeeze.

"Be happy, Tracy. If a fling with your resident writer is what it takes, go for it."

CHAPTER TWENTY

Tracy stepped over the long extension cord connected to the floor buffer in the lobby and was pleasantly surprised when she discovered Wade waiting for her near the registration desk. It was momentarily silent inside, Diego and his crew having taken a break after helping themselves to Styrofoam cups of coffee, fresh date bread, and yesterday's pumpkin muffins. She found herself jittery as a teenager and resisted an urge to reach up to see if her hair was in place.

"More coffee?" She glanced at the buffet after Wade shook his head. "Do you need anything else?"

"I'm fine, thanks. I was just thinking about heading into town. Do you need anything from Twilight Cove?"

She shook her head. "Nothing I can think of."

When he didn't move, she took a deep breath. Then she flattened the palm of her hand against her midriff and expected to feel the movement of a hundred butterflies flitting around her insides. She remembered how peaceful he'd looked sitting out on the bluff, staring out to sea. "I saw you outside enjoying the view."

He studied her for a moment before he said, "It's spectacular."

"You should see it from the widow's walk."

Closing the distance between them, he was close enough to touch. "Is that an invitation?"

"I guess it is. When would you like to see it?"

"How about right now?"

What are you doing? What are you thinking? The butterflies were getting frantic. She glanced around the empty lobby. Showing him the walk meant that she would be taking him through the apartment. Letting him see a more intimate, personal side of her life. Opening up to him.

She couldn't seem to stop herself.

"Why not? Everyone else is on a break."

The intimacy forced by the trip up the narrow stairwell wasn't lost on her as they went up to the apartment. She was aware of his every step as he walked close behind her through the rooms and down the hall to the door at the end. More stairs after that, steeper, just a bit wider than his shoulders. Time and use had worn depressions in the center of each step.

Curious, she found him just one step below her. Their faces were level. His deep brown-eyed gaze locked with hers. Her hand tightened around the handrail. She was able to break the spell, to continue climbing, aware of the sound of the slide of his jeans as he moved. Their footsteps kept time with each other until they reached the top. She opened the door to the rooftop and stepped outside.

She walked to the railing, grabbed it with both hands, and gazed out at the view. The ocean was fairly calm. Swell lines moved toward shore, forming waves in the cove. A slight onshore breeze was blowing.

He followed, stood beside her, his shoulder touching hers. She felt him take a deep breath, hold it, then let it go.

"You were right. This is something."

"I love it up here, above everything. I feel as if I'm floating on the breeze, like a gull." She raised her face to the heat of the sun, closed her eyes. Beside her, he shifted but remained silent. The sound of the workers' voices carried up from the garden below, lyrical Spanish phrases, an occasional laugh that drifted above the sound of the waves.

She let the seconds lengthen into a stolen moment that she savored as the warmth of both the sun and the man beside her slowly replaced the chill that had settled around her heart.

When she grudgingly opened her eyes again, she found that Wade had turned to face her. He was staring at her lips. Her heart stopped jogging and kicked into a full sprint.

"I should probably get back." She realized she hadn't meant to whisper, but she had, almost as if this interlude were somehow sacred. Perhaps it was — in that she would remember it for a long time to come.

"Lead the way." He stepped away from the rail, and as she passed by, she felt his hand riding at the small of her waist. The touch was so light, so fleeting, that she wasn't sure he had actually touched her at all.

"What's that second door to?" He paused at the top of the stairwell after they stepped inside.

"The attic."

She tried the old brass knob but, when it didn't budge, he reached around her to help and his forearm brushed against her. Searing, white-hot heat shot through her, radiated down her spine.

She tried to dismiss it. Told herself it was a perfectly natural reaction to his maleness, to the shock of physical contact with the opposite sex.

But she doubted she'd have felt the same way if she had accidently brushed up against the UPS man.

Once they were inside the stuffy little room under the eaves, Wade looked around at the boxes and crates piled on the floor.

"Most of these are full of things I didn't have room for in the apartment. The rest are old boxes that were left here. I don't want to have them hauled away until I've had time to look through them myself." Then she added, "Just on the off chance that one of them might be filled with gold bullion or old bonds worth millions now."

"You've had your hands full." He looked as if he were debating something and then asked, "Would you like me to go through these for you?"

"I couldn't ask you to do that."

"You're not asking. I'm volunteering. You said you'd think of something for me to do in exchange for lowering my room rate. How about if I go through these boxes, sort them all out, and have you look them over? Then I'll haul away what you don't want. If there's anything of interest, I'll set it aside."

"Like a chest filled with Spanish doubloons?"

When he laughed, his whole face lit up. It was such a transformation that she couldn't do anything but stare.

"Be happy; Tracy. If a fling with this guy is what it takes, go for it."

She couldn't help but think that this wasn't only about what she wanted. She was a mom.

What about Matt? And Chelsea?

Would they see her interest in him as a betrayal of their father? Neither of them was completely aware, as far as she knew, of the problems she and Glenn were having. If she were to start dating after only six months . . .

"Who's talking about dating?" Carly had asked.

"What are you thinking about?" He walked away from the window.

You. My kids.

"Nothing," she lied, and then turned the tables. "What are *you* thinking about? Besides this mess?"

"I've been wondering who might have lived here, thinking that a man would be crazy to ever leave, if the place were his." He looked away, as if he'd said too much.

Her gaze lifted to the cobwebs hanging from the rafters. Dust and must were trapped in the air. She was pretty sure that if she held her breath she would be able to hear the termites crunching away inside the walls.

She thought of all she'd accomplished downstairs, of all there was left to do. The Heartbreak Hotel project had started as a means to an end for her. Sure, she'd had enough vision to see it restored, inch by inch, but she hadn't really chosen to live here and probably never would have in a million years. Then she pictured the sunroom the way it looked now, how lovely it looked with the sun streaming through the windows. There was no view comparable to those she had from almost every single window.

And the moments of contemplation and peace she'd found on the rooftop walk were priceless.

"I have to admit," she said grudgingly, "the Heartbreak is starting to grow on me."

He moved closer. "Do you get an odd feeling here? Something that you don't feel anywhere else?"

Slowly she shook her head to deny it. What she was experiencing right now had absolutely nothing to do with the hotel and everything to do with him. The color of his eyes reminded her of chocolate fudge —

and there was nothing she liked better than chocolate.

As she studied his face, she made the fatal error of looking at his lips.

His voice was so low she barely heard him when he asked, "What are you thinking about?"

"Chocolate." She felt his hand on her arm. Felt the warmth of his palm as he ran his hand down her arm to her hand.

"Hungry?" His tone caressed.

Her mouth went dry. She licked her lips. "Starving."

There was a tug on her hand and then she was in his arms, locked in a crushing embrace. His mouth covered hers, his lips relentless, his hands strong and sure as he pressed her hard against him.

A shock to her senses, his touch was rough and at the same time gentle, communicating not only heat, but a sense that she had nothing to fear. He would stop if she said the word, she knew it. Instead, she closed her eyes, savored his taste as she frantically kissed him back.

So long.

She hadn't been touched like this for so long. She was compelled to open up to him, to kiss him back, to let go and lose herself in him. Soaring on sensation, she caught hold of the front of his shirt and hung on as his lips claimed her kiss. Aware of the erratic beat of her heart, of their ragged breathing, she lost track of time and place. She let go of all conscious thought, drowned in sensation — the scent of soap on his skin, the musty air around them.

For the first time in what seemed like forever, she felt alive, vital. Young again.

This is insane. This is dangerous.

This is what I want. What I need . . .

Without warning, the floor suddenly creaked behind them. Tracy heard a gasp before Chelsea's voice rang out, "Tracy? Ohmygod!"

She pulled away so quickly that she nearly brought them both down onto the boxes at their feet. If he hadn't held on to her, her knees would have given way and she'd have ended up in a heap.

With her own heart sinking, Tracy watched all the color drain from Chelsea's face as she stood there framed in the doorway, staring at them. Her freckles stood out in bright relief against her pale face.

"Chelsea —" Tracy knew there was nothing she could say, no lame excuse she could make for what had just happened. Chelsea was old enough to see through a lie —

though Tracy would never consider lying to her.

Before she could offer an apology, Chelsea turned and ran back down the stairs.

It wasn't until Tracy raised her hands to her lips that she realized her fingers were shaking badly. And that Wade was still holding her.

"Please," she whispered. "Let me go."

"Are you all right?"

She wasn't, but she nodded anyway. "I'm okay, but obviously, Chelsea's not."

He opened his arms slowly, as if afraid she might fall. She clasped her hands together and stared at the empty doorway.

"What in the world am I going to say to her?" She was thinking aloud, not really expecting an answer.

"Tell her that you're sorry she was upset."

"But —"

"There's no need to apologize for what we did, Tracy. It was a perfectly innocent kiss."

Perfectly innocent kiss?

Innocent? She didn't know whether to be ashamed or disappointed. What she'd experienced had felt far from innocent; for her it had been an earth-shattering encounter, but she wasn't about to admit that to him now.

"I need to go talk to her." She would

rather jump off the bluff at this point, but Chelsea meant too much to her to leave her downstairs alone in an emotional upheaval.

Wade reached for her hand, effectively stopping her in her tracks.

"I'm sorry she walked in on us like that," he admitted, "but I'm not sorry I kissed you. What about you?" His deep brown eyes bored into hers and, in their depths, she saw all the confusion she was feeling. "Are you sorry I kissed you?"

"I'm not sorry, but . . ." She had no idea what she was feeling. Embarrassment, certainly. *Shame?* No.

"Will you be all right?" He reached for her hand. "Do you want me to go talk to her with you?"

"No!" She took a breath. Calmed down. "No. I'll be fine."

She almost laughed. *Fine? Fine?*

"I hate for you to go like this."

"Wade . . ."

"I'm heading to Twilight, but I'll be back." He shoved his hands in his back pockets, meeting her eyes. "I'll leave the next move up to you."

After Wade left the attic, Tracy took a minute to pull herself together. She took a deep breath, pressed her fingertips to her lips. Every nerve in her body was pulsing.

She'd never been hysterical before, but right now she felt on the verge of both laughing and crying. Elated, buoyant, she was at the same time heartbroken for inadvertently upsetting Chelsea.

She'd seen the hurt in the girl's eyes and knew without a doubt that Chelsea saw the kiss as an ultimate betrayal of Glenn's memory.

CHAPTER TWENTY-ONE

Tracy found Chelsea in her room and ignored the girl's sullen request for her to go away. She walked in and halted a few feet from the bed.

"Chelsea, I'm so sorry."

"Hey, you don't have to apologize to me," she shrugged. "It's still a free country. Kiss whoever you want." She sat up and slipped off her black sandals. Her toenails were coated with glossy, summer-pink toenail polish. "You were so busy with your boy toy you forgot to call David Sylvester," she added.

Tracy felt like a deer caught in the headlights, but she sat down on the foot of the bed anyway. Chelsea scooted away.

"Oh, honey, I apologize again." Her words drifted into silence. "Things got a bit hectic around here. Willa stopped by and then, well, it . . . slipped my mind. Did you talk to David?"

Chelsea nodded. "He gave me an application and said there shouldn't be any problem."

"I'll give him a call the minute we've settled this. I promise."

Chelsea sat up. "There's nothing to settle."

"I'm sorry this happened, honey."

"Sorry you let him kiss you? Or sorry I walked in?" She crossed her arms, stared over at Tracy with more confusion than anger in her eyes. "I'd have expected this out of my mom, but not you. You always tried so hard to be the perfect wife, the perfect soccer mom. I thought you loved Daddy."

"Chelsea . . ."

"You don't even know this guy. He's just using you. How old is he, anyway?"

Tracy shook her head. "I have no idea."

"He's younger than you are."

"A couple of years, maybe."

"So. Don't you get it?"

Tracy stared at her, considering. "Get what?"

"That he's probably just out for sex. You're just lonely without Dad."

"Not enough to make a fool of myself. I wanted to kiss Wade, Chelsea."

She could tell she'd embarrassed Chelsea with her honesty. The girl got up, grabbed her purse off the chair, and dug around inside for the folded intern application. "I really ought to get this filled out."

Tracy refused to leave with Chelsea this upset. She walked over to the girl and laid her hand on Chelsea's shoulder.

"Look at me," she said softly.

Slowly, Chelsea turned.

She wanted to reassure her that, yes, she'd loved Glenn, and she wanted to sound sincere. All the doubt and anger that she'd lived with the last few years of her marriage were not Chelsea's burden. She didn't want to tarnish the girl's memory, so she tried to remember what she and Glenn once had. How much they'd loved each other once.

"I loved your dad. You know that, but now he's gone."

"Have you been sleeping with that guy?"

Tracy shook her head. "No. I haven't."

"Are you going to?"

"I don't know what's happening here. I don't know what I'm feeling for, or about, Wade Johnson. You have to understand that I'd never do anything to purposely hurt or embarrass you." Then she asked, "Are you going to be all right, honey?"

"Oh, yeah. Sure. My dad died, and my life sucks. I'll be fine."

"I can't bring your dad back —"

"I know that. I'm sorry, Tracy. I've just been kinda bummed lately."

"Do you need any help with that application?"

Chelsea shook her head. "I don't think so. I looked it over earlier. It's pretty standard stuff. They'll send for transcripts, check my grades and references."

"Then if you're all right, I'll go call David and then fix us some lunch."

Eating was the last thing she wanted to do right now, but it would be a way to get Chelsea out of her room to keep communications open. She left the room praying that she hadn't done irreparable damage to what had sometimes been a tenuous relationship. Unfortunately, there was no easy way out of this. Chelsea had seen what she'd seen. There was no going back.

CHAPTER TWENTY-TWO

School wasn't any fun with Christopher in Taos. Matt wished he could skip school, too. At least Carly had promised that Chris would be back for the class party on the last day.

It wasn't much fun hanging around the Ear Ache either, not with Mom running from room to room making sure everything was perfect for the open house. Today when she picked him up after school, she bought him an ice cream cone like always, but she was in such a hurry to get back that she made him eat it on the way home instead of at a table outside of Sweeties.

He turned off the portable television in his room and headed downstairs. The lobby was deserted, so he wandered down the hall past the guest rooms.

Looking around, he pressed his ear to the door of Wade Johnson's room, but he didn't hear anything. His mom was in another room down the hall pounding a picture hanger into the wall above a dresser. She didn't see him in the doorway, so he walked back to the lobby and out the front door.

The sun had been shining earlier, but now it was overcast, so gray and gloomy that he thought it might start raining. Noticing a ladybug on a bush near the porch, he walked over to see if he could get her to walk up his finger.

The ladybug flew off and Matt sighed, hoping he wouldn't have bad luck for seven years.

Scuffing his Skechers, he trudged along the stone path until he reached the end of the garden. When he turned the corner, he saw Wade's Harley parked beside the building.

Even without the sunshine, the chrome on the motorcycle gleamed like the brightest silver. After glancing around first to make sure no one was watching, he walked up closer to check it out.

He ran his hand over the wide leather seat and touched the glass covers on the gauges. The motorcycle had a kickstand just like his bike, only much thicker. He wondered how hard it would be to kick up the stand.

Reaching out, he gave the bike a little nudge but it didn't even budge, so he pressed a little harder first with one hand, and then both. Nothing happened.

He glanced up and down the road as far as he could see. There wasn't a soul in sight, so he took a deep breath and climbed up on the Harley, straddling the wide seat. He grabbed the handlebars and wished he could get somebody to take a picture of him.

Leaning forward, gripping the handlebars, he began to mutter low and deep in his throat, trying to imitate the Harley engine's purr.

"Potatopotatopotatopotato." With his eyes closed and the breeze off the ocean stirring his hair; it was easy to imagine cruising along the coast, leaning around the curve that hugged the bluffs, tearing down the stretch of road that turned onto Cabrillo Avenue. He imagined himself slowing down as he rode into Twilight Cove, and the look of surprise on Selma Gibbs's face when he waved to her and rumbled past the Plaza Diner.

Pretending to shift gears, he was just about to burn rubber in front of Twilight Cove Elementary. And his heart stopped when Wade Johnson said, "Having a good ride, Sport?"

Matt's eyes flew open and he froze right there on the big black leather seat. Wade was standing a few feet away with one hand in his back pocket and a black helmet under one arm.

He wasn't smiling, either.

Matt tried to say something, but nothing happened. Finally, when he was able to talk, he could only squeak "I'm sorry" in a voice that sounded just like Mickey Mouse — which was almost as embarrassing as getting caught.

When he was a little kid — a couple of years ago — he had a habit of throwing up whenever he was upset or scared. Right now he was afraid everything in his stomach was working its way north.

He wanted to jump down and tear off into the hotel, but he was too scared to move.

Wade Johnson shifted his scuffed cowboy boots and watched him for another minute before he said, "That model's called a Fat Boy."

"Oh."

"It weighs about six hundred pounds."

"Wow. I'm sure glad it didn't fall over." Matt envisioned himself flattened like a cartoon character beneath the big chrome bike.

"You couldn't budge it if you tried," Wade told him.

"I know. I already tried."

Wade nodded. "I figured."

"You gonna tell my mom?" Matt's stomach lurched again. He tasted mint chocolate chip ice cream.

"Tell her what?" Wade pretended not to know what he was talking about.

The ice cream in his stomach slowly settled as Matt slid off the Harley. He had to tip his head back to look up at Wade.

"You going someplace?" he asked Wade.

"Thought I'd go into town for dinner. Got any suggestions?"

Matt didn't want to like the guy, mainly because he didn't think Dad would want Wade Johnson hanging around Mom, but today Wade seemed a little friendlier than when he first checked in.

Besides, Mom said that he'd have to do his part to help the guests. He didn't really think anyone would ask a kid something like where to eat, or what to see, but maybe Mom was right.

"If you want a good hamburger and fries or some chicken, you can go to Selma's Plaza Diner. Do you like Mexican food?"

Wade nodded. "Some."

"Then you could go to Enrique's. It's on the road out of town."

"Thanks." Wade nodded.

Wade looked like he was thinking about

something really hard.

"How's it going with you?" he asked.

A rush of something Matt hadn't felt in a long time filled him up inside and suddenly he didn't feel like a kid anymore. He felt the way he did whenever he and his dad went someplace by themselves, or whenever he'd looked up into the bleachers during one of his ball games and spotted his dad sitting there watching the game.

Then he remembered he'd never, ever see Dad again, and the good feeling whooshed out of him as fast as air out of a loose balloon.

He hung his head and stared at his Skechers. "It's going okay."

"Just okay?"

He shrugged. "Yeah."

Wade Johnson didn't leave and Matt thought somebody ought to say something. "Mom said you write stuff."

"I do."

"She wants me to write, too. She thinks I'm good at it."

"She told me."

"She did?" That made him feel better, to know Mom was bragging about him. "She wants me to write about how I *feel* in a dumb journal. For *therapy*."

"Do you think you need to?"

He thought about it for a minute and answered honestly. "I dunno. She wants me to write how I feel about Dad dying."

"How do you feel about that idea?"

He shook his head, thinking of the journal with Spider-Man on the cover. It was full of *thousands* of blank pages. More than he could fill if he wrote for the rest of his whole life.

"I don't like to think about it."

"What if you just wrote letters to him?"

Was this a joke? Didn't the guy know his dad was dead?

"He's never going to read 'em."

"You could pretend. You could tell him about how you and your mom are fixing up this place . . ."

"I *hate* this place."

Wade Johnson glanced out toward the ocean and then looked like he just got a great idea. "Write to him about the Harley."

The more Matt thought about it, the more he wished Dad could see him on the Harley.

"I don't spell very good," he admitted.

"I don't either." Then Wade kinda smiled and it made him look much nicer. "Besides, journals are just for you, not anyone else. The spelling isn't as important as what you write."

"I'll think about it."

Wade put on the helmet before he reached into his front pocket and pulled out a key. Matt stepped away from the Harley and stood back, watching closely as Wade righted the heavy bike and straddled the wide seat. He turned the key and pushed a button and the big engine came to life.

Wade gave him a nod before he turned the bike toward the driveway. Matt felt the rumble of the motor down to his toes and wished like anything that Wade would ask if he wanted a ride, but he knew he'd have to ask his mom and she'd *never* say it was okay. No motorcycles. Not ever. That's what she always said.

Wade saluted him with two fingers and slowly rolled down the driveway. When he got to the end, he revved the engine and took off. Matt ran down the driveway after him. Watching the chrome wheels spin and hearing the roar of the engine made him want to fly.

He stood at the end of the driveway and watched Wade ride away.

Later that night, after his mom tucked him in, he waited a few minutes, turned the light back on, and picked up the journal. It took him a minute to find a pen that felt just right in his hand and then, thinking about Wade and the way he'd seen him sitting on the floor writing, he sat down on the floor, too. He leaned back against the bed and propped the journal on his knees, opened it to the first blank page, and in his most careful printing wrote *Matt Potter's Journal.*

Then he decorated the page with a few rockets and stars and a full moon, then a crooked crescent moon, and a rainbow arcing over some puffy clouds so it looked like heaven.

On the second page he wrote the date in the top right corner and then he wrote *Dear Dad.*

All of a sudden he couldn't see the page because his eyes were blurry. Then a tear plopped down on a line right in the middle of the page.

Matt closed the journal, tossed it on the floor next to him, hid his face in the crook of his arm, and cried.

CHAPTER TWENTY-THREE

For days Tracy had made it a point to not be alone with Wade for more than a few minutes of necessary conversation. She thought that given time and lack of opportunity, her attraction would fade, but unfortunately, the more she avoided being alone with him, the more she wanted to see him. At night she tossed and turned, wondering if he was thinking about her at all or if he was asleep.

Kissing him had been like having one piece of chocolate and trying to ignore the rest of the box.

Alone in the lobby that morning, she turned off the local radio news and weather report and tried to convince herself that meteorologists didn't know everything. It had been raining for two solid days. Not occasional showers. Not drizzle. There had been forty-eight hours of constant downpour, uncommon for California in any month, let alone June.

"What happened to global warming?" she mumbled as she walked over to straighten an already neat pile of magazines on the low coffee table in front of the fireplace. The sitting room was chilly and damp, which encouraged the slight smell of mildew that tended to linger in old buildings by the sea. If she weren't intending to leave for town in a few minutes, she would have started a fire just to dispel the gloom.

She was about to head upstairs to get Matt and her purse when Wade walked in, wiping his hands on a rag.

"I'm finished." He absently rubbed a spot of paint off his thumb as he crossed the room. "The last room is ready to decorate as soon as it's dry. I can set up the bed frame, if you'd like."

"I don't know what I'd have done without you." Three days ago, when Diego called to tell her that Immigration had picked up all but two of his regular workers and bused them back across the border, she had no option but to take Wade up on his offer to help out. Though Diego promised to be back with a crew as soon as possible, she couldn't wait — not with the open house date looming.

"I don't know how to thank you," she said lamely.

"I can think of a couple of ways."

Tempted to follow his line of teasing, she dropped her gaze to the cold fireplace instead. His nearness had quickly dispelled the chill. She knew that the sooner she got away from temptation, the better.

"I'm going into town for the last few linens and baking supplies," she told him.

"Would you mind picking up a pack of spiral notebooks for me?" When he started to dig in his pocket for some money, she raised her hand in protest.

"The least you can do is let me get them for you," she insisted. She wasn't looking forward to driving in the rain or dashing across the parking lots with her packages, but she'd put off the trip to town as long as she could.

The wind outside was howling. Slanting rain pelted the windows. She walked over to a table lamp and turned it on, chasing the shadows out of the room.

"I'll drive," he volunteered.

"I can drive myself."

"I know you can, but I'd like to go along anyway. I can't get out for lunch on the Harley."

"Matt's going, too," she added. *There. The*

ground rules are clear. Nothing would happen, nothing *could* happen with Matt along.

"That's fine." He shoved his free hand into his back pocket. "I don't mind at all."

"In that case, I insist you let me buy you lunch."

One corner of his mouth lifted in a half smile. "Whatever makes you happy."

Whatever makes you happy?

She wished her imagination weren't open to so many options.

"Speaking of happy . . ." She smiled back. "Yes?"

"I hope you like Happy Meals."

Wade pulled the bill of his cap lower and glanced across the front seat as Tracy directed him into the parking lot of the Super Kmart.

"Last stop, guys," she promised.

"Aw, Mom," Matt grumbled from the backseat, where he was almost buried under a mound of packages already.

"I'll bet you're ready to groan, too." Tracy smiled over at Wade as he waited for a minivan to vacate a parking space near the entrance.

He'd like to groan all right, but not because they'd made stops all over San Luis Obispo. Being with Tracy made him forget to watch the crowd. Every so often he'd look up, realize he was out in public, and panic that someone might recognize him. Then he'd try to tell himself to get over it. It had been months. He was old news.

She glanced down at Matt and then turned to Wade apologetically. "I need to check in at customer service. They called to let me know that the curtains I ordered are in. Maybe you two could hang out in the toy section until I'm finished?"

Wade turned to Matt. "How about it?"

The boy thought for a moment and then shrugged. "Okay."

"We'll meet you at the checkout in ten minutes. How's that?" Wade asked.

"Great."

He followed Matt through aisles of housewares, sporting goods, and electronic equipment. They stopped in stationery long enough for him to grab some roller ball pens and a three-pack of notebooks.

"You filled up that journal yet?" Wade eyed some with SpongeBob SquarePants on them.

Matt shook his head. The boy had been silent and withdrawn all day. Wade figured that his having come along didn't sit well with him.

"So," Wade attempted to make conversation as they continued on to the toy section, "have you tried writing any of those letters I suggested?"

"Yeah. I tried."

"Well, that's a start."

"Are you almost ready to leave yet?"

Wade glanced at his watch. They'd left Tracy no more than three seconds ago.

"We've got time to look around."

"I mean are you about ready to leave the *hotel*?"

Nothing like a kid to get right to the point. "Does my staying bother you?"

It was Matt's turn to look uncomfortable. "Kinda." Though Wade thought he already knew the answer, he asked anyway. "Why's that?"

"My friend Chris's real dad died and he got a new one."

Suddenly all the ramifications of what he was doing hit Wade square in the gut. Tracy wasn't a single woman. She was a widow with an impressionable young boy. A boy who'd suffered a tragic loss.

"I . . ." Wade had no idea how to respond.

Before he could stumble through a response, Matt volunteered, "I don't want a new dad. Ever."

Wade glanced at his watch and wished he could come up with a great one-liner.

201

Something prophetic and sensitive, something a character in a novel might say. A few words or phrases that would put Matt's mind at ease — but just then he was a writer without words. "What do you say we head back to the checkout and get in line?" It was all he could come up with.

Matt looked up. "Can I have a Combo Blaster?" Wade stared at the display of plastic space-age military toy hardware in front of them.

"What would your mom say?"

He could tell what Tracy's answer would be by the way Matt stalled. "She probably wouldn't care."

"Probably means I'd better say no."

"If you're not sticking around, what do you care if she gets mad or not?"

"I need a ride back to the hotel, you know."

Matt finally smiled. "She wouldn't leave you here. It's raining outside."

"I don't want to take a chance." Wade scanned the shelves. "How about an Operation game?"

"Dumb. I had one."

"Okay. How about Uno? I like Uno." Wade grabbed a deck of Uno cards off the shelf.

"I don't have anyone to play with. Mom's

too busy. Chris isn't home."

"I'll play with you."

The kid's expression communicated a "big wow," but Wade added the card deck to the items in his hands. On the way to the checkout stand, Matt suddenly stopped in the camera aisle.

"Can I have a disposable camera?"

"You like photography?"

"I wanna take some pictures on the last day of school."

"Sure, why not?" He waited while Matt chose a thirty-six-shot camera and then said, "We'd better go get in line."

Matt nodded and led the way.

Wade realized he'd picked the slowest checker in the place, and as they inched forward he grabbed a *People* magazine and started thumbing through it. He glanced at the Pages section and read a glowing review by a well-established writer, which he responded to with mixed emotions. He liked the guy, an affable but not very talented popular fiction writer. The competitive side of him wished he were still in the game, still giving the guy a run for first place.

He flipped through the rest of the magazine and nearly dropped it along with everything else he was holding. He found himself staring down at his own headshot.

In an article entitled "Whatever Happened To Last Year's Headliners?" by Jeannie McCabe, his photo was prominently featured along with a dozen other faces that figured in the news a year ago.

There was a sidebar next to one of his book jacket headshots. He was wearing his signature black turtleneck and tweed sport coat, and it was a shock to see himself with light brown hair, a full beard, and blue eyes. He quickly scanned the copy.

Edward Cain, object of a spate of sensational murders inspired by his novel, *An Even Dozen,* and succeeding court cases, dropped out of sight almost a year ago. Although his agent had no comment, Cain's former publisher, Sally Reinhart, hints that Cain just might be back soon, and with a vengeance.

"Wade?"

He found Tracy smiling beside him, her arms full of Martha Stewart curtain packages.

"Hi." He snapped the magazine shut and shoved it back into the rack, earning a glare from the checker when the cover tore with a distinct ripping sound. He wished he had the nerve to grab the entire stack of *People*s and toss them across the aisle.

"Anything interesting?"

Before he could divert her attention, she picked up the magazine and stared at Prince William on the cover. The handsome young man's photo, displaying features so reminiscent of Princess Di, assured top sales.

"Not much, as usual." Wade held his breath as Tracy set the curtain packages on the rubber conveyor belt.

She stared at the cover a few seconds more, and then sighed. "As if I have time to read." She fingered the slight tear on the cover before she put it back in the rack.

Matt wedged his way between them. "Wade bought some Uno cards. He's gonna play with me — since you don't have time anymore. And he got me a disposable camera, too."

"Did you say thank you?"

Matt shrugged. "Thanks, Wade."

"No problem, Sport." He set the notebooks, pens, the cards, and the camera on the belt and reached for some cash. When he looked up, he found Tracy staring up at him with one hand on Matt's shining sandy-red hair. She was looking at him as if he'd just bought the kid a new car.

He shrugged. "Hey, it's just Uno and a cheap camera."

As Matt squeezed between his mother and the counter and walked over to stare at the gumball machines, Tracy touched the back of Wade's hand.

"Thank you," she said softly. "He's having a hard time adjusting and I am always so busy . . ." She looked guilty as hell.

"He's used to having your full-time attention. I hear kids are resilient. He'll adjust." Wade glanced around at the checkout lines, suddenly aware of how many people spent their time waiting by thumbing through *People* magazine. He couldn't wait to get out of the store and head back to the isolation of Heartbreak Hotel.

"Are your parents still alive?"

He realized she was talking to him again. "My parents?"

"You know. The people responsible for your being born?" She smiled and tossed her hair back.

He'd almost forgotten that he had a past other than that as Edward Cain. He never talked about his life before the murders anymore. Never. Not even to Bob Schack.

"I never knew my dad. He died in Vietnam. My mom passed away about four years ago." He thanked God every day that she had gone before the murders and subsequent lawsuits. She'd died knowing he'd accomplished his goal of becoming not only a working writer, but one who even achieved a fair amount of success, even before *An Even Dozen* was released.

"You grew up without a father." She sounded thoughtful.

"I never knew what it was to have one." How different would his life have been if his father had come home from Vietnam? "You're doing a great job with Matt." He wanted to reassure her, even though he'd never been around kids much, but the boy seemed to be getting along all right, given the circumstances.

She sighed. "I hope so."

The checker made a slow and thorough comparison of Tracy's identification with the name and address on her check. Wade forced himself to not look around, certain that if he did, someone leafing through *People* might suddenly realize that Edward Cain was standing right there at checkout stand four.

He tugged on the bill of his ball cap again before he handed the checker his own twenty as she rang up his items. She took her sweet time counting out his change and then made a point of looking him right in the eye when she handed it back.

"Thanks for shopping at Kmart."

"Right."

Tracy was near the exit, where Matt was lobbying for change for the gumball machine. Wade started toward them.

"Hey, Mister!"

Wade froze when the checker called out to him. He had an urge to run, but slowly turned around while a fantasy scenario played out in his mind.

He imagined the clerk asking, "Are you Edward Cain?" Then she grabbed the microphone above the register and announced, "*New York Times* best-selling novelist Edward Cain on aisle four. *Edward Cain is on aisle four*!" she shouted.

It wouldn't be the first time he'd been a blue-light special. Early in his career he'd done plenty of book signings in stores just like this one.

He took a deep breath and reminded himself that his hair was black and his eyes were brown and he was clean-shaven. He prayed that Tracy and Matt would stay out of earshot.

"Yeah?" He kept his voice low, hoping the checker would do the same.

She picked up a plastic bag by the handles and dangled it over the end of the checkout stand.

"You forgot your stuff."

He grabbed it and mumbled thanks. As his heartbeat settled back to normal, he walked over to Tracy and Matt near the gumball machine and handed Matt all his spare change.

Rain pelted them as they sprinted for the car. He ran as he pushed the basket along, stood on the bottom rack, and coasted on it a few feet. Matt hooted uproariously when Wade dismounted right into a sizable puddle. Tracy ran along beside them with her jacket over her head and hustled Matt into the car. Together, they laughed as they tossed her purchases into the trunk.

Once they were all safe inside, Matt recounted the shock on Wade's face when he stepped into water up to his ankle. The windows steamed up before he could get the defroster going, and they sat cocooned in the car waiting for the steam to clear. Isolated from the world for a moment, it was almost possible to forget that he *wasn't* simply Wade Johnson, a copywriter with no cares or worries. A man whose guilt wasn't communicating itself into achingly real, sometimes terrifying nightmares.

"Now *that* was fun!" Matt shouted from the backseat. "Where are we going next, Mom?"

"Home!" she laughed. "We're all soaked

and it's almost five already." Then unexpectedly, she turned to Wade and said, "Would you like to have dinner with us tonight? I think you've earned a home-cooked meal."

It seemed like the most natural thing in the world for him to accept.

CHAPTER TWENTY-FOUR

"Uno!"

Tracy laughed as Wade groaned and feigned frustration when Matt finally slammed down his next-to-last card. She was certain that when he volunteered to play, he had no idea that one round could last over thirty minutes.

Matt jumped up shouting, "I won! I won, Mom!"

Watching from the doorway into the small kitchen, Tracy dried her hands on a dish towel. "Congratulations, honey. Tell Wade good night, okay? It's time for bed."

"Aw, Mom, it's only eight-thirty."

"It's ten to nine, actually. Get going. By the time you brush your teeth it'll be nine." She waited while Matt made a few more grousing noises but eventually trudged down the hall. After she'd tucked him in, she walked back out to the living room and joined Wade.

"Can I get you anything else?" She glanced back and forth from the sofa to the easy chair across from it.

"Sit here." He indicated the cushion beside him. She hesitated a moment before she finally joined him.

"I won't bite," he assured her.

"Chelsea will be home from work in a little while."

"How is she doing?"

"So far, she likes the job and the fact that she can carpool with her friend, Eric." She tried to sound casual, as if just the simple act of sitting beside him like this didn't make her all jumpy inside, even though he hadn't moved a bit closer.

"She's not still upset with you?"

"I don't think so. She doesn't act like it, anyway." She tried to relax. Found it impossible.

"What's on the to-do list for tomorrow?"

"I plan to finish hanging some pictures and setting out some flower arrangements. If you could hang the curtain rods and put the last bed frame together . . ."

"No problem."

She wondered if he noticed the way she blushed every time she used the word *bed* around him. Did the image send his thoughts careening down the same road?

She looked down at her hands, twisted the diamond ring. "I can't believe I'm almost finished. All the rooms will be ready for the open house on Saturday."

She sensed a stillness about him when he asked, "Are you expecting a big crowd?"

"About seventy-five, give or take a few. The RSVP is for regrets only, and so far, no one has called in to say they aren't coming. You know you're welcome to join us."

"Thanks. Maybe I will."

As they settled into an awkward silence, she wished he would pull her into his arms and kiss her the way he had the other day. Kiss her so long and so deep that she would forget about everything but him, but he'd made it pretty clear that the next move was up to her and apparently he was sticking to his word.

After a few more silent seconds she said softly, "I'm not getting any better at this."

"At what?"

"Being alone with you."

"You're doing all right." He reached out, gently took a lock of her hair between his thumb and forefinger, and rubbed it, waiting.

She closed her eyes for a second before she opened them and met his again. "I don't know what I'm doing. I mean . . . I keep finding excuses to be with you . . ."

Her admission was flattering, and yet it only added to Wade's guilt.

"I'd never do anything to hurt you, Tracy."

Unable to stop himself, he reached for her again. He meant every word, and yet he knew that she was bound to feel betrayed if she ever found out he'd lied about his last name and his occupation. There was so much he'd left unsaid about himself that the omissions would surely be seen as lies in her eyes.

She was so trusting that it scared the hell out of him. Creeps and perverts were real and they were out there. He'd not only read about them, he'd interviewed them in prison. He'd inspired a murderer himself.

"If I didn't trust you, I'd have never let you in the front door."

"How do you know you can trust me?"

"Let's just say that I can tell by the way a man plays Uno."

He wished he could stop staring at her mouth. "I want to kiss you again. I've been thinking about it for days."

"Me, too. Maybe you shouldn't keep me waiting."

He wrapped his hand in her hair, gently tugged until her head was on his shoulder and her mouth was there, tilted up toward his, lips parted, waiting.

He meant to kiss her tenderly, to make the kiss last forever.

Slipping her arms around his neck, she hung on tight, pulled him closer. They kissed until they were breathless.

He pulled away, breathing hard.

A torrent of rain pounded against the roof and yet inside, they were safe and warm.

Though it couldn't last, he found himself thankful for having had a glimpse into real life. A joyful life. Despite everything that had happened to her, she had stayed strong.

Loving her children, accepting love, returning it. Those things were as natural as breathing to Tracy Potter. She'd lost her husband, lost most of her resources, but she was battling back fearlessly, forging a new life and haven for herself, her son, and her stepdaughter.

I have absolutely no business ruining her life.

That first night, when he'd lied about his name, he had no idea that things would ever go this far. If there had ever been a time to make things right, it had already come and gone. If he told her the truth now, he risked breaking her trust in him. And he was certain that someone like Tracy would be as shocked and horrified by what he'd written as by the horrors that had occurred because of it.

Reluctantly, he let her go and moved a few inches away.

High color blazed across her cheeks. Her eyes looked twice as blue as usual.

"I should head back down to my room." He tugged on the front of his jeans and scooted to the edge of the sofa.

She fiddled with the hem of her top before she finger-combed her hair. "I have to be up early . . ." Her words drifted into awkward silence. Then they both spoke at once.

"Tracy —"

"Wade —"

Just then the door to the apartment opened and Chelsea breezed in. Wade had the urge to jump to his feet, but decided that would only make him appear guiltier.

"Wow! Is it dumping out there!" Chelsea laughed as she dropped her purse on the arm of a chair near the door. Water dripped from her hair. A wet circle stained the shoulders of her pastel-pink sweater.

She gave her long bangs a swipe, shifting them away from her eyes, and slowly took in the two of them sitting there. Her smile slowly wilted. Her mouth tightened.

"I'm soaked," she said, turning away. "I'm

going to take a shower and go to bed."

Tracy started toward the kitchen. "I was worried about you. Are you hungry? There's leftover chicken and . . ."

Chelsea slowly turned. Her tone could have set Jell-O. "No thanks. I already had dinner with Eric." She shot a withering glance in Wade's direction, then bid Tracy good night.

Tracy was staring down the hall after her. Wade crossed the room and reached for her chin, tried to pull her into his arms, but she stiffened.

"Are you all right?"

She slowly relaxed and sighed. "She and Glenn were very close."

"At least her timing wasn't as bad as last time." He was hoping she'd smile, but she didn't. "What time do we start work tomorrow?"

"I don't want to keep you from your writing."

"You're not. Believe me." He thought of the new notebooks he'd bought earlier. Page upon empty page. Would the dreams haunt him tonight? Would he feel compelled to write at all?

"How about I get to those boxes up in the attic after I put the bed together tomorrow?" he offered.

"If you can spare the time."

"I'll make time. Walk me to the door?"

Alone with Wade on the landing outside the apartment, Tracy was thankful for the low light in the hall. He glanced over at the door, which was closed, before he took her in his arms. She was amazed at how easy it was to step into his embrace. How right it felt. She didn't know what to expect and was surprised when he gave her what was almost a chaste kiss this time. He held her gently, took his time. It was slow, soft, and sweet.

When the kiss ended, she felt the warmth of his breath against her ear. "Thanks for dinner," he whispered.

"You're welcome."

He let her go and she resisted the urge to call him back. She watched him disappear down the stairwell.

She took a deep breath and when she was calm, when she felt more like the old Tracy, Matt's mom, she opened the apartment door and almost tripped over Chelsea. She was sitting back on her knees on the floor, shoving lipsticks, a mirror, pens, Palm Pilot, and her wallet back inside her purse.

"What happened?"

It was a second before Chelsea looked up.

"My purse fell off the chair and everything dumped out." She got to her feet, slipped the strap over her shoulder, and quickly started toward her room.

"Are you sure you don't want any leftovers?"

"I'm positive." Chelsea looked away and fiddled with her purse strap. Tracy couldn't tell if she was angry or not, but something was definitely wrong.

"How was work?"

Chelsea shrugged. "Fine. David's actually kinda weird, though."

Tracy remembered how Glenn had defended his accountant when she'd voiced a similar opinion. "How do you mean?"

Chelsea's brow furrowed. "I dunno."

"Does he make you uncomfortable?" She had never really taken to David, either, and couldn't exactly say why.

"Not really."

Tracy found herself wishing she heard less hesitation and more conviction in Chelsea's tone. "If working there bothers you, then you can always get another job."

"He told me the firm partners award a scholarship to one of the interns every year."

"They do? That's great news."

"I told him I was interested, and he said he'd keep that in mind. He wants me to go out to dinner with him and his wife."

"When?"

"Next week."

"Great, as long as it's not Saturday. I was really counting on you being here for the open house."

"Sure. I'll be here." Shifting uncomfortably, Chelsea started biting her thumbnail.

Tracy pictured Chelsea at eight, the year she'd married Glenn. The girl was at that awkward stage, her permanent front teeth had just come in and they looked too big for her mouth. She was stick thin with deep auburn braids and spattered with freckles the same color as her hair. It wasn't until she was eleven that Chelsea was finally convinced that Glenn wasn't going to leave Tracy and go back to living with her and Monica.

The lovely young woman standing before her now was nothing like the sometimes sullen child she'd met so long ago. But just now, that young woman looked like she'd rather be anywhere else.

"I need to go call Eric. I told him I'd let him know that I made it home through the rain and I forgot all about it."

"You sure everything's all right? You're not upset that Wade was here for dinner, are you?"

"No. Not at all." Chelsea shook her head and even smiled. "Really. I'm not. 'Night." With that she turned and headed down the hall.

Tracy knew her well enough to know that Chelsea might not be upset about Wade, but something was definitely up.

CHAPTER TWENTY-FIVE

Wade tossed and turned. Burning up, he kicked off the covers. A few minutes later, shivering, he tugged them back up to his chin. His dreams were intricate and vivid, so real that his body reacted as if he were living each experience.

At one point, after dreaming that he'd been tossed helpless upon a stormy sea, he was so exhausted he had to drag himself to the bathroom for a glass of water.

Gradually he felt better. He rubbed his face, blinked, looked around the bathroom, and wondered if he had been sleepwalking. Wide awake, he went back into the bedroom and turned on the bedside lamp. A few seconds later he was frantically pawing around the desktop for a pen. Finding one, he then grabbed one of the new notebooks and sat on the bed. As soon as he opened the notebook, his hand started moving across the page.

Almost home.

I was almost home when the storm hit, a monster storm that whipped the seas higher than I'd ever seen them. The wind howled like a banshee, tore the sails off the rigging, brought down the mainmast.

The ocean tossed the *Lantana* like a matchstick, threw her high and slammed her low, sending the crew sprawling. We fought like Spartans, but eventually she splintered into driftwood, casting one and all into the deep.

For the first time in forever, I prayed that dark night. Prayed as hard and fast as I could to a God I'd never believed in. I begged His forgiveness, all the time wondering why He should save me over the rest of the crew and spare my life.

All I could think of was Violette and my unborn son. I had to live, for them, if for no other reason. She'd lost her parents. She had only me.

Her words came back to me. "You've given your word to me, too, Ezra. Made a vow to love, to honor, and to cherish. We're bound by God . . . I'm afraid, Ezra."

The way she clung to me, begged me not to make this cursed voyage — Why didn't I listen? Why didn't I stay in her arms?

I grabbed for a piece of wreckage, held tight, and gave myself over to my fate. I awoke no better than a dead man with my cheek pressed into wet sand, the foaming tide tugging at my boots. I crawled out of the surf line, spit sand from my mouth as I dragged my weary bones to higher ground.

I slept having no idea if it was days or hours before I awoke again. When I did, the sun beat down on me.

It's been many weeks, perhaps months, by my calculations, since the sea spit me out on this godforsaken island. On clear days I can glimpse the mainland. I see the gold, fertile hills of California as plain as I see my ragged fingernails, my sun-ravaged skin.

I fear I'll starve before I get off this barren rock, fear that I'll not live to see my son. My child has been born by now.

I cannot bear to think of my sweet Violette and know how she's surely suffered. By now she knows the ship was lost at sea. Does she believe that I am dead? Can she feel me here, thinking of her, longing for her?

There are no others on this spit of land with me. I've walked the length and breadth of it, this knoll off Anacapa Island. There's no life here, barely a blade of

grass. I exist on mussels and crabs no bigger than quarters. For a man my size it's puny fare. My bones poke through my skin. My teeth are loose with scurvy even though I can see the land of plenty, not thirty miles away.

My mind wanders across the channel that separates us. I imagine Violette on the widow's walk, holding my child in her arms, pointing to a spot on the horizon.

Does she whisper to him? "There! Just there is where we'll see your papa's ship when he comes sailing home to us."

Does she cling to hope that one day I'll return, or has she given me up for dead?

I cannot signal passing ships. I have no fire. I have shouted my throat raw, waved my arms until I cannot lift them. No ship passes near enough to see or hear me.

My hope wanes. I know that if I die here, I will take the love I have for Violette with me to the other side.

Hours later, in a daze, Wade closed the notebook, set it aside. He glanced at the clock on the bedside table and figured he could get a couple hours' sleep before Tracy needed him.

Looking out the window into an ash-colored

225

sky the next morning, Tracy tried to not think about what would happen to the tourist trade if the weather got any worse. She rubbed her chilly arms, tempted to take advantage of one of the sofas and magazines in the sitting room, when Wade came walking in. His eyes were red-rimmed, his jaw covered with a night's growth of stubble.

"You look like a man who could use an espresso."

"I feel like a man who could kill for one."

She laughed. He didn't.

"Did you get any sleep?"

"Some. Did you?"

"Some." Preoccupied, he sat down at one of the tables in the sunroom.

"Maybe you should skip the coffee and catch up on your sleep."

"Sleeping is just practicing to die. Actually, I'm looking forward to sorting through those boxes for you."

"Really? Why?"

"Maybe there's a story up there."

She fixed a fresh pot of extra-strong coffee and knew that if she didn't go back upstairs and pay the bills she'd intended to pay this morning, she was leaving herself open to temptation.

"Help yourself to some coffee and come

on up. I'll be in the kitchen upstairs paying bills."

She was proud of the way she made an exit, proving to herself that she did have a shred of both decency and discipline left when it came to resisting him. She was barely settled at the small desk tucked into one corner of the kitchen when the phone rang.

"Heartbreak Hotel," she answered automatically.

"Tracy?"

Tracy recognized Carly's voice on the other end of the line and smiled as she tucked the phone between her ear and shoulder and licked the envelope on the phone bill.

"We're home," Carly announced. She sounded excited.

"You had a good showing."

"Fabulous. I'm really picking up a following in Taos. How about you? Are you finished? Have you got a full house?"

"I'm finished for now, but I've got plenty of vacancies. The weather has been the pits around here lately."

"It's bound to get busy as soon as school's out tomorrow."

"Wade is still here."

There was silence on the other end of the

line and then a very speculative, "Oh?"

"He's on some kind of sabbatical. Well, actually, he's been helping around here, too."

"No kidding."

"Most of Diego's crew was hauled off by Immigration last week, so Wade stepped in and finished up." Before Carly could say anything, Tracy asked, "Did Jake have time to look over the books? I'd imagine you had him hopping with the show and all."

"He's right here. I'll let you talk to him."

Tracy straightened, ignoring the rest of the bills. Outside, the sun was making a valiant attempt to break through the clouds.

"Hey, Tracy. How's it going?"

"If you can make the sun shine, things will be better," she laughed. "What's up, Jake? Did you find anything?" She pictured Jake seated at his desk in his home office. The Montgomerys' 1920s Craftsman home was situated high on a hill on an old dirt road aptly named Lover's Lane.

"If it's all right with you, I'd like to do a little follow-up work before we meet."

"Follow-up?"

Tracy knew his fees were way out of her ballpark. He'd insisted she not mention paying him, but now he was obviously putting in extra time. "Jake, I'm not a charity case . . ."

"You know this is something I want to do gratis, Tracy. For you and for Matt. Don't even mention money and insult me."

"You know how much I appreciate this."

"We'll talk in a few days. I may have something concrete for you by then," he promised.

Concrete.

As she hung up, she found herself wondering what he'd discovered.

What did he find? Something that David Sylvester had missed? Or had David kept the truth from her?

CHAPTER TWENTY-SIX

A gentle but steady rain fell as Wade carefully made his way over to the dormer windows in the attic. The frames were warped, swollen by weather and time, and he was forced to pound on the corners with the heel of his hand until he was able to open them enough to let some air inside.

On the left side of the attic he'd stacked the newer boxes that Tracy had neatly labeled *Potter*. The contents were carefully listed on the outside. Those would definitely stay.

In front of her household things and keepsakes, he lined up the old, weathered boxes with labels of products he recognized. Whatever was inside had probably been packed within the last thirty or so years.

On the opposite wall he lined up the boxes and crates that appeared to be the oldest. Not only were most of the old cardboard boxes falling apart, there were wooden crates tacked shut with nails that had rusted long ago.

These were the boxes in which he was most interested, the ones he secretly hoped might hold a key to the history of the Heartbreak.

He sat on the floor beside what appeared to be one of the three oldest boxes. It yielded nothing but odds and ends — a bent silver candelabra so tarnished it was blueblack, the color of a bad bruise, a frosted glass cream and sugar set, and piles of receipts from department and dry goods stores.

He left the candelabra and glass pieces out in case Tracy wanted them, and then scooped up armfuls of paper receipts brittle as fallen leaves, stacked them, and carefully put them back in the box.

Next he opened an old crate full of moldy leather boots and shoes, all used, cracked, and weathered, many with the soles separating from the tops. He shoved them back inside and thought that at this rate, he'd be done in no time.

He carefully opened the top of the next box, and when he saw more mildewed leather, he expected another pile of shoes. After pulling back the top all the way, he realized the box was full of ledgers.

Hopeful that they might contain book-keeping records or guest registrations, he carefully lifted the first volume, cradled it in his lap, and opened the cover.

Ship's Log
The Lantana
January 1889

As Wade's hands gripped the leather-bound volume, his chest tightened around his heart. For a full thirty seconds he could neither move nor breathe.

1889. The Lantana.

He opened the first page, not knowing what to expect.

It was dated January 27, 1889, and listed the ship's cargo and destination as well as a few other navigational notes. Wade turned the page and there, at the bottom of the second page, the name *Ezra Poole, Ship's Captain* had been signed in thick, bold cursive.

Wade stared at the signature, then rubbed his eyes, hoping the letters might suddenly shift and rearrange themselves into some other name. Any other name.

But nothing happened.

Quickly, carefully, he began to turn the pages. The signature at the bottom of every entry was the same.

He tossed the log aside and grabbed another. By the time he'd scanned through five of them, he was more confused and shaken than ever.

He'd never laid eyes on these logs before, never been inside these walls before. Hell, he'd never even been in Twilight Cove or anywhere near the coast of California until a handful of weeks ago.

And yet here he sat holding on to physical proof that there was nothing fictional about the man he had somehow been induced to write about. Captain Ezra Poole had been a living, breathing human being.

There was no explanation as to how he had tapped into the captain's heart, mind, soul, or whatever it was he had accidentally tapped into. No logical, *believable* explanation anyway.

He slowly looked around the attic, at the dusty floor, the collection of crates and boxes, the mummified moths trapped in what was left of a few tangled spiderwebs, and began to wonder if any of this was real at all.

Maybe I'm already locked up in some loony bin, being spoon-fed medication and chocolate pudding.

Maybe none of this is real.

233

Maybe I killed myself and this is hell.

"Wade?"

When he heard Tracy's voice echoing up the narrow stairwell, he realized that if she was here, then this couldn't be hell.

He closed the logbook and shouted, "Come on up."

Her soft-soled shoes padded up the stairs. She paused just inside the door. Her smile faded the minute she met his eyes, and she hurried toward him.

"Are you all right?" Automatically she palmed his forehead, the way she might check her son for fever. "You're white as a sheet."

"As a ghost, you mean." He wanted to tell her that he was fairly certain now that ghosts didn't float around as ethereal apparitions. They took up residence in your head.

"What's wrong?"

"Maybe it's just the light."

"And maybe I'm Britney Spears." She glanced down at the dirty floor beside him, then dragged over a box labeled "books" and sat down. "I think maybe you should go downstairs. If you pass out, I'll never be able to get you out of here and neither will the paramedics."

"If I pass out, lock the door and leave me

up here to rot."

Hearing her laughter settled his nerves, at least a bit. If this whole thing was part of some vivid hallucination, then he was damn thankful she was in it.

"What's that?" She pointed at the leather-bound book on his lap.

"A ship's log."

"It looks old."

"It is." What would she say if he came right out and admitted to losing his mind?

When the candelabra caught her eye, she picked it up.

"This is amazing." She turned the heavy piece over and over in her hands before she set it down on the floor. "I'll see if I can bribe Matt into shining it for me. It would be fun to display it in the sitting room." She then picked up the sugar bowl.

"The creamer is cracked," he told her. It seemed like it was years ago, not mere minutes, that he'd unpacked them. When he looked away from the glass pieces, he found her staring at him intently.

"Your color is a little better, but not much." She sounded relieved. He wished he actually felt better. He wished he knew what in the hell was going on.

Their eyes met and held, until Tracy's

dropped to the log again. "Interesting read-ing?"

"It's from 1889."

"You're kidding." She held out her hand and he gave her the log, relieved to be rid of the thing. Tracy opened the cover, slowly, reverently, like someone who treasured old things for what they were. She leafed through a couple of pages, closed it, handed it back.

Wade ran his hand over the nubby front of the ledger; traced with his fingertip the worn gold leaf letters that spelled out *Ship's Log,* and pictured the signature at the bottom of every entry.

Ezra Poole, Ship's Captain.

"Listen, Wade, you don't have to do this now. I really think you should go lie down."

Go back to his room and get caught up in those dreams again? Go back and perhaps start writing things he didn't know one damn thing about? That wasn't an option right now.

First the copycat murders. Then the lawsuits. The death threats.

If he were smart, he'd burn the damn papers and notebooks and leave Captain Ezra Poole where he ought to be — ashes to ashes, dust to dust.

"Wade?"

236

"What?" He discovered that she was no longer perched on the box of books, but kneeling beside him in the dust. Suddenly her hand slid warmly over his, her expression a study in concern.

"Something's wrong," she said softly. "What is it? Please tell me."

Slowly he shook his head, never taking his eyes off of hers, clinging to them, hoping she could help save the last vestiges of his sanity.

"When I checked in here, I was . . . at a low point in my life. I didn't ever want to write again."

"Why? What happened?"

"Too much stress." Better that she thought him a stressed-out copywriter — one of those writers who comes up with catchy jingles and phrases to sell people all the crap they thought they needed — it was better than the raw truth.

"The night I checked in, I started having odd dreams. Odd in the sense that they were more real than dreams. I'd wake up compelled to write. I didn't want to, but I couldn't stop myself."

"That's good, isn't it?"

"The words were pouring out of me, but I had no notion of where they were coming from and very little recollection of what I'd written afterward." He couldn't bring himself to look at her, afraid of what her reaction might be. "It took me a few days before I had the courage to read what I'd written."

When he finally looked over at her, he found her leaning toward him, intent, listening. Caring. She nodded, encouraging him to go on.

"It was the story of a sea captain, a man who owned a sailing ship at the turn of the nineteenth century."

She sat back on her heels and smiled. "We hear the ocean day and night. I've seen you out walking the bluff. Surely the atmosphere inspired you."

He shook his head. "There's a lot more to it than that." Used to stroking a beard, he ran a hand over his lower jaw, wondered if he'd ever adjust to being clean-shaven. "I've written pages and pages, in great detail, about things of which I know nothing."

"You're an educated man . . ."

Like everyone else, she assumed he had a degree, but it didn't take a master's degree in English to be a storyteller.

"But I don't know a thing about navigating a clipper ship, or about life in California in the late 1800s."

Her fingers curled around his hand, her

eyes were warm and full of concern. He imagined that this was the way she spoke to Matt when he was upset, the way she'd given her husband unflinching support.

"You probably remember more than you realize from grade school. Matt's class has been studying early California this year; the settlement of the state, the missions, the gold rush. Kids are immersed in this stuff . . ."

"I wasn't raised in California." *And I was in and out of formal schooling.* "Believe me, I've never studied anything like this before."

She searched his face. "I don't understand."

"I don't either." He held the logbook toward her. "Take a look at the bottom of the first entry."

Her slim, tapered hands reverently cradled the large, musty book. She opened it slowly, taking great care with the yellow, brittle pages, and scanned the first entry. She turned the page, came to the bottom, and read aloud, "Ezra Poole, ship's captain."

Then she looked up, expectant.

"The story I've been working on is in the first person. The character narrating the tale is Captain Ezra Poole."

"Maybe it's just a coincidence," she said softly, though she sounded far from convinced. "Ezra is an old name. It certainly fits a character from the 1800s."

"*Captain Ezra Poole?* I even nailed his last name and the name of the ship."

She flipped back to the first page. When she looked up again, her expression was no longer thoughtful. She frowned, trying to piece the impossible together.

"You've never seen these logs before today, have you? You haven't been up here going through these boxes before today."

"You know I haven't."

Over the past few days when he'd been working for her downstairs and in the evenings, she'd been up in the apartment. She'd have to have seen him come in, or would have heard him walking around up there. Whenever she left to run an errand, she locked the apartment.

She gently laid her hand on his shoulder. "There has to be a logical explanation for this," she said softly, almost as if talking to herself.

"There is. I'm losing my mind."

CHAPTER TWENTY-SEVEN

He's either an Oscar-caliber actor who's lying about this whole scenario, or I'm lusting after a borderline nutcase.

Tracy didn't know whether to laugh or cry as she sat in the middle of the cluttered, dusty attic listening to him trying to explain something that made absolutely no sense. She realized that *if* he was telling the truth, then he was either insane, or he believed in the impossible.

"Okay," she said slowly, trying to come up with a rational explanation. "So after you checked in, you had strange dreams and felt 'compelled' to write. Consequently, you just *happened* to name your main character after a real ship's captain who lived in the 1800s."

He nodded. "A man who may have lived right here in the Heartbreak Hotel." His gaze shot to the box beside him, one that contained what looked like many more volumes of the *Lantana*'s logs.

241

"And you've written things you say you don't know anything about."

"I *know* I don't know anything about them. At least I never did before." He was still pale, though not as much as when she'd first walked in. Fabricating a story like this was one thing, but actually being able to make himself appear physically ill was another.

"I think we should go through the rest of the logs."

"I don't." He wouldn't give the box even another glance.

"Why not?" *Because they'd prove he's lying?* She didn't need another liar in her life.

"Because I already know what happens to him."

"To your character, you mean."

"*If* my character *is* Ezra Poole. I've written about how the *Lantana* was lost at sea during a storm sometime in 1901." He looked around the attic. "I think he may have lived here. I think that's why these logs were up here in the first place. Maybe that's why I'm here. Ezra needed someone to write his story."

In some secret spot in her heart, she had wanted to believe he had stayed because he was attracted to her on more than a physical level. That he was falling for her, as she

242

suspected that she was falling for him.

Was he trying to now tell her that he was here because some *spirit* wanted him here?

Slowly she got up and brushed off her pants. His eyes never left her.

"I want to read what you've written." It wasn't a request.

"You don't believe me?"

"I believe that *you* believe what you're telling me. I don't believe in ghosts."

"You don't have time to waste. You have other things to worry about right now."

"Like what? Who's going to rent the eight empty rooms I've got downstairs? Or about how long it might rain? Or if the roads are going to wash out like they did a few years ago? Should I sit around and stew about going broke before I can get this place off the ground?" She offered him a hand up. "Come on. It's still drizzling, the perfect kind of day to make a pot of tea and read by the fire. Maybe your story will keep my mind off of my real worries."

He took her hand but got up under his own power. He didn't let go of her fingers while they stood beneath the eaves, staring into each other's eyes.

He pulled her close. She didn't pull away.

She couldn't have walked away from the desperate need and confusion in his sad, dark eyes, not even if she'd wanted to. She went up on tiptoe and brushed her lips against his.

"Thank you," he whispered.

"For what?" She gently stroked his cheek with her fingertips.

"For not running screaming from the room."

She smiled slowly. "Hey," she said, squeezing his hand, "give me a chance. I still haven't read what's in those notebooks."

When I think I can take no more, when I'm certain I've endured my final day, my final hours on this desolate rock of an island, a pleasure craft sails into the cove and drops anchor.

Two young men, carefree, with too much time and money on their hands — what shock they must feel, watching me use my last burst of strength to scrabble to the top of the highest outcropping of rocks along the shore and wave the ragged scrap of what's left of my white linen shirt in frantic circles above my head.

I shout, but my voice is weak, like that of an ancient man who has outlived everyone he knows and yet refuses to die.

To have rescue so close, to have them sail away without me is unthinkable. I squint against the sunlight reflected in the dappled crescents that bob on the surface of the ocean.

And I am rewarded when they wave back. They sail closer, as close as they dare without risking their craft. Beside myself, I search the shore for just the right piece of driftwood, one small enough so I can still drag it into the water, one large enough that I can cling to it as I try to kick and float out to the sailboat.

Somehow I make it. Shocked exclamations, wide eyes, and warm hands greet me as the two men pull me onto the sailboat, where I lie like a fish out of water, gasping for breath.

"Where? How? Who?"

Their words and questions swirl around me. So foreign are the sounds of other voices by now that I struggle to make sense of what they are asking.

A year and a day. It sounds ridiculous. A year and a day since the *Lantana* went down with all hands and a full hold.

They recognize my name and that of my ship. Made the news we did, all of us lost souls. I learn that a few of the men survived, lived to tell the tale of the storm that came out of nowhere, of the way the ship broke up beneath us, and before we had a chance to man one lifeboat, she was gone.

They turn their craft and under full sail we cross the channel. They want to take me directly to Ventura, for immediate medical care.

I will not have it. I turn into the madman I must appear to be, with my tangled beard and gray hair streaming around my shoulders, with my wild eyes.

I want no doctor; no prodding. None of it. I must get home.

"You want to go sailing," I tell them, "then sail. Take me home, take me back to Gull Harbor." From there I will hitch a ride to the inn on the bluff. From there I'll go directly to my love.

They do not argue, but thankfully sail straight away. The sky is as blue as a robin's egg. The wind steady. The young men are on the adventure of a lifetime.

They'll tell their children's children of this day when they grow old. They'll tell of the day they plucked Captain Ezra Poole off the rocks and saved his life.

At Gull Harbor, old friends drop their lines, stop mending nets, run down the dock to greet my two companions, who are shouting and waving their straw hats above their heads.

"He's alive. Captain Ezra's alive!"

I am alive. Over and over I am forced to remind myself that God's little joke is over.

Everyone stares. Surely I must look like the walking dead, but then Refugio De La Raza steps up to me, takes my hand, and pumps my arm up and down before he pulls me into a bone-crushing embrace. The others crowd around.

It's a grand excuse to open a pint of whiskey. A grand way to celebrate a living wake for a dead man come to life.

"I'd love to stay, my friends," I fairly shout above their joyous congratulations, "but I've a fair young wife awaiting me and I've tarried long enough."

I expect them to greet the comment with peals of laughter and ribald jokes, but a pall of utter, deafening silence descends over one and all.

"What is it?" I say, my voice made weak again by the looks on their faces, and then by the way they all turn away without meeting my eyes. Terrified, I find the strength to roar, "What is it?"

Refugio takes my arm. I try to shake him off, but he clings like a wounded terrier. "Come with me, Ezra, old friend. Come along now."

I want to refuse, but the crowd has

drifted slowly away, one by one, two by two, with heads together.

Numb, quaking, I let him lead me over to a rotting bench that, like me, has been exposed to the elements, the salt air and the sun, the wind and the sea, for far too long.

He gently touches my shoulder and I slowly lower my brittle self to the bench. Ignoring the splinters protruding from the wood, my fingers wrap themselves around the edge, clinging.

Refugio sits beside me and stares out across the docks, past the boats bobbing at anchor.

"Violette is not there, Ezra." He speaks softly, reverently.

"She grew tired of waiting," I say. She was so young. So much younger than I, and so very lovely. The world would be too tempting for a young woman like her. A young woman believing herself a widow.

Refugio shakes his head. "No. She didn't leave you. She never gave up hope. Long after everyone else was convinced that you were gone, your wife, she clung to hope."

"But then —"

"Then it came time for her to birth the child."

"A boy?"

The dark-eyed sailor nods again. "A boy."

"I have a son." I turn and look into his eyes, old eyes sunken in a face dyed by the sun and creased by time. "Where have they gone?"

"She was a good girl. A good woman, the perfect wife. Every day she waited, watched for you. Every night passersby would see her on the widow's walk, watching for your ship. Long after we all knew the *Lantana* had been lost, she refused to believe."

"Where has she gone? Where are they?" I cry.

"Gone to heaven, Ezra. Gone together. The babe was stillborn. Violette died a few hours later. If it's any consolation, she died with your name on her lips."

I make him take me there, to the inn. He has an old buckboard wagon that bumps and tilts as it lumbers over the pocked dirt road that edges the bluffs.

I see the hotel, her father's folly, jutting tall against the sky. A place that demands to be noticed, the only silhouette where nothing else made by man mars the coastline.

The windows are tightly shuttered. I stumble down from Refugio's wagon and wave him on. "Go! Get away! Leave me!"

I've no use for him now. I've no use for the sorrow on his face. His sympathy means nothing to me. I do not yet believe it's all over.

It's not true. None of this is true. It can't be happening.

The door is locked. I reach over my head, feel along the doorjamb, and find the key. I turn the lock and, out of habit, replace the key before I step inside.

Without the sun streaming in the windows, the lobby is dark. The furnishings are gone, the room cavernously empty.

My bare feet slap against the fir floor as I cross the room, calling her name over and over and over.

"Violette! Violette! Violette!"

The emptiness echoes the sound of my own voice until I'm hoarse. I climb the stairs, search our rooms on the second floor. Where once there was so much love, so much laughter and joy, there is only a hollow void.

Someone has taken out all of the things that were left behind. I don't care. The only thing on earth I ever cared about was my beauty, my Violette, and later my unborn child.

And just as Refugio said, I find they

are gone.

I stagger down the dark, narrow hallway to the door that hides the stairs. I take them slowly, one at a time, barely able to lift my feet now that everything I once lived for has been taken from me.

At the landing, I choose the attic door. Her things are piled there, boxes of clothing that still hold her scent. I find her yellow dress, press it to my face, inhale.

I drop the silk into an empty cradle that has already gathered dust, and leave the attic.

I open the door to the widow's walk and step outside. The wind has picked up. It howls around the eaves and dormers, daring to caress this place that is filled to the rafters with heartbreak.

With heavy steps I shuffle to the center of the walk and stare out to sea, out to that spot on the horizon where she must have trained her gaze a thousand times or more, standing firm, clutching for hope with both hands when others tried to tell her to let go.

As I stare out at that far distant place where the sea and the sky become one, I am convinced that if there is a God, he is the most cruel of devils.

Why has he spared me, and not them?

Does he truly expect me to live without them?

The waves pound against the rocks below the bluff; singing a sirens' song, they call to me.

Somehow I make it back down the stairs. I find the strength to shuffle outside and head toward the light of the setting sun.

I look like Father Time standing there half naked on the bluff, my long hair turned silver; my beard blowing in the breeze.

I stand there on the precipice of sandstone and listen to the waves as they crash upon the rocks below. I stare directly into the sun as it quickly slips lower, until it has almost reached that place where it will sink beneath the green waters of the Pacific.

I wait, poised on the edge, knowing there is only one way I can be with them, knowing I haven't the courage or the nobility it would take to live out the rest of my life alone.

I take a deep breath, and at that exact moment when the sun touches the water, I lift my arms and shout, "Violette!" and with her name on my lips, I dive headfirst over the bluff.

And I smile. Finally, I smile again as I plummet toward the rocks below.

CHAPTER TWENTY-EIGHT

Tracy pressed her lips together and slowly closed the spiral notebook on her lap. Tears blurred her vision. The flames in the fireplace wavered and smeared as she watched them dance behind the screen.

Her breath hitched on a sigh. She looked over at Wade, who lay sprawled on the second sofa. He had been watching her from the moment she opened the first notebook. Drawn into the story, she'd quickly become immersed, almost forgetting he was there.

Almost — but with him so near, it was impossible to forget about him entirely.

She could tell he was awaiting a comment. She had so much to say, but struggled for the right words. Running her hand over the cover of the final notebook, she realized there was only so much that mere words could convey.

"It's beautiful," she said.

"It's downright weird. That's what it is."

"It's a wonderful story. But do you honestly have any idea whether or not this is true to Ezra Poole's life?"

He sat up, staring at her across the low, wide coffee table covered with magazines and travel guides. "I have no idea. I never even knew he actually existed until I found those logs this morning."

The shuttered emptiness she'd seen in his eyes the night he'd checked in was back. She made an instant decision.

"I'm going to call Carly and have her pick up Matt when she picks up Christopher. Go get your jacket." She stood up, sore from sitting in one position for so long. She glanced at her watch, couldn't believe how long it had been since she'd first sat down.

"Where are we going?"

"To Twilight, to talk to the one person who might know something about Ezra Poole. If we're lucky, we can kill two birds with one stone."

Palmer Biggs was a fixture in downtown Twilight who spent most of his time in front of the post office with his cronies, but he could almost always be found at mealtime in Selma's Diner.

He was also a past president of the Twilight Cove Historical Preservation Society, one of the groups that had blocked Glenn's bid to tear down the Heartbreak, and he was still on the board in an honorary position.

Palmer's lunch was spread out before him, half a tuna sandwich on wheat toast, a bowl of tomato soup, and a cup of coffee. The cellophane wrapper on a pack of saltines crackled as Palmer tore into it, crushed the crackers in his thick-fingered hand, and then sprinkled them on top of his tomato soup.

The minute Tracy and Wade walked in, Palmer recognized her. His smile revealed a set of teeth yellowed with age beneath a thick, white moustache. A San Francisco Giants ball cap covered his bald head.

"I saw Chelsea in here a while back, and she told me to stop by the hotel and see what you've been up to."

"I wish you would," Tracy invited. "I'm having an open house Saturday night. Please drop by, and bring some of the society board members if you like."

He nodded. "I'll do that."

"It starts at six-thirty."

Palmer's gaze strayed to Wade and stalled.

"This is Wade Johnson." She introduced them, looking over at Wade. "Would you mind if we join you, Mr. Biggs?"

"Nope. It's still a free country."

They slid into the booth together and sat thigh to thigh.

"Wade's from L.A. He's here doing some historical research," she explained. "I was hoping that if anyone could help him, you could."

"Maybe. Depends on what he's after."

Wade answered for himself. "I've been dabbling with a piece on turn-of-the-century life in the area."

"Writing something, you mean?" Palmer relaxed a bit.

"Yes. Exactly."

Palmer took a big bite out of the sandwich half, swallowed, and then nodded to Tracy. "I was afraid you were going to tell me he had some cockamamie plan for the hotel like your husband's. Thought maybe you would try to enlist my help in getting some changes past the board."

"Not at all."

Selma interrupted long enough to see if they wanted anything. When Wade ordered a hamburger with fries and a milk shake, Tracy thought: *What the heck? Why not challenge her cholesterol count, too?*

Wade slid to the edge of the seat and leaned on the table. "You know anything in particular about the Heartbreak Hotel?"

Palmer swallowed his last spoonful of soup and shoved the bowl aside. After he centered his coffee cup on the saucer, his gaze slowly drifted over to Tracy, then back to Wade.

"Like what?"

"Are there any records left about who might have built it, or the names of any former owners?"

"All the old building records burned in a fire in 1930."

"You know anything about the California sea trade back in the late 1800s?"

"Some. Want to narrow it down a bit?".

"Did a Captain Ezra Poole ever live around here?"

"Why would you be asking about old Ezra?"

"Did you actually know him?"

"Hell, I'm not that old!" Palmer chuckled and then sobered. "He lived around here, sure. But I suppose you already know that or you wouldn't be asking. What are you up to?"

Tracy felt Wade's hand on her knee. He gave it a gentle squeeze. When she looked over at him, he was still leaning across the table, toward Palmer, his expression intent.

"I was helping Tracy clean out some old boxes in the attic this morning when I came across some ship's logs that had belonged to Ezra Poole."

For the first time since they had sat down, Palmer perked up and looked genuinely interested. "Ship's logs? From 1900?"

Wade nodded. "Some from the late 1800s. There are quite a few."

The conversation lulled when Selma came back with the shakes. Palmer was ignoring his coffee, pinning Tracy. His eyes were thoughtful beneath frosty eyebrows sprouting every which way like overgrown hedges.

"So what do you know about Poole?" Wade wanted to know.

Palmer finished his coffee and signaled Selma for a refill.

"He sailed the coast for thirty years, lived in a small settlement above Gull Harbor. There's nothing over there now but a small boat harbor and a restaurant."

Tracy felt Wade's fingers tighten on her knee. She didn't know whether to reach for his hand beneath the table and hold on tight or to get up and run as far and as fast as she could. None of the pieces fit anymore.

If Wade had researched Ezra Poole before he knocked on the hotel's door that cold and misty night, why not come right out and tell her? What motive would he have for fabricating this whole bizarre scenario? She would have gladly helped him. Not only that, but the trepidation she felt that first night would have been diminished had she known that he was a writer on a research mission.

"Do you know if Ezra was ever lost at sea?" Wade's voice was low and hesitant, almost as if he didn't really want to hear the answer.

"I thought you didn't know anything about him," Palmer said.

Wade shrugged, noncommittal. "I'm not sure how much of what I've learned is true."

"His ship went down, oh, I can't remember the particulars, I think sometime around 1900. Ezra washed up on one of the small islands near Anacapa. Survived like Robinson Crusoe for almost a year. When he finally made it home, he learned his wife had died in childbirth." Palmer stopped, taking a dramatic, pregnant pause. He heaved a great sigh and slowly shook his head.

A shiver slipped down Tracy's spine. She whispered, "Then he killed himself," effectively taking the wind out of Palmer's sails.

The old man's lips tightened. "Nobody knows what happened to him." He looked at them both. "So what did you come to me for, exactly?"

While they were talking, Selma had slipped up to the table with two hamburger combos. It was a rare moment when Selma was rendered speechless.

She set down their lunch order and wanted to know, "Then how *did* the captain kill himself?"

Tracy was afraid she already knew, but she waited for Palmer to verify it. Palmer was eyeing Tracy and Wade curiously. "Like I said. Nobody knows. He disappeared the day he was rescued. The day he found out his wife and child were gone. Never saw hide nor hair of him again."

Selma shook her head. "Haven't you all got anything better to do? It's gloomy enough with this damned weather," she grumbled. She grabbed a coffeepot from the table behind them and filled Palmer's coffee cup before she turned to Wade and Tracy, indicating their plates. "Eat up, kids."

Then she leaned over the table, winked at Wade, and gave him a flirtatious smile. "Handsome devil like you has to keep up his strength."

Doubting if she could taste the burger now that Palmer had confirmed what Wade had already written about Ezra, Tracy forced a smile. "Thanks, Selma. This looks great."

"I've got some really tasty strawberry pie for dessert. You want some, Palmer?"

"You buying?" he asked Tracy.

"I am," Wade said quickly.

Palmer nodded to Selma. "I'll have a piece." The minute she was gone again, he turned to Wade. "There's more to this than what you're both telling me, I can see it on your faces." He glanced around the near-empty restaurant.

"Don't you wonder why no one has ever made a go of the Heartbreak Hotel?" Palmer looked directly at Tracy. "You aren't the first person to try. The last owners were a couple from San Francisco. Came down here in the late sixties, kept the place open for a year and a half before they went belly-up. They locked up and left without looking back. Never able to sell the place even, not until your husband came along and bought it off them for a song."

Her appetite gone, Tracy picked up a fry, barely dipped it into a puddle of ketchup, bit the tip off of it, set it back down.

"Some folks in my father's generation might have been able to recall some stories about Ezra from when they were kids. I don't know any particulars, just that they used to say there was something strange about the place."

Selma arrived with Palmer's pie. He waited until she'd walked away. Tracy realized she'd been holding her breath. She let it go, fought to relax.

"My father always claimed the place was haunted."

Great. Almost flat broke and I own a haunted hotel.

It was easier to believe that Wade had lied about not researching Ezra Poole long before he checked in. But did that mean that he somehow knew about the logs and had gotten close to her in order to have access to the attic? Had he somehow *known* that the *Lantana*'s logs were there?

How?

And if so, why had he looked so genuinely stunned and shaken when she'd found him sitting there this morning? Why was he so shocked to find exactly what he'd been looking for?

Palmer milked the moment, taking time to eat the whole piece of strawberry pie and then wipe his mouth on the paper napkin before he raised his eyes.

"You really ought to try some of this. It's great," he urged.

Tracy was ready to leap over the table and

choke him. Instead, she clenched her hands together in her lap.

"Why doesn't anyone talk about the hotel being haunted now? I've lived here almost ten years and I've never heard that before. Why didn't anyone mention it to me before I moved in? I would have thought that someone would have said something, or joked about it anyway."

"Anyone who was alive then is either gone, or was too young at the time to remember much about it now. The hotel has had a run of bad luck almost since it was built, with no real explanation for it. The place was empty for over forty years before you moved in."

Run of bad luck? A hundred years, give or take a few; is more than a run of bad luck.

Palmer set down his fork and stared at the pie plate as if contemplating licking it clean before he looked at Wade again.

"Whatever made you start researching Captain Ezra anyway? The only piece we have about him is a short clipping from a San Francisco paper. Tells about his being rescued, and about how he disappeared the same day. Never was seen or heard of again. That's it."

Tracy couldn't take her eyes off Wade. This was his chance to prove that she hadn't made a fool of herself by trusting him. He leaned back against the booth, stretched his arm around Tracy's shoulders. She could feel him toying with a lock of her hair. His posture appeared casual, as if he were completely relaxed, and yet she could feel tension radiating from him.

"I stumbled across his name one day and thought he might make an interesting subject."

"You still have the article or piece you 'stumbled across'?" Palmer wanted to know.

"Not with me."

Tracy's heart felt as if it were caught in a vise. She was having trouble breathing. It was all she could do to not get up and walk away.

CHAPTER TWENTY-NINE

She's pissed.

Wade saw all the doubt and questions in Tracy's eyes and wished that he could take her hand and pull her out of the diner, take her to some quiet place overlooking the ocean, and set her mind at ease.

But he couldn't exactly reason with her when there was nothing reasonable about any of this.

Ezra Poole, it seemed, had lived and breathed and died — and if what he'd written was true, he'd jumped off the bluff behind the Heartbreak.

And if, *if* any of this was possible — and he still had serious doubts — then why?

Why me? And, more to the point, *how?*

How had he tapped into the story? How had he gotten all of the facts right?

The old man across the table was eyeing him suspiciously now, perhaps taking a clue from Tracy, who'd gone very still. She'd barely touched her burger.

He kept his arm draped around her, tried to reassure her — pretty impossible when he was a ball of confusion himself. Gently squeezing her shoulder, he watched her turn her wide, troubled gaze his way.

"I should be getting back." There was no smile in her eyes now, none of the warmth in her voice he'd grown accustomed to. "Matt gets out early today."

He nodded in understanding. Matt had nothing to do with her need to get home, and they both knew it. No doubt she was making an excuse, needing to put distance between them.

Wade signaled Selma, and she immediately hurried over to the table. After he asked for the check, the three of them sat in uncomfortable silence in the booth.

Palmer folded his hands and rested his forearms on the table. "Maybe old Ezra will make an appearance at that open house shindig you're throwing on Saturday night," Palmer laughed. "That would sure have everybody talking about him again."

Tracy seemed preoccupied, though Wade watched her attempt a smile. "That's all I'd need."

"Could be good for business," Palmer speculated, "having a resident ghost."

"You think so?" Wade asked.

Palmer shrugged. "It takes all kinds."

Before Tracy slid out of the booth, she looked at each of them in turn and then said, "I'd appreciate it if *neither* of you says one word about Ezra Poole to *anyone* on Saturday night."

It was drizzling again by the time they finally left the diner. A gunmetal gray sky draped with low clouds matched Tracy's mood as she drove back to the Heartbreak.

Her mind was racing faster than the engine of the BMW as she replayed their conversation with Palmer over and over, thoroughly convinced that she obviously couldn't tell the truth from a lie.

Glenn had kept the truth from her, and now Wade? She could understand Glenn not wanting to admit his failure. His ego wouldn't let him admit to her that they were ruined. Perhaps he hadn't even been able to admit it to himself.

But why would Wade lie his way into her life?

Was Chelsea right? Was he looking just for sex? She let her gaze slide over to where he sat silent and brooding in the passenger seat. With his looks and intelligence, he could get sex anywhere.

267

Obviously, he specifically came to locate the *Lantana*'s logbooks.

How much would he have to gain by getting his hands on Ezra Poole's logs, other than to verify his research? Had he been searching for other documents that might have been stored in the attic? If so, what had led him to believe they might be there?

What did he have to gain from writing Ezra's story?

She waited until they were alone inside the empty lobby before she confronted him.

"Did you come here intentionally looking for those logs?" she asked without preamble, unwilling, unable, to suffer any intimacy. Fearing that if she gave him the chance to touch her first, his charm might melt her anger. "Did you come looking for research material on Ezra Poole?"

She was so upset that she was shaking, so she paced over to the fireplace and took her time straightening its screen until she heard him step up close behind her.

"Look at me, Tracy."

Just as she feared, he reached for her, his hands closing around her upper arms, gently but firmly, forcing her to look at him.

"I never heard of Ezra Poole in my life before I walked through the front door."

"You had to have known something about

him. There's no way I can believe anything else."

"Believe what you want. There's no way *I* want to believe what happened, either; but I'm telling you the truth." Frustration creased his brow. When he raised his eyes, there was obvious confusion in them. "I have no idea what in the hell is going on."

"Have you actually *seen* anything?"

"If you mean a ghost? No."

She felt trapped between him and the fireplace, but not afraid. She lifted her chin, dared him to try to cajole her into believing him. He pulled her closer, raking her face with his gaze.

"I haven't lied to you about any of this," he said softly.

"You say that as if you have lied about something." She searched his eyes for the truth, prayed she'd be able to recognize it if it was there. Despite her doubts, her anger and distrust, she wanted to kiss him. She wanted him to make this whole thing go away, to make her forget about the logs and the heartbreaking story she'd read in his notebooks. It was impossible to tear her gaze away from his lips.

He lowered his voice to a whisper. She felt his warm hands on her arms, felt the heat of his palms through the sleeves of her jacket. She could almost taste him. "I wish to God I knew what was going on here."

"And I wish I could believe that, but I find it impossible." She lowered her eyes, hoping to break the spell he had on her.

She refused to be taken advantage of. No matter what else she might feel for him, she *had* to be able to trust him. She wasn't so desperate or so lonely that she would allow herself to fall in love with someone who couldn't be completely honest with her. Not again.

He was so close, she inhaled the scent of the wind and the salt and the sea mingled with his soap and shaving cream. She closed her eyes, wishing they could go back to the easy camaraderie they'd shared before he found the logs. She ached to kiss him. Longed for the thrill, the rush she'd felt last night when he'd held her in his arms.

It hurt to realize that she was already addicted to him even though he'd given her no reason to think that anything would come of their time together. She hadn't planned on falling for him, hadn't thought beyond the moment. She couldn't — not while doubting his motives.

Tugging out of his grip, she started to walk away.

He reached for her, catching her by the

wrist. "Tracy, listen —"

A gust of damp air hit them as the front door opened and Matt and Christopher came racing in. Wade let her go.

"Mom! I won a Citizen of the Year award at the last-day assembly." Matt ran around the sofa and thrust a construction paper folder at her.

She opened it, saw the certificate with an official-looking gold seal inside. He had, indeed, been chosen as one of Twilight Cove Elementary's Best Citizens of the Year.

"I'm so proud of you! We'll have to get a frame for this right away." She handed it back and went down on one knee to give Matt a hug, closed her eyes, and held on tight. This was truth. This was real. This was her world.

Fortified, she straightened.

He beamed up at her so proudly that she couldn't resist cupping his smooth cheek and smiling down into his eyes before she greeted Christopher, too.

"Wanna see, Wade?" He held the certificate up for inspection.

"That's great, Sport."

As Matt beamed up at Wade, Tracy focused on Christopher.

"Where's your mom?"

"She'll be here in a minute. She's in the

car checking her voice mail."

"How was your trip to Taos?" Tracy hoped Wade would leave. She couldn't face him right now. She needed time to think, impossible with him so close by.

Chris shrugged. "It was okay. Mom had to do a lot of art stuff."

"Wanna go upstairs and play Game Boy?" Matt asked Chris.

"Sure."

"There are some cookies in the jar," Tracy offered. "If you pour yourselves some milk, try not to make a mess."

With a rush of backpacks, rain jackets, and heavy athletic shoes, they ran out of the room. The silence the two exuberant boys left in their wake was deafening.

When Wade took a step in Tracy's direction with his hand extended in open invitation, she wanted so badly to take it, to believe him, that she ached all over — but he was asking her to believe the unbelievable.

"Carly's on the way in." She glanced at the front door, willing Carly to appear. She was mentally exhausted. She could ignore his hand but not his eyes, and as much as she'd like to, she was powerless to dismiss him, to walk away.

"I know it's asking a lot for you to believe

me," he said softly.

"Can we just drop this for now? *Please?* I have a day and a half before the open house and I don't need this right now." She met his eyes at last. "Any of it."

"You want me to leave?"

"You mean —"

"Check out."

"That's not necessary." Was her heart showing?

I want you to stay. I want you to tell me this was all some kind of a bad joke. Instead she said, "You're paid up through Monday."

He closed the gap between them again. "If that's the only reason you want me here, forget it, keep the money."

"Wade, please."

"Please what?"

"Give me time to think this through."

Just then Carly walked through the door. The spell was broken.

"I'm going out, but I'll be back," he promised. He nodded to Carly but didn't smile, and walked out without looking back.

Tracy watched Carly follow Wade with her eyes and answered Carly's question before she asked it.

"Wade's still staying here." She tried to hide her confusion, but Carly knew her too well.

"But something's up. Are you all right?"

"I'm fine." Tracy started toward the apartment stairs. "Come on up and tell me all about Taos. Would you like a glass of wine?"

Carly followed her through the lobby. "Since when do you have a glass of wine this early? I'll take a diet soda."

Since I started acting like an idiot over a guy who communicates with a ghost.

"I guess since it's the last day of school and the open house is almost here. And to welcome you home." Her steps faltered when she heard the Harley start up. It was none of her business where Wade was going. None at all.

Once they were upstairs and settled, Carly kept up a steady stream of chatter, filling her in about the art show in Taos.

Finally able to think of something other than Wade, Tracy commented, "Jake said there were a couple things he wanted to look into before he talked to me about the accounts, but he didn't go into detail. Has he said anything to you about what he's looking for?"

"No. He wouldn't ever do that without talking to you first." Carly finished her soda. "Are you sure everything is ready for the open house?" Carly asked.

"Pretty much. I'm going to start working

on the appetizers tomorrow, the ones I can do ahead. We're just having finger food, coffee, tea, and wine in the sunroom. I'll have some guest rooms open for viewing."

"Sounds great. I'll come over early to help you set up."

"You don't have to. Chelsea will be here."

"I know I don't *have* to," Carly told her. "I want to."

"Are you sure?"

"Of course." Carly smiled. "I'm looking forward to it. Jake can join me later and bring Chris. I know everything is going to be just perfect. Pretty soon this will be the hottest place on the coast."

The hottest place on the coast.

Tracy couldn't help but wonder what Carly would say if she told her that not only was Palmer Biggs predicting the hotel was doomed to fail, but that the mysterious hunk living downstairs was trying to convince her that he was channeling the resident ghost's life story.

Wade rode slowly down an avenue where jacaranda trees grew so tall and so full of lavender blossoms that their branches arched over the street, creating a tree tunnel alive with color. Well-manicured homes lined both sides of the street.

Sparing them quick glances, he wondered what it would have been like to grow up in a town like this, to know the neighbors, to make friends. What would it have been like to attend the same school for years, go to parties, play on a sports team?

Would he have written *An Even Dozen* if he had grown up here instead of in seedy apartments in New York? Would he have been able to plumb that level of darkness in his soul? Probably. He was a writer. Former housewives from the Midwest came up with equally gruesome thrillers.

He pulled over to the curb near a corner and asked directions to the local library. It was situated on a small grassy park, not much more than a triangular wedge of grass with some ficus trees for shade and a couple of benches. The library itself was light and airy inside. Two walls were a combination of bookshelves and floor-to-ceiling glass windows. The one-story layout was nothing like the old brick-and-mortar libraries he'd haunted when he lived in the city. Compared to those, this one was in its infancy. Still, he found the collection of local archives fairly complete.

But just as Palmer had said, there was nothing on Ezra Poole except for a newspaper article that had been photocopied and added to a small pamphlet detailing the beginnings of Twilight Cove and nearby Gull Harbor. The librarian affirmed that Twilight Cove's original building department records had been destroyed when the old wooden city hall structure had burned down in the thirties.

He spent three hours reading through volumes on the history and importance of shipping up and down the California coast, and then went through a stack of picture books that had detailed drawings of clipper ships and steamers. It should have amazed him when the drawings and paintings validated his descriptions. It should have, but it only stirred more questions than answers.

He couldn't shake the vivid images he'd had of Ezra and Violette. Given all that had happened, there was no longer any doubt in his mind that she had existed, but, unlike Ezra, who had made a name for himself only in that he'd survived the shipwreck, she had joined the legion of others who passed through the pages of history without leaving a discernible mark — unless there was some way to find a birth, marriage, or death certificate for her.

On his way out, he stopped at the information desk again to ask the librarian, "Would the birth, death, and marriage records prior to 1930 have been in the old city hall?"

She nodded immediately. "I'm afraid so."

"There wouldn't have been copies filed anywhere else?"

"Not that I know of."

Another dead end. He didn't know whether to feel frustrated or relieved.

"You're paid up through Monday." Tracy's words echoed through his mind.

He picked up some Thai takeout food before heading back to the hotel. With every passing mile he thought about the doubt, the hurt, and the confusion in Tracy's eyes. How did he expect her to believe him, to trust him, when he didn't believe what was happening himself?

He had never intended to fall in love with her. He didn't think he had it in him to let anyone in anymore. He'd stayed because he wasn't ready to walk away from her. He'd also stayed in order to help her. He'd never meant to hurt her, and yet he had.

What would she do if he told her he was a novelist? And about his pseudonym and why he hadn't been perfectly honest with her from the beginning?

"You're paid up through Monday."

He wanted to stay and yet he wasn't ready to reveal who he was, not even to Tracy. He thought he could trust her to not tell anyone. Surely she wasn't upset enough to expose him and turn his world upside down. But if he stayed, if she *let* him stay and become more a part of her life, he'd have to tell her everything, and he'd be handing her yet another reason to not trust him.

She and her son were putting their lives back together. If his identity were exposed, he'd be risking their privacy. Seeing that *People* magazine yesterday proved that.

She'd be better off without him around.

CHAPTER THIRTY

At 5:30 on Saturday evening, Tracy made certain that her pearl earrings were on tight and gave her retro French twist hairstyle a last glance before she walked out of the bedroom.

"Chelsea? Carly?" she called down the hall. "I'm going on downstairs."

"I'll be right down," Chelsea shouted from behind her closed door.

On a cloud of steam, Carly stuck her head and shoulders out of the bathroom. "You look great, Trace! I'll join you in five minutes. All I have to do is get dressed." She'd been there since two in the afternoon, helping to set up.

Downstairs, votive candles were scattered all over the sitting area and the sunroom. With the low-light sconces on the walls, the romantic lighting hid the imperfections that no amount of paint would cover.

Carly had picked up flowers at the farmer's market and arranged a multitude of small bouquets. They'd set out wineglasses and put chilled bottles of white wine in an old-fashioned aluminum tub of ice on a side table.

The cold buffet was a combination of appetizers Tracy had made herself along with finger sandwiches and tidbits she'd ordered from the local bakery and deli. It was a splurge, but one she'd carefully budgeted for.

Everything in the rooms and public areas looked just the way she wanted it to. In an hour, the sunroom windows would show off the spectacular sunset view, the bluff, and the coastline. A peaceful, relaxed atmosphere pervaded the sitting room. For a heartbeat she wished she could cancel the evening's affair and sink into the overstuffed sofa with a glass of wine and simply relax.

If she could turn back the clock two days, if she and Wade could go back to the way they'd been then, she would like nothing more than sharing the quiet, romantic atmosphere with him in private.

She'd heard him come and go the past couple of days — the sound of the Harley's distinctive engine hard to miss. Last night she'd almost ventured downstairs to knock on his door; but she was afraid that instead of voicing her concerns again, she would end up in his arms. This morning he'd left around ten and was gone most of the day. She'd been out picking up the party trays when he got back.

It was hard not to be moved by the setting she'd created here tonight. The rooms were perfectly romantic, a candlelit glimpse back to the turn of the century. She'd even talked Matt into polishing the candelabra that Wade had found in the attic. Complete with tall ivory tapers, it graced the middle of the coffee table.

She tried to convince herself that it was the candlelight and flowers, not her feelings for Wade, that stirred such longing in her and had her wishing they could be here alone tonight. She'd been planning the open house for so long that the idea of calling it off to be with Wade took her by surprise.

When the front door opened, she stopped musing and headed across the lobby to greet the first arrivals. Not surprising, Palmer Biggs, accompanied by Eloise Simpson and Vivian Ames, members of the historical society board.

Eloise, the senior of the two, took her time studying the lobby and sitting room and then announced, "I haven't been in here since I was a child. It's a shame this place was hardly ever open. It's such a stunning piece of turn-of-the-century architecture."

"The century just rolled around again," Palmer reminded her. Eloise snorted.

At Palmer's insistence, Tracy began to give them a tour until Carly came downstairs and quickly volunteered to take over. After they walked away, the huge empty lobby echoed with silence. Tracy walked over to the registration desk, straightened the huge registration logbook, then wandered over to the front window and arranged the folds of the lace curtains.

No one else appeared until Jake and Chris walked in a few minutes later.

As Chris took off upstairs to find Matt, Jake gave Tracy a hug and his congratulations. "Where's my wife?" He looked around the empty rooms.

"Giving a tour. Let me get you a glass of wine." Tracy led the way into the sunroom with Jake following close on her heels. Though his greeting had been filled with warmth, she'd sensed a hesitation. An uncomfortable silence stretched between them as she poured him a glass of wine and handed it to him with a cocktail napkin.

He seemed hesitant about something. She watched him take a sip of wine and look around before he said, "I was wondering if you'd have time to meet with me about Glenn's books tomorrow."

She knew by his tone that something was wrong, but whatever he had to tell her about Glenn would be better than not knowing what had gone wrong — and from the look on Jake's face, something was definitely wrong.

What if Glenn was into drugs?

What if that was where the money had all gone?

What had he kept from her?

"Certainly. What's a good time for you?" She tried to sound as if she weren't nervous, as if meeting with a P.I. was something she did every day. But this was, after all, Jake, and he was a friend.

"How about two o'clock tomorrow? We usually go out to breakfast on Sunday mornings."

We.

Two years ago, Carly had been a single mother struggling to make ends meet. Who would have thought their roles would have been so completely reversed? Tracy tried not to envy them, Jake and Carly and Chris. They were a family now, with family traditions to uphold.

"Two is great." She wished they could go upstairs right now and that Jake could lay it all out for her. Two o'clock tomorrow was a lifetime away.

"There's my girl." Jake spotted Carly walking into the sunroom with Palmer and the others. "I'll take her some wine and save her from Biggs."

Tracy watched with mixed emotions as Jake walked over to the tub of chilled wine bottles to get his wife a drink.

"You look beautiful tonight."

The sound of Wade's warm voice so close to her ear sent ribbons of chills unfurling along her spine. Resisting the urge to lean back into him, she took a deep breath and slowly turned around. The moment she laid eyes on him, she was stunned by the change.

Instead of his usual black T-shirt and Levis, he wore a long-sleeved ivory polo shirt and pleated chocolate slacks that matched his eyes. A pair of designer loafers completed his outfit.

The upscale look was so totally incongruous to the way she'd come to think of him that for a moment she was speechless.

"Are you all right?"

She slowly nodded. "Just surprised. You look . . . you look so . . ."

"Good?" He never teased. Somehow it raised the level of intimacy between them another notch. Strangers didn't tease.

Handsome. Delicious. Sane. She couldn't stop staring.

"Different." She realized that he must have been out shopping most of the day. "You look different."

He stepped closer. "I thought I'd better not show up looking like hired help."

He reached over and straightened her collar for her and his hand brushed the back of her neck. Heat spread from the nape of her neck to her hips, knees, and then toes. She reminded herself to breathe.

"Truce for tonight?" he offered.

"Truce," she agreed softly.

He turned and picked up a small plastic box that she hadn't noticed before. A florist's box. A corsage box.

Her heart started slamming against her rib cage. No one had given her a corsage since her high school prom in Marshall.

"For me?"

He shook his head no. "I was going to wear it myself but it doesn't go with my shirt."

She watched him carefully pry open the corner of the box. The plastic lid popped as the top flew up to reveal a perfect gardenia blossom.

She bit her lips and savored one of his rare smiles, surprised at the care he took as he lifted the corsage and held it out to her.

"Can you . . . would you mind?" She adjusted her collar so he could pin the corsage on her shoulder.

He drew the long pearl-headed corsage pin out of the florist's tape around the stem, and hesitated.

"I've never done this before," he confessed.

"Never?"

"No."

They both moved at once. She stepped closer. He leaned over her and they bumped heads.

"Sorry," she apologized.

"No. I'm sorry."

"Don't be," she whispered, half ashamed of all the things she suspected him of, still afraid that he had lied.

But tonight was special. Tonight was the night she'd worked so hard for. He'd helped her get here, too. Worked alongside her most of the week.

Tonight they'd called a truce and she intended to enjoy the fruits of her labor.

She tried to see the corsage on her shoulder. "It's beautiful."

"No, you're beautiful." His low, husky voice sent another shiver down her spine. "And as much as I hate to let you go, you should circulate." He reminded her that they weren't alone, and for that she was thankful. There was no telling what she'd do if they weren't. No telling what she'd be willing to believe tonight.

She looked over at Palmer Biggs, who was working his way through a tray of appetizers as his friends from the society awkwardly stood by.

Aside from Carly, Jake, and the boys, they were still the only arrivals. Chelsea was downstairs now, stationed in the sitting area near the front door.

"What if no one shows up?" With literally no outside invited guests there yet, she couldn't help but worry.

Wade took her hand, held it between his where no one in the room could see that they were touching.

"Then the others would probably leave early. Would that be so bad?" he said softly.

She looked up in surprise, caught him smiling. His dark hair glistened blue black in the candlelight. His eyes were warm, his smile inviting.

He made it oh so easy to forget her concerns. Forget what he'd told her about Ezra Poole.

Seeing him now acting perfectly sane, looking like something out of *GQ* magazine with his hand, solid and warm, around hers, she realized that it wouldn't take much to convince her that maybe *she* was the crazy one for doubting him.

As much as he hoped for her sake that everyone she had invited did show tonight, Wade had been relieved when he walked in and found the room nearly empty.

Though he risked being recognized tonight, the look on Tracy's face when she saw him made taking the chance worthwhile. She'd been shocked by his appearance — which wasn't surprising given that he'd been wearing the same Levis for two weeks. What astonished him was the depth of his relief when he realized that her anger and doubt had diminished.

He found himself wishing that he could lead her down the hall to his room and make love to her.

Damn the party. Damn Ezra Poole.

Damn his own past.

Since the first time he'd kissed her he'd fantasized about losing himself in her, slipping the pins from her upswept hair, letting it fall loose and free around her shoulders. For the first time in forever, he truly wanted to get to know a woman deeply.

"That would be awful," she said forlornly.

"What?" Shaken out of his fantasy, he looked into her worried eyes and remembered that he'd asked her if it would be so bad if no one showed up.

"It would be just terrible if no one came."

Her disappointment and anxiety were clear as she gave his hand a quick squeeze, let go, and looked around the nearly empty public rooms.

"Why wouldn't they come? Free food and wine, a chance to see a great new hotel right on the water?" As much as he wanted her all to himself, as much as he wanted to hide, he still wouldn't wish this night to be a disaster. She'd worked too hard, planned too long.

"At least it's not raining." He hoped to put her mind at ease, but she wasn't smiling.

"There's always so much going on around here. People are so busy —"

"Give it a while. It's early yet."

She glanced over at the trays of appetizers. "I ordered too much food."

"Palmer looks like he's doing his share to remedy that."

Mentioning Biggs brought back the scene in town, but Tracy's thoughts were obviously elsewhere. He followed her gaze and noticed a well-dressed couple walking

through the front door.

"That's Natalie Barnes, president of the Twilight Cove Chamber of Commerce, and her husband," she said in a hush.

When she started to walk away, then suddenly stopped and looked back apologetically, he encouraged her. "Go. I'll help myself to some wine."

"Thank you for the corsage." She reached up, tenderly fingering the blossom.

He didn't move until he'd watched her walk across the lobby. When he turned around, Palmer Biggs and two companions near Palmer's age were bearing down on him.

"Johnson," Palmer nodded, staring up at Wade from beneath his bushy brows.

"Mr. Biggs." Wade introduced himself to the women.

"You able to find out anything more about Ezra?" Palmer wanted to know.

The taller of the two women was beaming at him. "I'm so glad that someone your age has taken up an interest in one of the area's most colorful and least-known personalities, Mr. Johnson."

"Thanks, but call me Wade." He tried to keep his mind on the conversation, but his gaze kept drifting over to Tracy, who was still with the chamber president. They were moving closer, headed for the sunroom. The last thing he wanted was for her to overhear him discussing Ezra again. Not tonight.

He casually glanced at his watch and then tried to appear as disappointed as possible.

"I'm really sorry, but I need to check on something for Tracy. Will you excuse me?"

The ladies looked upset, but Palmer was already gazing over at the buffet again.

Wade made a quick exit out the side door.

CHAPTER THIRTY-ONE

Natalie Barnes complimented Tracy on all the progress she'd made and asked important questions about her plans for the Heartbreak. All the while, Tracy was completely aware of Wade as she watched him smoothly escape Palmer, Eloise, and Vivian.

"I'm glad that you've listed the hotel with the chamber secretary. Tourists are always stopping in the visitor center looking for last-minute accommodations. You're sure to pick up some bookings through us. I can't imagine you'll have many vacancies, though." Natalie paused to look around. "This is beautiful. Isn't it, Patrick?"

Patrick Barnes looked more interested in the view outside the sunroom windows. The setting sun performed on cue, staining the sky with red, orange, and peach hues just above the horizon line. The ocean surface was glassy this evening with gently undulating swells rolling toward the bluff.

Natalie took the glass of wine that Tracy offered. "I've never been in here before; then again, neither has anyone else. As far back as I can recall, this place has been boarded up. You're certainly lucky it wasn't a complete teardown."

Lucky? As Tracy looked around, she realized she was lucky. Much more than she thought the first time she set eyes on the interior of the Heartbreak.

Natalie shook her head. "I hope you get a good crowd tonight. We almost didn't make it on such short notice."

Tracy didn't think three weeks was short notice.

Natalie smoothly grabbed a cocktail napkin and an appetizer. "I'm so glad Chelsea called Wednesday to give us a heads-up about the invitation being on the way."

"Did you say Chelsea called?" Tracy thought she had surely misunderstood.

"Yes. Wednesday. To give us a heads-up about the invitation. That was good thinking."

"I'll have to thank her." Tracy glanced around and saw Chelsea beside Carly near the French doors that led out to the porch. They appeared to be in an intense discussion.

Carly looked as serene as always. Though

casually dressed in a sleeveless pastel knit top and a long black skirt, her natural beauty and inner glow made her the kind of person that everyone felt comfortable with, old, young, or in between.

Twenty minutes later, Tracy had made all the excuses she could make to the Barneses without embarrassing herself and them. Time and again, Natalie reiterated that earlier invitations would have *certainly* helped fill the room. Tracy walked them to the door and bid them good night.

No one had to tell her that her open house was a complete disaster. The sunroom was dismally empty except for herself and the Barneses and Palmer, and his friends, who had taken up squatters' rights at one of the sunroom tables, loaded plates with appetizers, and helped themselves to more wine. The senior contingent was settled for the night.

Jake, Christopher, and Matthew had all disappeared.

Wade, too. Even Chelsea and Carly were no longer inside.

She couldn't blame them all for hiding out. If she didn't have to be there, she'd be looking for the exit, too. Tracy lingered on the front porch after the Barneses drove away. She had even lined the steps and railing with cheerfully glowing votive lights here, too. The Heartbreak was all dressed up for a party that wasn't happening.

She refused to give in to despondency as twilight gathered. She thought about Palmer inside stuffing himself on her appetizers and wondered if he would blame this disaster on the ghost of Ezra Poole.

Maybe so, but not her. *She* was going to have a little talk with Chelsea.

"Isn't it the coolest thing you ever saw?" Matt couldn't help but feel proud of the big Harley parked beside the hotel, even if it did belong to Wade, who was only a guest.

He could tell that Christopher wanted to touch it, and if Wade and Jake hadn't both been standing there, he'd have let Chris sit on the bike, as long as he was careful. Heck, they could both fit on the big seat and there would still be room for one more.

"It's waaaay cool," Chris admitted. "Can we get one, Dad?"

Matt was always surprised when Chris called Jake "dad." He did it all the time now. Back when Jake first married Carly, Chris still called him Jake, but things had changed pretty quick.

Chris had always wanted a dad more than anything. Now Matt knew why. He missed his own dad so much that sometimes it was hard not to start bawling like a baby. After a couple of tries, he was finally able to write some letters in the journal, like Wade suggested. Now, sometimes, he found himself looking forward to sneaking into his room to write another one.

Writing to his dad wasn't the same as having him around, but it wasn't as bad as not being able to talk to him at all.

He listened as Jake asked Wade all kinds of questions about the Harley — like how's the mileage and how long has he had it. He was asking so many questions that Matt started to worry that maybe Jake would actually buy one. Then Chris would be able to ride on it anytime — but after Wade left, then he wouldn't even have a Harley to look at, or sit on and pretend.

Just when he was feeling really sad, he felt a hand on his shoulder. He looked up to find Wade standing right there beside him, like they were friends. Like Wade knew how he was feeling.

He hadn't really liked Wade Johnson at first, but the guy turned out to be pretty nice after all.

Besides, his mom smiled a lot more since Wade was around, and if Mom was happy, then the whole place didn't seem so empty anymore.

In fact, when his mom was happy, the whole world seemed a lot brighter.

Chapter Thirty-Two

When she couldn't find Chelsea or Carly downstairs, Tracy paused long enough to reset the CD player, and instantly Elvis Presley's smooth, mellow love songs filled a silence broken only by Eloise's constant chatter. It wasn't like Chelsea to be vindictive, no matter how upset the girl might be about Wade, but Tracy could think of no other reason for her to sabotage the party.

She forced a smile, waved to Palmer and his friends, and headed for the apartment stairs, but before she could start up, a car horn blared out front. Not just any car horn, either, but one that played the first stanzas of "La Cucaracha."

There was only one person in Twilight with that kind of horn — Joe Caron, the cook at Selma's Diner. Car doors immediately started slamming, followed by the sound of excited chatter. Abandoning her plan to find Chelsea, she hurried across the lobby.

Selma Gibbs came breezing in on Joe Caron's arm. As soon as she saw Tracy, Selma opened her arms in an expansive gesture that took in the entire room.

"This is something else!" Selma's booming voice reverberated around the huge lobby. She paused long enough to gaze around, and then pressed her hand to her ample bosom, as if overwhelmed. Then she threw her arms around Tracy and gave her a bear hug, nearly choking the life out of her.

Drowning in Selma's overly powerful perfume, Tracy laughed and hugged her back.

"Thanks for coming," she said, fighting back tears. "Isn't the diner open tonight?"

Selma beamed. "Miss a grand occasion like this?" She turned to Joe, who looked more than a little uncomfortable in dress slacks, a starched white, long-sleeved shirt, and bolo tie. She jabbed him in the paunch with her elbow. "We're thrilled, aren't we, Jose?"

"Let me show you two around," Tracy offered, ready to usher them into the sitting room.

Selma shook her head. "You go ahead and

greet your other guests. We'll help ourselves to refreshments and show ourselves around."

"What other guests?"

"The ones in the cars that pulled in behind us."

As Selma and Joe made their way into the sunroom, Tracy looked over and saw Geoff Wilson, owner of the Twilight Cove Gallery, and his partner Vincent Smythe walk through the door. Geoff had the exclusive rights to sell Carly's paintings in California.

The minute she saw Geoff, Tracy realized that this sudden influx of unexpected but very welcome guests had to be Carly's doing.

"Tracy!" Geoff grabbed her hands and leaned back to look her over. "You look *absolutely fabulous.* Doesn't she, Vincent?"

Vincent concurred. "Stunning. I *really* like what you've done with your hair."

Self-consciously, she fingered the French twist.

"Very retro," Vincent winked. "Very old Hollywood."

"Very Grace Kelly," Geoff added.

"Thanks . . . I think. I take it the gallery is closed tonight?" Overwhelmed with gratitude, Tracy wanted to cry. Downtown Twilight Cove was fast becoming a ghost town tonight. "Thank you two for coming."

"Mind if we look around?" Geoff asked, ignoring her question.

"Of course not. That's what tonight is all about. I have some guest rooms open down the hall to the right." She pointed the way. "There's plenty of wine and munchies in the sunroom."

They were a few steps away when Vincent suddenly turned around. "By the way, Tracy, if you ever, *ever* need help in a pinch, I've always wanted to play innkeeper."

Touched, she promised, "Thanks, Vincent. I'll remember."

Geoff rolled his eyes. "I'd pay you to hire him, just to get him out of my hair." The men laughed and continued on into the sunroom.

No sooner had they walked away when a trim young brunette with a deep tan and an exotic lilt to her eyes came through the front door. She paused to look around with obvious admiration for the setting. Spotting Tracy, she quickly walked up to introduce herself.

"I'm Kat Chandler." She offered her hand.

"I've heard all about you from Carly," Tracy said. "I'm glad to finally meet you in person."

"Same here." Kat Chandler was Jake's

former partner in his private investigating firm in Southern California. House-sitting for the Montgomerys had led to Kat's subsequent marriage to a Twilight Cove local.

"My husband would have loved to have seen this place, but he's away on business for a couple of days." Kat's gaze lingered on the fireplace and the sitting area. "What a great room!"

"I'm glad you like it. It's my favorite." She explained that there were guest rooms open for viewing, and then Kat Chandler asked, "Are you booked up for the end of July?"

Don't I wish?

"Not yet."

"How many rooms do you have?"

"Nine, but one is occupied."

"I'll book the other eight and the ninth if it's available then. We'll need them for a week beginning Thursday the twenty-second of July."

"All my rooms for a week?"

Kat nodded. "My family is coming over from Hawaii, and you know how it goes. At first only three of them were coming, then it was down to two. Then seven of them, and now more of the kids have decided to fly over. There'll be around fourteen in all, so I'll reserve all the rooms to be certain."

"Are you sure?" Tracy couldn't believe she was reserving all nine rooms in one fell swoop until it hit her. "Did Carly and Jake put you up to this?"

Kat laughed. "No. Why?"

"They've come to my rescue a lot lately."

"Actually, the Montgomerys are innocent this time. The idea is all mine. We've been trying to figure out where to put everyone at our house, which would be impossible." She turned and pointed out the open front door. "See those lights on the point a couple of miles down?"

Tracy nodded.

"That's the Chandler house. That's where we live."

They chatted a few more minutes while Tracy led Kat over to the reception desk and penciled in reservations for the eight rooms. When they finished, Kat strolled into the sunroom and Tracy realized that there had been a little over a dozen late arrivals, not all of them Carly's mercy calls. She made the rounds, speaking to travel agents and bed-and-breakfast booking service owners who gave her advice on internet sites and brochures. Two of them took digital photos of the rooms.

When Carly finally reappeared a few minutes later, Tracy excused herself, leaving behind travel agents who were singing her praises.

"Thank you." At a loss for words, she threw her arms around Carly's neck.

"For what?" Carly's smile was infectious.

"For this." She indicated the guests with a sweep of her hand. "For coming to the rescue and calling out the troops." Tracy took a deep breath and wiped away a tear from the corner of her eye. "Most of all, for being such a great friend."

"That's what friends are for, isn't it?" Carly asked softly. "You've been there for me so many times over the years."

"Friends don't keep score," Tracy reminded her.

"Exactly." Carly reached over and carefully wiped a tear from beneath Tracy's lower lashes. "Enough, okay? You're going to ruin your mascara." She glanced around the room. "Have you seen the boys?"

"I thought I saw them go outside with Jake. Have you seen Chelsea? She's got some explaining to do."

Carly didn't try to pretend she had no idea what was going on.

"She is a wreck," Carly admitted, but she didn't make any excuses for Chelsea. "She forgot all about mailing the invitations until two nights ago, when she found them in the bottom of her purse. She tried to make up for it by calling everyone on the list to tell them the invites were on the way."

"Why didn't she just tell me?"

"She wanted to try to salvage the situation first. She really hated to let you down." Carly glanced around. "I see that quite a few of the travel industry guests made it after all."

"Fourteen out of seventy-five isn't a very good showing." As she gazed around the room again, she caught Selma in deep conversation with Geoff and Vincent, watched Joe and Palmer charm the ladies. Vincent was talking to Kat Chandler. New friends, old friends.

Tracy found herself fighting back tears again. "Actually, it's worked out even better than I expected," she admitted, smiling through tears as she gazed around at all the people gathered in the sunroom. "If this hadn't happened, I might never have known just how many truly special friends I have in this town."

Wade was on his way back inside when he saw Chelsea step out onto the porch and pull her cell phone out of her purse. She looked as if she'd been crying.

Looking down at the phone as she hurried along the garden path, she nearly walked right into him.

"Are you okay?" He'd have to have been blind to miss the dark look she shot him.

"Do I *look* okay?"

He held up both hands. "Sorry I asked."

She looked like she was going to sidestep him and walk away, but suddenly changed her mind.

"What are you doing here, anyway?" she wanted to know.

"I was just checking on my bike and was headed back inside."

"I meant, what are you doing *here,* at the hotel? When are you going to check out?"

"Has Tracy said anything about wanting me to leave?"

"Tracy is way too nice to kick you out. Besides, she needs the money. Unlike her, I know what you're really after."

"You think so?" He tried to ignore the insult. "Tracy's a grown woman," Wade reminded her.

"My dad's not around to stick up for her, so I will. If you're waiting around for her to sleep with you, forget it. She was crazy about my dad. She's just lonely right now. You're nothing but a substitute for what she's really missing."

"You've got me all wrong, Chelsea."

"Oh, yeah? And what makes you different from most other guys on the planet?"

"I'm not most guys." She'd been upset when she walked outside, and he was pretty certain he wasn't the cause of her anger, but he was getting the brunt of it.

"If you're in a rotten mood, maybe you should go and pick a fight someplace else."

"Really? Where? There's no place to go in this town."

Just then, a red Corvette driven by a kid wearing glasses and a letterman's jacket pulled up at the end of the driveway. Chelsea waved to him, then turned around.

"Do me a favor, will you?" she asked.

"Sure."

"Tell Tracy I went out with Eric for a while."

"When should I tell her you'll be back?"

"Whenever you want to."

"I meant what time?"

She called out over her shoulder as she headed for the Corvette, "I know what you meant. Tell her not to wait up."

CHAPTER THIRTY-THREE

Wade slipped into the foyer without drawing attention to himself and lingered in the shadows. His gaze unerringly found Tracy, and the moment he laid eyes on her, his heartbeat quickened.

He knew he was in serious trouble. A woman had never gotten to him so fast without even trying. She was in deep conversation with Carly Montgomery, her features alive with animation, her delicate fingers wrapped around an empty china teacup.

The light and shadows in the room danced over Tracy's porcelain skin, kissed her blond hair with highlights that sparkled like a halo of jewels.

Observing without being observed, he noticed every minute detail about her. He wondered: What was she like as a child? Then a teen? Had she always been so focused?

She had been thrown into a situation that

could have destroyed a weaker woman, but she was bound and determined to make this venture work. He hoped for her sake that she was on the brink of success.

Not even half of the guests she'd expected had showed up, but there was no lack of love in the room. Those gathered around were laughing and chatting, and so was Tracy as she tried to make the best of a bad situation.

Tonight he was content to remain in the shadows, watching, wanting the best for her, wondering what might have happened if they had met years ago, before she'd married. Before he'd made the biggest mistake of his life in the name of success. If he'd met her then, both their lives could have taken a different journey, one they would have traveled together. He was sure that whenever, wherever he'd met her, he would have fallen in love with her.

She wasn't like anyone else he'd ever met. She was the ideal he thought he'd never find. Beautiful, intelligent, a woman who wasn't afraid to get her hands dirty. A great mother. A caring friend.

He was a man on the run from himself and the public. A man haunted not only by the memory of twelve murdered young women, but now, one very persistent ghost.

Any dream he might nurture about a future with Tracy would forever be just that — a dream.

That's what I want someday. That look. That feeling.

Tracy tried not to envy the way Carly and Jake smiled at each other across the room when they thought no one was watching. Though the Montgomerys had been married for over two years now, they still acted like newlyweds.

So as not to get caught staring at them, she quickly glanced down at her watch and realized that time had flown. It was nearly nine, almost time for the gathering to come to an end. When she looked up again, she saw Carly making her way across the room.

"I'll start cleaning up the kitchen," Carly offered.

"Absolutely not. I can handle it. You've been here all day. Go on home."

"Are you sure there's not something I can do?"

Tracy thought for a moment. "Since you and Jake brought separate cars, do you think he'd mind staying after everyone leaves to go over whatever he found out about the accounts? If he'd prefer to wait until tomorrow, I'll completely understand, but I know

I won't be able to sleep thinking about what he's going to say."

Carly's long, sun-bleached hair swayed around her shoulders when she nodded. "I don't think he'd mind at all, as long as you're not too tired."

"Not at all." *Tired?* Sleep was the furthest thing from her mind. When she hadn't been thinking about Wade, she'd been worrying about what Jake was going to tell her.

As Carly walked away, Tracy headed for the buffet. Tossing used napkins in a nearby trash basket, she turned around and found Wade right behind her.

"You still look beautiful." He had the uncanny ability with just a look to make her feel as if she were the only one in the room.

"Thank you. And thanks for the gardenia. It's still fresh." She turned her head, inhaling the heady scent that had reminded her of him all night and made her feel as if he'd been right there beside her, though she hadn't really seen him all evening.

"I wish for your sake more people had shown up." His eyes spoke volumes.

The last thing she wanted was him feeling sorry for her. "There was a little snafu with the invitations, but thanks to Carly, things worked out. The point of tonight wasn't just to make contacts, but to celebrate. So instead of networking, I had a chance to share my accomplishment with old friends."

Whenever she thought of everyone who'd come over at a moment's notice, her heart felt lighter.

When he took her by the elbow and stepped toward the bank of windows behind them, that light heart started tripping over itself. Though her mind was still full of questions, her heart was powerless to resist him.

"I saw Chelsea out front."

She felt a touch of lightness ebb. "I was looking all over for her."

"She went out with Eric. She told me to tell you not to wait up."

His voice lowered to a more intimate level as he leaned closer. "I have a bottle of champagne on ice in my room. After everyone's gone and you've tucked Matt in, would you share it with me in celebration of all you've accomplished?"

No one had ever said anything remotely as romantic. The idea that Wade wanted to celebrate what she'd done nearly brought her to tears again.

"You really are an enigma, you know." She was tempted to reach up and rearrange his artfully tousled hair.

"How so?" He gave her a half smile, no

more, as if some deep, lingering sadness prevented him from ever being completely happy. On him, that half smile was enough to intrigue, and entice. And to warm her to her toes.

She thought of the night he'd walked in out of the rain carrying nothing but his motorcycle saddlebag and helmet, how he'd said no more than half a dozen words to her before disappearing into his room.

That man was a far cry from the one she'd come to know as a talented writer, a professional who wasn't afraid to pitch in. And yet there was still so much to learn. He never talked about his childhood, never mentioned his family nor one single friend, not even in passing. She had no idea where he'd gone to school, how he chose his profession, or what he wanted out of life. She had no idea where he lived or where he was headed.

And she still hadn't gotten to the truth about his knowledge of Ezra Poole and how he knew about the location of the *Lantana*'s logs.

All she did know for certain was that for tonight it didn't matter. Tonight they'd agreed to not discuss it.

"You're still quite a man of mystery," she said, thinking aloud.

"Is that good or bad?"

"It's . . . interesting."

"Interesting enough to tempt you to have champagne with me?"

She looked around the room and located Matt. He waved to her, his smile perhaps not as bright as it used to be, but he was smiling again. She sighed, and when she turned to Wade, she knew she could give him only one answer.

"I'm afraid I'll have to pass on that champagne." She tried to hide her regret but failed miserably. "I wouldn't feel right, being alone with you in your room."

Hoping you would do God knows what with me.

She reminded herself that he had invited her only for champagne. She was the one assuming that things would go further.

"I could come upstairs," he suggested.

She shook her head. "That wouldn't work either."

"I didn't think so, but it was worth a try."

"I'm sorry," she finished lamely, wishing he weren't so close. She was tempted to reach for him. "I hope you understand."

"I knew it was a long shot, but you can't blame a guy for trying."

Did he sound as disappointed as she felt? She wondered what he would think if he knew just how close she'd come to saying yes.

CHAPTER THIRTY-FOUR

After everyone left, Tracy tucked Matt in and hurried back downstairs, where Jake had slipped out of his casual sport coat, rolled up his sleeves, and was seated at a bistro table in the sunroom, looking over papers in a manila folder. As she walked into the room, he closed the file.

Her mouth was suddenly dry, but she walked straight over to the table without stopping for anything to drink. Oddly enough, her palms were damp. She pressed them against her linen pants and then sat down across from Jake.

She would never forget that morning in David Sylvester's office when the accountant had told her about her financial status, or rather *lack* of one. She had that same hole-in-the-pit-of-her-stomach feeling now as she'd had then.

It didn't matter that she was surrounded by the fruits of her labor, that she'd pulled things together somehow and made a home for herself and Matt, or that she was on the brink of establishing a very viable business. She was waiting for another ax to fall.

Snap out of it, she told herself. *There's* nothing *you can't handle.*

The soft strains of the Eagles's "Hotel California" drifted in from the CD player in the sitting room. The scent of cinnamon coffee rose on the steam above Jake's cup.

She clasped her hands together in her lap, reminding herself that nothing he could tell her could hurt them now. Glenn was gone. If he had a drug habit, if he was heavy into gambling or God knows what else, that was behind her now. Knowledge is power. Hopefully she would learn something from whatever Jake had to say, but looking at his deeply concerned expression, she knew that whatever he had discovered was troubling. He seemed hesitant to begin.

"It's bad, isn't it?" She leaned forward, perched on the edge of the chair.

"I went over all of Glenn's books, looking for any misappropriation. I thought maybe someone who worked at the brokerage, a secretary or one of the other agents, might have found a way to siphon off money. It was a long shot, but that was my suspicion when I started digging."

318

He sounded perfectly calm, as if he were so used to dispensing terrible revelations on a regular basis that he had grown immune to it. But his eyes were still too expressive. The news wasn't good.

"That wasn't it, though, was it?"

He shook his head. "Glenn simply spent way more than he made. When money ran low, he took out second and third mortgages. Eventually he ran through an equity line of credit and wasn't able to borrow any more."

"Damn it. Why? Where did all the money go? Three years ago we had more than enough put away. It was money that was not commingled with the business."

She thought about the move from Twilight Cove to Canyon Club, the way Glenn spared no expense on decorating or buying himself a new Mercedes, all the investing he'd done in so many new development projects. Of course, she had worried, but he was constantly assuring her that everything was fine.

Jake's voice pulled her back.

"I'm not going to beat around the bush," he said. "There were things in the books that to the untrained eye wouldn't necessarily be seen as red flags. Things David Sylvester might not have questioned, but I can't believe he didn't."

"Glenn hired him because David is the best around."

"Were they close?"

She thought back. "I thought just acquaintances. They met through a business group, Rotary or something, in San Luis Obispo." She took a deep breath, twisted her wedding ring around and around. "We never went out socially with David and his wife." She tried to recall Glenn talking about David on a personal level.

"Tracy, Glenn had a mistress," Jake said quietly.

She froze, locked up from head to toe, and nearly stopped breathing.

A mistress.

"Are you certain?" She had no idea that she could feel such anger, or such betrayal.

"He had an affair with a woman for over three years before he died."

"Three years?" Suddenly, as if she'd been living life behind a fog bank, the mist began to clear.

"Honey, I'm afraid I'm going to be late again. I hate like hell not to get home for dinner, but there's no way around it. Don't wait up."

"Trace, I'm sorry, but I'm going to have to go back to Santa Barbara tonight. I've got a big meeting with the contractors on the Plaza

town house project. I'll be back Tuesday."

Liar. All lies.

She'd suspected. Just before he died, she'd confronted him, and still he'd lied.

"Are you having an affair, Glenn? If not, what's happening to us?"

"I don't know how you can even ask me that. I love you, Tracy. I love you and Matt and the things we've built together."

She had swallowed the lie, now she was choking on the pain.

He was *cheating on you.*

He had a mistress.

"How do you know? How do you know that for certain?" The blood in her veins was turning to ice, and slowly, her heart began to freeze, too. She could barely feel it pumping.

"Glenn was withdrawing large amounts of cash, large by most people's standards anyway. Ten and twenty thousand at a time. He purchased a very pricey fixer-upper in Montecito, nothing on a really grand scale, but you know how much property goes for down there."

Numb all over, she tried to fathom it. "A house? In Montecito?"

"I checked at the recorder's office, looked for grant deeds and holdings in his name. One was originally held in joint tenancy with the woman. The amount he paid in cash certainly accounts for the money shuffling he'd done. The house was transferred to her name a couple of months later.

"I also linked her to him through some checks he wrote to her personally. On the surface, some appeared to be legitimate business transactions."

"Who?" Who was the woman he'd ruined all their lives for?

"Tracy, there's something more."

"What?" *What more could there be?*

"They had a child together."

When the room started to spin, she unclenched her hands and propped her forehead on her palm. Jake was beside her in an instant, steadying her with a hand on her shoulder.

"Do you want to put your head down?"

She licked her lips. Her tongue felt coated with cotton. "No," she whispered. "I'll be okay."

"Maybe we should go into the sitting room. Or do you want me to take you upstairs?"

"No." She shook her head and the dizziness slowly passed. Jake walked over to the sideboard and poured her some water. She took a sip, but it made her nauseous. "How old is the . . . their child?"

"Almost two."

Somehow, though her heart was numb, her mind was still functioning. Her anger raw and real. "You're absolutely sure?"

"I drove down to Montecito and took photos." He sounded as if he hated to admit it.

"Photos?"

"Surveillance photos."

Surveillance. She felt as if she'd suddenly been cast in a bad B movie. She must have looked stunned, for he gently reminded her, "Tracy, it's what I used to do for a living."

She'd forgotten. Now she tried to imagine Jake — big, smiling, kindhearted Jake Montgomery — skulking around behind shrubbery, sneaking photos of the woman who'd been sleeping with Glenn.

A woman who'd had a child with *her* husband.

"Who is she?" She almost welcomed her anger. It was at least an assurance that she wouldn't live out the rest of her life unable to feel at all. She tried to focus on Matt instead. He would need more than a brittle, angry shell of a mother in his life, but right now, she could see only red.

"Who is she, Jake? What's her name?" She wanted somewhere to direct her rage and, damn him, Glenn was gone.

Jake's shoulders rose and fell as he took a deep breath and let it go.

This isn't easy for him, either.

"Willa Conner." Jake shifted toward the edge of his chair as if ready to vault around the table and catch her if she fainted.

"What did you say?" She wasn't certain she'd heard him correctly. She couldn't *believe* she'd heard correctly.

"Willa Conner," he repeated.

Willa.

Her oldest friend. Willa, who had shared her high school years. Her college roommate. Willa, who had made the move to California with her. Willa, who'd sat in her living room a few days ago and wished her well.

"I thought she was ill." Incredulous, she remembered how worried she'd been about Willa.

"You know her?"

"She was here just a few days ago." A hollow laugh she couldn't stop bubbled out of her. There was no joy in it. "We've known each other for years. We were close once, a long time ago."

She had been the one who'd pushed Glenn into choosing Willa to decorate the Canyon Club model homes. She had been instrumental in getting them to work together. Willa was a talented designer, an artist, not to mention a beautiful woman, but Willa had never had much luck with men. She'd always claimed to be completely fulfilled by her career, but Tracy thought she'd seen a quiet longing in Willa, one she hadn't noticed until the first time Willa saw Matthew right after he was born.

"Do you have a picture of the . . . child?" She still couldn't believe it. She wanted to see for herself.

Jake slowly opened the file folder. Her gaze dipped to the photos lying there — upside down from where she was sitting — but there was no mistaking Willa's sleek dark hair and porcelain skin. Then Tracy saw a flash of red gold before Jake picked up the top photo and handed it over to her without a word.

She didn't need further proof than this. No paternity test in the world would shout the truth as loudly as the photo of Willa holding a toddler who had hair the exact same reddish gold as Glenn's and Matt's. The child's eyes were the same cerulean blue. Her little button nose matched Matt's at that age. Their baby photos could have been interchangeable.

And Willa? The image showed her carrying her little girl from what must have been her house to the Volvo. Impeccably dressed as always, Willa's arms were wrapped tightly around the child. She wasn't smiling. Violet smudges stained the shadowed hollows beneath her eyes.

She's grieving, not ill. Tracy couldn't tear her eyes away from the photograph of her friend. Willa was grieving for Glenn on a deep level of her own, grieving the way Tracy should have, had her memories not been shrouded with the strain their marriage had been under.

Willa was grieving for the lover she'd lost. Her baby's father. *For Glenn.*

She slid the photograph back across the table, finally met Jake's eyes. He must think her the biggest fool on earth.

But Jake was a professional. Amazingly, he comprehended her thoughts without her having said a word.

"There's no need to feel ashamed. Most people never suspect a thing in these cases, Tracy. Probably very few people who knew you and Glenn would ever suspect, either."

She thought of David Sylvester, his anally neat desk, his smug smile. His condescending charm.

"David Sylvester knew." She was sure of it now. Somehow, some way, David had known but hadn't told her. She was sure of it, but now that Chelsea was working at his office, hoping to land a scholarship, she hesitated to confront him.

Jake nodded in answer to her remark. "Maybe. Maybe not. He had to have seen the one-way cash flow. He may have even cautioned Glenn at some point."

She sniffed. "Believe me, Glenn never took well to being cautioned. Not once he set his mind on something." Her gaze traveled slowly around the room. "Look at this place. Surely someone must have told him he was crazy when he bought it, but did he listen?"

"Are you going to be all right?"

"Yes. Sure. Fine." She had no idea if she'd ever be *fine* again. One thing was certain, she'd never be such a blind idiot again. Never.

"Why don't you let me call Carly and have her spend the night?"

Instantly she looked up and shook her head. "No." The humiliation was too much when she thought of Carly knowing. "Did you tell her?"

"Not at all. I handled this whole thing as confidentially as I would have if you'd hired me."

"Would you . . ." she looked at her hands, "would you tell her for me?" She was on fire with embarrassment, but she didn't want to shut Carly out. She'd become too trusted a friend. Besides, she knew that Carly was not one to spread gossip.

Tracy reminded herself that she'd trusted Willa, too. Trusted her with Glenn. Pushed them into business together . . .

"Of course, I'll tell her." Jake sighed. "I just hate leaving you alone."

She thought of her precious boy asleep upstairs, and for a fleeting second she wondered where Chelsea was and if she was safe.

There was no way she could ever let either of them find out about Glenn and Willa. It was enough that her own love and trust had been dealt the final blow tonight — broken into an infinite number of blunt, jagged pieces. No, they didn't need to know.

"You'd better get home, Jake. It's late and Carly will be wondering where you are." She tried to smile, wondered if she'd be able to stand, if her legs would even hold long enough for her to walk him to the door.

"This is what I hate most about this job," he said.

"Being out late?" She couldn't think straight. Her mind was still reeling, still seeing the images in the photograph.

Jake pushed away from the table, gathered

up the file, and offered it to her. She re-
coiled, as if it were a bomb about to go off.

"I don't want it. Burn it, for all I care."
She tried standing. Miraculously, her knees
held. "What was it you were saying? Something about what you hate?"

"Having to be the one to tell people that
they've been cheated on. Telling them that
the one person in the world they care about
the most has betrayed them. It's why I quit
taking on marital cases and started writing
'how-to' books."

"You know what *I* hate about this?" As
they crossed the wide lobby, their footsteps
sounded hollow against the bare wood floor.

"The whole thing, I imagine."

They paused just inside the front door.
Jake looked so very concerned that, for his
sake, she forced herself to smile.

"It's bad enough finding out that Glenn
was unfaithful for years, but what really fries
me is that he's already dead. Now I won't
be able to kill him myself."

CHAPTER THIRTY-FIVE

At least she left Jake smiling as he walked out the door. She turned out the lights as she hurried upstairs, needing to see Matthew, needing to ground herself in the reality of her new life — in this place that didn't feel like a real home. In Matt.

Matthew was her world now. She didn't need to remind herself of that, she just needed to touch her baby, to make sure he was sleeping soundly, that he was warm and alive.

Because she was surely dead. She still couldn't feel a thing.

A pyramid of light streamed out of Matt's room as she walked down the hall. He'd fallen asleep propped up against his pillow. The lamp on his bedside table was turned low, the journal she'd given him lay open atop the comforter. His pen had rolled to the edge of the bed.

She picked up the journal, set the pen on

the nightstand, and then gently sat down beside her sleeping son. Her initial anger receding, she was amazed at how calm she'd become. Her hands weren't even shaking anymore. Then again, she no longer felt anything, so why wouldn't she be cool as a cucumber?

Looking down at the open journal in her lap, she glanced at the last entry Matt had made and ran her fingertip over his unevenly spaced letters. Penmanship had never been his strong suit.

Saturday nite.

Dear Dad,
   Tonight Mom had a party. It was really grate. Chris was here and so was a lot of people that you know. That guy Wade is still living downstairs. He shooed his Harley to me and Chris and Jake. Jake liked it a lot and you wood, too.
   I think Wade is kinda nice now.
   I still miss you so much, tho.
         You're dear son, Matthew A. Potter.

The letters blurred. Her vision smeared behind tears. Tears Glenn certainly didn't deserve. She scanned Matt's first entries and then closed the journal and set it on

331

the table.

She pulled the comforter up around his shoulders and reached out to touch his hair. Her hand stopped poised above his strawberry-blond hair. The image of Willa and Glenn's daughter flashed across her mind. A child with hair the exact shade as Matt's.

And Glenn's.

She smoothed Matt's hair back off his forehead with a feather-light touch. His lashes fluttered on his smooth, lightly freckled cheeks, and then his eyes slowly opened.

He smiled up at her. "Hi, Mom." His voice was thick with sleep. She knew he wasn't really awake.

"Hi, honey."

Still groggy, he rolled over to his side. "If you wanna talk to Dad, you can use my journal." His words drifted off to a whisper as he gently slipped back into his dreams.

She'd *love* to talk to Glenn right now.

But nothing she had to say was fit for her son's ears.

She turned off the light and made her way through the darkness to her own room. Light from the bathroom spilled across the king bed, a field of emptiness that dwarfed the compact room. There was no way she would sleep tonight. She found herself wondering if she'd ever get a good night's sleep again. Before she realized what she was doing, she'd pulled off her wedding ring and was walking toward the dresser. She opened the top drawer, dropped the ring inside, slammed the drawer.

The walls closed in on her. The room suddenly became claustrophobic. She left the room, ran up the attic stairs, and burst out onto the widow's walk.

The wind had picked up. It was howling around the eaves again. She wrapped her arms around herself as a gust whipped long strands of hair out of her French twist. She didn't care. The air was damp with moisture off the water, the sea spray carried on the stiff breeze was chilly tonight. Another unseasonable storm was on the way. She didn't care.

"Damn you, Glenn!" Knowing her words would be muffled by the wind, she cursed aloud but found no real release, no satisfaction in cursing a man who couldn't hear her.

Unable to breathe, she grabbed the railing and clung to it, leaning over, drinking in gulps of air, but she couldn't catch her breath. She looked down, saw the light from

Wade's window spilling out across the garden.

She wondered if he was awake, if he was writing. Maybe he slept with the lights on now that he'd made friends with Ezra Poole.

He had champagne on ice in his room.

"Would you share it with me in celebration of all you've accomplished?"

She'd turned him down because she always did the right thing. Always the good girl, she'd done the right thing all her life. She'd suspected Glenn, but hung on to hope, believing in him long past when she should have, daring to hope that things would turn out fine. She'd put her belief in him though he hadn't deserved it. He hadn't deserved an ounce of her love, or her loyalty.

She took a deep breath, filled her lungs with cold, damp salt air, then she let it go in a rush.

She didn't want to be good or right anymore. She just wanted to *feel* something again.

Wade's mind was wandering in a million directions at once.

He'd tried reading through his notebooks, tweaking sentences here and there, tightening the writing. When he heard an unexpected knock on the door, he gathered up the notebooks and deposited them in the top drawer of the small bureau on his way across the room.

The instant he opened the door and took one look at Tracy's swollen eyes and tearstained face, he knew that something terrible had happened. Her smile was a caricature of the genuine article she always wore. Strands of golden hair had escaped the pins that held it in an intricate twist. Wisps straggled alongside her pale cheeks.

She hadn't changed. Nor had she taken off her corsage. She looked pale and shaken as she stepped past him into the room and looked around.

"Good. I see you still have that champagne." She nodded toward the plastic ice bucket on the low bureau. A bottle of Dom was standing in water with a few bits of ice floating around it.

"It's not ice-cold anymore."

She shrugged. "I don't mind. Am I still invited?" Her gaze barely grazed the bed before moving on.

"Certainly." He picked up the champagne, and droplets of water trickled off the bottle. He swiped the surface of the bureau with his bare hand and shrugged apologetically.

"Sorry."

She blinked, looked up at him. "For what?"

"Making a mess."

She shrugged, made no other comment.

"I'll be right back." He was half afraid to leave her alone.

He grabbed a hand towel from the bathroom and hurried back. The cork popped smoothly and he pulled it out, held the bottle up to the light, and watched the champagne bubble up inside.

Across the room, Tracy remained silent, her arms wrapped around herself in a protective, telling posture. He'd never seen her like this, and she was scaring the hell out of him.

He filled two champagne glasses he'd bought at the liquor store and walked across the room to where she was staring out the window into the darkness.

"Cheers," he said, handing her a glass and then touching the rim of his flute to hers.

"Cheers." The word came out on a barely audible whisper, and when her eyes met his, he saw such deep, raw sorrow in them that his heart contracted.

She finished the champagne in two long, smooth swallows and held the thin flute out to him again. He set down his own glass, walked back over to the bureau to refill hers.

"What made you change your mind?" He glanced over his shoulder, hoping she would open up to him.

She shrugged. "I felt like talking."

He indicated the only chair in the room before he sat down on the bed, leaned back against the headboard, and crossed his ankles. She sat.

"So talk." He noticed she'd already polished off half of the second glass of champagne.

She held the stem of the flute between her thumb and forefinger, lifted it to the light, and studied the bubbling liquid as if it were a science experiment. Finally she turned to him again. Tonight her eyes were pale, liquid turquoise, shimmering with unshed tears.

He set his glass down, got up, and crossed the space that separated them, then went down on one knee beside her chair. Strands of her hair had come loose and curled in soft wisps around her temples, like stray sunshine. He reached up, hooked his finger in one of the curls, and gently pulled it away from the corner of her eye. Her skin was as cool as the night air.

When he took her hand and then cupped her jaw and said, "What's wrong, Tracy? What happened?"

Silent tears began to slide down her

cheeks. She bit her lips together, gave a slight shake of her head, and closed her eyes.

He took the glass from her hand, set it aside, took both of her hands in his, and led her over to the bed so that he could sit beside her. With his arm around her shoulder, he drew her against him and let her cry.

She didn't make a sound, something even more disturbing than having her break down sobbing. She sat there with silent tears streaming down her face.

Not knowing what else to do, he drew her against his chest and held her. The moment she lay her cheek against his heart, she started sobbing in earnest. When her heart-wrenching sobs slowly subsided and she rested her head on his shoulder, he brushed her tears off her cheeks and kissed her brow.

He wanted to throttle Chelsea for the mix-up with the invitations. Obviously, all the work, the pressure, the poor turnout, had finally gotten to Tracy.

Her head moved against his shoulder. He felt her breath catch on a mingled sigh, and then her hand slowly covered his. She slipped her fingers between his and held on tight.

"What would you do if you found out your whole life was a lie, Wade?"

His whole life *was* a lie right now. *Does she know?* If she'd somehow found out, she wouldn't be sitting here crying about it. She'd be kicking his sorry ass out onto the street.

"In what way?" he asked.

"In every way," she whispered.

He slipped his fingers beneath her chin, gently forced her to look at him. Her lashes were spiked and matted, her complexion mottled red. Still, she was beautiful to him. He was so very tempted to kiss her, to try and make her forget whatever had upset her so, but he couldn't take advantage of her weakness.

"Tracy, what happened?"

She took another ragged breath. "I met with Jake after the party."

"Carly's husband."

She nodded. "He's a private investigator."

He'd been afraid of discovery, and all this time Tracy's closest friend's husband was a P.I.?

"He told me . . . he told me . . ."

She pressed her fist against her lips and stopped. Her shoulders heaved beneath his arm. Slowly, she calmed again, pulled herself together.

"Tracy, I'm so sorry." *Jake told her; Jake had discovered the truth and now she knows*

I've lied to her.

"There's no need for you to be sorry," she said, shocking him. "It's not your fault. I *knew,* damn it, but I didn't press him. I lived with it. I swallowed his lies."

"Who? Press who about what?"

"Glenn was having an affair for more than three years and I didn't do a damn thing about it." A short burst of sound escaped her, something between a laugh and a sob. "Is it still called an affair when it lasts that long?" She looked to him for an answer. "Do you know?"

"I have no idea." The schmuck who'd left her penniless had been screwing someone else?

"They even had a child together." She pulled away, blinked, and wiped her hand across her eyes, a valiant effort that only destroyed her mascara. He reached over, tried to thumb off the dark streak beneath her eye.

"And what did I do about it? Miss Merry Sunshine? Miss The-World-Is-Such-A-Wonderful-Place? I let him convince me that things would be all right. That he was working himself to death to provide for us, to give us the world. Not that I'd ever asked for it, mind you, but because he said he wanted the best for all of us."

340

She was working herself up to a full boil, which he suspected he could handle a whole lot better than the misery she'd been mired in a moment ago.

"And all that time, he was sleeping with her." She covered her cheeks with her palms, but her blue eyes shone over the tops of her fingertips as she stared back. "She had his daughter, and I had no idea."

She was trembling now, her hands shaking violently when she pulled them away from her face. She was no longer wearing her wedding ring.

He picked up her glass, filled it to the top along with his, and carried it back to her.

"Here's to starting over." He lifted his own glass to toast her, knowing without a shadow of a doubt that starting over wasn't all that it was cracked up to be. Sometimes it was downright impossible. "You're a fighter, Tracy. You'll be all right. If I had to bet money on anyone putting this behind them and moving on, it would be you."

"You want to know the best part?" Ignoring his last comment, she knocked back half the glass of champagne. "I'm the one who threw them together."

"You know her?"

"Oh, yes, I know her. She's an old friend." With a quick shake of her head, she gave another bitter laugh. "Her firm was allied with Glenn Potter's development projects. We were friends back in Indiana."

He took the glass from her, set it aside, took her in his arms. As he held her tight, he gently swayed back and forth. Her arms tightened around his waist and she drew closer, burrowing deeper into the security of his embrace.

Gingerly, he pulled the pins from her hair and then ran his fingers through it, watched it fall around her shoulders. The blond skeins were soft as silk, light as moonbeams.

Her breath came on a soft, warm sigh against his neck. For a moment his own caught and held when he felt her warm fingertips tease the skin above his shirt collar.

She turned her face up to his. Her eyes were closed, her lips kissably close.

No man in his right mind could resist her, though he was pretty well convinced that he wasn't in his right mind most of the time now anyway.

Hungry for the sweet, alluring taste of her again, he kissed her without hesitation. There was no resistance on her part as she kissed him back.

"Make love to me," she whispered, her voice throaty, full.

He wanted her more than he wanted to see the sunrise in the morning. Wanted her more than he'd ever wanted anything in his hopelessly damned life. In a blinding flash of realization, he knew that he'd do anything for this woman, give her anything, give up anything, just to make her happy.

And in that moment he also knew that making love to her tonight would be the worst thing he could ever do to her, or for her.

He took a deep breath, slowly shook his head. Her smooth brow slowly creased. Questions filled her eyes.

"Not like this, Tracy. Not tonight. Not out of anger, Tracy."

"But —" She shook her head, tried to deny it.

He wouldn't hear of it. "You don't want this any more than when you turned me down earlier. You're here because you're hurt. You're here because you've been betrayed, not because of what we might find together, or what we can give each other. You want to get even with your husband."

She grew very still, unmoving. Then she lifted her head and stared up at him. The turmoil was raw and real in her eyes, and then he saw the one thing he had feared seeing before he turned her down.

Her cheeks flamed before she quickly paled. She lowered her eyes in shame.

"Don't, Tracy. *Don't.*" He tried to lift her chin, to get her to meet his eyes again.

She tried to pull away, to slide off of him, but he held her tight.

"There's no shame in your coming to me tonight. The shame would be mine if I took advantage of your weakness. I can't do that to you and I won't. I care about you too much."

"Please," she whispered. "Let me go."

Her hair fell like a gossamer curtain across her face, hiding her expression from him, hiding her embarrassment. He brushed it back, tucked it behind her ear.

"I'm sorry," she whispered, getting to her feet, slipping on her sandals. "I'm so sorry, Wade."

"Don't be." He wished she'd look at him again, but she was already walking toward the door.

In two long strides he'd outpaced her, grabbing the door handle first to keep her from running out. He refused to move until she raised her eyes.

"If we were to make love tonight, you'd never forgive yourself for acting on impulse. You'd never forgive me for letting you. I don't want to hurt you, Tracy. Not ever. I know that when you're thinking straight again, you'll realize I'm right."

Tears sparkled in her eyes, but she didn't look away.

"Come on, I'll walk you upstairs." He opened the door. Lamplight spilled out into the dark hallway ahead of them.

"I'll go up alone."

"Are you sure?"

She nodded. "I'm sure."

"I'll see you in the morning, okay?" He kissed her softly, tenderly. "Meet me in the sunroom."

She stepped out into the hall, and he thought she was going to walk away without another word. Suddenly she stopped and turned around. The smile she gave him was bittersweet and wistful. Her eyes were sad, but luminous.

"Thank you, Wade," she whispered. "Thank you for being so honorable."

CHAPTER THIRTY-SIX

All around her, shadows filled the deep pockets of darkness in the far recesses of the lobby and adjacent sitting room. She clutched her bra, trying to move soundlessly across the bare wooden floors. Her breathing was rapid and shallow, the sound filling the emptiness.

She felt Wade watching her. She'd seen him lean against the doorjamb after she walked out, his arms crossed, his mouth drawn in a tight line. When she reached the bottom of the stairs, she finally heard the door to his room close.

Dear God in heaven, what was I thinking?

She nearly tripped on the wide hem of her pants, let go of her blouse to brace herself, and dropped her bra. Ashamed of sneaking through her own house, she shook herself and pulled her blouse together.

By the time she reached the apartment, she was shaking like a leaf, her head already pounding from too much champagne. Her conscience screamed as she stepped into the dark living room and felt her way past the overstuffed chair and ottoman before inching her way down the hall to her room.

A night of revelations. She'd learned more about her life and about herself tonight than she would have ever thought possible.

Why paint a pretty picture? Glenn was a bastard. He'd cheated on her, ruined their lives, put Matthew's and Chelsea's futures in jeopardy. And for what? So that he could carry on a long-term relationship with Willa?

And Wade Johnson? Yesterday she'd suspected him of lying to her in order to get into the attic. Tonight he'd proved that he had more scruples than Glenn ever had. Thank God Wade was the man he was, that he had the honor to do what only a handful of men would have done in the same situation. He'd sent her packing.

Not only had she discovered the depths of his honor tonight, but she had finally faced the truth. She had gone to him seeking solace, longing for his touch, needing him to soothe her battered ego, and somewhere between acting on her pain and hearing Wade turn her down, it hit her with blinding clarity that she wanted him because of who he was and what she felt for him. Not merely to get back at Glenn. Not to salve her own ego, but because she'd fallen in love with him.

She wanted him with a need kindled that first night when she'd taken a chance and let him into her hotel and into her life.

Her anger and sense of betrayal paled beside her explosive desire for the man downstairs.

Even knowing that Wade intended to walk back out of her life as surely and as suddenly as he'd walked into it, she still wanted him.

When she heard the soft sound of a footstep in the hall, Tracy's first and only thought was *Wade.*

A heartbeat later, there came a quick knock on her half-open door. She whirled around, the slip of her white lace bra clutched in one hand, holding the front of her linen blouse closed with the other. It was Chelsea, not Wade, who pushed the door the rest of the way open.

Tracy was suddenly paralyzed, right there in the middle of the room.

"My sorority sisters are always sneaking back into the house like this." Chelsea's disbelief was loud and clear. It was a night for surprises.

Tracy tried to straighten her tangled hair and gave up. "I'm not sneaking."

"You look like a deer caught in the headlights. I looked for you when I came in. I went up to the widow's walk, but then I figured you were with him." Then Chelsea whispered something Tracy barely heard.

"What did you say?"

"I said, what about *Dad*? He loved you so much! How could you do this?" The words were loud and bitter, filled with hurt.

Tracy crossed the room on long, angry strides, walked right past Chelsea, and quietly closed the door. "Keep your voice down or you'll wake Matt." She fought for calm, struggled to sound in control.

Chelsea didn't move. "You wouldn't want Matt to know you've been downstairs with Wade, would you?"

Tracy's hand shot out before she knew that she had even moved. The sound of her palm connecting with Chelsea's cheek cracked unbelievably loudly in the silence of the night, imprinting itself forever on her mind and her heart.

Before a second passed, Tracy grabbed Chelsea, and though the girl struggled, she refused to let her go until she had succeeded in wrapping her arms around her.

"Oh, my God, Chelsea. I'm so sorry. I'm

so, *so* sorry." She'd never struck anyone in her life. Never laid a hand on Matthew or Chelsea before. She'd never laid a hand on anyone in anger.

"I loved your father." She was quaking so hard she could barely stand, ashamed and appalled at what she'd done. "Once I loved him with all my heart."

Slowly, carefully, Chelsea slipped out of her arms but she didn't run out of the room as Tracy expected.

"This isn't about Dad, is it? It's about tonight. You're pissed because I didn't mail the invitations on time, aren't you?"

Tracy shook her head, feeling completely disjointed. "The party is already light-years away now."

"I'm sorry about the invitations. I put them in my big leather bag, the one I haul back and forth to work. They ended up on the bottom and I forgot all about them. Once I found them, I tried to call everyone."

Tracy held up her hand. "Please. It's all right. That doesn't really matter anyway, does it? What matters is what I just did." She closed her eyes, pressed her fingertips against her forehead, and rubbed it. "I don't deserve your forgiveness, honey, but I want you to know that I'll never, ever forgive myself for slapping you." She dropped her hand, met Chelsea's eyes, on the verge of tears again. "I'd do anything to take it back, but I can't."

Chelsea shrugged. "My mom wouldn't have thought twice about it."

"I'm not Monica."

"Definitely. That's why I've been so worried about you and this Wade guy. My mom's a pro when it comes to men, but you're so different. You and my dad had something special, and for a long time I was jealous. Tonight, on top of the mess I made of your party tonight, when I came in and saw you standing there with your eyes all puffy and your hair and clothes all messed up, I snapped."

"There are worse things than a low turnout at an open house." Tracy felt as limp as a wet washrag.

"But it was your big night to show off the place, and now . . ."

It was my big night all right.

"Go to bed, Chelsea. It's late, and we're both tired."

Chelsea didn't move. Instead she stared back at Tracy, her gaze sweeping her from head to toe.

"Did he attack you?"

"What?" Tracy drew back, startled.

351

"Wade Johnson. Did he attack you down-stairs?"

"Of course not." She walked over to the low dresser on the other side of the room and stared out the closest window. The sky was ink black. There wasn't a star to be seen. She closed her eyes and took a deep breath, wishing away all the things Jake had told her, wishing she could take back slapping Chelsea. Wishing she could start the whole night over again.

Then she thanked God that the girl was so resilient and, apparently, so forgiving.

Then she quietly admitted, "I'm lucky Wade Johnson is the man he is. *He's* the one who kept things from going too far tonight."

Chelsea hesitated. "What's really wrong, Tracy? If you aren't upset about the party, what is it?"

"Nothing you need to worry about. Nothing either of us needs to worry about tonight. I'm just tired. Everything will look better in the morning."

"Are you sure?"

Tracy nodded. "I'm sure."

She somehow held on until Chelsea said good night and left. Then she ran into her bathroom and threw up.

■ ■ ■ ■

"Mom?"

Lost in a dense fog, Tracy struggled toward the sound of Matthew's voice.

She was asleep and yet completely aware that she was dreaming — a strange, convoluted saga in which Glenn and Willa had shown up at the Heartbreak, luggage in hand, asking for the best room in the place.

Wade, walking around in low-slung Levis and nothing else, was the bellboy. He tried to serve them a plate of cinnamon rolls burned to the size and consistency of charcoal briquettes while Palmer Biggs danced around the sunroom with a naked Selma Gibbs. Palmer was so short that his nose was wedged between Selma's ample breasts. And now Matthew was there dressed as Spider-Man, calling her name.

"Mom?" Matthew again, shaking her shoulder.

She opened her eyes, finding herself face down in her pillow. The inside of her mouth tasted like the Gobi Desert. She sat up too fast and her head started clanging like the bells of Notre Dame. She'd fallen asleep completely dressed.

Shoving her hair out of her eyes, she

stared over at Matt, who was beside the bed in pajama bottoms and a fleece sweatshirt, his arms folded across his chest, his brow creased in a deep frown.

He looked exactly like Glenn.

Glenn. Suddenly the awful truth came rushing back. *Glenn and Willa.*

They had a child together.

"What is it, hon?"

"The roof is leaking."

"What? Where?" She clamped the sides of her throbbing head with both hands.

"In the kitchen. It's dripping all over the kitchen. I put bowls and pans under the drips, but water is pinging out onto the linoleum."

"Did a pipe break?"

"It's *raining,* Mom."

Raining. Again. And hard, too, if the sound of it was any indication.

She glanced over at the clock on the bedside table and realized she'd slept right through the alarm.

Jumping up was a bad, bad idea. Her head started to spin, so she braced a hand against the wall and closed her eyes.

"Mom? Are you okay? How come you slept in your clothes? Your eyes are all puffy."

She swallowed. "I'm fine. I ate something salty. I got to bed late. Have you had breakfast?" She wondered what Wade was thinking when she didn't take coffee and rolls downstairs.

"I had Cap'n Crunch."

"Where's Chelsea?"

"Gone to meet Eric someplace."

"Go down to the laundry room and bring back the yellow plastic bucket to put under the worst drip, okay?"

He nodded, suddenly important for having been given a real chore. "I will."

She looked up, remembering that her room was beneath the attic. She'd have to go check it for leaks up there, too.

"If you run into Mr. Johnson, tell him that I'll bring the coffee down shortly."

"Okay, Chief." He saluted before he charged out of the room.

She refused to look in the mirror as she walked past on her way out of the room. The kitchen felt cold and damp. Rain streaked down the windows facing the ocean as the storm blew onshore.

She measured out coffee before going back to her room to clean up.

It took fifteen minutes to shower, pull her hair into a ponytail, and use enough eyedrops and makeup to hide some of the damage.

She poured herself a cup of coffee and,

355

before she could change her mind, dialed Willa's number. Clutching the phone to her ear, she closed her eyes and thought she was ready, but she wasn't prepared for the shock of hearing Willa's voice.

"This is Tracy," she managed somehow after Willa said hello.

"Tracy!" There was a slight pause. "How was the party? I'll bet it was fabulous."

Hot coffee sloshed over the rim of the mug. She barely got it into the sink before she let it go. *Willa.* The woman had no idea she knew everything.

Her hand tightened on the phone.

"Tracy? Are you still there? Can you hear me?"

A blessed, icy calm came over her. "Yes. I'm here." She took a deep breath. "The party was fine. Great." *Just peachy.*

"I'm sorry I had to miss it."

I'll just bet you are.

Willa sounded drained. No wonder. Her lover, the man who'd given her a child, the man who'd bought her an expensive home in one of the most exclusive areas on the coast, was dead.

"How are you doing, Willa?"

There was a pause. "Fine, why?"

"I was worried about you after you left the other day. You looked so . . . sad."

Another pause. "I'm all right."

"That's good." Tracy paced over to the middle of the room and watched rainwater plunk into her pottery mixing bowl. She felt completely disconnected, thoroughly un-emotional. As if she were another woman entirely.

"You know, your visit got me thinking. It's been *way* too long since we've had lunch together. How long has it been? A couple of years?" Using the toe of her tennis shoe, she adjusted the position of the bowl beneath the drip.

Willa's voice was so soft, Tracy could barely hear it. "I have no idea when I'll be up in your area again."

"No problem. I have to drive down there to pick up a special order this week anyway," Tracy lied. "I'd love to take you to lunch."

"I'm not sure —"

You're not getting off that easy.

"Oh, come on. It's been years. I'm not taking no for an answer. What day this week is best?" She heard Willa shuffling pages, imagined her at her desk, checking her calendar.

"Tomorrow at one. That's probably too soon."

Not even if I have to walk all the way.

"I'll be there. Should I pick you up at your office?"

"I'll meet you at the Brown Pelican."

"That would be great. I haven't been there in ages."

"If the weather stays bad . . ."

Tracy glanced toward the window. Rain smeared the glass, distorting the view.

"I'm sure it will clear, but I'll call if I can't make it. I'll see you tomorrow at one, Willa."

They said good-bye. It wasn't until Tracy hung up and set the phone down that she realized what she'd done. She leaned against the kitchen counter, staring at the coffee mug in the sink and the coffee staining the porcelain around it.

"Mom?" Matt came running into the kitchen with bucket in hand, barely missed the mixing bowl, and pretended to be gasping for breath. "I saw Wade and told him to come get his own coffee."

"Oh, no!"

"Well, I already told him to." He set the bucket on the floor and started to pick up the mixing bowl.

"Let me do that." She started across the room and almost died when she realized that Wade had followed Matt in.

"I'll get it." Wade picked up the full mixing bowl and Matt swiftly replaced it with he bucket between drips.

Tracy's heart stumbled when Matt held up his hand and exchanged a high five with Wade the way he used to do with Glenn.

Dear Dad. I still miss you so much.

"Can I watch Nickelodeon, Mom?"

Trying to keep it together, she nodded. "Okay, but keep the volume down."

He started to run out of the room and then halted in the doorway, his expression serious. "I turned on the vacancy sign."

When she thought she hadn't any left, she felt a rush of tears. "Thanks, honey." She collected herself and then told Wade, "If he keeps this up, I'm going to have to put him on the payroll."

Wade walked over to her as soon as Matt was out of sight. She looked everywhere but into his eyes. He touched her shoulder, ran his hand down her arm to her wrist. His fingers were warm and gentle where they rested against her pulse point.

"How are you doing?"

Drawn by the kindness and genuine concern in his voice, she smiled. It was feeble, but it was a passable smile. "Not as bad as I thought I would be. I'll live."

"Good." He smelled like soap and shampoo and filled the small galley kitchen with his raw masculinity. Hard, but giving.

"Coffee?" She had a hard time forming a complete thought whenever he touched her.

"Sure."

She kissed him as he poured himself a cup of coffee.

"I'm sorry," she apologized. "I overslept."

"I was worried you wouldn't sleep at all."

She shrugged and admitted, "I was up most of the night."

He leaned back against the counter, crossed his ankles, and blew on a sip of black coffee.

She collected her own cup from the sink and started over.

"So, you're meeting Willa tomorrow?"

She glanced up quickly, as if caught doing something forbidden. "You heard?"

"I didn't mean to. I followed Matt in. I'm sorry."

He didn't look sorry. He looked curious and, more than that, he looked concerned. "She doesn't know that you know everything yet."

It wasn't a question, merely a statement. He'd crossed the room to stand in front of her. She felt drained and hollow, tempted to lean into him, to tap into his physical strength. "No, she doesn't know."

"Why put yourself through it, Tracy?" When he reached for her, she let him pull her within the circle of his arms.

She closed her eyes, pressing her cheek against his shirtfront. A button on his new denim work shirt dimpled her cheek.

"Because I still don't know everything, and I need to. I don't know when it started. I don't know how she could do this to me and Matthew and Chelsea." The memory of slapping Chelsea hurt as much as the actual act. She took a deep, shuddering breath. "I need the truth."

"I can't see you wanting to make her suffer, not even if she deserves it."

"I'm *not* doing this to make her suffer. I'm doing this for *me*. I need to see her face when she tries to explain. *If* she even tries."

He moved slightly, and she heard the clink of his coffee mug against the counter. Then he pulled her closer with both hands, nuzzling his lips against her hair.

Drawing strength from his comforting embrace, she remembered the look on Chelsea's face last night, her anger, her shock.

I'm human, too, not some perfect sitcom mom who has all the answers. I'm flesh and blood. I need love, too.

Even if it's not forever.

As Tracy slipped her arms around Wade, she couldn't help but think of how differently things could have gone last night if not for this man's honor.

She raised her face to him and whispered, "Just a kiss?"

"Of course." He brushed her lips, slowly, tenderly.

And suddenly she was lost in sensation — until the *Rugrats* theme song drifted in from the living room.

"Thank you," she said. Though her world was still rocking, she found herself able to smile, to step back. "That was nice."

More than nice, it had sizzled. Right now though, the last thing she needed was a stimulant.

He reached for his coffee. "Don't go to Santa Barbara tomorrow."

She shook her head. "I have to."

"What about Matt?"

"I'll call Carly. She won't mind having him over."

"Are you going to tell her where you're going? Does she know about Glenn?"

"Jake was supposed to tell her for me. And no, I'm not going to tell her I'm meeting Willa." She hoped she made her point when she added, "And you aren't either."

"What about guests? What if someone wants to check in?"

She remembered Vince, Geoff's partner,

offering to help out last night.

"I have someone who can fill in for me."

"I see you have this all thought out, but I can fill in for you," he offered.

"You've already done more than enough, Wade. Besides, it's a good idea for me to train someone to take over if I ever need help. Vincent will be great." *And you won't be here forever.*

She glanced out the window again. The rain was a hazy gray sheet still battering the coast. The swells were dark and angry, topped by whitecaps that rose and sank beneath the roiling water.

Captain Ezra Poole flashed through her mind.

Her whole life was riding out a typhoon and only she had the power to keep it from capsizing.

"Why don't you take some time to go through the *Lantana*'s logs in the attic?" she suggested.

"I'm not opening *that* can of worms again." He sounded determined not to discuss the logs or his writing again. Their argument seemed light-years away now.

"For whatever reason, you've come here to tell Ezra's story . . ." she began.

He cut her off. "Tracy, look, I didn't come here to tell Ezra's story. I still have no idea

363

how it came to me."

"Please, Wade. I don't *care* how it happened right now. Please, use the logs. Learn all you can about Ezra Poole."

"You still don't believe me."

She searched his eyes, knowing that *he* believed what he was telling her.

"Everyone deserves a little personality quirk."

"The other day you weren't as forgiving."

"I've been on a roller-coaster ride since then. Finish your story. It's wonderful. People need stories about lasting love, today more than ever."

He was silent, thoughtful. She could tell that he didn't approve of what she had planned for tomorrow — but he didn't try to argue.

No matter what he might have said, come hell or high water, she was going to talk to Willa face-to-face.

CHAPTER THIRTY-SEVEN

Monday the sky was brilliant blue without a wisp of a cloud in sight. The storm had washed away the smog, and every tree and shrub, every blade of grass sparkled with vibrant shades of green — lime, emerald, chartreuse.

A few minutes before one, Tracy pulled into the parking lot and walked down the curving sidewalk lined with fan palms toward the Brown Pelican, a restaurant tucked into a cove on the beach in Santa Barbara.

It was a casual, popular spot right on the sand of a broad, level beach. The decor was typical funky waterfront with rough, weathered wood siding and old pier pilings cut in staggered heights bordering the flower bed. A wall of windows faced the ocean. Today the Pacific was so calm, it was hard to believe the storm had ever happened.

Glancing at her reflection in the window,

forcing herself to walk slowly, Tracy hoped that her nerves didn't show. She'd chosen her outfit carefully, changing three times before finally deciding on her favorite Tommy Bahama beige silk slacks, a matching sleeveless shell, and in case the mercurial weather changed again, a thin silk sweater tied around her shoulders.

Tracy saw Willa immediately after stepping through the front door. She paused at the hostess station.

"I see my party," Tracy told the twenty-something hostess. The shapely, tanning-bed-bronzed blond grabbed a menu and led the way to Willa's table.

As yet Willa hadn't seen her. She was sitting at a table for two beside the front window, staring out at the water with her chin propped on her hand, her eyes deeply shadowed. She looked completely miserable.

And why wouldn't she? Her lover is dead.

Did betraying her best friend ever enter her mind?

Willa looked completely startled when she realized Tracy was already there, standing beside the table. The hostess quietly slipped away as Tracy pulled out her chair and sat down.

"You're here." Willa's smile faltered, then

slowly reappeared.

"Is everything all right?"

Willa slowly nodded. "I've been wanting to see you again, actually."

Tracy fingered the napkin wrapped around the silverware, took a deep breath, and forced herself to stay calm.

"It's been a long time since we've done this." Her voice sounded far off and tinny, as if escaping an old Victrola.

There was a distance in Willa's eyes as she nodded. The even, blunt ends of her smooth dark hair brushed her jawline.

Tracy unwrapped her silverware and spread her napkin on her lap. There was a lull while the waitress took her order. She chose a simple garden salad, knowing she would have to force-feed herself. Actually tasting anything would be impossible.

Tempted, she denied herself a martini, deciding to stick with club soda and lime. She didn't want to end up on *Eyewitness News.*

Betrayed wife kills husband's mistress in local eatery.

"Remember years ago, when I first met Glenn and would vent about all the little things that bugged me about him? All the dumb little things that didn't really matter? You were such a good listener. So sweet to put up with it."

Willa didn't flinch, but there was a faraway look in her eyes again. Tracy swiftly changed the subject. "How's the decorating going?"

"Fine. I'm finishing up a few projects."

Their salads were delivered to the table along with a small basket of bread. Tracy chose a piece and tore off the crust, one crumb at a time.

Willa didn't even lift her fork, but kept her hands in her lap. "How are you doing now that you aren't focused on the open house?"

"Funny you should ask." Tracy popped a bite of hard crust into her mouth. It could have been cardboard for all she cared. Willa seemed to be dissolving right before her eyes.

She took a deep breath, swallowed the bread crust. "Life is always interesting, don't you think? I mean, six months ago I was married. Everyone thought I had a devoted husband and was living a fairy-tale life. But now . . ." She paused, leaned back, and realized that she wasn't nervous at all now.

There was so much strength in knowledge. So much power in having the upper hand.

"But now Glenn's gone and I'm running a hotel on my own and . . ." She paused again, leveling her gaze on Willa, ". . . and not only is my husband dead, but I found out that he had been sleeping with an old friend for years."

Slowly what little color that was left in Willa's cheeks drained away. The violet circles beneath her eyes deepened as her hand went to her throat.

She opened her mouth, but nothing came out. Not a sound. Tears welled in her eyes. She did nothing to stop them as they slipped over her bottom lashes.

The woman looked positively pitiful.

Tracy felt nothing. Not even triumph when she played her trump card. The betrayal was still too raw, still too real.

When Willa finally spoke, Tracy could barely hear her over the chatter around them.

"How long have you known?"

"Long enough."

"You didn't say anything when I came by . . ."

Tracy thought about that day. How sad Willa had looked. How she'd assumed that her friend was simply sharing her pain. Empathizing with her.

"I didn't know then."

"Who told you?"

"A private investigator."

Willa's mouth dropped. She leaned forward. "You hired a private investigator?"

"To go over Glenn's books. To see if I could find out how he got into such debt. The trail led back to you. To his cash withdrawals. To the house he bought for you" —

"Tracy —"

— "to the daughter you had with him."

"I know what you must think of me."

Tracy shook her head. "No. You have no idea. Actually," a tight, angry laugh escaped her, "it's funny, but there's really no way to express what I feel, or what I've been thinking since I found out."

Willa shoved her plate aside, shook her head, and leaned forward. "Believe me, I never planned to fall in love with Glenn. It just happened."

Tracy quickly cut her off.

"How did you let it happen, Willa? How does a woman let her feelings go beyond attraction for another woman's husband? To an old friend's husband? What kind of woman lets that happen? How could you, of all people, let that happen?"

"I couldn't help myself."

Glenn's handsome, boyish smile came to mind. His shining sandy hair, deep blue eyes. His ready laugh. He'd always been at-

tractive to women. Handsome and successful. It was a tough combination for some
women to ignore.

Willa turned toward the window as the
waitress approached them. The girl glanced
down at their untouched plates.

"Is everything all right?" she asked.

Tracy dismissed her with a nod and a
quick, "Fine, thanks."

It was another moment or two before
Willa could even look at Tracy again.

"He loved you, Tracy." There was no trace
of spite or envy in Willa's tone. She sounded
sincere, caring as always. "He said he'd
never divorce you. He made that clear right
from the start, and I would never have asked
him to."

"So, you were content to sleep with him
and take his money?"

"It wasn't like that."

"No? Then how was it, Willa?"

"It was . . . like nothing I've ever felt for
anyone. I didn't care that he could only give
me stolen hours. I knew going into it that
he'd never, ever leave you. He wouldn't do
that to you, or to Matthew."

Most especially to Matthew.

Tracy knew how much Glenn always
regretted the effect his divorce from Monica had had on Chelsea. She could see him

371

wanting to avoid doing the same to Matthew.

"I can believe he stayed for Matthew, but if he *truly* loved me, he would never have slept with you."

"Don't you think it's possible to love more than one person?"

Two nights ago she had been ready to sleep with Wade, and she'd known him a month. If she were completely honest with herself, she knew she had been attracted to him almost from her first glance. But if she'd still been married? Or if Wade was married?

She didn't have to think twice about what choice she would have made then.

"Glenn took a vow to be faithful, Willa."

"You must have suspected something," Willa said softly.

"Certainly, things were . . . different." There was no way she was going to let Willa know exactly how things had been between her and Glenn those last few years. She changed the subject, asking one of the questions she'd been wrestling with for two days now.

"What about your child? What were you going to tell her when she was old enough to understand? 'Your daddy has another family? A real family?' "

"I was going to cross that bridge when, and if, I came to it."

"So, you *were* hoping Glenn and I would divorce."

"No."

When Willa reached for her water glass, Tracy noticed that her hand was trembling wildly. For a second she thought the woman was going to drop it.

Willa took a quick sip of water, no more, and looked pained.

"My daughter's name is Mary Jane."

"After the shoes?"

"After my grandmother."

Tracy tried to not care what Willa and Glenn had named their daughter. She tried to forget how much the child looked like Matt.

"I know about all the money, Willa."

"No," Willa shook her head, "you don't."

"I know that Glenn gave you a sizable stipend every month for the last year, and that he bought you a house in Montecito."

"It was all for Mary Jane."

"And you."

"But you don't —"

"What? I don't *what*? I know everything, thanks to Jake Montgomery."

"Tracy, let me finish a sentence."

Tracy didn't want to *let* her do anything.

How Willa could sit there and justify any-thing was beyond her. Her anger at Glenn, at both of them, was back — hard, cutting, and bitter, and she hated feeling this way. All this anger didn't fit. It hurt like nothing she'd ever felt before — like walking a mile in a pair of shoes that were two sizes too small.

She looked down at her salad, at the crumbs of bread crust scattered everywhere, and resisted the urge to sweep them onto the floor.

"Fine, so finish." She dared Willa to make any more excuses.

"I'm dying, Tracy. I have leukemia and it's reached the terminal stage."

CHAPTER THIRTY-EIGHT

Tracy's gaze quickly touched on Willa's sunken cheeks, the dark circles beneath her eyes, the way her veins showed like blue lines on a road map across the backs of her hands.

"Dying?" Not mourning Glenn so deeply that she had lost an inordinate amount of weight. *Dying?* "Are you sure?" The woman was only in her midthirties.

"They've tried everything. The last experimental drug nearly killed me."

"Did Glenn know?"

"Of course. That's where most of the money went. The disease showed up when I was pregnant with Mary Jane. I couldn't have treatments then, of course. After she was born, it came on with a vengeance."

"Does she have it, too?" Dear God. Tracy could never wish that for a child, any child.

Willa's face mirrored her deeply embedded relief. "No, thank God. She's fine." She took a deep breath. "My insurance would pay for only so much. Glenn is . . . *was* paying for my treatments. The cost was exorbitant." She looked down at her hands as if more ashamed at having to take the money than for the affair.

They fell into an uncomfortable silence.

Tracy's anger had fizzled like a bad Fourth of July bottle rocket. The hurt was still there, deep and searing as a terrible burn, but the fury of her anger was gone.

As she looked across the table at Willa, at this new, pale, emaciated version of Willa, those long-ago years full of laughter and friendship they'd shared in Indiana battled the weight of her hurt and anger.

Her positive outlook on life had always been her mainstay. It had pulled her through the worst of times and kept her going. It had given her the strength, the will, to start over with nothing but the Heartbreak Hotel and a vision.

Now the attitude that she'd fought so hard to nurture all her life was fighting her need to strike back for what Glenn and Willa had done.

"The house . . ." Willa's words drifted away. She looked as if she were about to collapse as she reached for her water again.

"Maybe you should try to eat something."

Willa shook her head no and set the water glass down without taking a drink. "The house was a fixer. It was in terrible shape when Glenn bought it, but he saw the potential in buying in Montecito. He had one of his contractors remodel it and we moved in. The house was never for me, Tracy. It's for Mary Jane. The equity in it is her trust fund. Glenn promised to take care of her." Her lower lip trembled as her eyes filled with tears again. "Now he's gone."

Tracy tried not to care, but that was simply too tiring. She felt like a ship becalmed. All the wind was out of her sails and she was exhausted.

Willa rested her elbows on the table and rubbed her temples.

"I had my mind made up to tell you today. I know you probably don't believe me now, but it's true. When I dropped by the Heartbreak in May, I didn't come to visit. I was there expressly to tell you, but I couldn't do it. Now there isn't much time left, and I wanted you to know."

"So now I know." Tracy thought of how she'd walked into the restaurant ready to take no prisoners. Ready to see Willa squirm.

"I need your help, Tracy, though I don't have the right to ask for it."

"No. You don't. I can't forgive you, Willa. Not this." Her mind suddenly flashed on Chelsea. *"I'm so, so sorry, honey."*

She forced herself to focus on Willa.

She's my oldest friend. In my life long before Glenn. Before California.

"I'm not asking for your forgiveness," Willa said. "I know that would be asking too much. What I want is for you to take Mary Jane after I'm gone."

"What?"

"Raise my daughter, Tracy. I have no family. No one else. Besides, there's no one on earth I'd trust her with but you."

The image of the smiling redheaded little girl flashed through Tracy's mind. The little girl who looked so much like Glenn. So much like Matthew.

As if Willa had read her mind, she quickly reminded her, "She's Matt's half-sister, Tracy."

She's Glenn's child.

Would Glenn have come to me? Would he have laid it all on the table, the affair, the money, the house in Montecito? Would he have asked me to raise his and Willa's daughter after Willa was gone?

"Was that Glenn's plan?"

"For the first time in his life, Glenn had no plan. He refused to believe the treatments wouldn't work. He kept going from day to day, pushing his projects, pushing himself. I tried to tell him that it was past time he told you. I only have a few more months, maybe even a year, but only if I'm lucky. Who knew Glenn would go first?"

Reeling, Tracy sat in stunned silence, staring.

Willa shuddered. "I know that if things were different, if I asked you to raise a child of mine who wasn't Glenn's, that you wouldn't bat an eye. You wouldn't hesitate to say yes."

"But this is too much."

"I know."

"I feel like I'm the lead in a soap opera. The next thing you know, Glenn will walk through the door telling me it wasn't really him we buried, but his evil twin, one that no one even knew existed." Despite the gravity of the situation — or perhaps because of it — Tracy laughed.

Even Willa smiled, though weakly. "*That's* what I want for Mary Jane, Tracy. I want her to be able to laugh in the face of adversity, to make lemonade when life gives her lemons. It's something I've never been able to do. I want you to pass that on to my daughter."

"Willa, I *can't.*"

"Don't refuse me outright. Go home and think about it. I know that if anyone can make sense of this situation, if anyone truly understands what would be best for Mary Jane, it's you."

"Just because I'm able to laugh when I feel like crying, don't make me out to be Mother Teresa. I'm human, Willa, and right now I'm mad as hell."

"You're the one who has always done the right thing. You're the one who truly believes in herself. That's why I want you to raise Mary Jane."

Somehow Tracy managed to pay the check. She left Willa sitting at the table and walked out of the Brown Pelican. She was across the parking lot, standing beside her car, before she realized she'd even moved.

Just as she pressed the lock button on her key ring, she heard the sound of a Harley starting up across the lot and thought of Wade. As she opened her car door, the sound grew louder. Looking up, she realized it was Wade as he came riding across the parking lot, headed in her direction.

He pulled up in the empty parking space beside her and killed the engine. He was off the bike, taking her in his arms in two long strides. "Tracy."

"Is something wrong at home? Is Matthew

all right?" Her words were muffled against the front of his leather jacket.

"Matthew's fine. Everything's fine. I was worried about you."

She drew back, still in his arms.

He was frowning as he thumbed away her tears.

"You don't sound happy about it."

"Yeah, well, I don't much like to worry. I wanted to make sure you weren't too upset to drive home."

"Some tough guy you are."

"Hey, it was a beautiful day for a ride anyway." He shrugged, trying to make light of the fact that he'd ridden all the way down here just to be sure she was capable of driving herself back.

She looked around, not wanting Willa to walk out of the Brown Pelican and see her wrapped in Wade's arms. She didn't want to see Willa at all. She took a deep breath and stepped away from him.

"I'm okay. Really." *Confused. Empty.* She tried to smile and failed miserably.

"How did it go?"

"Certainly not the way I expected."

"Want to talk about it?"

"I don't know how to explain what just happened in there." She hadn't yet come to grips with what Willa had asked of her. She certainly wasn't ready to try to tell anyone about it. Not even him. "How are things at home?"

"Vincent actually checked in three guests. A couple on their honeymoon, and a single man."

"Maybe I should leave more often. Maybe it's me," she mumbled.

"I'm worried the single guy might be competition."

She found herself smiling. With Wade beside her, the whole sordid stew her life was in seemed a little less bleak. She couldn't bear to think of him leaving tomorrow, let alone ask if he were still planning to go.

He rubbed her arm. "You ready to head back? I'll follow you."

"I'm ready. I'm so ready."

Despite the turmoil inside her, Tracy realized that she was desperately looking forward to getting home. There was so much to think about, so much she didn't want to face yet — though she would have to sooner or later.

Willa and Glenn. Willa's illness and her impossible request.

And Wade. His life, his work, was in L.A.

They hadn't spoken of his leaving since Saturday night.

She hadn't been foolish enough to believe that he would stay, that at the very least he'd ask if he could keep in touch, if he could see her again.

She chose to deal with things later. She'd had enough for now.

She slid into her BMW, started the engine, and headed out of the lot. As she headed up the coast, she realized that for the first time ever, she was thinking of the Heartbreak as home.

CHAPTER THIRTY-NINE

The sun had already set and the sky was getting dark as Matt sat on the top porch step waiting for Wade. He watched the tall man come walking up the bluff path and waited until he reached the garden walk behind the hotel before running out to meet him.

"Hey, Wade. Mom says you're leaving tomorrow." The Harley was way cool and Wade wasn't so bad. He might even miss him a little.

"I'm heading out in the morning." When they were at the back steps, Wade sat down on the porch and stared out at the ocean.

Matt sat down beside him. "You coming back sometime?"

"Maybe."

"You gotta go back to work or something?"

"Something like that."

Matt noticed that Wade sure wasn't talking much tonight. Neither was Mom. He hoped that she wasn't going to be too sad after Wade left. He hadn't thought about it much before, but maybe she needed a grown-up around to talk to. He didn't know how to talk Wade into staying a little while longer, so he just sat there thinking about how much he'd miss sneaking out to sit on the Harley. He remembered the day Wade went shopping with them, and then he had a great idea.

"Wait here, okay, Wade?"

"Sure."

Matt jumped up and ran back into the house and up to his room to grab the disposable camera off his dresser. When he ran back out to the porch, Wade was still there.

"Here," he said, holding out the camera.

"Want me to take a picture?" Wade turned the camera over in his hand.

"I used all the film. You can have it."

"Don't you want to get them developed?" Wade was looking up at him, trying to figure it all out.

Giving Wade the camera made him feel really good. So good he couldn't stop smiling.

"You can take it with you and keep the pictures. That way you'll always remember your vacation here."

Wade tried to hand the camera back. "That's really nice of you, but it's yours."

"It's a going-away present. I want you to take it with you." Matt sat down beside him again. It was getting darker out. It was hard to see the ocean now, but he could still hear it.

Wade didn't say anything. He just sat there holding the camera in his hands, staring at it. Finally he looked over and said, "How about this — I'll get doubles made of the photos and send them to you."

"Wouldja?"

"Sure."

"Way *cool.*" Matt wondered if he'd feel this bad every time guests checked out. He thought about the new guy who had checked in earlier and decided: *probably not.* He had a feeling that Wade was different. That if he stayed a little longer, they might get to be real good friends. Then he had another great idea.

"Since you're leaving, you think you could give me a ride on the Harley?"

This time, Wade laughed. "Is that why you gave me the camera? Is this a bribe?"

"No. I gave you the camera so you won't forget us. So how about the ride?"

"Your mom would kill me if I gave you a

ride. I think you know that already."

"Yeah. I know. I just thought I'd ask." He rested his elbows on his knees and his chin on his fists. The porch lights came on, making it even harder to see what was out beyond the garden.

"Matt?"

"What?"

"Thanks again for the camera."

"That's okay."

"Even without photos, I won't forget you."

Alone in his room a few minutes later, Wade carefully stacked the *Lantana* logs on the dresser. That evening he'd sorted and scanned through fifteen years of shipping details from the late 1800s, right up to the year Ezra Poole's ship had been lost at sea.

Ezra was through dictating. The renovations were finished. It was time to go.

His saddlebags were packed and lying on the chair across the room. Leaving wasn't something he wanted to do. For the first time in his life he'd met a woman who he could actually imagine sharing his life with, someone he would look forward to waking up with every morning. But Tracy deserved far more happiness than he could offer her.

She'd never know how much her trust, her smile and determination, her warmth and caring meant to him. She'd never know that his taking refuge here for a few weeks had saved his life. He would never forget her or the Heartbreak.

He reached for a log written the year before the ship went down and headed for the bed, intent on making a last few notes, when there came a soft knock on the door. It was late, too late for Matt to be up, and knowing it could be only Tracy, he wondered if his longing to see her had somehow conjured her up.

"Hi." She was carrying an open bottle of Pinot Grigio and two wineglasses. "May I come in?"

"Of course."

She glanced over at the stack of ship's logs. "If you're working —"

"No. I was making a few final notes." He closed the door behind her.

She walked immediately to the desk and poured two glasses of wine. He couldn't take his eyes off her as she crossed the room and offered him one.

The confrontation with Willa had affected her deeply. She not only seemed a world away, but there was a hesitancy about her, an uncertainty, as if she were treading very rocky ground, watching every step.

"Here's to life." She lifted her glass in a toast.

"To life." He raised his own goblet, touched it to hers. His mouth touched the rim of the cool glass. He would rather be savoring the sweetness of her lips.

"How's the writing coming?"

"The dreams stopped the day the story ended with Ezra taking that swan dive over the bluff." After another drink, he shrugged and added, "It's still a goddamn romance."

"Literary fiction has its place, but give me a happy ending any day. I wish I still had time to read." As she laughed softly, the sound settled heavily around his heart.

"Ezra killed himself," he reminded her. "You call that a happy ending?" He thought about his own ending — which may not have been much different than Ezra's if he hadn't checked in.

"So, that proves that technically, you *didn't* write a romance. The hero never, ever dies in a true romance novel." She walked over to the French doors. He saw her become perfectly still when she noticed his saddlebags lying on the chair.

"You're really leaving," she said softly.

"Yes." He ached with the wish that he had made love to her that night.

She set her empty wineglass on top of the

dresser. When she turned to him, a wistful smile lifted the corners of her lips. "What if I asked you to stay?"

He set his glass down, crossed the room, and stopped short of holding her.

"If you asked me, I'd have to tell you that that was impossible."

"But you won't tell me why."

"No."

Her eyes searched his face. "Have you done something illegal?"

"It's nothing like that, believe me."

"What if someone asked the impossible of you, what would you do?" She was watching him closely.

A few weeks ago, he thought writing again was out of the question, that living was impossible. Staying here any longer would make it impossible to ever leave. And eventually, that would make life impossible for all of them.

"I can't stay, Tracy." It hurt to say the words.

"I'm not asking you to."

She stepped closer to the window and stared out into the dark night. "Willa asked me to do something today that would require me to be a far better person than I am. I don't have it in me."

"She asked you to forgive her?"

"She's dying."

Shocked, he had no idea what to say.

"Willa's dying, and she asked me to raise her and Glenn's daughter."

"No one would blame you if you refused." He went to her, took her hands in his. There were no tears in her eyes tonight. Only confusion. Only questions. "What about her family?"

"She doesn't have anyone."

"Before she was Glenn's lover, she was your friend. Someone like you, someone with a heart as big as yours, would find her request hard to ignore."

"Her daughter is Matt and Chelsea's half-sister."

"Exactly."

"I'm no saint, Wade. People would think I'm crazy."

"From what I gather, they thought you were crazy for taking on this place."

"I had no choice."

"There's always a choice. I learned that the hard way. But tough choices don't scare you. You've proven that here. If anyone can do what Willa's asked, you can. I know the welfare of that child means more to you than what people would think."

"What would I tell Chelsea and Matt?"

"Chelsea is old enough to handle the

truth." He thought of the disposable camera tucked in his backpack. "Someday, when Matt's old enough, you'll explain it to him. He'll know you made the only choice you could make."

"How can you be so sure?"

"He's your son."

"It won't be easy."

Unable to resist, he went to her, took her in his arms, and struggled to find the right words. "Life isn't ever easy. But I've learned something being here with you, watching you pull your life back together. It's not what happens to us that matters as much as how we take the experience and make something out of it."

"Thank you," she said softly, holding tight to his hands. "You've given me a lot to think about."

"You'll do the right thing."

"I hope so." She seemed in no hurry to leave his arms, and though it was sweet torture, holding her close, he couldn't let her go.

"Matt fell asleep early," she dropped her gaze to their hands, "and Chelsea agreed to work late tonight."

He went perfectly still, unwilling to break the spell, sensing a distinct change in her.

She pulled away slightly, just far enough

to look up into his eyes. "I want you to make love to me. I guarantee that I'm not hysterical tonight. I haven't had too much to drink, either."

"Tracy —"

She sighed and pressed her fingertips against his lips before he could respond. "Hear me out. Please." Refusing her once was the single hardest thing he'd ever done. He had no idea how he was going to do it again.

"This has nothing to do with what Glenn did, nothing to do with salvaging my ego. I want this night to remember you by when the days are long and the nights are longer. I want *you* tonight, Wade. I'm not asking for anything else. You're leaving. I know that. My own life is in chaos. If you don't feel safe enough to tell me whatever it is that's going on with you, I'll accept that . . ."

"Tracy, I *would* tell you if I thought it would change things, make things better, not worse —"

"Don't make me beg you," she whispered.

"You make it impossible for a man to say no."

"I don't think there are many men who would have said no the first time."

"Just the fools."

She shook her head as she wrapped her

arms around his neck. "Just the heroes."

"I'm no hero, Tracy, believe me. I am no hero."

"You could have fooled me."

"You don't know me."

"I know that you've got a kind heart. That you're willing to help someone in a bind. That you're caring, intelligent, and talented. I've looked forward to talking with you, to being with you, kissing you. Isn't that enough?"

When she drew his head down, stood up on her tiptoes, and pressed her lips to his, so pliant and willing, he lost the will to resist. Her lips parted beneath his, her hands moved to gently frame his face. They were both breathless when the kiss ended.

He opened his eyes, found her staring into them with a need that matched his own. "I can't do this without telling you everything."

She put her fingertips against his lips. "*Don't.* Not if it will change things between us."

"Tracy —"

"Will it? Will it make me see you differently?"

"Probably. I don't see how it wouldn't."

Unshed tears glistened in her eyes. "I really can't take any more right now," she whispered. "Please, just leave it alone. Leave things the way they are and make love to me."

"Come here." He led her over to the bed, waited until she sat down before he left her, collected their wineglasses, and refilled them. After handing her the wine, he sat down on the edge of the bed. It sagged beneath his weight. Her heart was pounding in her ears, drowning out the sound of the sea. She took a hearty sip of wine, keeping her gaze riveted on his face.

She could see that he was still haunted by what he had wanted to tell her, but she didn't want to hear it. Not any part of it. Not tonight.

She wanted *him* — the Wade she'd come to know. She wanted to remember him just the way she'd known him, but he looked so grave, she had to lighten the mood.

"Are you afraid Ezra is watching?" She pretended to be looking for someone and even peered into the corners.

At that, Wade finally smiled. She slipped her arm around his waist, amazed at how perfectly she fit against him.

"Now that I've written his story, Ezra's through with me." He finished his wine and leaned around her to deposit the glass on the nightstand. "I don't want to waste what precious time we have left talking about a ghost. Besides, you're the only one haunting my dreams lately." She missed his warmth when he left her to close the curtains.

This should be the beginning, not the beginning of the end.

She wanted to be able to remember this night for the rest of her life. To remember the gentle touch of his hand, the scent of the salt air mingled with that of their bodies. She wanted this to be a night that Wade would never forget — no matter how far away he went. She wanted him to think of this night, to remember her, for the rest of his life.

"Promise me something." He slipped his arms around her again, held her close, stroked her tenderly.

"Anything." She owed him that much. She'd begged for this. Initiated it. She would never, ever regret this night.

"No good-byes," he whispered.

She knew why. She couldn't bear it either. "No good-byes." Suddenly her heart was breaking. The image of Ezra and Violette standing on the widow's walk flashed through her mind. Their parting had been forever.

"Promise?" He kissed her temple.

"I promise."

Afterward, Wade opened his eyes and found her lying on her side, her chin propped on her hand, smiling down at him.

She'd never know that he would be dreaming of this night for a long, long time to come. Him, the guy who couldn't remember the name of the first girl he'd ever slept with. Until now, until Tracy, none of them had ever mattered. He never thought he'd experience this kind of desire, this kind of sharing. It was the stuff of trite novels, of sappy love songs.

He'd never believed in this kind of emotion, this kind of need. Then again, he'd never believed in ghost stories, either.

The saddest thing in the world was that he believed now — and it was too late.

Not only would he be haunted by her memory, but by the thought that someone else would eventually check in to the Heartbreak who would surely fall in love with her, seduce her. Worse yet, maybe even break her heart.

She was a warm, vibrant woman.

She had so much to give. She deserved to love and be loved. She deserved more than what her husband had done to her.

She definitely deserved better than he was.

He found her gazing down at him from beneath her lashes, eyes lazy, glazed with passion and desire.

The room was dark when Tracy opened her eyes again and found herself alone in Wade's room. Exhausted, satiated, she'd drifted off to sleep in his arms.

A glance at the clock and she knew she'd slept no more than twenty minutes. She reached over, touched the indentation in his pillow. The fabric was still warm.

"Wade?" The only sound beside the ocean's roar was that of her own breathing. She slid out of bed, ran to the bathroom, and pushed the door open. It was dark inside. He was already gone.

A sound escaped her, a cry that came from the depths of her soul. She covered her mouth with both hands, her shoulders heaving, dry sobs welling up from her toes.

Suddenly a rumble of sound cut through the night.

Wade's Harley.

She'd never hear a motorcycle again without thinking of him.

He had to have walked out a moment before she woke up. Had he been somewhere in the hall? Heard her stir before he let himself out? Had he been tempted to turn around? To take her in his arms and stay?

"No good-byes."

"No good-byes. I promise."

She ran to the French doors, threw them open, and ran out onto the porch. From there she could see the driveway. Helpless, she watched him turn the bike in the direction of the road.

If he looked back, he might see her standing exposed to the elements, her heart stripped bare, too. Did he know he was taking it with him? Would he care?

He gunned the engine, pulled out of the drive, and headed south. He didn't look back.

The chill of the sea spray kissed her skin as she focused on the Harley's taillight. Tears blurred the red glow that grew smaller and smaller until it was reduced to the size of an ember, bobbing in the darkness as the bike hugged the curves in the coast road.

She slipped back inside, locked the doors, gathered up her clothes. She thought of taking a shower, then decided she wanted to wear Wade's scent awhile longer. She threw on her clothes and went upstairs.

Chelsea's bedroom door was closed, which meant she had come in sometime earlier. Had the girl looked for her down-stairs? Had she walked down the hall? Heard them making love?

She hoped not. Things had been all right between them since the confrontation after the open house. Chelsea may have forgiven her, but every time she looked at the girl, she still felt ashamed.

Tonight she felt no shame about what she'd done with Wade, though. No shame at all.

She looked in on Matt. One of his plastic Transformers lay on the floor beside the bed. She picked it up, set it on his bedside table, kissed him on the forehead, and went into her own room.

Wrapping her favorite faded terry robe over her clothes, she went up to the widow's walk. Her skin still tingled from his touch. The cool night air was damp, but it didn't faze her.

She didn't know she was crying until she reached up to brush her hair back off her cheek and found her skin wet with tears.

For a while, couldn't she simply pretend that he was still downstairs, still in his room? Wouldn't it be easier to pretend, at least for now, that she would see him again in the morning? That she'd find him sitting in the sunroom, sipping hot coffee, going over his notes, leafing through the morning news?

It was easier to think about looking up to see him coming down the hall in his loose, easy stride, his jeans riding low on his hips, that slow, sensual half smile on his lips.

Easier to pretend, just for a little while, that she would see him again.

She was still alone, but no longer lonely. She had added a new chapter to her own story. A new memory. She'd survived Glenn's death and ultimate betrayal.

She would survive Wade leaving. She had to, no matter how much it hurt.

As she wiped her face on her sleeve, she pictured a secret spot deep inside her heart, a corner where she could safely tuck away a scrap of hope that their paths would someday cross again.

CHAPTER FORTY

The next morning the sun was struggling to shine through a cloud bank as valiantly as Tracy struggled with her aching heart while serving coffee to the guests who had arrived while she was at lunch with Willa.

Henri Brochard was a Frenchman in his mid-seventies who wore a bad toupee that stuck out around the sides of his head. His skin was the color of grade school paste, his hands and fingers long and tapered. He waved them around his head whenever he spoke, which was often.

Henri was taking his coffee and date nut bread with cream cheese in the sunroom at a table where he could sigh over the view. He wore a long silk dressing gown over striped pajamas. A burgundy fez rode his toupee.

A bittersweet ache filled her as she remembered Wade teasing her about the single male guest who might steal her heart.

A couple from South Dakota had taken their breakfast into the sitting room, where they sat opposite each other on the two sofas. Both of them were deep into novels, the wife so absorbed that she merely nodded and didn't even look up when Tracy asked if they'd like their coffees topped off.

She noticed the woman was reading a paperback, *An Even Dozen,* by Edward Cain. What seemed like light-years ago, someone at Global Mortgage had given Glenn a hardcover copy of the book when it first came out. She wondered if it was upstairs in a box someplace and then thought: *Who am I kidding? As if I have time to read.*

She left the guests to themselves and went back upstairs, where she found Matt in his room, drawing. Needing a few minutes to catch up on paperwork and balance her checkbook, she was on her way to her room when she heard the water running in Chelsea and Matt's bathroom.

Chelsea usually left for work at seven and it was well past eight. She gathered up her bookkeeping, intending to work at the small breakfast bar. On her way, she knocked on the bathroom door.

"Chelsea? Are you going in to work today?"

She hoped there wouldn't be another confrontation about Wade this morning. *Not today. Please.*

"I've got a headache. I called in sick."

"Want some breakfast?"

"No, thanks."

Great. Exhausted from lack of sleep and feeling as if she were constantly picking up the pieces of her life, Tracy went back to the kitchen and dived into the bills, a daunting job to say the least. By the time she looked up, a good thirty minutes had passed. She stretched and went back to knock on Chelsea's door, wanting to see for herself that Chelsea was all right. Needing to talk to her if she was upset about last night.

She had to knock twice. "May I come in?"

There was a long pause before Chelsea finally answered, "Sure, come on in."

The girl was curled up in an overstuffed chair by the window and didn't turn around when Tracy stepped into the room.

"Is there anything I can get you? A Motrin, or anything?"

"I'll be okay." The answer was a little too quick. It also lacked conviction.

"If this is about last night, I was with Wade when you came in." Tracy closed the door and walked over to the bed.

"I figured." Chelsea chewed on her bottom lip.

"He's gone. He checked out." She hated saying the words aloud. Hated making it real.

"He did? Really?" Chelsea sounded surprised but not relieved.

There was a gnawing hollow in Tracy's stomach as she confirmed it. "Really."

"Is he coming back?"

Is he coming back? She pictured the hopeful corner of her heart and shrugged. "I have no idea. Not anytime soon, anyway."

"Are you okay with that?"

Surprised that Chelsea cared enough to ask, Tracy crossed the room and sat on the corner of the bed closest to Chelsea's chair.

"No. I'm not okay with it. I'm going to miss him. I . . . I came to care for him deeply." She was surprised at how easily the truth came out this morning.

"Why didn't he stay?"

"He just couldn't. The timing wasn't right for either of us."

Finally Chelsea turned her gaze away from the window. Her usually bright eyes were dull, filled with sadness and confusion. "I hope he didn't leave because I was rude to him."

"When?"

"The night of the party. I was pretty upset about the invitations and all." She took a deep breath. "I told him he was just a substitute for Dad."

"Honey, that's not true. You know that."

"I was so bummed that night, so mad at myself. But when I saw Wade, I took it out on him. I was going to apologize, but I didn't get the chance."

Just then the sun broke through the haze and came streaming in the window. Tracy couldn't keep her gaze from drifting to Chelsea's cheek, to the spot where she'd slapped her. Every time it happened, her stomach tied itself into a knot. The slap hadn't even been hard enough to leave a mark, but the memory would forever be a stain on her own heart.

"You're white as a sheet, honey." Gently, she laid her hand on the girl's shoulder and Chelsea reacted with a shudder. Tracy's heartbeat accelerated. Something was going on that had nothing to do with her or Wade. "You know you can tell me anything, don't you?"

She watched tears well up in the girl's eyes and spill down her cheeks. Instinctively, she slipped her arm around Chelsea's shoulders and drew her close, the way she did with Matt when he was upset. Chelsea's breath hitched and, after another second, she buried her face in her hands.

"I hate David Sylvester."

He wasn't at the top of Tracy's list of favorite people, either. He never had been. Since Jake had told her about Glenn's affair, she'd been fairly certain that David had known, and kept the truth from her.

Rubbing the girl's back, Tracy coaxed her over to the bed to sit beside her. She let her cry without questioning her, waited until Chelsea wiped her eyes and sat with her hands clenched between her knees.

She could think of only one thing that David might have done to upset Chelsea so much, and then she remembered that Chelsea had been working late last night. Anger erupted out of a reserve deep in every mother's heart, anger reserved for those times when they need to fight for their children in any way they can.

"Did he do something inappropriate? Did David come on to you?"

Chelsea shook her head no, but continued to stare at her hands.

"Tell me, Chelsea."

"He asked me to work late, and then when everyone else was gone, he . . . he offered me a glass of wine." Then she shrugged. "That's no big deal. We . . . I've had wine at parties." She finally looked up, met Tracy's eyes. "You know that, right?"

Tracy nodded. She knew very well what went on at sorority and fraternity parties. The first time Chelsea came home from college, Glenn had even offered her wine with dinner. But for David Sylvester to do so, especially at the office, was inexcusable. He knew better than to put himself in a compromising position with a nineteen-year-old girl.

If he didn't, he was certainly going to hear about it as soon as she was out of this room.

"Did you have a glass of wine with him?"

"I told him no. I wanted to leave because I didn't like the way he was looking at me, you know?"

Again, Tracy nodded. Chelsea was a vibrant young woman, full of energy, ripe with sensuality, still possessing the innocence of youth — a tempting combination.

"He told me I was beautiful," Chelsea said. "I told him I had to get home. But he said 'What's the rush?' I said that Eric was waiting for me downstairs, in the lobby."

Thank God for Eric Nichols. A freshman at Cal Poly, San Luis Obispo, Eric was on the tennis team. From what she could recall, he was well-mannered and soft-spoken. He had curly brown hair and always wore dark-rimmed glasses. She had no doubt that he was probably head over heels in love with Chelsea, though they didn't seem to be officially dating.

"What did David say? Did he tell you to go on home?" Tracy rubbed Chelsea's shoulders and back, thankful that the girl was confiding in her.

"He said he was attracted to me. I told him I wasn't into married men. That's when he said he wasn't *that* married." She finally faced Tracy again. Her breath hitched, but she didn't break down this time. Her own anger was finally taking hold. "It made me sick to my stomach. He told me things weren't going all that well at home, that his wife Kathy was overly devoted to their daughters, and that she didn't have time for him. I guess I couldn't hide how disgusted I was.

"He said he didn't like the way I was looking at him. How was I *supposed* to look at him? He's married, for God's sake! He's got his wife's and kids' photos all over his freaking desk! He said making passes was what guys did. *All* guys. Then he started talking about Dad, Tracy. He told me that Dad had women on the side, too. I called him a liar, and he laughed at me. He said that Dad had a lot to hide. A *whole* lot to hide."

Tracy's suspicions confirmed, her own anger was simmering close to a boil. How dare he throw Glenn's infidelities in Chelsea's face, thinking it would help him plead his own case? How dare he tell her?

"Did he keep you from leaving? Did he touch you?"

She shook her head. "No." A smile flitted across her face, but then dissolved a heartbeat later. "Not after I threw a glass of wine in his face and ran out without looking back. I left the sweater you loaned me in my cubicle." Her eyes filled with tears that started rolling down her cheeks. "It . . . was . . . your . . . your favorite pink one," she sobbed.

Tracy knew she wasn't crying over the lost sweater as much as her lost innocence. She held the girl close, desperately angry at David Sylvester, so furious that she could barely sit still. Her anger was tempered only by the pain she felt for Chelsea.

It wasn't but two minutes later that Chelsea mopped her pajama sleeve over her face and turned red-rimmed eyes on Tracy. "Did Dad play around?"

Tracy knew that the minute she didn't immediately deny it, that the instant she hesitated and weighed the consequences of telling Chelsea the truth, the girl would see through her.

"Tracy, tell me it's not true."

"Honey . . ."

"Dad fooled around? Did you *know*?"

"No." Easy, so easy to tell that truth. She hadn't known, not really. "Not for certain. Not until a couple of nights ago."

She had no recourse but to tell Chelsea what Jake had discovered when he went over the account books. How, apparently, Glenn had had a mistress, but she stopped short of telling Chelsea about Willa and Mary Jane.

"Oh, my God, Tracy. I can't believe it."

Suddenly the tables were turned and she found herself the recipient of Chelsea's sympathy. It was nearly her own undoing when Chelsea took both her hands and clung to them.

Slowly, she admitted, "I didn't want to believe it, or I'd have pursued it sooner. And I would have done everything in my power to keep you from finding out. I'd have told you myself before I let you find out this way." It was easy to see that Chelsea was still in shock. So much so that she was no longer crying.

"I never thought Dad would do something

like this to you. I thought he loved you so much."

So did I. "There's no doubt that he loved you, honey. No doubt. This doesn't change the way things were between the two of you."

"You don't think so? He was living a lie."

"Just remember, you were his princess." She wondered what Chelsea would say if she knew that Glenn had had another daughter.

Chelsea sighed and pushed her hair back over her shoulder. "I told Eric to get my sweater for me when he went in today. Obviously, I won't be going back there again."

"Don't worry about the sweater. I'll get it myself."

Chelsea's hand tightened on Tracy's. "You *can't.*"

"Oh, yes, I most certainly can, and I will. There's no way I'm letting that man get away with this."

Chelsea jumped up. "Please, don't. I'm *all right.* Nothing happened. If you go in and make a big deal of this, people will talk. David's wife might find out. His little *girls* might find out. He has two precious little girls."

Tracy remembered the photo of those darling children in their matching tartan dresses. It was on display, front and center, on David's desk. She couldn't wait to see the look on his face when she went marching into his office.

"We can't let him get away with this."

"But I don't want those girls' lives shattered the way mine was when Dad moved out and left me behind with Mom," Chelsea cried.

It was the first time she'd ever opened up about how her parents' divorce had affected her. The first time she'd ever admitted how deeply she'd been hurt, though her pain and confusion had been evident from the minute Tracy had met the sometimes sullen, more often sad-eyed little eight-year-old.

"I understand your feeling that way." Tracy hoped that she appeared calm, when what she was really feeling couldn't be further from the truth. "But I can't look the other way and give David a chance to do this sort of thing again." She stood up and walked to the middle of the room. "Now, you go shower and have some breakfast. I'll need you to stay with Matt until I get back."

"Are you really going to David's office? Right now?"

"You bet I am." She started for the door, ready for an argument, determined not to be swayed.

"Tracy, wait." Thankfully, Chelsea sounded resigned, not angry.

Tracy paused with her hand on the doorknob. "What, honey?"

The girl summoned a trembling smile and whispered, "Thank you."

Two hours later, the employees bustling around the offices of Sylvester, Lease & Lynch all appeared to be intent on what they were doing, all definitely in a no-nonsense mood when Tracy walked in.

An attractive twenty-something receptionist with long straight hair and a conservative shirtwaist blouse that failed to hide an ample bustline looked up from her desk. She made the mistake of giving Tracy a practiced smile behind the phone headset she was wearing.

"May I help you?"

"Tracy Potter to see David Sylvester. I don't have an appointment, but I'm sure he'll see me."

The brunette blinked a couple of times. "Why don't you have a seat?" She indicated a bank of chrome-and-leather sling chairs lined up between huge potted palms.

"I'm fine right here." Tracy silently dared her to argue.

The receptionist picked up the phone.

"Yes. A Mrs. Potter. Okay." She hung up and smiled apologetically. "He's all tied up for the rest of the morning. He said he's sorry, but that if you make an appointment — Hey!" She jumped up so quickly that she pulled the headset out of the phone. Tracy was already through the doors to the right of the desk. "You can't go in there!"

Once she was in the hallway beyond the waiting-area doors, Tracy ignored the receptionist and kept going past a maze of cubicles and doors until she reached David's office. She hadn't been here more than a couple of times since that terrible morning last March, but she knew the way. She didn't bother knocking, not as long as she'd gotten this far. She barged all the way in.

Shoving the door open, she marched across David's paisley-print carpet and didn't stop until she was standing across the desk from him. He'd jumped to his feet the moment she'd stepped through the door and quickly concealed his shock. Carefully, with a great show of purpose, he slipped his Montblanc pen in the ebony holder on his desk, shot his cuffs, and noted the time on the gold watch on his wrist.

Then he did the worst possible thing he could do, given the circumstances. He smiled.

"You bastard," she said softly. "How dare you stand there smiling when you know very well why I'm here."

"And why is that?"

"You not only tried to seduce Chelsea last night, but you told her that her father was a player."

"Prove it."

"It's her word against yours, is that it?"

"No one else was around. Obviously she's been unstable since Glenn died. She was under the false impression that she had a chance at the scholarship we award to a deserving intern every year, and she thought that seducing *me* would be the way to assure she got it. Unfortunately, I had to fire her last night." He raised his arms, shrugged. "I'm sorry that she's angry enough to accuse me of something so sordid."

"I see you've got it all figured out." Tracy stepped away from his desk, her gaze traveling over the well-appointed office. "In fact, you've got such a well-rehearsed answer that it sounds like you might have thought this all out *before* you sexually harassed Chelsea." It was a moment or two before she saw what she was looking for.

"Do I need to call security to show you out?"

Though she knew it would be his word against Chelsea's, she didn't count herself out yet, and he shouldn't have, either.

"Actually, no. But I'm sure your assistant has been in here this morning. And you've already seen clients, haven't you?"

"So?"

"You no doubt have a cleaning service that comes in every evening to straighten things up, right?"

"What are you getting at, Tracy?"

"I'm sure all of them, if forced to testify, would tell the truth if they were asked if they noticed that red wine stain on your carpet."

She watched the blood creep up from the tight button-down collar around his neck. He shot a glance down at the carpet right in front of her feet, where there was, indeed, a red wine stain the size of a dinner plate. It was obvious that someone had tried to clean it up. It was faded, but noticeable right there in the open.

"Chelsea told me she threw red wine at you."

"I spilled that myself. I was so shocked by her behavior."

"Did you wear your dirty shirt home? How did you explain what happened to Kathleen?"

"I spilled it myself."

"Chelsea threw wine in your face. It would be on your collar. All over the knot of your tie. Maybe even your shoulders. Not exactly where you'd spill it on yourself. How would you explain that?"

His confidence was paling as his face grew redder. "Who do you think you are?"

"A mother. A mother who is mad as hell. Nobody messes with one of my children without paying for it, David. Nobody."

"She's not even yours."

"Oh, yes she is. She's been part of my life for ten years, and no matter what Glenn has done, no matter whatever happens from here on out, she's still mine. Now, will you admit what you did, call Chelsea, and apologize, or do I call Kathleen and tell her everything?" She knew that in the long run, she'd be doing Kathleen a favor by calling her.

"You keep the hell away from my family."

"You keep the hell away from your interns from now on. And stop covering for your clients. I found out about Glenn before you said anything to Chelsea. I had help from a private detective, and I won't hesitate to have him dig up everything he can on you, David. Every sordid detail he can uncover. I'm sure that this isn't the first time you've harassed one of your employees."

"What is it you want?"

"I want you to tell me that this will be the last time you try to take advantage of a woman. And I want that scholarship money for the fall semester."

"Blackmail? You'd resort to blackmail?"

"I think the politically correct word is reparation." She took a deep breath. "And David? I'd resort to almost anything where my kids are concerned."

CHAPTER FORTY-ONE

A complete calm washed over Tracy the minute she walked out of Sylvester, Lease & Lynch with her pink sweater in her hand and a hefty check for Chelsea's fall tuition in her purse.

Now, alone in the kitchen in her apartment, she was concentrating on scooping a measuring cup full of flour and dumping it into a white crockery mixing bowl. She heard footsteps behind her and turned to look over her shoulder.

Chelsea walked up beside her and stared at the recipe card for scones. She picked up a stick of butter, and then, shoulder to shoulder with Tracy, measured out three-quarters of a cup by slicing through the silver wrapper.

"I hated you when you married my dad," she said softly.

Tracy knew how hard it was for the girl to admit to what she thought was a secret she'd been harboring for years.

"I know." Tracy leaned toward the sink and filled a smaller cup with water.

"You did? You knew?"

"Kids are pretty obvious."

Chelsea's complexion reddened. "I wanted Dad to come back home, not marry someone else. I blamed you for him not coming back to us."

"You were only eight." Tracy's hands stilled. "I didn't break your parents up, you know that, don't you? I didn't even meet your dad until after he was divorced."

"Mom used to tell me that you two had something going on before he left us."

"That simply wasn't true. I hadn't even been living in California long enough."

"I figured that out when I was in high school." Chelsea picked up the recipe card and turned it over and over. "Tracy, I'm so sorry."

"It was a long time ago. We've both grown a lot since then."

Chelsea wiped away a tear. A small laugh escaped her. "I haven't cried this much since the day you called and told me Dad died. I just hope you know how sorry I am. I treated you pretty badly for a long time, and all you've ever been is good to me. You didn't deserve it."

She wiped the back of her hand across her eyes. "You were so great this morning, listening the way you did. Taking my side. Mom would have told me not to make such a big deal out of what happened. She'd tell me to go back and apologize to David, that if I wanted that scholarship, I should have been nicer. She probably would have told me that I should have let him . . ." She closed her eyes, unable to go on.

"Look at me," Tracy said softly. Chelsea opened her eyes. "You did what was right. Your dad would be proud of you. And I'm proud of you."

"I'm sorry for all the times you made my favorite dinners and I wouldn't touch them."

"Chelsea —"

"And I'm sorry for the time we went to the Grand Canyon and I didn't talk to you all week."

Tracy laughed. "You insisted on wearing a towel on your head in the car so you didn't have to look at me. I'd forgotten all about that trip."

"After you let me move in with you this summer, I told you that I wouldn't be caught dead cleaning rooms in this — dump. I feel like crawling under a rock and never coming out. I'd be more than willing to have that job now, if you still need me."

Tracy took her by the shoulders. "Enough. Stop this now or . . . or I'll have to send you to your room for a time-out."

At that, Chelsea finally smiled.

"Clean slate. Okay?" Tracy offered. "From here on out we start over. Deal?"

Chelsea nodded, though she did so slowly. "I still can't believe what David said about Dad, but I believe you, so I know it's true."

"The best thing you can do is let it go." Tracy wished she could follow her own advice. "Just remember that he loved you."

Tracy embraced her and Chelsea hugged her back. Tracy picked up a wooden spoon, her heart fuller than it had been in months. Then she heard Chelsea ask, "How did you end up being such a good person?"

Good person?

Tracy set the spoon down and closed her eyes. Willa's face, her voice, filled her mind.

"I want you to raise my little girl."

Her gut reaction had been to laugh in Willa's face, but she'd been too stunned. Wouldn't a truly *good* person, a selfless person, be able to forgive and honor Willa's request?

According to her Baptist grandmother, a truly *good* woman would never have slept with a stranger, a man she would never see

423

again, especially with her son asleep under the same roof. "I'm not that good, believe me."

"Yes, you are. You're exactly the type of person I want to be, if it's not too late."

"You're already a good person, Chelsea."

"You think so?"

"I know so. You made the right choice last night."

Chelsea left the kitchen with a smile on her face.

She left Tracy frowning down into the scone batter. Chelsea only meant to compliment her, she knew that, but unknowingly, the girl had forced her to consider the biggest challenge she would ever face.

A few minutes later she was just about to put the scones in the oven when the phone rang. She answered and heard nothing but silence on the other end of the line, a silence so still it was deafening. When she heard her heart beating through it, she knew without a doubt who it was.

"Wade?" Her fingers tightened around the phone.

"How are you doing?"

"I miss you." She released a long sigh. Hearing his voice again jolted the truth out of her.

"I wasn't going to call," he said.

She wrapped her arm around her midriff. "I watched you ride away."

"I thought you were asleep."

"Where are you now?"

"Down the coast. How is everything?"

"Let's just say life is never boring around here." She cut out the last scone, set it on the baking sheet, and brushed her hands off over the sink. He didn't need to know what had happened this morning, though she was proud of standing up to David. Wade wasn't part of their lives anymore.

"Have you had any more guests check in?"

"No. The weather stinks." Then she thought of Henri and smiled. "The Frenchman is still here, though."

"Still in his robe?"

"It's growing on me."

They laughed, too short, but very sweet sounds, before they fell into silence. She closed her eyes. Imagined Wade right beside her.

"There's a package coming in the mail for Matt. FedEx," he told her.

"Really?" She wondered what he'd found that Matt would enjoy. "That's so thoughtful. He'll be so excited to get a package."

There was such a long pause that she thought the connection had been broken, but then he said, "Tracy, last night with you —"

"I know," she whispered. "I know."

They drifted into silence punctuated by the distance between them. There were no words for what had happened for her last night. She could only hope it was half as good for him. *Just come back. Why don't you just come back?* She wanted to scream at the injustice of fate.

How could she have possibly fallen in love so soon?

Even an amateur psychologist could see that she was rebounding. She'd needed reassurance, needed to rebuild her self-esteem, and she'd fallen into the arms of the first man who'd looked her way. Literally, almost the first man who had walked through the door. That was the most rational explanation.

But when was love ever rational?

Deep down inside, she wanted to believe that what she felt for Wade was more than an easy fix, more than a knee-jerk reaction to her loss, her pain, and ultimate humiliation.

It certainly felt as real and as true as the love she'd once had for Glenn.

But the voice of reason warned her to remember how that had ended.

She tried to remember, too, that Wade had reasons of his own for moving on. Reasons that she'd refused to let him talk about last night. Things that he was convinced would change the way she saw him, the way she felt about him.

"I've got to go, Tracy," he said softly.

"I know." She bit her lips together to stop their trembling, refusing to cry any more. She'd proved just how strong she was this morning in David's office. Her heart was strong, too. Strong and resilient, and hopeful.

The silence deepened. She was afraid he'd already hung up, but then she heard him sigh. "Be safe, Wade," she whispered.

"You, too," he said. And then the line went dead.

The scones forgotten, she hung up and stared down at the phone.

"Mom! Mom!"

As Matt came charging into the apartment, she hung a smile on her face.

"What's up?"

"You better get downstairs quick. That crazy old French guy is walking around in the lobby in a striped Speedo!"

CHAPTER FORTY-TWO

The Best Western Inn by the Sea on the Pacific Coast Highway in Dana Point held none of the charm of the Heartbreak, but Wade wasn't looking for charm when he checked in.

In a room decorated in eighties mint green and peach pastels, a standard-issue motel television was bolted to the dresser. For three days the local news channels had focused on "the storm of the century." Obviously the producers had already forgotten that they had dubbed last month's storm the century's worst.

He'd been on the road for a month now and didn't have to watch the news to know the weather sucked. All he had to do was look out the window. Not only had an El Niño weather pattern hit the coast from San Diego to Seattle; in a move that further crippled the tourist industry, the Department of Homeland Security had raised the terrorist alert level from yellow to orange.

Travel plans had been canceled all over the country.

Neither the weather nor the alerts had ever mattered to him back when he'd been mired in his own egocentric world, working to keep his Edward Cain books in front of the public eye.

Edward Cain, national bestseller, wouldn't have cared if a widow living in a monstrosity outside of a burg like Twilight Cove was affected by the latest catastrophic storm, fire, *or* pestilence. Before he became the notorious author of *An Even Dozen,* Edward Cain had never cared about anything but his career.

But Wade MacAllister, a.k.a. Wade Johnson, did care.

He cared a hell of a lot, and now that his sensitivities had kicked in, there was no turning them off.

Staring out the window at the downpour that was sending a river of water pouring down the gutter and into the storm drains along the highway, he dialed the number of the Heartbreak Hotel for only the second time since he'd left there.

He recognized Chelsea's voice the moment she answered.

"Chelsea, this is Wade."

"Oh!" Her surprise was more than evident. He expected a curt reply and a hang-up, but instead she quickly said, "Tracy's not here. She ran into town to pick up some milk and the mail. She'll be so disappointed."

He pictured Chelsea in the lobby, leaning against the dark oak registration desk, and strained to hear the Elvis music in the background.

"How are things going?" he asked.

"Not good," she admitted. "It's really slow everywhere. Even Pismo is nearly deserted. The shops in Twilight are empty. We've only got a couple of rooms rented this week, but that's better than last."

"I'm sorry to hear it." He realized it wasn't just an empty phrase. His heart ached for Tracy. He thought about having Bob send her money. He'd even thought about Schack arranging to buy the place for him through a broker so that she could move out and not have to worry about money at all.

But if she ever found out what he'd done, she might never forgive him, and he still wasn't ready to live with that yet.

"Wade, I never got a chance to tell you how sorry I was about the way I acted the night of Tracy's open house."

The girl's apology took him completely by surprise. He wondered what caused such a change of heart. "Apology accepted, but I can't fault you for looking out for Tracy."

"Thanks."

"You keep it up, okay? Take care of her." He stopped short of adding — "for me."

"Why not come back and take care of her yourself?"

He couldn't tell her that by keeping his distance, he was doing them all a favor. "I wish I could, but that's not possible." He walked over to the dresser, where the photos Matt had given him were lying in plain view. He picked up one of Tracy standing on the front steps, smiling into the camera. "Listen, I've got to go. Thanks for the apology, Chelsea."

"She misses you, Wade. She hasn't said anything, but I can tell."

He closed his eyes, still saw Tracy's smile. "Thanks again," he said, helpless. Feeling low, he hung up after Chelsea told him good-bye.

Debating how to help Tracy, he realized that apart from donning a clown suit and waving a cardboard arrow at passing cars in front of her hotel, the only thing he knew how to do, besides spend money, was write.

If he really wanted to help, then he had to

do the one thing he did best.

Before he could talk himself out of it, he phoned information for the number of the *L.A. Times* features editor and then had the number put through. Thankfully, he didn't get a voice mail. He had no intention of leaving a callback number.

"Jim Kemerer."

Wade recognized the voice immediately, though he hadn't spoken to the man since Jim had been an editorial assistant at Ballard Publishing.

"Hey, Jim. This is Edward Cain. How's it going?"

"Holy shit!" There was dead silence on the other end of the line before Kemerer recovered. "Where are you? Man, everyone thinks you dropped off the face of the planet."

"Good. That's how I want to keep it."

"Do I get an exclusive? Is that why you called?"

Wade knew that Jim was already seeing dollar signs and a Pulitzer nomination for an interview with the elusive Edward Cain.

"Maybe down the line. Right now, I need a favor. Big-time."

"Shoot."

"I'd like you to run a travel article about an inn up the coast."

"A travel article."

"Right."

"What's the hook? Aside from the fact that I assume you're staying there."

"I'm not there. Actually, I'm on the other side of the continent," he lied. "I'm doing this as a favor to a friend — and there is a hook."

"Okay. Shoot."

"The place is haunted."

"Haunted. As in, by a ghost?"

"Right."

"That's it?"

"Come on, Jim. You know people are attracted to that kind of thing. Ghostly mansions, haunted museums and hotels, all of that — stuff." He would have said "all that crap" before. Not now.

"Have you actually seen the ghost? Got any photos of it?"

There was no way he was admitting he'd been anywhere near the place, or even in California. "No, but I have it on really good authority."

"Hell, I'll run anything you want to send me."

"Yeah. Well, there's a catch. I don't want an Edward Cain byline. Use Staff Writer if you want. Anything but the Cain name. Got it?"

"Why did I have the feeling you were going to say that?"

"Will you keep the name Edward Cain off it?"

"Is that how it has to be?"

"It's important to me, Jim."

"I hear ya. When do I get the copy?"

"I'll FedEx it to you with a couple of photos. You'll have it by five tomorrow. You think it'll make the Sunday travel section?"

There was a long pause. "I'll have to kill the lead feature, but for you, sure. I'll put it on the AP wire, too. Where can I reach you in case any questions come up?"

"Nice try. You can't. There won't be any problems. Count on it."

"What do you get out of it?"

"Like I said, I'm doing a friend a favor."

"Okay, fine."

"And the Cain name stays off."

"Sure."

"Thanks, Jim. And if Edward Cain ever surfaces, you'll get the first interview."

Wade hung up, grabbed his jacket, and headed out to buy computer time at a Kinko's a couple of miles inland.

On Saturday afternoon, Tracy sat curled up on the couch with Matt tucked in beside her. There were no guests downstairs, and since it was pouring buckets outside, she had popped some corn as they settled in to watch a *Trading Spaces* marathon.

"Mom?"

"What, hon?"

"Do you think Wade's been riding his Harley around in all this rain? Or you think he got a car?"

She stared at the television, watched as a too-cute carpenter sawed an old table in half to make a recycled bookshelf, and imagined Wade riding through the rain. She had no way to contact him, no way of knowing if he was even in California at all. He could be very near, or he could be a thousand miles away. All she knew for certain was that a day didn't go by that she didn't think of him and remember every second of the night they'd spent in each other's arms.

"I doubt it." She hoped he was warm and dry. But more than that, she hoped he wasn't holed up in another hotel somewhere, charming the pants off of someone else.

"He hated for all that chrome to get dirty," Matt mumbled around a mouthful of popcorn.

"He told you that?"

"I could tell. He was always polishing it." He reached for another handful of popcorn, leaving a trail of kernels between the bowl and his mouth. "I kinda miss him. Do you, Mom?"

"What?"

"Do you kinda miss Wade?"

She refused to lie to a nine-year-old. "Yes. I kinda do."

"Maybe he'll come back."

"Maybe." She'd begun to doubt it, though.

Earlier in the week, she'd come in toting plastic bags full of groceries. Sopping wet, she almost made it through the front door when Chelsea appeared and helped with the bags. She'd said that Wade had called to see how they were doing, and Chelsea had told him all about the bad weather and lack of guests.

Hearing that she'd missed his call, Tracy had fought the urge to sit down in the middle of the lobby and bawl her head off. Instead, she'd calmly trailed Chelsea up the stairs, emptied the grocery bags, and told herself that, even if she hadn't spoken to Wade herself, at least he'd called. At least he was still thinking of her.

Suddenly the phone rang unexpectedly. She hoped it was him and that he could sense how much she'd been thinking of him. She grabbed the portable phone off the sofa beside her.

"Heartbreak Hotel."

"Do you get the early weekend edition of *The Tribune*?"

Tracy immediately recognized Carly's voice and smiled. "Nope. I get it on Sunday. What's up?"

"I hope you have a good supply of cinnamon buns and scones in the freezer."

"Of course I don't. I serve them fresh. Why?"

"Because your phone is going to be ringing off the hook, that's why. There's a travel article that's going to be in the Sunday edition. It's credited to the *L.A. Times* travel section."

"If it's about how tourism is sucking bigtime right now, *puleeese,* you don't need to read it to me."

Carly laughed. "Actually, it's about a very colorful, very romantic inn on the central coast. A place named Heartbreak Hotel."

Tracy sat up so quickly that Matt tipped over and spilled half a bowl of popcorn.

"Someone stole our *name*?"

"No. Someone wrote an article about *your* Heartbreak Hotel."

"Henri. It had to be Henri. I knew there was more to that old codger than the fez, Speedos, and silk robe."

"Not Henri. Edward Cain."

"Edward Cain?" She frowned. "The name rings a bell, but I can't put a face to it."

"Edward Cain is that novelist. *The* novelist. The one who wrote *An Even Dozen*? Remember?"

"Kind of. Oh, yes! The woman from South Dakota was reading it while she was here last month. Is it good?"

"The big deal about it is that a real killer committed twelve murders that he copied *exactly* as Cain wrote them. It was pretty grisly. Eventually the killer was caught, but Edward Cain was sued by some of the victims' families. He even received *death threats,* and then dropped out of sight as soon as the trials were over. I just saw an article about him in *People* a few weeks ago. I've still got that issue around here some-place . . ." Carly muffled the phone, but Tracy could hear her yelling to Jake to hunt through the back issues of *People.*

"How would Edward Cain know anything about the Heartbreak?"

"Tracy, the article was also about *you.* There were paragraphs singing your praises. He said there was a ghost haunting the place. Specifically, a ghost named Captain Ezra Poole. The article had some details about Ezra's past, and Twilight Cove. It

438

even mentioned Palmer Biggs and the historical society. How come you never told me you had a ghost?"

"Because I *don't* have a ghost, Carly."

"He described you, your delicious coffee, and fabulous home-baked goods. He made the place sound so romantic and inspiring, and he even went so far as to say it was a better stop on the coast than Hearst Castle." Tracy thought back through the handful of guests who'd checked in over the last few weeks. She was barely making enough money to keep the lights on, let alone break even. She'd just about decided that if things didn't pick up soon, she'd have to think about signing the place over to the historical preservation society just to keep from having to pay the utilities and taxes.

"There was even a picture of the place. A photo of you standing on the front steps. And there was a crooked shot of the neon sign out front."

"That sounds like one of Matt's photos from the set Wade sent to Matt the day after he left . . ."

"Tracy, don't you get it yet? *Edward Cain.* Edward Cain is obviously a pen name for the only writer who ever stayed there long enough to know the place so well."

There is only one guest who knows anything

about Ezra Poole. One guest who ever admitted to being a writer. Only one person who had access to those photographs.

"Ohmygod. Wade?"

"Right! Wade." There was a pause and then Carly added, "Tracy, the guy has to be worth millions."

Her Wade — with his worn-out cowboy boots and low-slung jeans, his slow smile and dark, sad eyes that looked into her soul. Her Wade, the man who'd walked in a stranger and become so much more. *Wade writes as Edward Cain?*

She thought she knew all she needed to know about him. She'd slept with him and she hadn't really known him at all.

"Tracy? Are you still there?"

"I'm here." *Somewhere. I'm in here somewhere.*

"Want me to bring the article over?"

Outside, it was still raining cats and dogs. She thought about Carly making the winding drive down Lover's Lane and then through Twilight Cove. The carpenter on the TV was painting the recycled bookcase a puke shade of green that reminded her of strained Gerber peas.

"That's okay. Matt and I will run down to the Paper Sack and get a copy."

"Unless I miss my guess, you'll be so busy

from now on that you won't be going much of anyplace. I still can't *believe* it. Wade is Edward Cain. I never even saw him in anything other than Levis and a T-shirt except for the night of the open house."

The night I begged him to make love to me. He tried to tell me. He wanted to tell me the truth. She thought back to that night, tried to recall every word.

"I can't do this without telling you every-thing."

"Don't. Not if it will change things between us. Will it make me see you differently?"

"Probably. I don't see how it wouldn't."

"Tracy?" Carly's voice shook her out of her reverie. "Are you there?"

"Yes. I'm here."

"I can't *believe* Jake didn't recognize Wade as Cain. I told him he must be losing his touch. He was so into that whole case. He is going through a stack of old *People* magazines right now. If we find it, I'll save it for you. Why don't you go Google Edward Cain?"

Tracy promised she would before she said good-bye. Matt was still eating popcorn off of the sofa. The cute carpenter on TV was trying to squeeze the bookcase through the door, but he'd measured wrong and it didn't fit. A paint-spattered couple in *Trad-*

ing Spaces shirts didn't look hopeful.

Wade is Edward Cain.

She remembered that Chelsea had told him exactly how badly things were going at the beginning of the week.

The travel article was his valiant attempt to try and save the Heartbreak for her.

CHAPTER FORTY-THREE

For three solid days it had rained almost nonstop, and even so, the hotel had been surrounded by news vans and reporters on Edward Cain watch. The phone had been ringing off the hook with reporters and publicists, and despite the barrage, she couldn't turn it off, because amid the flurry, people were calling with inquiries about legitimate reservations.

It was afternoon and still raining outside as Tracy put the finishing touches on a bouquet in the sunroom. When she heard footsteps in the lobby close by, she whipped around, wielding her pruning shears, prepared for just about anything.

It wasn't a reporter, but Chelsea, who came walking in wearing a baseball cap and sunglasses.

"Calls still coming in?" Chelsea glanced at the phone. "Who knew the Heartbreak Hotel would end up being *the* place to stay on the coast? And the only one filled to capacity."

Tracy had opted to not step outside after she'd opened the front door to answer it and nearly been toppled by reporters, microphones, and cameramen. Sunday night had been so unbelievable that they'd smuggled Matt out to Carly's car in a pile of linens, and she'd driven him up to their place for an overnight.

"I hope things calm down soon," Tracy said. "We're already all booked up clear through next summer." She set the shears down. "Are you going out?"

"To the store. Did you notice that most of the news crews have left? There's only one truck left out there." Chelsea had all of her long hair wound up beneath the baseball cap. "Where did they go?"

Tracy charged over to the window and drew the curtain back an inch. "Do we really care, as long as they're gone?"

"It seems weird, though. First they all descend, and now they've taken off again like a swarm of locusts." Not only had the press descended, but two days ago an exorcist called, guaranteeing he could get rid of Ezra Poole for five thousand dollars. Tracy told him she wanted to keep Ezra. A publicist for New Zealand's world-famous

444

medium Jennie Crawford called, proposing a seminar and psychic training sessions at the hotel for those who wanted to hone their ability to speak to the spirit.

A couple from Roswell, New Mexico, phoned to say they didn't believe that Ezra Poole was a ghost. No, they had proof that Ezra was a code name for an alien being known as Arze. After she hung up, she realized Arze was Ezra spelled backward.

Yesterday the FedEx carrier delivered a resume from a self-certified ghost-buster.

Matthew was already charging his classmates for tours. He'd tried to bribe Chelsea into hiding in the closet draped in an old sheet to scare his customers. She would have been more upset about his new enterprise, but he hadn't been this happy in months. Chelsea was getting adept at sneaking out of the hotel in disguises, sometimes using the guests as shields.

"Sylvester, Lease and Lynch called while you were in the shower," Tracy told her.

Chelsea paled. "Did they say what they wanted?"

"It was Lease himself. David Sylvester quit. He relocated to Denver. They wanted to know if you could come back and work for them next summer. He also apologized for any 'inconvenience' we may have suffered."

"What does that mean?"

"That's exactly what I asked him. He said that they received an anonymous letter suggesting that they look into David's 'indiscretions,' and it seems there were quite a few. He was asked to take a payout and leave."

"Did you write the anonymous letter?"

"I wanted to, but I didn't. I know how strongly you felt about David's family finding out."

Chelsea was thoughtful a moment. "I have a feeling it might have been Eric. I think he's the only other one who knew."

"Don't be angry with him, Chelsea. He obviously cares a lot about you." Tracy then added, "Mr. Lease said that they would be happy to have you back next summer, if you are interested. He insisted that you keep the 'scholarship' check David wrote, whether or not you decide to go back."

"There's no time to go back this year." Chelsea finally smiled again. "Maybe when you sell this place, Jake will take you on as a P.I. You certainly took care of David Sylvester like a pro."

"Has Wade called back?" She hadn't given up hope.

446

"Not yet."

She sighed, still battling her confusion. As much as she wanted to talk to him, she was jumpy and nervous about it. He wasn't just Wade Johnson, writer on hiatus anymore, he was a bestselling novelist, extremely wealthy, and a hot topic. Certainly not the man she thought she knew. In her heart of hearts she knew he hadn't written the story to hurt her, but she found herself wishing he had given her some warning before the story broke, and she was blindsided.

She'd researched Edward Cain on the Internet, found his website. The information there hadn't been updated for over two years, and of course, there was no mention of the murders. His bio was scanty at best, and in his photos he was barely recognizable as the man she'd come to know. She'd read plenty of archived news articles that detailed not only the grisly murders but the subsequent hearings that Wade had endured.

She longed to talk to him, but she didn't know where to start.

When the front doorbell suddenly rang, she and Chelsea both jumped at once.

"It looks like a woman." Tracy headed for the door. Check-in wasn't for hours yet. She glanced through the window in the door

447

and noted that the caller was a young woman in her early thirties, dripping wet, carrying a sopping canvas overnight bag. Dressed in a wraparound skirt and T-shirt that looked as if she'd slept in them, the caller looked harmless enough.

Even so, Tracy opened the door cautiously. "Do you have a reservation?"

"Not really." Before Tracy knew what hit her, the woman shouldered her way right past her into the lobby and shook out her tangled, curly hair like a wet puppy.

"I'm sorry. I'm afraid we're completely booked." Tracy hated to send her off in the rain. She thought of all the nights the place had been empty over the last month. Now she didn't have even a cot to spare.

The young woman set the overnight bag down. She didn't look at all disappointed or worried. Nor did she look like she was going anyplace. Chelsea stepped out from behind the reception desk and joined them.

"You must be Tracy Potter." The young woman turned to Tracy first and extended her hand.

"Do I know you?" Tracy tried to place her.

"Lauren Westin, from *World* magazine." She pulled a business card out of a side pocket in her purse and handed it to Tracy.

Tracy tried to hand it back. "We aren't

448

talking to reporters."

Lauren turned. "You must be Chelsea."

"We aren't giving interviews. If I have to call the police, I will," Tracy warned her.

"Hear me out first, okay? Surely you've heard of *World.*"

"All the news that's not fit to print." Tracy reached for the woman's overnight bag. It was so light that it had to be empty. "Since you won't be staying, I'll just carry this out to the porch for you."

Lauren Westin snagged the handle and a brief tug-of-war ensued. "Hey, we're the biggest little newspaper in the world. We're at every checkout counter in every English-speaking country on the planet."

"I've seen your rag," Chelsea told her. "What was the headline a couple of weeks ago? 'Cro-Magnon man comes out of cave dwelling to abduct Bush daughters'?"

"One of our all-time bestsellers." Lauren actually looked so proud that Tracy laughed.

Her laughter quickly halted when Miss Westin, seeing an opening, turned on her. "Is it true you had an affair with Edward Cain?"

"Who said that?" She jerked the suitcase out of the woman's hand and headed for the door.

Lauren Westin was hot on her heels. "So

449

it is true?"

"I didn't say that."

"You didn't deny it, either."

Chelsea stepped between the reporter and Tracy. "Look, leave us alone."

"*World* will pay for a story. Just give us what you can on Edward Cain. Give us anything you can. How long ago was he here? Where did he go? How has he managed to stay out of sight for so long? Has he had extensive plastic surgery?"

"You need to leave." Tracy opened the door and set the suitcase outside, fully prepared to pick up Lauren Westin and toss her out after it if she had to. "Bye now."

"Did you sleep with him? How often? How did you two meet? How long was he here?"

"I've never met Edward Cain." Not exactly a lie.

"We wouldn't reveal your name. We'd quote you as 'a source close to Edward Cain.' My publisher is prepared to pay as high as twenty-five."

"You have to be kidding." *Sell out Wade for twenty-five dollars?*

"Okay, fifty thousand, but that's all I'm authorized to offer without calling my boss."

"Fifty *thousand* dollars?" All she had to do was tell this hungry reporter with the

450

sloppy fake-leather purse and run-down shoes what she knew about Edward Cain and she'd make *fifty thousand dollars?*

Tracy glanced over and noticed that Chelsea was stunned and staring at the reporter. Fifty thousand dollars would go a long way toward paying for the rest of her education. Tracy held her breath.

"How about you?" Lauren focused on Chelsea, on her obvious interest. "That's a lot of money. At least think about it." Lauren pulled out a pen and wrote "$50,000" on her card, and then she handed it to Chelsea, who stared at it in disbelief.

"Think about what fifty thousand can buy, and call me when you change your mind. Just remember, no one wants old news, so don't wait too long."

Lauren Westin sailed through the door, grabbing her overnight bag as she crossed the porch. Tracy shut the door behind her.

Chelsea was still staring at the card, running her fingers around the edges. "Can you believe it? Fifty thousand dollars?"

Tracy's heart caught in her throat. Chelsea was no doubt thinking about how she could make a small fortune if she chose to tell *World* magazine, or any other media outlet, that the night before Edward Cain checked out, he and her stepmother had slept together. If anyone got wind of what Chelsea knew, or thought she knew, there would be a bidding war for the rights to the story.

Then Chelsea slowly smiled. "You know what I was just thinking about?"

Tracy didn't know if she wanted to hear. "No. What?"

"Out of nowhere, I suddenly flashed on those hokey birthday dinners you always make me. One for every single year since you married Dad. And those old tacky paper cone hats we always wore, and that pitiful kitty candle you've saved since I was eight — and all I could think was, *as if. As if* I'd sell you out for a *measly* fifty thousand dollars."

Chelsea laughed and tore the business card in half, then quarters, then eighths before handing it to Tracy. As the pieces sifted into her palm, Tracy couldn't say a word. She was too busy fighting tears.

The legendary Hotel Del Coronado on Coronado Island in San Diego opened in 1888 and boasted resident ghosts in rooms 3312 and 3505. Since both rooms were already booked, Wade decided that having a drink in the hotel's Babcock & Story Bar would be as close as he wanted to come to another ghostly encounter.

Despite heavily overcast skies, surf lessons were under way on the beach in front of the hotel as he sat at a table on the outdoor terrace. He punched Bob Schack's number for the first time since the article came out on Sunday and took a sip of a tall, icy mint *mojito.*

"Bob-o." He had a feeling his agent would be in as sour a mood as he was himself.

Bob didn't even bother with hello. "You could have warned me you were doing that article, buddy, so I could cover my ass. You know what it's been like in this office since your name surfaced again?"

"Yeah? Well, that article wasn't *supposed* to have my name on it." He'd bought the *Los Angeles Times* the day the story ran and was thankful he was a three-hour drive from L.A. or he'd have come out of hiding long enough to track Jim Kemerer down and give him more than a piece of his mind.

As it was, he'd had to wait until Kemerer was "at his desk" and settle for a far from cordial phone conversation that left him frustrated and angry, but it was far too late to do anything about it.

"You didn't bother to get anything in writing, obviously," Schack chided.

"Exactly what Kemerer told me. I didn't think I'd have to. He says he never gave me his word, but then he tried to blame the byline on his copy editor. Jim *conveniently* left the office for the weekend *after* telling his assistant that the story was by Edward Cain. He claims he gave the assistant specific instructions to leave the name off, but that the story was nothing unusual without it and the assistant editor acted on his own."

"Well, buddy, the good news is, book sales have spiked again. I don't have to tell you the bad news. The media is all over that hotel."

"Yeah, I know. That's the last thing I wanted." Thinking about the aftermath that hit Twilight still set Wade's teeth on edge.

"I take it the blond in the photo was behind your writing that piece. Am I right? I would have never guessed a woman could flush you out of hiding."

Tracy. He'd done it for her, to help her. He'd wanted to spotlight the hotel, not turn her world upside down. He'd watched the television reports taped outside the hotel on all the local news spots. The Heartbreak had already been featured on *Entertainment Tonight* and *Extra.* The copycat murders were to be revisited on *20/20* and *48 Hours Mystery* at the end of the week.

Palmer Biggs and the mayor of Twilight Cove had already given interviews.

Tracy was refusing to talk to the media. Reporters had dubbed her "Mrs. Muir," after the *Ghost and Mrs. Muir* movie. It seemed that the lovely, mysterious widow who'd lured Edward Cain out of hiding was refusing to make a statement.

He'd tried calling over and over but never got past the hotel answering machine. He couldn't leave his number, so he'd hung up, hoping that, eventually, Tracy would have to answer.

"Wade? Are you there?" Bob's voice jarred him back to reality. He watched a big set of waves roll in, tossing amateur surfers right and left in its wake.

"Yeah. I'm here."

"Are you in or near Twilight Cove right now?"

"No."

"Thank God. I've been going nuts, praying you'd call in again. The day after that story hit, I had a frantic call from Geraldine Farley."

The woman's face came to mind immediately. Sixties, overweight, the pale skin of a Midwesterner in midwinter. Her daughter had been victim number seven. Mrs. Farley was one of the survivors' relatives who hadn't sued him.

"She's decided to sue after all?" It would

455

mean going back to court, facing life as Edward Cain.

"That would have been better than what she had to say. A couple of days after the story broke, her son, Franklin, went missing."

"What do you mean, missing? As in kidnapped?"

"No. As in he left home." Bob suddenly paused, as if hesitant to go on.

Suddenly Wade remembered Farley. Early thirties, mentally unstable, his sister's death had hit him hard. He'd made death threats already.

"Let me guess —"

"His mother is afraid he's headed out to the coast looking for you."

"He really dangerous?"

"Does the phrase 'He's off his meds' mean anything to you?"

Wade broke out in a cold sweat.

"Why don't you come to L.A.?" Bob suggested. "Let me put you up someplace."

"I'm not worried about myself, damn it." He couldn't care less what happened to him, but his mind raced ahead of the implications. It was imperative that he live long enough to get back to the Heartbreak.

"When did this guy leave Minnesota?" Wade calculated driving time.

"Three days ago."

"He could already be out here."

"Look, Wade —"

"I'll call you back."

"Wade, wait —"

He hung up before he wasted any more time. Knocking back the rest of his drink, he stood up and tossed a ten-dollar bill on the bar and walked out.

As soon as he got back to where he'd parked his bike in the parking lot, he pulled out his cell phone again and dialed the Heartbreak Hotel.

In the mess that was her kitchen, in the middle of the cracked linoleum floor, Tracy was carefully lifting cinnamon buns off a hot baking sheet with a spatula when the phone rang. She paused, listening to an intercom connected to the answering machine on the reception desk downstairs.

"Tracy? Are you in there? *Pick up the phone!*"

Her breath caught and her heart started hammering. It was Wade, a.k.a. Edward.

She raced across the room, realized she was still balancing the bun on the spatula, stopped halfway to the phone, and headed back to the cooling rack on the counter.

"Don't hang up!" Though she knew he

couldn't hear her, she hollered at the phone anyway as she dumped the bun. She tossed the spatula in the sink on her way back across the room.

"Tracy, this is Wade. It's important. For God's sake, pick up. I'm afraid you might be in —"

The intercom went silent.

"Damn!" She grabbed the phone and picked it up. "Wade? Wade?" All she heard was dead silence on the other end of the line. She flicked the receiver up and down but couldn't clear the line. Nor could she get a dial tone. The weather had played havoc with the phone lines. For the last couple of weeks, service had been on again, off again all over the area.

She hung up, ran out the apartment door, and headed downstairs, yelling, "Chelsea? Grab the phone, would you?"

She mumbled to herself as she ran downstairs. "*I'm afraid you might be* — what?" What was he going to say?

Might be mad? Up to my ass in reporters? Trapped in the house, afraid to go out onto my own porch? Afraid someone will shove a microphone in my face and ask for the "real" story?

"*Have you met Edward Cain? When did he stay here?*"

"Did you have an affair?"

"What does he look like now? Is he planning another book?"

Wade — no doubt he was calling to apologize for turning her life upside down, for creating a media frenzy outside her door — for giving her what she'd wished for — a successful inn with a calendar full of reservations.

She could forgive him the circus outside. The spotlight would eventually move on. All the vans but one were already gone. All she had to do was wait out the storm.

"Chelsea?" She ran to the reception desk and finally remembered that Chelsea had slipped out for groceries. The answering machine light was blinking so she played back the messages, skipping ahead until she got to Wade's. There was nothing more than what she'd already heard. *"I'm afraid you might be —"*

She clicked the receiver button up and down. There was no dial tone on the downstairs phone, either.

She had no way to reach him, even if she used her cell. He'd never given her his number.

Listening, hoping the lines would be working soon, she stared out the front windows, watched the rain fall, and waited. A few minutes later she checked the line again. The phones were definitely dead.

CHAPTER FORTY-FOUR

"Operator. May I help you?"

Wade forced himself to speak slowly and distinctly. "I'm trying to get a call through to a number in the Twilight Cove, California, area." He'd pulled over at the rest stop at Leucadia, given the operator the number, and waited while his intestines wound themselves into a coil.

"The lines are down in the area due to heavy rains. They'll be operational again as soon as possible."

"Can you try the Twilight Cove police?" *Surely they have a contingency for a phone outage.*

"Sorry, sir. The line for the Twilight Cove sheriff's station isn't working, either. If this is an emergency, I can connect you to the San Luis Obispo police."

"That would be great."

Within seconds he had the 911 dispatcher in San Luis Obispo on the line.

"I need you to send a squad car to the Heartbreak Hotel. It's on Route 1, just north of Twilight Cove. Their phone lines are down and —"

"What's the emergency?"

"Tracy Potter, the owner of the hotel, may be in danger."

"*May* be in danger? And your name, sir?"

"Wade MacAllister."

"Mr. MacAllister, what makes you think Ms. Potter is in danger?"

He wanted to yell, *"Shut the hell up and send over a squad car!"* — but he knew that would get him nowhere. He forced himself to sound calm instead.

"Someone is out to get me and I'm afraid he might go through her to do it."

"And who might *he* be?"

"Franklin Farley. He's from Minnesota and he's made threats on my life."

"Do you know for certain he's in Twilight Cove at the hotel at this moment?"

"We think he may be headed there."

"You and Ms. Potter?"

Wade sighed and clenched his teeth so hard he was afraid he'd crack a crown.

"Look, my agent called and said that Farley's mother warned us that he's been off his meds. He's out for revenge against me. I'm Edward Cain."

"You said you were Wade MacAllister."

"Do you read the papers at all?" Sarcasm won out.

"Look, sir, we're short-staffed here as it is. I can't send out a squad car just because you think someone from Minnesota *might* be headed to the hotel."

"Farley threatened my life. He may believe I'm at the Heartbreak Hotel. He may try to lure me out of hiding by using Mrs. Potter."

"Are you in Twilight Cove?"

"No. I'm just north of San Diego, but —"

"And you're hiding because?"

"Because of the media and —"

"Hey, wait a minute. Are you *that* writer?"

Finally. He'd never been so glad to have his name recognized.

"Yes."

"We still can't send anyone out there on a hunch."

"I can't get through to the Twilight Cove sheriff's office."

"There is a bridge closure four miles down the highway, which is where most of their squad cars are needed."

"The bridge is out?" His heartbeat slowed. If no one had access to town, then Tracy would be safe until he could get to her. "No one can get into Twilight?"

"Yes, sir; they can. The canyon route is

open but it's slow and go. We've got a couple of small landslides up there."

"You won't send anyone to the hotel?"

"We can't do anything until there's an actual emergency in progress."

Wade hung up and cursed. The weather was cloudy with occasional drizzle this far south, but he'd be heading into worse weather on the bike. No picnic. It would be a miserable ride in the rain, but all his time on the road had conditioned him to riding in any weather. Once he got there, he'd have the advantage of being able to skirt backed-up traffic.

He quickly punched in Schack's number. This was no time for pleasantries. "Have you heard from Mrs. Farley again?" he asked the instant he heard Bob's voice.

"She still hasn't seen or heard from Franklin."

"Okay, listen. I want you to call the top security company in the San Luis Obispo area. Hire a guard to watch the Heartbreak Hotel and get him there right away. If Tracy Potter walks out of the hotel, I want her trailed. If anything looks the least suspicious, have them follow up. I don't want the occupants of the hotel alarmed or alerted."

"They'll need a photo."

He described Tracy and then added,

"Have them check the Net. Try Twilight Cove real estate sites. She used to have a license, and Realtors always have headshots. There's a long shot of her in front of the hotel that ran with the article. It might be online on the *L.A. Times* site. If not, have them check the archives."

"Right. Okay. I'll get on it."

"I've got to go."

"Wait!"

He gave Schack one more minute. "What?"

"Be careful, Wade. I don't represent dead authors."

Matt was having the time of his life. He couldn't believe it when Tucker Hannah and Willie Schmidt showed up at four that afternoon. They were the most popular guys in the sixth grade and would never have given a fourth-grader the time of day — unless that fourth-grader had access to a real live ghost.

"So, this is the room, huh?"

Tucker stared at the door to Wade's former room and Matt nodded. He'd turned the hall lights off earlier, just to make it spookier. His mom kept asking why the lights kept going off, but he'd just shrugged and hoped she wouldn't call an electrician.

She'd told him to stop with the tours, but she was so busy that he was still able to sneak kids in.

He pointed to the door and lowered his voice.

"This is where Edward Cain met the ghost of Captain Ezra Poole." He'd memorized the article about the hotel, at least the parts about the old sea captain and how he had been marooned on an island like Tom Hanks in *Castaway,* how Ezra almost starved before he got rescued. Then he'd pause dramatically and lower his voice before he told how Ezra jumped off the cliff behind the house and splatted on the rocks below.

He now knew why Wade was always in his room scribbling. He was thinking about becoming a writer himself. He'd almost filled the whole journal with letters to his dad, and some of them were whoppers. It was a gift that he didn't know he had, but he figured he ought to be able to make up some really good stuff and get paid for it.

He put the key into the keyhole and slowly cracked the door ajar.

"Can we go in?" Willie whispered.

Matt pretended to think about it. "I dunno."

Willie nudged Tucker with his elbow.

466

Tucker said, "We'll give you seventy-five cents extra."

Matt sighed and pretended to think about it. "Okay. I guess. But don't touch anything."

Chelsea and his mom would kill him if the bedspread got wrinkled or messed up before the guests checked in later.

"And *be careful*," he warned the guys. "Ezra won't come out if he doesn't like you."

"What's not to like?" Tucker elbowed Willie hard and laughed. A shoving war ensued.

"Hey, keep it down or you'll scare him off."

The older boys quieted down and walked into the room, their eyes wide and full of awe as they turned full circle to take it all in. When the curtains at the oceanside window billowed up, lifted by the breeze, they both jumped, bumping into each other.

Willie shoved Tucker. "Fartface."

Tucker shoved back. "Shithead."

"I'll have to end the tour if you don't shut up," Matt warned, suddenly feeling a rush of power. He waited in the hallway so that he could keep an eye out for Chelsea and Mom. If Mom caught him again, she'd for sure make him give the guys their money back.

When a deliveryman walked into the lobby, Matt glanced back into the room to make sure Tucker and Willie weren't touching anything before he hurried down the hall.

The deliveryman was holding a huge vase of roses with a card sticking out of it. He lowered the vase. "These are for Tracy Potter. Is she here?"

"My mom's upstairs." He was afraid that if he called her, she'd come downstairs and he'd get busted for operating the tour again.

"Just leave 'em on the registration desk," he suggested.

"Sorry. She has to sign for them."

Matt sighed and impatiently pointed to the stairway on the opposite side of the lobby. "She's up there. Go on up."

As soon as the flower deliveryman started toward the stairs, Matt hurried back to Wade's old room. It was time to slam the door on the guys and pretend it was Ezra's doing. It was the best part of the tour as far as he was concerned. Even better than the quick peek and maybe even a walk around the haunted attic.

Christopher had called last night to say that he heard from one of the kids in their class that the Haunted Heartbreak Hotel tour was almost as good as Disneyland.

Matt couldn't help but smile. By the end of summer, he was going to be a *gazillionaire.*

Tracy was headed for the stairs when she turned the corner and nearly ran into a deliveryman already halfway up with a bouquet of huge ivory tea roses in his arms. They almost hid him from view.

The man peered around the roses. "Are you Tracy Potter?"

"How did you get in?"

"The kid told me to come up."

Remembering Lauren Westin posing with an empty overnight bag, she asked, "Are you a reporter?"

"No." He had a vacant look, as if he had no interest whatsoever in his surroundings or her. His job was to deliver the roses and leave. Charm wasn't a requirement. "The Daisy Drop sent me."

"Come on up." She stepped aside to let him pass when he reached the landing and then ushered him into the apartment, where stuff was piled everywhere, a sure sign that her life had gone haywire.

I'm going to need more help.

"Put them on the coffee table." She found her purse and started digging for a tip as he set the flowers down and then pulled a receipt out of his pocket.

She glanced at the bouquet, anxious to read the card stuck on a plastic pitchfork. The roses were lovely — breathtaking in fact. The Daisy Drop was the oldest and best florist in Twilight, and they always did an outstanding job.

The delivery boy was no boy. He had to be close to thirty. His hair was thinning, nearly the same length all over. His eyes were deep-set. He was looking around the room.

"Sorry the place is such a mess." She immediately stopped when she realized she was apologizing to a deliveryman. "Here you go."

She handed him three dollars. He stared at it for a second before he pocketed it, looking more uncomfortable by the second.

"Well, then." Surely he wasn't stalling for a bigger tip.

"Thanks for bringing them upstairs." She started for the open door, hoping he'd get the hint and walk out before she had to tell him to go ahead and leave.

"So, where's Edward Cain?" He glanced around the room.

"You *are* a reporter." She shook her head, closed her eyes, and prayed for patience.

"I'm getting really sick and tired of you people."

"I'm not a reporter. Just curious."

"Edward Cain is *not* here. Now please, leave."

"Is he coming back?"

"I really have no idea." The guy was beginning to creep her out, but she couldn't exactly put her finger on why. Maybe it was because his lackluster gray-blue eyes never really settled on anything. There was nothing suspicious about him, really. He seemed mild-mannered, almost shy. His features were so average that he would easily blend into a crowd and barely be remembered.

She glanced into the kitchen, thought of going for the phone. Last time she had checked, the line was still dead, but he couldn't know when service would go back on. She opted to walk out into the hall and if he didn't follow her out, she was going to bolt down the stairs, find Matt, and head outside to where the news van was parked across the road.

"Well, then —"

She was three feet from the door when he came bolting past her, slammed it shut, and leaned against it.

As her pulse shot up and her ears started buzzing, she fought to focus.

Where are you, Matt? She prayed he wouldn't come upstairs. Chelsea was out shopping and due back soon. She didn't want her walking in, either. There was no other way out except through the door to the widow's walk, a fine alternative in case of fire, but not with someone trailing after her. Still, if she could get there before he could stop her, if she could run to the stairway that led upstairs, get there before he —

Her thoughts were hopping around like a jumping bean. She decided to keep him busy, keep him away from the kids at all costs. He was between her and the stairs to the lobby. She could try to get to the kitchen, to the knives, if she had to.

But with a knife in her hand, she might be putting herself in greater jeopardy.

I have to do something.

"Whatever you're thinking, don't." With more speed than she would have given him credit for, he pulled a switchblade out of his pocket. It sprang to life, a glittering silver stiletto that flashed deadly, even in the gray light streaming through the front window.

Not today, she thought. *I don't want to die today; I won't die today. Matt, stay downstairs. Please, please. Chelsea, take care of him. You're a smart girl.*

She prayed that Chelsea would somehow divine that something wasn't right. *But how?* Finally she managed to find her voice again. "What do you want?"

"Edward Cain."

Death threats. Wade had received death threats. She'd wondered just how bad things could be that he'd had to change his looks and keep moving. Now she knew.

This is how bad it can be.

"He's gone. I didn't even know he was here."

The intruder shook his head as if shaking off a pesky fly. He frowned. "But he knew you."

He leaned against the door, a casual posture that belied the way his gaze was darting around the room and back. He pulled a piece of crumpled newspaper out of his pocket. She stared at it. The Heartbreak feature story, creased and faded.

Quoting the article word for word without even looking at it, he recited, "Tracy Potter, innkeeper. A consummate hostess who serves baked goods that melt in your mouth. She met a challenge head-on by creating a welcoming, homey atmosphere that tempts guests to linger by the fire on a chilly day, or take in the view from the sunroom. Who can go wrong lingering a while in a place where a rose garden grows wild beneath the California sun, and gulls play over the water?"

He shoved the article back into his pocket. "How *cozy* were you two?"

When she didn't immediately respond, he laughed. The sound chilled her blood.

"Please, my son might come in. Tell me you won't hurt my son," she pleaded.

"I don't hurt kids." He didn't sound all that convincing, though. "I don't really want to hurt you either, but Cain has to pay."

"For what?" Keep him talking, she decided, thinking of all the detective series she used to watch while she was waiting up at night for Glenn to come home. *Keep him calm. Keep him away from Matt.*

"Cain deserves to die. My sister was one of the even dozen. She was pretty, just like you. She was younger, though. She never asked for trouble, but because of Edward Cain's book, she's dead. And so are all the others. He got off easy, but I'm going to make him pay. God told me I have to make him pay. Now, I want you to call him. Get him back here."

Chapter Forty-Five

"I don't know how to get ahold of Edward Cain." Despite the cloudy weather, Tracy could feel sweat trickling down her temple.

"Do I look stupid?" her assailant asked.

"Not at all." *You look dangerous. Demented, but not stupid.* "The phone lines are out. They've been out since this morning."

"Don't patronize me. I can read your thoughts through your eyes, Ms. Potter."

"Try the phone."

He made her get it for him, bring it to him. She obeyed, and when he punched it on, there was no dial tone. Raising his arm as if to throw it across the room in frustration, he immediately thought better of it and shoved it into his waistband.

"I have no idea where Wa . . . Edward Cain is —"

"Where's your room?" He moved quick as a snake, grabbing her arm.

"Why?" She dug her heels into the carpet.

475

Though he didn't appear to be in all that great shape, she was no match for his strength.

He stepped away from the door and dragged her across the room. She bumped into the coffee table and winced.

"My son is downstairs. If he comes looking for me, the first place he'll go is my room. You don't want him to find us, do you?" *Oh, Mattie. Think. Think. Breathe.* "There's an attic. No one ever goes up there. Take me to the attic." She prayed she hadn't just signed her own death sentence.

He stopped in the hall just outside the door to her room. "Show me."

The front window in the attic looked down on the news van still parked out front. All she needed was to attract the attention of someone, anyone, a reporter or member of the crew. Maybe someone would see her if she waved, if she could just attract their attention. Maybe someone could help her. Save her.

If she could just get someone's attention . . .

His fingers dug deep into the tender underside of her arm as she pointed toward the door at the end of the hall, and he dragged her through it and then up the steps. At the landing he paused.

476

"Which door?"

She pointed to the attic door.

"What's the other one?"

"It goes outside. Onto the roof."

He opened the attic door and, once inside, hooked the door lock. The space was tidy now, thanks to Wade. The boxes and crates were all labeled and stacked. There was nothing in sight that she could use to defend herself. At least nothing that jumped out at her. Wade was the last one to touch most of the boxes. Somehow, the thought comforted her.

She thought about darting over to the front window, but he was right there, breathing down her neck. Though it was raining out, the air held a hint of tropical moisture. It was stuffy in the room.

"How long do you intend to keep me up here?"

"Until the phone works and you can call him."

"I already told you —"

"We'll sit here until he comes back!" he yelled.

Tracy groaned. "But he's *not* coming back. What part of that don't you understand?"

His voice dropped almost to a whisper, and as if he were explaining to a three-year-

477

old, he fell into a singsong rhythm. "Sooner or later someone's going to notice you're missing. It will make the news. Then Edward Cain will come back to help you, to look for you."

She thought for a second she was going to throw up. Not Wade, but eventually the kids would be looking for her. Then what? Knowing how often she went out there, they would naturally look on the widow's walk, and then they would think to check the attic, too.

Her gaze flew to the small iron hook that he'd latched on the inside of the door.

"My children will notice I'm missing and they'll come up here. How do you plan to keep all three of us quiet?" The question gave him pause, heightened his nervousness.

"I don't know. I don't know. I don't know." His gaze shot back and forth. "Shut up."

"Have you thought this through? What's your name?"

"Franklin."

"Franklin, you know, you still have time to walk out of here before you get yourself into real trouble. I won't hold it against you if you change your mind right now and let me out. You can walk out. Did you drive? Is your car out front?" Surely someone had seen him come in with the flowers. Wouldn't they notice that he hadn't come out?

"Please *shut up.*"

"Cain will never come to my rescue."

"If I kill you, he'll come then. He'll come after me because he'll know it should have been him, not you. He cares about you. I can tell by what he wrote about you."

Her hands had been trembling, but now they were shaking uncontrollably. She clenched them together; tried to make herself look weak, thankful that he hadn't tied her up. It was obvious Franklin had no idea what he was doing, but with the stiletto in his hand, he was holding all the cards.

"I really don't want you to die, like my sister and the others. But if I have to kill you to get Cain's attention, I will. Now please sit down."

She stared around the room. Glanced over at the front window. Too far. She wouldn't have a lot of chances, but she could try to get to it. If she had to, she'd kick it out, scream bloody murder. But that might enrage him and he would still have time to kill her, run downstairs, and find Matt.

"Where should I sit?"

"On that one." He pointed to a box in the middle of the floor. It was filled with Ezra's logs. She'd boxed them up herself the day

479

after Wade left and brought them back up here.

He sat within arm's length of her, stretched his legs out in front of him, and was tucked into the dark space where the angled ceiling met the floor.

"How? How did your sister die?" She tried not to choke on the question. Her one goal was to keep him talking.

"You haven't read the book?"

"No." She knew now that she never would be able to bring herself to open it. And she knew why Wade had looked so desperately lost and lonely that first night.

"My sister was number seven. Simple murder wasn't good enough for Mr. Cain. The killer he created, the spawn of his imagination, not only raped his victims, but at the end, he slit their throats. And Cain even took it a step further with each victim."

She saw the knife in his hands. He was staring at the gleaming tip.

"Cain's killer dismembered them before he killed them. One piece at a time. Toes. Fingers. Feet. Hands. He tied off the wounds, made certain they didn't bleed out. Kept them alive, in pain, in terrible agony, Ms. Potter. He did different horrible things to each of them. Tortured them in twelve different ways before he slit their throats.

Killing them was actually the most merciful thing he could do. And it was all Cain's design."

"It was fiction," she whispered.

"It became fact. My sister didn't deserve to die that way. None of them did," he said sadly.

"Edward Cain is certainly not the only author writing that kind of novel. What about the people who buy and read them? Aren't they just as guilty? Is it Edward's fault that someone decided to replicate the murders?"

Franklin drew his legs up close to his body and looped his long arms around his knees. The knife was ever in his hand.

He was glaring at her, his eyes focused for the moment. Determined. His expression made her shiver. "I suggest you shut up, Ms. Potter. This isn't something you can fix by mixing up a batch of 'mouthwatering cinnamon rolls.' You should start thinking about what I might have to do to you."

If he was waiting for her to break down, to grovel, then he was going to have to wait until hell froze over. She was determined to stay strong, to not show fear. "Edward cares only about himself. He won't care what happens to me."

Nothing was further from the truth. Her

death would be one more burden for Wade to bear. In writing the travel piece about the Heartbreak, he'd risked his own anonymity for her. How many people like Farley were out there seeking revenge?

She broke into a cold sweat when she heard a creak on the stairs outside the door.

Franklin shot up lightning fast and without a sound. In a second he crossed the room and covered her mouth with his hand. She felt the hot prick of the cold blade at her throat.

"Don't move. Don't make a sound." His breath was stale, his skin so cool it felt reptilian as he whispered in her ear. "If you even twitch, I'll kill you. I swear on your kid's life."

Her eyes widened above his hand and she watched as the door handle slowly turned back and forth, back and forth. Then her heart almost stopped when she heard Matt's voice on the other side of the door.

"Weird," Matt said.

"What's weird?"

She didn't recognize the second voice, but it sounded like another boy.

"The door is supposed to be open, but it's stuck. Or maybe it's locked from inside." Matt sounded puzzled.

The knob rattled as he tried to open it.

Tracy willed him to give up and leave.

After what was only heartbeats that seemed like hours, she heard his voice again. "I guess Ezra doesn't want us in there."

"Yeah, right. Somebody else locked it."

"There's no keyhole, see?"

There came the sound of a scuffle to see and then a third voice complained, "What a gyp."

"Come back and bring friends — maybe Ezra will let us in next time."

The stairs creaked and footsteps echoed hollowly as the boys went back downstairs. Tracy's relief was as great as her fear when she knew that Matt and the others were leaving.

Suddenly her mouth was free. Franklin had let her go. He walked across the room but hovered beneath the eaves where he could see her, where he was close enough to reach her if he had to.

She told herself to hang on, to think straight. She was still alive. She'd come too far in the last few months to give up now.

Stay alert. Stay strong. Wait for a chance to escape. Surely he'll get tired, if he doesn't crack first. He can't watch me every second.

As long as she was alive, there was a chance.

■ ■ ■ ■

Thank God for the Harley.

Wade skirted the traffic jammed along the canyon road as if it weren't there.

The minute he cleared the bend in the old road and saw the Heartbreak standing on the bluff against the misty, smoke-gray sky, an odd mix of relief and anxiety hit him at once.

Carefully negotiating potholes and puddles, he tried to temper his anticipation with caution. There was no need to panic, or to panic Tracy, either. Farley might very well be back in Minnesota. He could have just been making idle threats.

The hotel, with its eclectic mix of architectural styles, its widow's walk and dormers and wide porch, gave him a sense of homecoming — the likes of which he'd never known in all the years of shuffling around New York from apartment to apartment.

That sense of homecoming was surely inspired not by the sight of the hotel, but by his feelings for Tracy. He'd been a fool not to tell her who he was and how he came to be there, even though she'd told him that she didn't want to know.

As the bike quickly ate up the last half

mile to the Heartbreak, his desperate need to hold Tracy again, his need to see her safe, to feel her in his arms and tell her how much she meant to him, was almost overwhelming.

As he drew nearer, he finally and completely understood Ezra, his love for Violette, and how it had kept him alive — and why he couldn't live without her.

A news van was the most recognizable vehicle on the road, with its tall antenna and bright station logos painted on the sides. Also noticeable was the nondescript navy-blue sedan parked at the curb. A three-hundred-pound security guard was taking up half the front seat.

Noting a couple of other cars out front, he blew past the *Eyewitness News* van and pulled into the driveway, continuing on up to the house as if he had every right to be there. He left his helmet on, with its tinted face shield, dismounted, and hustled up the walk to the side door. He was inside so quickly that no one from the van had time to move, let alone stop and ask questions.

He didn't pull off his helmet until he was safely inside the lobby, where he found a couple standing beside their suitcases at the registration desk.

"Do you work here?" the woman wanted

to know.

"No, but maybe I can help. What do you need?" He glanced around, wondered where Tracy might be.

"We're here to check in. The Korman-icks?"

Wade opened the big drawer in the desk and pulled out a room key.

"Here you go," he said, tossing it to them. "Mrs. Potter will take a copy of your credit card when she gets in. The rooms are right down the hall. Make yourselves comfort-able."

He pointed them in the right direction, then checked the sunroom and the laundry. Both were empty. He headed for the apart-ment stairs, taking them two at a time.

Relief washed over him when he heard Matt's voice coming from inside the apart-ment.

Matt was fine. Tracy was fine. Everything would be fine. It had to be.

Matt was headed down the stairs with two older boys trailing behind him. He stopped the minute he recognized Wade, and his two friends ran into him. Launched into the air, Matt came flying at Wade, who caught him before he ended up knocking them both all the way back to the lobby.

"Wade! Wow. You came back. Did you see

486

the *Eyewitness News* van outside? There were five of them out there yesterday, until the mudslide. They were waiting for —"

Wade cut him off immediately. "Will you come upstairs with me, Sport?"

"Sure." Matt drew himself up, suddenly important. "Bye, guys," he told the other boys. "Be sure to tell everybody about the tour."

Wade started up the stairs behind Matt. "Tour?"

"Yeah. The Heartbreak Hotel Ghost of Captain Ezra Poole Tour." Matt stopped, forcing Wade to stop in his tracks, too. "You're a writer, Wade. You think I should name it something else?"

"You could add the words 'world famous.' The World Famous Heartbreak Hotel Ghost of Captain Ezra Poole Tour."

"I think that's too many words."

"It worked for Sergeant Pepper's One and Only Lonely Hearts Club Band."

"Who?"

"Never mind."

"Maybe I'll try it." But he sounded doubtful.

Wade took a deep breath as he stepped over the threshold of the apartment. Everything seemed quiet inside. The windows were slightly open to the view and the ocean, just wide enough to let the salt air in and keep the rain out. There was still a hint of cinnamon in the air mingled with that of roses. He thought of Tracy. Ached to see her again.

He and Matt called out to her at the same time. "Tracy?"

"Mom?"

Emptiness echoed back. Wade walked into the kitchen, where everything looked to be in place, but the longer he stood there, the longer he had the strangest feeling that something was wrong. The feeling grew stronger when Matt came running back into the kitchen.

"She's not in the bedroom or the bathroom. Maybe she went to the store." He sounded more than a little hesitant. "She would'a told me she was going, though."

"Is Chelsea here?"

Matt shrugged. "Mom wouldn't have left me by myself."

They moved into the living room together, Matt sticking to him like glue. It wasn't a bad feeling at all. "You wanna watch TV, Wade?"

He wondered how he'd missed seeing the gargantuan bouquet of roses in the middle of the coffee table, but then he realized he'd been looking for only one thing — Tracy.

The bouquet was so huge it was better suited for the lobby.

Wade walked up to it and gently pulled the card out of the plastic flower pick in the middle of the bouquet. He opened the small envelope and stared at the card.

Tracy,
Thinking of you.

Love, Edward.

The Daisy Drop was the local florist where he'd bought Tracy's gardenia corsage.

He stared at the card from "Edward" and his blood ran cold.

He hadn't sent her flowers, and if he had, he certainly wouldn't have sent them signed from Edward.

He dropped the card on the coffee table and turned to Matt.

"Where did these come from? Do you know? When were they delivered?"

The boy shrugged. "Some guy brought 'em a while ago."

"When did he leave?"

Matt turned on the TV and started channel-surfing. Wade walked over and stood in front of the screen.

"Did you see the flower deliveryman leave?" He tried to keep the strained ur-

489

gency out of his tone, but Matt immediately picked up on it and looked concerned.

"I was busy giving the tour. I never saw him leave. I told him to bring the flowers up here, and then he did." Wade paced over to the front window, stared out at the news van. The security guard was sipping something in an oversized take-out cup.

Wade shoved his hands into his pockets.

"Hey," Matt said, hopping to his feet, "maybe she's in the attic. Or on the widow's walk."

Wade's pulse picked up as he pictured the close, pitched roof. The room where he'd found the *Lantana*'s logs and questioned his own sanity. Matt was talking, calling his attention back. "What did you just say?"

"I said, the attic was locked when I tried to show the guys. Right before you saw us. There's no key, but there's an old hook on the inside of the door. The kind you slip through a little ring. I told them Ezra locked it, but it had to be Mom, right? Ezra's not real, is he, Wade? Mom said you made him up so we'd get more business, but I'm not supposed to tell anyone that part of the story. Did you make him up?"

There is an old hook on the inside of the door.

"Sure. Did you knock on the door?"

490

Matt nodded. "Maybe Mom went in there to take a nap. It's been kinda weird around here. We got all kinds of people trying to talk to her and —"

"Listen, Matt. I'm going to need your help."

Matt turned off the television and jumped to his feet. "Cool. What are we gonna do? Wash the Harley?" Wade pulled out his cell phone and dialed 911. He was connected to the San Luis Obispo dispatcher again. He told her to hold on a second. He went down on one knee and put his hand on Matt's shoulder.

"Listen up, okay? This is really important. Go out front and ask the big guy parked out there in the dark blue car if he has a two-way radio. Ask him to have his company call the police. Tell him to stay out there with you and watch the house, okay? Can you do that?"

"Sure." He didn't look sure. He looked scared. "Where's my mom?"

"Probably at the store, like you thought. Or maybe she did go to the attic to get away from all the newspeople."

Matt shook his head. "Not my mom. Why do you need the police?"

Wade told the dispatcher to hold on again and then told Matt, "Time to get going.

You ready?"

"But . . ." Matt dragged his feet.

Wade started to walk him to the door, but before Matt could step out into the hall, Chelsea breezed in with two plastic shopping bags dangling from her hands.

Wade automatically took them from her and set them on the kitchen counter. Chelsea looked none too pleased to see him. She followed him into the kitchen.

"What are you doing here? Where's Tracy?"

Wade nodded to Matt. "Go ahead. Take off. Now." He looked to Chelsea for support.

"Go ahead, Mattie. I need to talk to Wade alone."

"Why?"

"Just go."

As soon as the boy was out the door, Wade got back on the cell. The line was dead. He walked over to where he'd dropped his saddlebags, opened one, and pulled out the Colt.

"What are you doing?" Chelsea started backing toward the door.

Wade tossed her his cell phone. "Call 911."

The gun had been loaded since Bob warned him about Farley. Wade took the safety off. "If you can't get anyone, try San Luis Obispo. Tell them there is an armed robber in the house."

"Is there?" Her eyes went huge and her face drained of color.

"I don't know."

"But . . ."

"Tell them whatever they need to hear, just get them out here. Go outside and wait with Matt. Stay with the security guard out front."

"*What* security guard?"

"The guy in the blue car."

"I saw him sitting out there. I thought he was a reporter." Her gaze flashed between the gun in his hands and his face. Her blue eyes were wide with fear and confusion. Her freckles stood out like specks of cinnamon across the bridge of her nose.

"I don't understand." She shook her head. "What's going on, Wade? Why are you doing this?"

"Tracy's in trouble."

"She's been in trouble since she let you in the front door."

Frustrated, he took a step toward her and when he saw her recoil in fear, he remembered the gun and quickly backed away. "I'd never do anything to hurt any of you," he swore.

"Then why are you standing here with a gun in your hand? Where is she?"

"There's someone out to get me and I think he may have walked in here earlier posing as a flower deliveryman. Matt never saw him leave, and Tracy's not around. Matt said the attic is locked from inside."

"Ohmygod," she whispered. "I thought the copycat murderer was dead."

"Someone else threatened revenge."

She punched 911 into the cell phone.

"What should I tell them?"

"The only thing that'll get them here. Tell them there's an armed intruder inside the house, then get out and go stay with Matt."

Already on her way out, she paused at the door. "Want me to send the security guard up?"

He shook his head. "He's a rent-a-cop. I'd rather wait for the police."

"But if Tracy's up there, if someone does have her —" Someone was on the other end of the line. "Hello, this is an emergency."

Wade signaled that he was headed upstairs.

Chelsea ran back in and grabbed the sleeve of his jacket. "Maybe you should wait for the police, too."

The gun was awkward and heavy in his hand. He was a writer, not a hero. Not by a long shot, but he had created a monster in *An Even Dozen,* and in turn that monster had infected the mind of another crazed and tormented soul.

Unfortunately, he knew exactly what his own monster had been capable of — but he had no idea what was going through Franklin Farley's head. Nor did he have the luxury of time to find out.

As Chelsea demanded immediate help over the phone, he tried to silently run down the hall to the stairway, hoping he had jumped to conclusions. Maybe the attic door was jammed. Maybe his imagination was working overtime. But he couldn't take a chance.

He crept up the stairs with his heart hammering out of his chest, stopping at every creak and groan. When he reached the top, he pressed his ear to the door, heard nothing.

Slowly, barely breathing, he reached for the old brass doorknob, turning it gingerly so that it didn't make a sound. He tried opening it, but Matt was right, it was barred from the inside.

CHAPTER FORTY-SIX

When Tracy heard the Harley, she covered her face in her hands, afraid her reaction would give Wade away. She listened, knowing he had pulled into the driveway and stopped.

Wade's here. Wade's back. Dear God, Tracy prayed, *don't let him come up here.*

Seconds became minutes. Her mouth was dry and her butt was numb from sitting on the box. A second ago she thought she saw the doorknob move ever so slightly, but her vision wavered and she decided she was hallucinating.

Farley was becoming more disoriented and confused with every passing minute. At one point he'd taken to softly humming a meandering, unrecognizable tune. Absorbed, he almost seemed to have forgotten she was there.

"Could you open the window, please?" She tried to sound as casual as she would talking to anyone. If Farley wanted to see her scared, he had a long wait coming. She'd be damned if she'd let him know how petrified she was, not for herself, but for Wade.

When he didn't answer, she turned to look over her shoulder and found her captor seated against the far wall, staring at her with a glazed look in his eyes.

"Franklin, *please* open the window a little wider. It's stuffy in here."

"Wrong. It's raining outside. But you'd like that, wouldn't you? You'd like me to show myself to those newspeople out there, wouldn't you?"

"They don't even know you."

"No, but they will."

"Don't you realize that while you're sitting here, Edward could be getting farther away? It might be hours before anyone starts looking for me."

He shook his head. "I don't think so. Soon your boy is bound to notice you're not around. Boys notice things like that . . . like when their moms are gone. Or when their sisters are killed. They notice."

His voice sounded distant, as if he were slipping back to another time and place.

A place he inhabited only in his mind.

■ ■ ■ ■

Wade closed his eyes and released a pent-up sigh when he heard Tracy ask Farley to open the window.

He bowed his head. The gun in his hand wavered like a mirage, but this was no mirage. No dream. No fantasy he'd concocted. This was as close to hell as he ever wanted to get.

For now, Tracy sounded as if she were holding her own. All he had to do was sit tight and wait for the police. They were the experts. He'd researched enough police procedure to know that they knew the best tactics for getting Tracy out alive.

Hang on, Tracy. Hang in there.

He crouched outside the door on one knee, listening — recalling how Ezra had prayed to a God he never believed in for rescue, prayed that he and his Violette would be together again.

Interminable silence on the other side of the door was finally broken by the screech of tires against the pavement out front. Footsteps echoed behind the attic door.

And then, Farley's voice. He sounded frantic. "It's the police!"

Wade's hand involuntarily tightened

around the gun. He pressed his palm against the door. It was old and locked — if Matt was correct — by a flimsy hook and eye.

You're only a writer. You're no damned hero.

Suddenly it didn't matter who or what he was — if he didn't hear Tracy say something by his next heartbeat, he was going in. He whipped the gun behind him, shoved it into the waistband of his pants, and covered it with his jacket.

"The police are out there!" Farley scooted across the floor, crawling away from the window like a disjointed crab, heading right for her with the switchblade open.

Tracy gauged the distance to the door, thought about trying to make a run for it. She knew she'd never make it.

There had been no sirens, no slamming of car doors, just a screech of tires that had immediately sent Farley darting over to the window. She could see that he was frantic. There was no guessing what he might do now.

"It's not too late to let me go. I'll convince them this was all a big mistake," she offered.

"Shut up! Let me think." He reached her in seconds, sweat beading his thin upper lip.

"You aren't going to get out of this any other way. The police aren't going to let you go unless I assure them that you're in-nocent."

His gaze darted from one side of the attic to the other, to the window, back to her face.

"*Now* Cain will come."

She dropped her gaze, terrified that he would see the truth in her eyes, that he would surely realize that the man he knew as Edward Cain had come back.

Wade was out there somewhere. He was here because he must have known about Farley. He had to have been the one to call the police. She remembered his voice over the answering machine earlier. *"Tracy, I'm afraid —"*

Now what he'd tried to say was all too clear. He'd called to warn her about Farley.

He'll have taken care of Matt, and Chelsea, too. She knew it in her heart. Wade would make sure her kids were out of harm's way.

Without warning, Franklin grabbed her by the arm and jerked her to her feet. She'd been sitting in one cramped position for so long that without thinking, she cried out in pain.

"Shut up! Or I'll kill you! I swear I will!" He shook her, whipped her around, and wrapped his arm around her in a viselike grip. He pulled her up against him, pressing the deadly knifepoint against her throat. His hand was shaking so violently that the switchblade jabbed into her throat.

A loud crash ripped through the room. The old door frame splintered as the door flew back on its hinges and banged into the wall.

Wade rushed into the attic and froze. "Let her go, Farley. It's me you want."

"Wade!" The minute she opened her mouth, the knifepoint pressed deeper into her throat. Something warm and terrifying trickled down her neck.

"Why not let her go, Farley?" Sounding as casual as if he were asking the man to pass the salt, Wade took another step into the room. He was unarmed, but he looked and sounded completely calm, perfectly in control.

"How does it feel?" Farley's voice had gone up an octave. "Now you can watch her die. You won't have to imagine what it's like to have someone you care about carved up into pieces. You can witness it firsthand. You'll have a chance to see what a *real* murder looks like."

Tracy was afraid to breathe. Every time she inhaled, the point of the blade was that much closer to sliding into her throat. She hung on Farley's arm, watching, listening. Wishing she could tell Wade to get out, to save himself. Wishing she could say all the things that she had been foolish to not tell him before, foolish to think it was too soon.

It's never too soon to tell someone you love them. Never.

Better too soon than too late.

She had to tell him now, before it was too late. "Wade . . . I . . ."

"Shut up! Shut up!" Farley's arm had tightened so tight that she was afraid he'd break her ribs.

Wade hadn't moved an inch, but his tone was no longer casual. He was furious, no longer hiding it. "You want to carve someone up, Farley? Make it me. Prove what a man you are. Come on. Kill me." Wade spread his hands wide, stepped closer.

"No!" Tracy cried.

Farley shook her. "Shut up!" he hollered.

"The police are downstairs." Wade was deadly calm again, speaking slowly, as if explaining the situation to a five-year-old. "If you want me, you're going to have to take me before they get up here." Wade spread his arms wide, palms up, in surrender. "Come on. You want me? It's her or me, Farley. You make a move to kill her, and I'll be on you before you can stop me."

Farley was humming now, a low, strained, wandering tune that sent chills down Tracy's spine. And now he was quaking like a leaf, scratching the switchblade across her throat.

While Farley wavered with indecision, her gaze was drawn to shadows shifting in the stairwell behind Wade. Then, without warning, the stairs creaked loudly. Farley shoved her aside and sent her reeling. Struggling to keep her balance, she hit her head on the low underside of the ceiling.

As she fell to the floor, she saw Farley rush Wade with the switchblade aimed at his chest. She screamed, and as if seeing everything in slow motion, watched Wade whip one arm behind, and a gun instantly appeared in his hand.

Farley lunged at Wade at the exact moment an armed sheriff's deputy burst into the room. Wade fired at Farley. The officer fired at Wade. The two rounds echoed simultaneously.

"Wade!" Tracy screamed as she watched him pitch forward.

Farley clutched his side and staggered back before colliding with the low ceiling and crumpling to the floor in a heap. As the fingers of his outstretched hand opened, the switchblade fell onto the floor.

"Wade! Oh, God. Wade!" Tracy pushed herself up onto her hands and knees and started crawling toward Wade as a flood of sheriff's deputies poured into the room. Seeing stars, she staggered, got to her feet, and started toward Wade just as a deputy nudged the gun out of Wade's hand with his toe.

"What have you done?" Blood was pouring from a wound in Wade's back, low on his shoulder. Falling to her knees beside Wade's prone body, she shouted at the deputy, *What have you done?*"

A young, blond deputy, his thick chest fortified by a Kevlar vest, reached for her arm to help her up, but she shrugged him off.

"We got a call about an armed assailant." He stared down at Wade and the gun lying beside him.

She pointed over at Farley's crumpled form. "That's the assailant. He was holding me hostage, threatening me at knifepoint." Kneeling beside Wade she cried, "This man was trying to save me."

She struggled to turn Wade over as another officer went down on one knee and pressed his fingers against Wade's neck, feeling for a pulse.

"Get the paramedics up here!" he shouted. "He's still alive."

An officer across the room was kneeling

beside Farley, handcuffing him. "This guy's just grazed," he said.

Tracy covered the wound in Wade's shoulder with her hands, leaned over to try and stop the flow of blood.

"Get some help up here!" she screamed at the county sheriffs as Wade's warm blood pumped through her fingers. "I need some towels! Where are the paramedics?"

"They're on the way, lady."

Around her there was nothing but noise, deputies yelling for the paramedics, two-way radios squawking, the heavy footfalls of men running up and down the stairs and moving around the crowded space.

She ignored them all as Wade's face drained of color.

"Wade?" She leaned her lips close to his cheek as she pressed down on the wound. She could feel his heart beating, almost beneath her hands. *So close,* she thought. His heart was too close to where her hands were covering the bullet wound.

"Please, hold on, Wade. Please stay with me. You're going to be all right." His skin had gone ashen. Behind her, the sound of another two-way radio crackled as paramedics finally hustled in. The attic was crowded with men in uniforms. "Wade? Listen to me. I love you. I love you. Do you hear me?"

She watched his face, desperate for a sign, the flicker of his eyelids, the merest trace of movement on his lips. Something. Anything to let her know that he had heard, that he understood that she loved him. That it wasn't too soon.

She prayed that it wasn't too late.

Someone knelt beside her — a woman, one of the emergency medical response team. They exchanged a look that conveyed feelings without words. *Finally,* Tracy thought. *Finally someone who understands.*

"Let me," the young Hispanic woman said softly.

Finally Tracy let go and moved aside, relinquishing Wade to the young woman's capable hands even though she wanted to wrap her arms around him, to cup his face and will him to open his eyes, but he needed more than just her will now.

She looked down at her hands, helpless, and saw that they were covered in blood.

"We need to move him, ma'am. We need to get him out of here." A paramedic who didn't look any older than Chelsea was kneeling on the other side of Wade.

"I want to go with him," she appealed to the woman. "May I please go with him?"

A deputy stepped between her and the

stretcher they were carefully shifting Wade onto. "We'll need a statement from you first, ma'am."

"But —"

"I'm sorry, but you'll have to stay here."

CHAPTER FORTY-SEVEN

Though Carly and Jake were waiting downstairs, she didn't see Chelsea or Matt anywhere. It wasn't until the Montgomerys came rushing toward her that the grim reality of what had happened hit her all at once, and she started sobbing.

"Where's Matt? Where's Chelsea?" She grabbed Carly, forcing her friend to look her in the eyes. In her heart of hearts, she felt Matt and Chelsea were safe, but she needed to hear it from her friend.

"Chelsea called and told us to come over. We had her drive Matt up to our place. They're with Christopher. Geoff and Vince are both on their way over there, too, so the kids won't be alone."

She knew that Geoff and Vince would pamper the kids, comfort them with food, exhaust themselves cheerleading.

It wasn't until Jake took her arm and walked her toward the small bathroom off the sunroom and said, "Let's get you washed up," that she remembered there was blood all over her hands.

"I'll run up and get you a clean top," Carly volunteered, but the sheriffs wouldn't let her up the stairs.

When Tracy heard a siren blare outside, she tried to veer toward the lobby.

"Where are they taking him?"

"They're headed for the hospital in San Luis Obispo."

"But —"

"Let's get you washed up, and then after you talk to the sheriff, we'll drive you straight over there."

Jake handed her over to Carly when they reached the small half bath off the solarium. Carly started the hot water and then pumped hand soap onto her friend's bloody hands. Tracy closed her eyes rather than watch the deeply red-stained water swirl around the bowl and down the drain.

Once she was cleaned up, Jake led her back into the solarium, where the deputies were waiting.

"Some of the guests were supposed to have checked in by now." She glanced around. Real life — bookings, check-ins, room rates, vacancies — seemed light-years away.

"We sent the early arrivals to Selma's, where she's giving them complimentary dinners. I called Kat Chandler, and she's going to come over and sit at the desk until you get back. She'll check the guests in and send them to Selma's. The police said that as long as no one goes upstairs, they'll be allowed to get into their rooms in a couple of hours."

Tracy thought her emotions were under control, but upon hearing of Selma's kindness as well as that of a woman she'd so recently met, her tears started flowing again.

"I don't know how to thank you." She tried to wipe away her tears, but more kept coming.

"Don't even think about it." Carly hugged her, then grabbed a napkin off the buffet in the sunroom and tried to dry Tracy's tears. "Friends don't keep score, remember?"

"Is Mom dead?" Matt was shaking by the time he finally found the courage to ask Chelsea the question that had been haunting him since they'd left the Heartbreak.

He'd seen the sheriff's deputies pull up and run into the house. He'd heard gunshots. Right after that, he'd leaned over and hurled his lunch right there in the gutter beside the security guard's car.

No one told them what was happening when the paramedics rushed inside, not until Carly and Jake drove up a second later. Jake got real mad and showed everyone his P.I. identification and went inside, but Carly told Chelsea to drive him and Chris back to their house. Geoff Wilson and his friend Vincent came driving right behind them. They rushed them all into the house and then started cooking.

Geoff turned on the music video channel and took the remote into the kitchen with him, but not until after Vincent had threatened to drive them around in the car for hours if they dared to turn on the news.

It reminded Matt of the day his dad died. The Montgomerys had picked him up at school and taken him to their house. He'd stayed for dinner, and the whole time, everyone was acting really weird. Finally, by the time it was dark and cold outside, his mom had shown up and she was crying.

That's when she told him his dad was dead.

Now he was back at the Montgomerys' and everything was creepy and almost the same, except that this time Chelsea was with him. But she wasn't talking.

"Chelsea? *Is Mom dead?*" He realized he'd barely whispered before. This time he almost yelled at her.

Chelsea turned away from the TV screen and looked at him. Really looked at him.

"She's just fine. Jake and Carly drove her to San Luis Obispo to see Wade. He's in the hospital there."

"Did he get shot?"

"Yes."

"Is Wade gonna die?"

"I don't know." She shook her head and patted the sofa beside her. "Come here, Mattie."

He walked over to his half-sister and let her hug him. "Chelsea?"

"What?"

"Do you think Wade will die?"

"I hope not."

"Me, too."

She hugged him even tighter than before, and then she cupped his face between her hands and looked him right in the eyes.

"No matter what, you know you'll always have me, don't you?"

He used to think he'd always have his dad, too. Now all he had were some photos and a dumb old journal full of letters instead.

"Something might happen to you. Everybody dies."

"Mattie, Tracy's fine, and I'm fine. We're not going to die anytime soon. I promise."

He wanted to believe her, he really did, but ever since Dad died, he'd been feeling the way he had the year he was in kindergarten and somebody told him there wasn't really any Santa Claus.

He knew that nobody, not Chelsea, not anybody, could promise that they wouldn't die. Nobody.

And just like the truth about Santa Claus, it was something he wished he didn't know.

Two hours later, Jake ushered Tracy through a cluster of media people and into the Sierra Vista Regional Medical Center. Suddenly the weather and bridge closure were old news. The latest up-to-the-minute reports were all about Edward Cain, Franklin Farley, and the drama that had unfolded at the Heartbreak Hotel.

It took ten minutes, Jake pulling out every piece of identification he had on him and having an intense discussion with the deputy stationed at the front door, to get Tracy up to the waiting room near where Wade was still in surgery.

The minute she walked into the waiting area, she was approached by a harried but handsome man, tall, balding, confident, but obviously very shaken.

"Ms. Potter? I'm Bob Schack." He extended his hand. "Wade's literary agent. I recognized you from the news clips." He led her over to a chair.

"How is he?" she asked. Her nerves taut as wire, she perched on the edge of the vinyl chair when both Schack and Jake started encouraging her to sit.

"He's in surgery. The doctor said the bullet went clear through him, which is the good news. They don't know what damage he's sustained though."

"Did he ever regain consciousness?"

The agent shook his head. "Not that I know of."

"What about Farley?"

"The good news is, Wade is a lousy shot and Farley was barely nicked. He's under arrest in the psych ward."

Hating this helpless, useless feeling, she thought of Wade in surgery, visualized the doctor's capable hands on him, healing him, helping him. Short of praying, there was nothing she could do to help Wade. Nothing.

He risked his life to save me.

She clasped her hands together, refusing to break down, refusing to give up hope.

"He wrote that article to help me fill the hotel," she whispered, thinking aloud. Thinking of how he'd unwittingly put himself in danger by having his pen name surface again.

"The Cain pseudonym wasn't supposed to be on it." Schack sighed and rubbed a hand over his bald head.

The air-conditioning was set on arctic. Chilled, Tracy rubbed her arms, got up, and started walking around the small room, giving in to the need to move. "Isn't there *anything* we can do?"

Bob Schack shook his head, failing miserably at smiling. "All we can do is wait."

By the time the surgeon in green scrubs appeared in the waiting area, Tracy felt like a used pillowcase — crumpled and empty.

He immediately walked over to where she was seated between Jake and Bob Schack. "Are you all here for Wade MacAllister?"

MacAllister? She watched Schack stand.

"We are. How's he doing, Doctor?"

"He's actually awake and out of recovery. You can see him one at a time, but only for a few minutes. His prognosis is great. Much better than I expected when he got here."

As he went on to explain the extent of Wade's injury and the surgery, Tracy tuned him out. She'd heard what she needed to hear. Wade would be fine.

She was as relieved as she was confused.

"Why don't you go in first," Schack offered.

Before she left to follow a hospital guild volunteer waiting to take her to Wade's room, she looked up at the literary agent. "MacAllister?"

He nodded. "That's right. Wade MacAllister."

"He told me his name was Wade Johnson."

"He used aliases to protect his identity."

She left him to follow the pink-smocked volunteer down the hall. The woman chatted all the way, no doubt hoping to put her at ease, but it wasn't working. She paused on the threshold of the private ICU room, not knowing what to expect.

It certainly wasn't seeing Wade awake and alert. He was lying in a web of tubes and wires, surrounded by monitors. The moment he saw her, he smiled.

Later, she wouldn't remember crossing the room, only that she was suddenly at his side. Carefully, she reached for his hand, and though he didn't say a word at first, he clung to her fingers.

"Oh, Wade," she whispered, fighting not to burst into tears in front of him as she stared into his eyes. "Your eyes are blue." She couldn't believe it. They were as blue as her own.

He blinked. "They must have taken out my contacts."

"What else, Wade? What else don't I know?" She remembered that he was not Wade Johnson, but Wade MacAllister, a.k.a. Edward Cain, grossly successful thriller writer.

She'd had him cleaning paintbrushes and putting together bed frames.

"My hair is really light brown," he confessed.

She sighed. It wouldn't matter if his hair were fluorescent purple. She rubbed her thumb over the back of his hand, content to just watch him breathe. "Are you in pain?"

"I feel like I have a sizable hole in my shoulder," he confessed. "Can you forgive me for lying to you?"

"You tried to tell me the truth, remember? I wouldn't let you." She smiled, and then added, "How can I be mad at someone I don't even know yet?" Then she shook her head. "Actually, I am feeling a lot of things right now. Grateful, relieved, concerned, confused. But not angry."

When he tried to move and winced, she immediately reached for him but didn't know what to do. "What is it? Do you need the nurse?"

"No. I need you."

She closed her eyes at the stark, horrendous memory of blood pouring out of his shoulder, the close air in the attic, the acrid smell of blood in the air. Over and over, she reminded herself that the doctor had assured her that he would be fine.

She opened her eyes, holding tight to his hand. A chair was wedged into a small space between the bed and the wall. She lowered herself into it.

"I'm so sorry, Tracy. I never wanted anything but good for you." He paused, tried to shift positions, and his pillow slipped sideways. She automatically leaped up to help him, gingerly reached around him, raised him just enough to adjust his pillow. As she drew back, she was so close that his warm breath was caressing her cheek.

"The article worked. The Heartbreak is booked up for the next year," she told him.

His eyelids drifted shut and, thinking him asleep, she tried to slip her hand out of his. His eyes flew open.

"You should get some sleep," she urged.

"Don't leave yet. I want to talk."

"I'll sit right here," she promised.

"The night I checked into the Heartbreak, I had no intention of checking out."

She couldn't tell if he knew what he was saying, for she had no idea. "What do you mean?" She wondered if he was talking about his writing, about how he knew about Ezra Poole and the ship's logs stored in the attic, if he was finally going to tell her why he'd showed up that night.

"I was going to commit suicide."

She thought she'd heard wrong. "Suicide?"

When he nodded slowly, she added, "In *my* hotel?" Vivid images flashed through her mind. She saw herself walking down the hallway, opening the door, finding his body. Calling 911. The police. The reporters. The room that would always be a reminder.

"How? Why?"

"How? I bought a gun for protection. Why? I was sick of running from myself and from the world. Sick of not having a life. Sick of the guilt I couldn't shake."

"You told me your name was Johnson, not MacAllister. Why?"

"One more level of protection. You didn't ask to see my driver's license. I didn't know if I'd ever talk to you again."

She rubbed his hand, had to know, "Why . . . why didn't you do it that night? Why didn't you kill yourself?"

"The nightmare. The dream. I don't know

what it was, but that night I had the first real sleep that I'd had in months. And I didn't dream about the Even Dozen murders. I dreamed of Ezra, almost as if I was there, reliving it with him. Maybe he wanted to keep me from doing what he'd done, from taking my own life the way he had. I don't know. But for whatever reason, those dreams forced me to write again and kept me alive."

He paused, took a deep breath, and winced.

"Wade, you need to rest. Please." She started to stand again.

"No. Not now. There will be time for sleep later." His gaze locked on hers. There was nothing but heat in his ice-blue eyes when he looked into hers. "It might have been the dreams, the writing, that kept me at the hotel at first, but it soon became you, Tracy. Your own attitude toward your situation, your determination, your vulnerability. I stayed because — whether you'd ever admit it or not — you needed help and I needed someone to help, someone to care about. I decided early on to stay until more guests started checking in and you and your kids weren't alone anymore."

"So you left me with Henri?" Though she was smiling, his simple admission had moved her more deeply than anything else he might have said.

"I left to save you from the very thing that ended up happening."

"I know. How well I know that now." She rose out of the chair, unwilling, unable to keep from kissing him. Aware of the IV line, of his bandage, she leaned over him, touched her lips to his. She kissed him lightly.

His eyes drifted closed again. This time he struggled to open them.

"I'm going to let you sleep," she said softly. "I need to see Matt, to let him know we're all right."

He mumbled, "As much as I hate for you to leave, I know he needs you, too. Will you send Schack in before I'm out for the count?"

He was right. She hated the thought of leaving him, but she couldn't wait to see Matt, too. To assure him that she was fine, that Wade was going to be all right. She kissed him again, quickly, carefully.

"Do you have family you want me to call?"

"No. No one."

The simple admission broke her heart.

"I'll send in your agent," she promised.

"How will you get back?"

"Jake is here." She turned away again,

reaching for the door.

"Tracy?"

She turned, barely hearing him when he said, "Come back soon?"

She would forever remember him bursting into the attic to save her.

"I'll be here in the morning when you wake up," she promised. When she found the courage to whisper, "I love you," she saw that he was already sound asleep.

CHAPTER FORTY-EIGHT

The next morning, Wade opened his eyes, and just as she'd promised, Tracy was there, making his heart beat faster, making the whole world brighter.

"Hi," she said softly, instantly on her feet, taking his hand, touching his cheek. "I thought you'd never wake up."

It hurt to swallow, but he managed.

"Hi." His voice sounded hoarse, and his shoulder hurt like hell, but her smile was the only drug he needed to make the pain go away.

"How are you feeling?"

"I've been better. More important, how do I look?"

She laughed. "You want the truth?"

"That bad, huh?"

"That bad."

To dispel her worry, he reached up and touched his hair, which was flattened against his head.

"I really need some gel. And contacts. Would that help?"

Her smile faded. "No more hiding, Wade. Not from me, anyway."

Her words, softly spoken but with her meaning perfectly clear, left him no room for argument.

"No more hiding. Bob and I spoke last night. I want him to fly me down to L.A. as soon as I'm released." He saw the disappointment on her face, the worry, but he wasn't going to lie to her anymore. He watched her gaze sweep the room and then rest on the monitor, which was beeping with a steady even rhythm.

She hesitated before asking, "Do you know how soon that will be?"

"Tomorrow, probably." He could see everything she wasn't saying in her eyes. "As soon as I'm able, I'll start giving interviews. Hopefully, if I give the press and the public what they want, sooner or later they'll get bored with me and leave me alone. It'll be easier to accomplish that in L.A."

"Are you sure that's what you want?"

He nodded. Catnapping off and on, lying alone in the dark last night, listening to the sound of his heartbeat echoing in the monitor, he'd had nothing but time to think about what he wanted. For now, for the future.

"I'm sure. I've had time to do some thinking, too. If I go home with Schack, it'll draw the media away from here."

A shadow crossed her face, but it was fleeting. "You think I can be intimidated by a few more sound crews and news vans? I'm getting used to it."

He wished he could joke about it, too, but the memory of hearing Farley telling her to shut up yesterday, hearing him threaten to kill her, was still fresh in his mind. "You've seen the dark side now, Tracy. You've seen what can happen."

Her smile slowly faded, but her hand tightened around his. "We made it through together, remember?"

"I don't want any of you in danger."

"I noticed there's still a security guard outside the hotel. This morning I spoke to him, and he said he was hired by the Schack Literary Agency."

"Something Bob Schack knew I'd want. There will be a guard there as long as it takes," he assured her. "I love you, Tracy. You know that, don't you?" He watched her carefully, willing her to understand. He couldn't take a chance with her life again. Couldn't put her and her family in harm's way. "I love you and I know you love me, too, or you wouldn't be here right now. If you *didn't* love me, you'd have never forgiven me for not telling you everything in the first place."

"I know," she whispered. "Just as I know I'll never forget that you almost died for me yesterday."

"Help me believe that I can work this out, that there will be a time when the worst of this will all be behind me and I can come back to you."

There was a wistful sadness in her eyes. "Do you really think that there's a right time, a perfect time for anything? We can't plan our lives that easily. Things happen, Wade. Things we don't expect to happen that suddenly do — things like birth and death and —"

"Falling in love?" he asked.

"And falling in love," she whispered. "I don't want you to leave."

"I don't *want* to leave you again, but if I can do anything to make all this go away — and sooner rather than later — then that's what I have to do. And I need to believe that you understand, that you'll wait until I work this out. I need to believe in your love more than I've ever believed in anything in my life."

■ ■ ■ ■

Trust him, her heart whispered.

Trust in your love for this man.

Tracy forced herself to smile down into unfamiliar blue eyes and fought a wave of anxiety. Letting him go again would be one of the single hardest things she'd ever do. She knew that Bob Schack would see that he was being well cared for, protected — but he would be in the spotlight, and after what had just happened, she feared for him.

"Tracy?" He pulled her close, slipped his fingers into her hair, kissed her lips. "Hopefully it won't be long. I'll call you every day."

When she drew back, she saw his determination. Just like before, he was doing what he thought was best for all of them. He was leaving.

Tears stung her eyes, blurred her vision, but she refused to cry in front of him. She silenced the nagging voice inside her that reminded her that she'd trusted once before, that she'd loved before. But this time things were different. This time she was walking into love with a heart that was a little battered, but wiser for it.

"Come here," he whispered, tugging her hand. She got up, leaned against the chrome bed rail, and was about to kiss him when the door opened and an Asian American nurse came breezing in carrying his chart. Her short, straight hair was bright fluorescent purple. She wore a smile from ear to ear.

"Nurse Robin!" Wade's face lit up just looking at her. Tracy couldn't stop staring at her hair.

He lifted a brow suggestively. "She's promised to give me a dye job."

"Not until you get me an autographed copy of your book," the nurse shot back.

Tracy saw that it was a struggle, but Wade finally laughed again. "Only if you can get me outta here in record time."

"Are you kidding? We need the room already." Then the nurse turned to Tracy. "Your daughter's waiting for you in the hall," she said matter-of-factly.

Tracy's heart rate spiked.

"What's wrong?" Wade looked as concerned as Tracy felt.

"I have no idea. She's supposed to be home with Matt."

He wouldn't let go of her hand until she promised to come back and tell him what was going on. In the hall she found Chelsea with her arms folded and her forehead creased with deep concern.

"Where's Matt?" Tracy could barely get the words out.

"He's at the Heartbreak. I called Vincent and he came right over. Everything's fine at the hotel."

"But *something's* wrong."

"You had an emergency phone call. I tried to call your cell phone —"

"They aren't allowed on up here," Tracy explained.

"I thought I should tell you myself, anyway." Chelsea took a deep breath. "A woman called about your friend, Willa. A hospice worker. She said Willa is asking for you."

Willa's home was surrounded by sycamore trees in an exclusive neighborhood dubbed the American Riviera, where parcels were at least an acre and homes cost in the millions.

Bone-tired and dreading what she was about to do, Tracy rang the doorbell and took a deep breath. Within seconds a woman with big, soulful eyes and long brown hair greeted her at the door.

"I'm Theresa Bonaducci, Willa's neighbor," the woman said. Tracy introduced herself and Theresa said, "I'll take you back to Willa's room."

Theresa led her through the beautifully

appointed house fit for an *Architectural Digest* spread. Custom furnishings of exotic woods, slate and hardwood floors, and high wood-beam ceilings all worked together to make what was once a simple, one-story, California ranch-style house into a lovely home.

Willa's room was decorated in calm, cool colors — peaceful shades of the sea and sky. Soft classical music filled the air. Another woman, who introduced herself as the hospice worker, welcomed Tracy and stepped out so that they could be alone.

Shocked when she realized that the person lying in bed was actually Willa and that she was watching her from across the room, Tracy said the first thing that came to mind.

"It's nice here."

"A nice place to die."

"Oh, Willa."

The longest walk Tracy had ever had to make was across the pale celery-colored carpet to Willa's bedside. Once more she found herself sitting beside a hospital bed, but in this room there was no relief, no hope for another, brighter tomorrow. She stared at the hollow shell of what was left of Willa. The woman's hair had thinned to next to nothing. Her skin was the color of ash.

Guilt nearly swallowed Tracy whole. She'd

avoided making any decision about Mary Jane, but — even consumed by her own drama, in Wade, in running the hotel — she'd never forgotten Willa's request.

She had almost waited too long to answer.

As if Willa could read her mind, she said, "I don't have long, they say." Her smile was a grotesque parody of itself, her speech halting whenever she paused to take a ragged breath. "I feel like . . . I'm already a hundred years old. I'm not even sure what day it is."

She paused again as if each word, each sentence, was an effort. "Theresa saw the story about the . . . intruder on the news yesterday." Willa seemed too weak to go on, but asked for details.

Tracy told her in as few words as possible about Wade's identity, how Farley had held her hostage, and how there were still reporters outside the Heartbreak.

"So you see," she ended on a sigh and added, "so you see, there's no way I would feel right exposing your daughter to that kind of —"

Willa interrupted, saying something Tracy couldn't quite hear.

"I'm sorry." She leaned closer. "What did you say?"

"Is . . . Matt . . . there? At the hotel?"

Tracy nodded. "Matt and Chelsea both."

531

"I want Mary Jane to be with them."

Tracy's heart sank. "Willa —"

"It's up to you," Willa added.

Tracy closed her eyes against the pain of seeing her former friend like this, tried not to think about Willa's daughter growing up without her mother, tried not to think of how and why all their lives had changed irrevocably because of the affair.

Her gaze strayed to a framed photograph on the table beside Willa's bed. Surrounded by pill bottles, a plastic water carafe, a plastic cup with a flex-straw, a box of tissues, the vibrant face of a lovely little redheaded girl was smiling back at her. Thankfully there were no photos of Glenn, or of the three of them together.

"That's her," Willa rasped. "That's Mary Jane."

Despite everything, Tracy's heart, a mother's heart, truly ached for the woman.

"Where is she now?" *Who is caring for her? Is she with strangers, or somewhere here in the house?*

"It's her nap time. Theresa's been Mary Jane's sitter since she was born."

"Have you made arrangements for her care? Since you didn't hear from me . . ." She had to look away and found herself wondering if perhaps Theresa was close enough to want to adopt Mary Jane.

"My lawyer . . . found a young couple who wants to adopt her."

The notion should have freed Tracy, but with stunning clarity she realized that the idea of a nameless, faceless couple waiting to adopt the child in the photo bothered her more than she could have imagined.

"I had the lawyer . . . draw up two sets of adoption papers. I told the couple to not get their hearts set on the adoption." Willa struggled to swallow.

When Willa started coughing, Tracy automatically reached for the carafe, filled the plastic tumbler, and shifted the flex-straw so that Willa could take a sip.

By the time Tracy set the tumbler back on the table, she was shaking like a leaf. She'd been more composed in the attic with Farley than she was now — seeing Willa like this — knowing that the woman she'd befriended so long ago was facing life's unavoidable, ultimate test. In that split second, as she watched Willa wince and struggle to swallow, Tracy knew that, right or wrong, there was only one choice she could live with.

Careful to not disturb Willa, she lowered herself to the edge of the bed, closed her eyes, and forced herself to forget everything else and remember the day they'd first met. Tall and gangly at thirteen, Willa had definitely been an ugly duckling, but she'd been blessed with hair the color of iridescent black satin and flawless alabaster skin. Both would help her create an image that was unforgettable.

"Tracy?"

She glanced down. Willa's eyes were closed, her breathing ragged.

"I'm here," she said.

"I'm afraid." A tear leaked out of the corner of Willa's eye and slid down her temple.

Tracy had to swallow a lump in her throat before she could speak. "I am, too." There was only one way she could help Willa find peace, only one thing she could do. "I'll raise Mary Jane for you," she promised.

"Are you sure?" Willa's eyes fluttered open.

Am I sure? She was sure of only two things right now — her love for Wade, and the fact that she wouldn't be able to live with herself if she didn't agree to adopt Matt and Chelsea's half-sister.

"She'll become part of our home and our lives, as dear to me as Matthew. As special to me as Chelsea."

"What will you tell her about me?" Willa

whispered.

"What do you want me to tell her?"

"That once, we were best friends."

Tracy nodded, fighting tears. "I'll tell her. I promise."

"Thank you," Willa whispered. "I thank you with all my heart. Someday, when she understands what you've done for us, Mary Jane will thank you, too."

When the hospice worker came back and told Tracy that it was time for Willa's pain medication, she left the room, shaken, but determined to live up to her promise to raise Mary Jane as her own.

It hit her that explaining Mary Jane to Matt wouldn't be as hard as telling Chelsea. Chelsea was old enough to take one look at Mary Jane and, if not immediately put two and two together, ask questions. Facing another truth about her father would be a second tremendous blow.

In the living room, Theresa smiled warmly, but it was obvious she'd been crying.

"I still can't believe it." She shook her head and sighed. "I prayed for a miracle." She pulled a handkerchief out of her pocket and mopped her eyes. "It's almost time for Mary Jane to wake up from her nap. Would you like to see her?"

Mentally exhausted, Tracy nodded.

"Can I get you a cup of tea?" Theresa offered. "You look like you could use one."

What she could use was a good, strong drink.

"Herbal, if you have some." She had a long drive home ahead of her. The last thing she needed was liquor or caffeine. She was too tired for alcohol, and the stimulant would only add to her anxiety.

"Are you . . . will you be adopting Mary Jane? I know how much Willa was hoping you would."

Tracy wondered exactly how much Theresa knew and decided that she was too tired to care at this point. What Theresa obviously knew was that Willa had chosen her to raise the child, so that's what she talked about. "I'm hoping you can help me make this a smooth transition for her," Tracy said.

Together they decided that it would be best if Tracy brought Matt and Chelsea down to meet Mary Jane here. Tracy hoped that she could make more than a few visits over the next days or weeks, just so the child could grow comfortable with her.

By the time she'd had two cups of hibiscus tea and a long chat with Theresa, they had worked out an arrangement.

Am I really doing this? Am I bringing this child into my life? Into all our lives?

She knew that what she was doing was bound to affect her and Wade's future, but there was no way to predict how until she could talk to him.

Theresa walked her back down the hall, past the closed door to Willa's room. This time Tracy was ushered into a nursery right out of the pages of a fairy tale. She found herself immersed in a world of sensory memory, of baby powder and lotion, plush toys, the melody of a wind-up mobile. Diapers, pairs of tiny socks, of soft flannel and sunshine-fresh cotton.

Across the room, Mary Jane was awake in her crib, her eyes still puffy from sleep. When Tracy and Theresa walked in, the child pulled herself up and stood at the crib rail in a buttercup-yellow sundress. Her plump bare legs and feet were pumping up and down.

"Ma?" She tried to look past Theresa as the sitter walked over to the crib.

Theresa's eyes filled with tears, and Tracy had a hard time holding on when Theresa rubbed Mary Jane's back and said softly, "No, honey, Mommy's sleeping right now."

She lifted Mary Jane out of the crib and held her high on her hip as she turned to

537

Tracy. "Say hi to Tracy, honey. This is Mommy's friend."

Mommy's friend.

Mary Jane silently took her in with huge, innocent blue eyes. Slowly, a trusting smile bloomed across features reminiscent of both Matt and Chelsea, and yet distinctly her own. Then she opened her arms wide, giggled, and strained toward Tracy, begging, without words, to be held.

Automatically Tracy reached for the little girl without thought or hesitation. Theresa handed her over, and when Tracy enfolded Mary Jane in her arms, all traces of doubt dissolved. She knew, deep down in her soul, that no matter what happened after today, she'd made the right choice.

Later, after Willa had fallen asleep, Tracy left the house and drove north with the radio blasting. Tears streaming, she forced herself to sing every oldie at the top of her lungs. By the time she reached San Luis Obispo, she had stopped crying and entered the state of euphoria that always hit her when she went beyond tired. She felt as if she'd crossed over some invisible threshold and was running on warp speed. Her mind was fooling her body into thinking she would never need sleep again.

After calling Chelsea to check in and hearing that she and Vincent had everything under control, she decided that for once she'd *buy* baked goods for the guests so that she could spend time visiting Wade before she headed down the canyon to the Heartbreak.

Once she reached the hospital, she had to talk her way around the nurse with the purple hair before finally walking into Wade's room with a new, determined spring in her step.

Chapter Forty-Nine

Wade was channel-surfing when she walked in. Clicking the remote off, he set it aside and watched her cross the room.

"You're glowing," he said, amazed. "Should I worry? I didn't expect to see you until tomorrow."

"I couldn't go back to the hotel without stopping by."

"I'm glad. How did it go?"

"The best and the worst. Willa's dying." There was no satisfaction in her voice, only sorrow.

"And Mary Jane?"

"She's coming to live with us." She seemed to be waiting for a reaction, as if her adding another child to her home would faze him, as if she was worried that he might think twice about having a relationship with a woman with not one but two kids at home and a part-time daughter in college.

"I knew you'd take her." He smiled to let

her know it was all right.

"I didn't. In fact, I tried to turn her down."

"And yet you didn't. Are you all right with it now?"

"Actually, I feel great. I'm not looking forward to telling Chelsea, but I can't put it off. There's no way to know how long Willa has." Her smile dimmed. "The hospice worker said it could be two weeks, or it could be days. I may be picking up Mary Jane before I know it."

"I wish you could get away, maybe come stay with me in L.A. for a while. Bob could hide us someplace for a week or so, until I'm really up and around. Whenever you needed to, you could come back and move Mary Jane into the Heartbreak." He could see that she was tempted, but she slowly shook her head and then sat down on the edge of the bed.

"It sounds like heaven," she said softly, "but I've got a hotel to run and a life I can't just walk away from anymore." She paused, traced the back of his hand with her fingertips, and then looked into his eyes. "I've been thinking about your going back to L.A. I thought about it all the way back up here. I've decided you're coming home with me when they release you. I want you to stay at the Heartbreak. I've already called Matt and Chelsea and they both agree. Matt volunteered to sleep in Chelsea's room on a futon until she goes back to school. You can have his room."

"You're coming home with me."

The idea that she still loved him after everything that had happened, that she wanted him back in her home after what he'd done to her life already, still astounded him.

"I can't ask you to do that, Tracy."

"You didn't ask. Come home with me. Let me take care of you. Let *us* take care of you."

"I can't let you do this," he insisted.

"Why? Because you'd rather have Bob hire some fake-breasted tall blond nurse in L.A. to take care of you?"

At that, he couldn't keep from laughing. "Yeah, that's it. You got me." He sobered when he realized how intent she looked.

"I'm doing this for purely selfish reasons, Wade. I don't want to let you go."

What she was offering was a life the likes of which he'd only briefly glimpsed during his stay at the Heartbreak. He tried to imagine himself settled in Matt's room, surrounded by LEGOs, Transformers, Hot Wheels, and plastic action figures. Tried to picture himself living in the heart of a family of more than two — something he'd never experienced in his life.

He knew what it was to be a loner, but not what it meant to be part of a real family that had just added one more. For as long as he could remember he had lived his life in self-imposed isolation, immersed in his work.

A writer writes. A writer needs solitude. It was his mantra.

But he wasn't a writer anymore. The problem was, he didn't know what he was.

She was staring back at him, waiting for a decision, looking at him as if he truly were a hero, as if he had all the answers. He didn't know if he could live up to her expectations, no matter how small. Nor did he for one minute believe that his troubles were behind him.

"As you just said, you've got a hotel to run and a family to care for."

"You don't think I can take care of you, too?"

"I *know* you can take care of me." He lifted the back of her hand to his lips, pleased when she blushed at his kiss.

"Then let me."

"Tracy —"

"You left before, Wade. You walked out of

my life because you didn't want to bring the media down on us, and look what happened."

"I'm sorry, you know that."

"I don't want you to be sorry. I want you to stop running. I want you to stay here. No matter what happens, we can survive it. There's no need for you to run anymore. Whatever happens, we can survive it together. The least we can do is try."

"Are you sure?" He didn't want to leave any more than she wanted him to.

"Willa asked me that same thing earlier, and you know what? I realized that one of the only things I was sure of was my love for you. I think we both deserve some happiness right about now, don't you? Give this a chance. See what happens."

"See if I pass the test, you mean?" He pictured himself riding down the coast road on the Harley someday soon, finally giving Matt that ride he'd been begging for.

"See if Matt, Chelsea, Mary Jane, and I pass. What do you think?"

"I think I'd better call Schack and have him cancel the jet."

The next day Tracy and Chelsea were having breakfast together at the narrow bar that separated the kitchen from the living room.

544

Each morning they went over the reservation schedule for the day, talked about which guests were checking out and which rooms had to be prepped for new arrivals.

"So is Wade going to be staying here or going back to L.A.?" Chelsea picked up a bear-shaped plastic container and started squeezing honey onto a piece of toast smothered in peanut butter.

"It was a hard sell, but I finally changed his mind." Tracy picked up the honey when Chelsea finished and dribbled some into her hot coffee. "We'll have the media to deal with again, but hopefully not for too long."

Chelsea smiled. "It won't be forever. Besides, we're getting pretty good at handling them, don't you think?"

"I think we are." Tracy would never have guessed that the trials they'd faced over the previous few weeks would have brought them closer, but they had. She just hoped that what she was about to say wouldn't jeopardize the new bond between them. She was finally having the kind of relationship she had always wanted to have with Chelsea — the kind she'd always hoped for.

"What a shock about your friend, Willa." Chelsea reached for more orange juice and poured herself another glass. "Did you know she was sick?"

Fate had just handed Tracy the perfect opening, and she knew she'd better take it.

"Not until recently." *There were a lot of things I didn't know until recently.* "Yesterday, when I went to see Willa, I made a decision that concerns all of us, but it was mine to make. I hope you'll understand."

Chelsea lowered the toast without taking a bite. "This sounds serious."

"It is." Tracy dived in headfirst. "It's about your father and Willa." She lowered her hands to her lap, clasped her fingers together.

"They worked together sometimes," Chelsea remembered aloud. "Didn't Willa decorate the Canyon Club models? I haven't seen her in years."

"She was —" Tracy's throat closed. She took a deep breath and blurted, "She was his mistress."

"Willa?" Chelsea's brow scrunched. "And my *dad*? Wasn't she an old friend of yours?"

Slowly, Tracy nodded. "Yes, she was."

Chelsea's eyes grew huge. "Is that . . . is she the one *David* was talking about when he said Dad was a player?"

Tracy had to clear her throat. "Yes." She took a quick sip of her own juice and let Chelsea mull over what she'd just said before she hit her with the second round.

"You didn't know?" Chelsea asked.

Tracy shook her head. "Not until the night of the open house."

"It really wasn't about the invitations. *That's* why you were so upset."

Another nod. "Yes."

"Did she beg for your forgiveness from her deathbed? My God, Tracy. I can't believe you went!"

"That's not why I went. I drove down there because Willa and your dad had a child together — a little girl. Willa asked me to adopt her."

"A little girl?" Chelsea paled. Her breakfast sat ignored, the toast going cold as melted peanut butter dripped over the crust and pooled on her plate. *"Dad?"*

"Yes. And Willa."

Chelsea opened her mouth to say something, closed it again, and slowly shook her head. "I can't believe it," she whispered. "Are you sure?"

"Yes. Her name is Mary Jane, she's almost two, and she looks a lot like both you and Matt."

"Do you have a picture of her?"

"I should have asked for one, but I didn't." She wondered if Jake still had the file of photographs, but decided it would be too painful to ask him, to see those photos again. If she'd only asked Willa for one, then she remembered. "I was hoping that you would go with me this week, down to Montecito, to meet her."

"Are you . . . I can't believe it. Are you actually thinking about adopting her?" She covered her lips with her fingertips. Her eyes searched Tracy's.

"Yes. Yes, I am."

"How can you even stand to look at her and not think of what Dad did to you?"

"I wondered that myself, believe me, but Mary Jane is the innocent one in all of this. She's just a baby, Chelsea. And indirectly, she's part of you, and part of Matt. She's not to blame."

"She's my half-sister."

"That's right."

"Just like Mattie."

"Just like Matt." Tracy slid her empty plate back and traced the edge of her place mat with her fingernail. "Willa found a couple who is willing to adopt her . . ." It wasn't too late to tell Willa that she'd changed her mind — but this wasn't about Willa or Glenn or even what Chelsea wanted anymore. This was about Mary Jane, about a two-year-old who had a half-brother and -sister who stood to gain as much as they would give by having her in their lives.

In the stillness that fell on the room, as the second hand ticked quietly on the fat-faced clock above the sink, Tracy waited for Chelsea to digest everything she'd just said.

"This couple," Chelsea leaned back on the bar stool, still frowning fiercely. "Who are they? Does Willa know them? Is she related to them?"

"No. Her lawyer found them. She doesn't have any relatives." It was the one thing they'd had in common growing up. Tracy was raised by her grandparents, Willa by a maiden aunt. If anyone knew what it was to want for family, it was Willa.

"Well," Chelsea stared down at her toast a few more seconds before her gaze drifted back over to Tracy, "we have to take her; don't we? I mean, she is my half-sister."

"I'm so glad you agree — because I already promised Willa that we'd take her." The second half of the hundred-pound weight that Tracy had driven home under yesterday suddenly lifted, and she felt like crying with relief.

"What about Mattie? What will you tell him?"

"For now, just that Mary Jane is my friend Willa's daughter, and that Willa died and wanted us to adopt her."

Chelsea nodded in agreement. "He'll be

excited, I think."

"I hope so."

Chelsea grew thoughtful again. "When do we get to have her?"

"It could be a week, maybe a little more, or it could be today. There's no way of knowing." Tracy couldn't help but think of Willa.

"There are only a few weeks left before I have to be back at school. Maybe I should move to Mom's until then since Wade is moving in, and now Mary Jane, too."

"I've been thinking about contacting one of the parties due in today to see if I can't work something out with them."

"Like what?"

"Like getting them booked into Rose Cottage in Twilight instead, and offering them a free booking next summer." She noticed Chelsea's hesitation. "Unless you *want* to move to Monica's."

"No, I don't want to go, but — what if the guests refuse to take you up on your offer?"

"Dealing with a couple of irate, disappointed guests is nothing after what I've been through this week. We'll manage. Just remember that I want you here as long and as often as you want to be here, Chelsea. This is your home, too."

"Thanks, Tracy."

"I love you, honey. I know you're going to love Mary Jane the minute you see her."

Just then Matt came strolling in, tripping over the hems of his sagging pajama bottoms, the oversized T-shirt he'd slept in hanging past his knees.

"Who's Mary Jane?" He rubbed his eyes, walked over, and started eating Chelsea's peanut butter and honey toast. It dribbled down the front of his shirt, but he didn't seem to care.

Tracy and Chelsea exchanged a glance.

"Hop up here." Chelsea indicated the empty bar stool beside her with a pat. "Tracy's got a really *big* surprise for you."

When they moved him back into his room downstairs at the Heartbreak, Wade felt more at home than he ever had in his upscale apartment in Manhattan.

Sitting up in bed on his fourth night back, he was content to watch the curtains billow in on the breeze and listen to the sound of the rolling surf. His shoulder was stiff and painful beneath his bandage, but he was diligently working on the exercises the therapist had assigned him. The therapist was due to stop by in the morning to check on his progress.

There had been a media mob in front of the hospital the afternoon he was released, but he and Bob had put their heads together to come up with a plan that had his agent as excited as a kid in a candy store. Schack held a formal press conference, promising that after a month of recovery and intensive physical therapy, Wade MacAllister, a.k.a. Edward Cain, would be available for interviews. Until then, Mr. MacAllister was going to be resting up in seclusion at a private home in Malibu — which Bob just happened to own.

Then, with much fanfare, "Wade" — or rather, an out-of-work actor from Pismo Beach posing as Wade — was swiftly wheeled out of the hospital covered by a lap robe and wearing a baseball cap, huge dark glasses, and a turtleneck pulled up to his lips.

He was filmed boarding a private jet at the airport and, again, disembarking at Van Nuys. Schack's Malibu house, the "undisclosed location," was covered night and day. Paparazzi had ample opportunities to get shots of "Wade" whenever he would occasionally dart past a window or quickly step out onto the sundeck for a second before ducking back inside the house.

In the meantime, the real Wade had

slipped out the back door of the hospital in scrubs provided by Nurse Robin, who, it seemed, was completely shameless as long as she could get her hands on autographed copies of his books. It didn't matter which books, just so long as his signature was in them.

Bob immediately started booking interviews, and the last time he called to check in, Oprah and Barbara Walters were butting heads over who would have the first on-air time with Wade.

Meanwhile, the real Wade was in his room at the Heartbreak, a room he no longer shared with a ghost. Someone was constantly at his side making sure he wasn't bored, hungry, or lonely. In the past few days he'd played more hands of Uno with Matt than he cared to recall, and much to Matt's chagrin, he was becoming an expert at Game Boy.

He was also adept at going over the USC class catalog and fall schedule with Chelsea. She confessed that she was tempted to major in journalism, that was until he told her that writers like Lauren Westin made hardly any money — their publishers kept it in reserve as payment for their sources.

Whenever Tracy could spare a few minutes, she'd been right there beside him, fluffing his pillows, asking if he was doing his shoulder exercises, plying him with food. She brought him every meal, ate with him, tempted him just by being in the same room. His first day back, he'd playfully asked if she'd sneak down and spend the night with him. She laughed and thought he was kidding.

According to his watch, it was 8:30 already, and she still hadn't come down to say good night. Last night they had sat out on the porch, listened to the waves, and talked for hours.

By 9:00 he was antsy and missing her, so he got up, tested his strength, and left his room for the first time in three days.

There was an intrinsic, peaceful stillness about the hotel. Even with every room filled, there was still a settled kind of quiet that was missing in most places these days. There were no distractions, no cars constantly humming along the road out front, no streetlights. Here, the night sky wasn't faded to gray by city lights. The stars looked close enough to touch.

The hotel seemed to glow with its own warmth, pulse with the beat of its own heart.

Passing through the lobby, he half expected to see Tracy at the reception desk and was disappointed when she wasn't there. Two couples were in the sitting area sipping wine and chatting amiably as he walked by. No one paid any attention to him other than to nod.

Everyone knew that Wade MacAllister was in Malibu recuperating.

Memories assailed him as he climbed the stairs. The aroma of cinnamon and spices lingered. Aged wood and the accumulation of years added to the homey atmosphere. As he started up to the apartment, he noted that the stairs still creaked. The wallpaper in the stairwell was faded almost beyond description, but it seemed right somehow, that aside from adding a new coat of paint and a bucketful of hope to the place, Tracy had hardly changed a thing.

At the top of the landing he had to stop and catch his breath, and hoped he hadn't popped anything under his bandages. He figured he could have walked right into the apartment, but it was a familiarity he hadn't yet acquired, so he knocked and waited.

It wasn't Tracy, but Chelsea, who answered.

"Wade! Are you all right?"

"Is Tracy around?"

She gently took his arm and led him in as if he were a centenarian out on the loose alone. "She's up on the widow's walk. Sit down and I'll run up and get her." She tried to steer him over to the sofa.

He motioned toward the hall. "I want to surprise her."

"Do you need help?"

"Not with what I've got planned."

She blushed to the roots of her hair. "Oh, Wade."

"I'm just kidding. Besides, I can barely stand." Not exactly a lie. The climb up one flight already had him feeling weak as a kitten.

She wouldn't let go of his arm until he told her he was only kidding again.

Down the hall, the light was on in Matt's room, the door open a foot or two. Inside, Matt was propped up against his pillow, writing in his journal. He must have sensed that someone was watching, for he looked up, and when he recognized Wade, he tossed the journal aside.

"Come on in!" He pulled himself up straighter in bed. Wade quickly held his finger up to his lips and walked into the room.

Matt whispered, "What are you doing up here? Are you better already?"

"I'm getting there. I came up to surprise your mom." Suddenly Matt was grinning from ear to ear. "She's up on the roof."

556

"I know."

The boy shrugged. "So are you gonna go up and try some kissie, smoochie stuff on her?"

"You think I should?"

"Women kinda like it. That's what Christopher told me." He lowered his voice and glanced toward the door. "Chelsea does. She's always out in the driveway smooching with Eric when she thinks nobody is watching."

"Maybe I'll give it a try." He noticed the journal. "That's not Spider-Man anymore, I see."

Matt looked proud. "Naw. I filled that one up already. I'm gonna be a famous writer. Like you."

When Matt beamed up at him, Wade's confidence stumbled. He'd certainly never published anything worthy of a child's praise.

"Go on up and surprise Mom, then come back and tell me what happened, okay?"

"It's pretty late. I think you'll have to wait until tomorrow to find out."

Thoroughly disappointed, Matt sighed, but he didn't argue.

"Will you please turn out the light for me?"

"Sure." Wade stepped close to the bed and

Matt handed him the journal. Setting it carefully on the night-stand, Wade turned out the light.

"Mom leaves the door open a crack."

"Okay. Night, Sport." Wade stepped out into the hall and made certain he left the door open a crack behind him.

CHAPTER FIFTY

Clear, warm nights were Tracy's favorite times on the widow's walk, yet there had been very few of those this summer. She'd splurged on two matching teak deck chairs, figuring she owed it to herself now that the hotel was constantly booked. Besides, she would have another windfall as soon as she sold her wedding ring.

Dressed in comfortable lightweight sweats, she stretched out on the deck chair and stared up into the night sky, content to watch the stars and listen to the song of the sea for a few minutes before she went down to tell Wade good night.

She liked to imagine that Ezra's Violette might have come up here at night, too, watching the same stars and constellations, listening to the waves' soothing, monotonous tune as they rolled in over the rocks, the sound soothing her as she waited for Ezra to return.

A moment ago she'd been thinking of Wade. She couldn't help but smile as she remembered the junk-food wrappers in his wastebasket. Twinkies and Cheetos. And tequila bottles. Not exactly brain food. After all that alcohol, sugar, and preservatives, it was no wonder he thought he'd heard Ezra's ghost.

She took a deep breath and closed her eyes — just for a minute.

The next thing she knew, someone was calling her name. She imagined it was Wade, that he was right there, beside her — so close that she could hear the sound of his voice over the waves. Slowly she opened her eyes and realized she must have drifted off to sleep.

"Tracy?"

She quickly sat up and there he was, kneeling beside her deck chair, staring into her eyes, as if he were trying to look into her very soul. It was a shock seeing him there, where she hadn't expected him to be.

"How did you get up here? Are you all right?" She reached out, cupped his jaw with her palm. His skin was clean-shaven and, looking at him now, she tried to picture him as he had appeared in his Edward Cain headshots. So sober. So cool and distant. It seemed impossible.

"I'm fine. I was downstairs all alone, missing you." Glancing down at her watch, she realized that, somewhere, she'd lost a good twenty minutes. "I either fell asleep just now, or," she looked up at the star-spattered sky, ". . . I was abducted by aliens. There's close to twenty minutes unaccounted for," she teased.

"I hear they can't possibly do all that testing and get you back to earth in less than forty-five. You must have just dozed off."

When she stopped laughing, she wanted to know, "So you really missed me?"

She watched his hair move with the wind off the water, tempted to run her fingers through it. She didn't know this version of him with his light brown hair growing out beneath the darker hue, and sky-blue eyes that seemed to see right into her heart — but he did look very, very good. Better than good, he looked delicious.

"Like crazy. I was forced to crawl out of my sickbed and come looking for you."

"I'm glad you did, but I hope you didn't wear yourself out." Whatever else she was going to say was swallowed by his kiss. She let the taste of his lips, the touch of his hands, sweep her away from everything, infuse her with the warmth and energy she needed tonight.

"That's the least of my problems tonight. You seem tired, though." He smoothed her hair back behind her ear.

"I'm not really tired, just running in too many directions at once. If you'll be all right alone, I thought I'd see if Vince can come in while I drive the kids down to Santa Barbara tomorrow to meet Mary Jane. The sitter called and said that Willa's much worse."

"I'll be fine. Don't worry about me. I wish I could go with you."

"It's a long ride, and besides, you're supposed to be hiding out. Earlier I found myself thinking about everything I have to do and wishing we all had more time. Time for Mary Jane to get acquainted with us before we bring her home. More time before Chelsea goes back to USC, because I'm really going to miss her this year." She got to her feet, took his hand, and walked with him to the railing. She wrapped her arm around his waist and lay her head against his good shoulder. "I wish there was time for just the two of us."

"We'll have plenty of time, Tracy."

"You think so?" She knew better than to count on it now. No matter how positive she tried to be, no matter how much she looked forward to the future, life had taught her some hard lessons over the past few months — lessons she wasn't going to forget anytime soon.

"I sure hope so," he whispered.

She closed her eyes and leaned into his embrace. "Whenever I come up here, I can't help but think about Ezra and Violette as I look out to sea or watch the gulls fly over the bluff. Do you think they're together now?"

"Ezra and Violette?" He smiled into her eyes. "I know they are."

"Did he tell you so?" The darkness hid her smile.

"He didn't have to. I could tell when I walked into my room again. There's a new lightness there. Ezra's definitely gone. Where else would he be, if not with Violette?"

His arm was hanging over her shoulder. She touched the back of his hand with her index finger, stroked it lightly, tenderly. Over the past few days they'd talked of many things, of Chelsea's coming school year, of Farley, the Even Dozen, the trials. She'd let him talk, sensing that he hadn't ever opened up to anyone else.

They'd talked of everything but their future. Though she hungered for him night and day, right now it was enough to have him near. They hadn't actually spoken of love again since that day in the hospital.

So she was completely caught off guard when he said, "I've never been in love before, you know. Not like this. Not with anyone. I never knew much happiness, Tracy. Not as a child, not as an adult. Sometimes I think I would have made a great poet. I was born melancholy. I was always looking toward the future, dreaming of becoming a star, of making my mark in the writing world. I was forever chasing the gold ring. I was never happy in the moment. I planned to be happy when I finally had it all. The trouble was, I wasn't happy once I had it all, either — because of the way I'd made all that money.

"I always thought that love and happiness were illusions until I walked in your front door and saw them in the way you treated Matthew and Chelsea, in your friendships, in your hopes and dreams for this place. I've seen how you derived happiness from the simplest of pleasures, setting out your china cups and plates, baking something fresh every day, making sure people felt at home here.

"I felt them both the night I pinned that corsage on your shoulder, and the night we made love — when you gave, asking nothing in return.

"Being with you has taught me that it's not the big events or achievements, not the 'wow' moments that make us happy, it's the little things, the humdrum ordinary things that happen between heartbeats that should bring us joy, love and happiness, and loving memories. Those are the moments we have to celebrate, and I want to celebrate all those everyday moments with you, Tracy." He slipped his arms around her and drew her closer. "I want to share all the joy and all the memories to come with you and your kids for as long as fate lets me."

He claimed to have never loved, and yet he'd just expressed his love in the most eloquent of terms. She turned in his arms, reached up, and carefully looped her arms around his neck.

"What about the not-so-joyful moments? Will you be willing to share those with us, too?"

"Love is what's seen you through the good times and the bad. If you'll marry me, I'll never give you reason to have to doubt my love for you."

"Marry you?" Despite everything he'd just said, she hadn't seen the proposal coming.

"Will you?"

"I love you, Wade. Most of the time, almost desperately. I thought of you today right in the middle of serving breakfast and wondered if anyone would notice if I just walked out of the sunroom, slipped down the hall and into your bed."

"I wish you would have."

"I believe you were in the middle of a hot hand of Uno at the time."

He groaned, kissed her, but didn't give up. "About that proposal . . ."

"This isn't something you should rush into —"

"Say you'll marry me, Tracy. It doesn't have to be this week, or this month. Not even this *year;* if you don't want to, but I need to hear you say you'll marry me."

"Marry a crazy writer who hears ghosts?"

"A crazy writer who's head over heels in love with you. A writer who happens to have enough money to hire a staff to keep this place running so that you can spend all your time with me if you want."

"I don't care about your money." Truth be told, she still had to remind herself about Edward Cain, his books, his success, his notoriety. To her; he was still just Wade. Her Wade.

"That's one more reason why I love you, and I don't want to let you get away." He laughed.

"I'm not going anywhere."

"I saw Matt on my way up. He gave me some man-to-man tips. Said women like kissie, smoochie stuff."

"Is this a conspiracy?" She couldn't help but laugh. "That's surprising. Lately whenever the subject of girls comes up, he can sum up everything about them with one word — 'yuck!' " She wrapped her arms tight around his waist, lifted her face to the stars. "I think this is where you definitely need to try some kissie, smoochie stuff," she whispered.

"You think a couple of good kisses will convince you that I'm not an invalid, and that you should come downstairs and tuck me in?"

"Try me." Her heart was soaring. She was ready to savor the moment, to celebrate the joy that was theirs right here, and right now. "Somehow, I have the feeling you can be very persuasive."

EPILOGUE

Four months later . . .

The Heartbreak was dressed for Christmas.
Carols were playing in the lobby. A huge
tree sparkled with lights and replica ornaments from the turn of the century, when
the building was constructed.

For Tracy, welcoming guests would never
be routine, not with such a wide variety of
people visiting from all over the world. She
was just finishing checking in a couple from
Hawaii.

"Thank you, Mr. and Mrs. Sparks, and
welcome to the Heartbreak Hotel. Let me
know if you need anything else. Once you're
settled in, you might want to wander out on
the back porch, where wine and cheese will
be served at sunset. It's a good time to get
to meet some of the other guests, if you care
to. Whatever you do, feel free to make
yourselves at home."

They thanked her profusely and headed

for the hall, stopping to ooh and ahh while they gazed at the Christmas tree. Then, as the Sparks wrestled their bags down the hall, Tracy crossed their names off the reservation ledger.

The day Tracy walked into the hotel for the first time, she would never, ever have guessed that she would find happiness here — but the Heartbreak had truly become a place where not only she had healed, but so had Matt and Chelsea — and Wade.

For all of them, time had soothed hurts, faded scars, and gilded memories. Willa's death had affected her more than she would have ever thought possible, given what had happened. In losing Willa, she'd lost the last connection to her own past in Indiana. Willa's death was one more reminder of how very short life is, and of how every precious moment is a gift.

Tracy heard footsteps on the stairs and watched Chelsea come strolling into the lobby with Mary Jane riding on her hip. The little girl started playing peekaboo with Tracy the minute she saw her, burying her face behind her hands and peeking out through her fingers.

"I've got the wine and glasses set up outside on the porch. All you need now are the cheese and crackers," Chelsea said.

Chelsea was home on holiday break, helping out with the rooms, taking care of Mary Jane, running things behind the desk, greeting guests, and generally filling in. She came home at every opportunity and always slipped right in to helping out. She enjoyed the challenges so much that she'd decided to major in hotel management.

"Thank you. Are you going out?"

"Eric called and asked me if I wanted to go to the boat parade of lights at Gull Harbor. Do you need me tonight?"

"Go," Tracy encouraged. "The last guests just checked in."

"Great, I'll call and tell Eric I can go, then."

The front door opened and Jamie, the FedEx deliveryman, walked in.

"Hey, Jamie. How are the kids?" Tracy took the box he handed her and set it on the counter, then she signed for it and listened while he gave them an update on his new twin boys.

The minute he walked out, she picked up the box and looked at the packing slip. It was from the Robert Schack Literary Agency in L.A., but addressed to her, not Wade.

"What is it?" Chelsea was at her elbow, trying to see. "Another package from Wade.

I think these Twelve Days of Christmas surprises he keeps sending you are just great. What did you get yesterday?"

Tracy blushed with embarrassment. "Tickets to Paris."

"You're kidding! Open this one." Chelsea nudged her. "Quick."

Tracy pulled the tab and the box opened. Inside was a book, hardbound, with an aqua dustcover and a picture of the California coastline below the embossed title, *The Life and Times of Captain Ezra Poole.*

She ran her fingers over the glossy finish, tracing the raised letters: "By Wade MacAllister and Capt. E. Poole."

"He did it. He published Ezra's story." Chelsea sounded awed. "But not as Edward Cain."

Wade had, indeed, given the press what they wanted for a good two months. He had entertained interviews from a hotel room at the Beverly Hilton and had gone on the talk show and news magazine circuit.

And so far, his plan was working. With Wade getting more air time than Michael Jackson, the press soon got their fill of him. Another Jennifer Lopez wedding scandal soon overshadowed the demand for Edward Cain appearances.

And somehow, through it all, he'd managed to put the finishing touches on Ezra's book and sent it to the publisher without telling her that he'd even finished.

"Is there a note?" Chelsea picked up the box and shook it, but nothing fell out. "Wow. Did you know this was coming out?"

"I had no idea."

Matt came downstairs and immediately walked over to join them. "What's up?"

Tracy looked at Matt standing next to Chelsea and wondered if he had grown a foot since summer. "Wade published the story of Ezra Poole."

"Cool!" The sparkle in his eye told her he was thinking of a new moneymaking scheme.

"Don't even think about giving tours again, young man."

"We could sell copies of the book," Chelsea suggested. "Wade could autograph them and we could show them here at the front desk." She automatically drew Mary Jane's hand away from her long hair and then untangled the strands wrapped around the toddler's fingers.

"See if Wade already autographed it," she urged.

Tracy set the book on the counter and, lifting the cover; realized there was something inside. She let the book fall open on its own, and there, pressed and dried, was the gardenia blossom from the corsage he'd given her the night of the open house.

"That's just about *the* sweetest thing I've ever seen," Chelsea said softly. "That's the kind of thing Eric would do."

"Who put a dead flower in the book?" Matt scrunched up his nose and winced. "Weird. What does it say?" He tried to see over Chelsea's shoulder. Mary Jane grabbed his hair and wouldn't let go. He started emitting painful yowls.

Chelsea winked at Tracy when they heard the Harley pull into the driveway.

"Looks like hubby's home." Chelsea grabbed Matt by the collar and turned him in the direction of the stairs. "Come on upstairs and I'll fix you a snack."

"Why? Why can't I stay here, Mom?"

"Because she and Wade need some adult time," Chelsea told him as she gave him a nudge.

"They sure need a lot of adult time. How about I go with you for a dollar?"

"Quarter," Chelsea countered.

"Fifty cents."

"Deal."

As they bickered their way up the stairs, Tracy carefully placed the gardenia back in the middle of the book and turned to the title page. There was no autograph written there.

Wade walked in the side door, set his helmet down on the bar stool behind the reception desk, and wrapped his arms around her from behind. She leaned into him, closed her eyes, and knew she was the luckiest woman alive.

"I missed you," she whispered.

"I missed you, too. And to think I only went to the post office," he laughed.

"Still —"

"You got the book!" One-handed, he reached around her and picked it up. "Did you see the dedication?"

She shook her head. "I looked to see if you autographed it."

He flipped the book open and put it into her hands.

When she looked down at the page, her heart skipped a beat as she read his words, printed for all the world to see.

Words more precious to her than any trip to Paris, than anything money could buy.

To my wife, Tracy,
Ezra and I both thank you.
Never forget . . . true love stands the

test of time,
I love you.

Wade.

ABOUT THE AUTHOR

Jill Marie Landis's novels have earned distinguished awards and slots on such national bestseller lists as the *New York Times* and the *USA Today* Top 50. She is a seven-time finalist for the Romance Writers of America's RITA Award in Single Title Historical and Contemporary Romance as well as a Golden Heart and RITA Award winner.

Some of her recent releases include the Irish Angels Series, inspirational historical romance from Zondervan, and *Mai Tai One On, Two to Mango, Three to Get Lei'd, Too Hot for Hula* and *Hawaii Five Uh-Oh,* her hilarious "Tiki Goddess Mysteries" set in Hawaii.

Jill Marie resides in Hawaii with her husband. When she's not writing or sitting on the beach reading, she enjoys visiting with family and friends, raising orchids, working in her garden, occasionally quilting, but most of all dancing the hula.

Visit Jill's website at www.jillmarielandis
.com
Join Jill on Facebook at www.facebook.com/
JillMarieLandisAuthor/
and www.facebook.com/thetikigoddess/
Follow Jill on Twitter at twitter.com/
jillmarielandis

The employees of Thorndike Press hope you have enjoyed this Large Print book. All our Thorndike, Wheeler, and Kennebec Large Print titles are designed for easy reading, and all our books are made to last. Other Thorndike Press Large Print books are available at your library, through selected bookstores, or directly from us.

For information about titles, please call:
(800) 223-1244

or visit our website at:
gale.com/thorndike

To share your comments, please write:
Publisher
Thorndike Press
10 Water St., Suite 310
Waterville, ME 04901